The Political
Imagination in
Literature   A READER

Edited by

PHILIP GREEN
DEPARTMENT OF GOVERNMENT
SMITH COLLEGE

MICHAEL WALZER
DEPARTMENT OF GOVERNMENT
HARVARD UNIVERSITY

The Free Press, New York

For Dorothy and Judy

Preface

The purpose of *The Political Imagination in Literature* is to provide (1) a new and useful tool for education in political science and (2) a source book and reader for all those who love the richness of political life and political thought.

It is a common teaching experience that beginning students, even upperclassmen and graduate students, sometimes find the standard institutional and theoretical readings in political science courses abstract, dry and dull, removed from their own lives and concerns. It is unfortunate that this should ever be so—that works having to do with one of the most significant areas of human affairs should fail to touch the imagination; that a process which so powerfully affects our lives should, for all the study we give it, remain distant, uninteresting, in no way personally compelling.

The world of literature, in contrast, is a storehouse of materials that *can* touch the political imagination, that have done so in the past. Good literature offers us an exceptionally keen perception of the vital elements in political life; the ways in which seemingly abstract ideas become dramatically realized in the behavior of individuals, groups, and even nations; the ways in which seemingly impersonal institutions become intertwined in the lives of persons; the ways, conversely, in which individuals and groups subtly mold institutions and abstract ideas to achieve their own ends. To see an idea or an institution in operation, to see political life as a personal problem, obedience and disobedience as complex human choices— all this adds a dimension to one's understanding of politics that can rarely be achieved by academic description.

Thus we conceive the function of this reader: to make political science concrete for students. Like the proliferating volumes of case studies which are being called into existence for much the same purpose, our reader is intended to supplement the standard materials of political science teaching. What it adds to the disciplined, scientific description of experience is, in a sense, *experience itself;* for as John Dewey observed, the perception of the meaning of a work of art—letting it flower in one's mind—is one of the deepest forms of experience. And in experience understanding begins.

Our belief in the virtues of the literary approach to politics, then, has led us to make some examples of that approach available in anthology form; at the same time, that belief has affected both the style and substance of our anthologizing in two important respects. First, since imagination and experience both are uniquely personal phenomena, we have tried to avoid assigning to our selections meanings that the authors themselves did not see fit to make manifest (although we have at times unavoidably imposed our own interpretations on ambiguous material). Second, insofar as possible we have used only works of real literary merit which can literally be experienced and so carry conviction in their views of the political world. Although our selections are grouped according to broad topic headings, we have not attempted to "cover the field," to illustrate every question that can conceivably arise in the study of politics.

Limited as we have been by considerations of space and the unavailability of a few pieces that deserve to be included here, we have only been able to suggest the scope of the political imagination in literature and have often had to make do with brief excerpts from works that should be enjoyed in their fullness. We hope that students of political science will find their interest in politics reinvigorated by this source book and so will be led to explore further in this great and continuing literary tradition and to recapture it for themselves.

✹   ✹   ✹

In preparing this anthology, we derived immense benefit from the advice of Lewis Coser and Irving Howe and from their (respective) books, *Sociology Through Literature* (Englewood Cliffs, 1963) and *Politics and the Novel* (Boston, 1957). Many other of our friends—too many to be mentioned here individually—made helpful suggestions to us. Among them, Daniel Aaron, Marshall Berman, and Peter M. Marin deserve special thanks, as do our wives, Dorothy Green and Judith Walzer.

Philip Green
Michael Walzer

Contents

Contents

Contents by Author

Chapter █

Origins: The State of Nature

The myth of a state of nature, a prepolitical condition out of which men long ago emerged to form societies and governments, is central to a great deal of political theory. In part this is because we are all fascinated by beginnings, perennially tempted by the genetic fallacy. But the myth also has real intellectual value. Theorists need to understand what it is that political association and state power add to human life, and they achieve this understanding by conjuring up the image of an unassociated and uncoerced man. They try to imagine how they and their fellows might behave (and feel) if they were free of all the restraints of convention and law. The tools of this exercise are at once rigorous analysis and free fantasy. Its products are so many maps of the prepolitical and then of the political universe, the one being conceived, in most cases, as the antithesis of the other. Do natural men, as reconstituted in the theorist's imagination, live in some fraternal harmony? Then it must be politics that brings conflict and war. Is the state of nature itself a state of war? Then the purpose of politics must be order and security. Is man by nature free, a creature of impulse and spontaneity? Then it must be society that enchains him and the laws that justify his slavery. Is nature ruled by the strong? Then the state is a confederation of the weak and equality a political creation.

There are an infinity of possibilities and none of them obviously true. Chiefly for this reason modern political scientists have turned away from speculations about genesis and nature, ceding the field to the anthropologists and metapsychologists. But if no theory of prepolitics has yet been scientifically demonstrated, it nevertheless remains true that not every mythic statement is of equal value. Some speak more directly to us than do others and tell us more about ourselves, explaining what we feel to be our immanent lawlessness or recalling a happier self we somehow remember having lost. Such myths, when we believe them, lay bare the human purposes that politics is meant to serve—and so suggest its failures. They make the state transparent; we pierce its various facades and find the men inside.

These are the myths seized upon by poets and storytellers and endlessly elaborated until they come, like the tales of paradise or the epics of the American West, to shape the political consciousness of a whole society. The literature of prepolitics clearly cannot take realistic forms; its imaginative effects depend upon its claim to penetrate reality and expose natural patterns and essential human types. It is consciously didactic and allegorical. Its characters have no personalities; they are embodiments and representatives of concepts: lust or love, fear or courage, natural ignorance or native sagacity. Its scenery is the primitive forest, the distant isle, the wild frontier. Its action is stereotyped: the invasion of paradise by the serpent (or, as in Anatole France's Penguin Island, by the priest); the dangerous advance of lawmen into the wilderness; the eruption of base instincts in some primitive setting. How many of our ideas about politics can be traced to these tales!

Two types of myth above all have dominated Western political thinking, and so our selections fall neatly into two groups. First, there are the myths of Eden and the golden age, which played such an important part in Christian and classical thought, retold here by Milton in a passage from Paradise Lost. In more modern form—the cautious sensuality of Milton becoming almost programmatic—the same dream of harmony and love pervades the eighteenth century literature of exploration. New lands are an ideal place to discover a lost nature: thus the legendary South Sea Islands, which offer the additional advantage of allowing paradise to coexist in time with the legalized oppression of advanced civilizations. Denis Diderot's Supplement to Bougain-ville's "Voyage" describes a dramatic encounter between a South Sea native and a European explorer, and through this device the author turns the ancient myth into a sharp challenge to his own contemporaries. For the French philosophe is in no sense philo-sophically disinterested; his work suggests that the Eden story is a perennial source of social criticism. But writers who accept this happy view of nature and make demands in its name must face the disquieting facts that paradise is distant in time or space and that it neither endures nor expands. Paradise is always lost, and this loss must be explained. In Penguin Island Anatole France elaborates one of the key mythic explanations: the intrusion of "advanced" men. Inspired in large part by Rousseau (though his literary style is closer to Voltaire's), France writes a witty philo-sophical tale of the simultaneous origins of civilization and degeneracy, of decent dress and sexual lust, of property and oppression.

The second type of myth is the precise opposite of the first: It includes tales of anti-Edens, descriptions of nature that em-phasize only egoism, aggression, and war. Thomas Hobbes's Leviathan is the finest philosophical version of this view, and the central theme of that work echoes throughout Rudyard Kipling's short story "How Fear Came." For "only when there is one great Fear over all, as there is now, can we of the jungle lay aside our little fears, and meet together in one place . . ." Society and the state are the products of a single shared fear, Kipling suggests; though he does not go on to show, as Hobbes does, that they are only preserved through the establishment of a single overall authority always feared by everyone. That never happens in the Jungle.

Perhaps the most important and the most complete cultural elaboration of the Hobbesian myth is to be found in the novels and films that deal with the American West. On the frontier all men are equal not because they share some universal human qualities, but because, as Hobbes wrote, anyone can kill anyone else. The Colt .45 is the "great equalizer." And the equality of ungoverned men breeds a general warfare and a general fearful-ness that is ended only by the arrival of a lawman who is a better

gunman than any of the others and so inspires a greater fear.
James Agee's film script for The Bride Comes to Yellow Sky
(adapted from a story by Stephen Crane) describes the final
triumph of the law: a confrontation between the last outlaw, who
still embodies the freedom of the frontier, and the last heroic
marshal, no longer a lone, masculine figure, but married now, the
herald of respectability and the police.

But there is another way into civilized and political life, and
perhaps a better one. It is open, or so Jean-Jacques Rousseau
thought, to men already at some remove from the primitive harmony of the first state of nature but not yet degenerate, not yet
evangelized by apostles of some "higher" culture. What such
people need is not an agreement to support a marshal and reg-
ulate their competitive wars, but rather an agreement to cooperate among themselves so that the wars do not begin. Jean
Giono's Joy of Man's Desiring contains one of the few explicit
literary descriptions of such an agreement—of Rousseau's social
contract—of that rare and moving moment when a group of
individual men and women unite to become, perhaps only briefly,
"one common body."

THE VISION OF PARADISE

John Milton

From *Paradise Lost*

. . . Thus was this place,
A happy rural seat of various view:
Groves whose rich trees wept odorous gums and balm;
Others whose fruit, burnished with golden rind,
Hung amiable—Hesperian fables true,
If true, here only—and of delicious taste.
Betwixt them lawns, or level downs, and flocks
Grazing the tender herb, were interposed,
Or palmy hillock; or the flowery lap
Of some irriguous valley spread her store,
Flowers of all hue, and without thorn the rose.
Another side, umbrageous grots and caves
Of cool recess, o'er which the mantling vine
Lays forth her purple grape, and gently creeps
Luxuriant; meanwhile murmuring waters fall
Down the slope hills dispersed, or in a lake,
That to the fringèd bank with myrtle crowned
Her crystal mirror holds, unite their streams.
The birds their choir apply; airs, vernal airs,
Breathing the smell of field and grove, attune
The trembling leaves, while universal Pan,
Knit with the Graces and the Hours in dance,
Led on th' eternal Spring. Not that fair field
Of Enna, where Proserpin gathering flowers,
Herself a fairer flower, by gloomy Dis
Was gathered—which cost Ceres all that pain
To seek her through the world—nor that sweet grove
Of Daphne, by Orontes and th' inspired
Castalian spring, might with this Paradise
Of Eden strive; nor that Nyseian isle,
Girt with the river Triton, where old Cham,

Book IV, ll. 245–355.

5

Whom Gentiles Ammon call and Libyan Jove,
Hid Amalthea, and her florid son,
Young Bacchus, from his stepdame Rhea's eye;
Nor, where Abassin kings their issue guard,
Mount Amara (though this by some supposed
True Paradise) under the Ethiop line
By Nilus' head, enclosed with shining rock,
A whole day's journey high, but wide remote
From this Assyrian garden, where the Fiend
Saw undelighted all delight, all kind
Of living creatures, new to sight and strange.
Two of far nobler shape, erect and tall,
God-like erect, with native honour clad
In naked majesty, seemed lords of all,
And worthy seemed; for in their looks divine
The image of their glorious Maker shone,
Truth, wisdom, sanctitude severe and pure—
Severe, but in true filial freedom placed,
Whence true authority in men: though both
Not equal, as their sex not equal seemed;
For contemplation he and valour formed,
For softness she and sweet attractive grace;
He for God only, she for God in him.
His fair large front and eye sublime declared
Absolute rule; and hyacinthine locks
Round from his parted forelock manly hung
Clustering, but not beneath his shoulders broad:
She, as a veil down to the slender waist,
Her unadornèd golden tresses wore
Dishevelled, but in wanton ringlets waved
As the vine curls her tendrils, which implied
Subjection, but required with gentle sway,
And by her yielded, by him best received
Yielded, with coy submission, modest pride,
And sweet, reluctant, amorous delay.
Nor those mysterious parts were then concealed;
Then was not guilty shame. Dishonest shame
Of Nature's works, honour dishonourable,
Sin-bred, how have ye troubled all mankind
With shows instead, mere shows of seeming pure,
And banished from man's life his happiest life,

Simplicity and spotless innocence!
So passed they naked on, nor shunned the sight
Of God or Angel; for they thought no ill:
So hand in hand they passed, the loveliest pair
That ever since in love's embraces met—
Adam the goodliest man of men since born
His sons; the fairest of her daughters Eve.
Under a tuft of shade that on a green
Stood whispering soft, by a fresh fountain-side,
They sat them down; and, after no more toil
Of their sweet gardening labour than sufficed
To recommend cool Zephyr, and make ease
More easy, wholesome thirst and appetite
More grateful, to their supper-fruits they fell—
Nectarine fruits, which the compliant boughs
Yielded them, sidelong as they sat recline
On the soft downy bank damasked with flowers.
The savoury pulp they chew, and in the rind,
Still as they thirsted, scoop the brimming stream;
Nor gentle purpose, nor endearing smiles
Wanted, nor youthful dalliance, as beseems
Fair couple linked in happy nuptial league,
Alone as they. About them frisking played
All beasts of th' earth, since wild, and of all chase
In wood or wilderness, forest or den.
Sporting the lion ramped, and in his paw
Dandled the kid; bears, tigers, ounces, pards,
Gambolled before them; th' unwieldy elephant,
To make them mirth, used all his might, and wreathed
His lithe proboscis; close the serpent sly,
Insinuating, wove with Gordian twine
His braided train, and of his fatal guile
Gave proof unheeded. Others on the grass
Couched, and, now filled with pasture, gazing sat,
Or bedward ruminating; for the sun,
Declined, was hasting now with prone career
To th' ocean isles, and in th' ascending scale
Of Heaven the stars that usher evening rose: . . .

THE ENCOUNTER WITH CIVILIZATION

Denis Diderot

From *Supplement to Bougainville's "Voyage"*

In the sharing of Bougainville's crew among the Tahitians, the almoner was allotted to Orou; they were about the same age, thirty-five to thirty-six. Orou had then only his wife and three daughters, called Asto, Palli and Thia. They undressed the almoner, bathed his face, hands and feet, and served him a wholesome and frugal meal. When he was about to go to bed, Orou, who had been absent with his family, reappeared, and presenting to him his wife and three daughters, all naked, said: "You have eaten, you are young and in good health; if you sleep alone you will sleep badly, for man needs a companion beside him at night. There is my wife, there are my daughters; choose the one who pleases you best. But if you wish to oblige me you will give preference to the youngest of my daughters, who has not yet had any children." The mother added: "Alas! But it's no good complaining about it; poor Thia! it is not her fault."

The almoner answered that his religion, his office, good morals and decency would not allow him to accept these offers.

Orou replied: "I do not know what this thing is that you call 'religion'; but I can only think ill of it, since it prevents you from tasting an innocent pleasure to which nature, the sovereign mistress, invites us all; prevents you from giving existence to one of your own kind, from doing a service which a father, mother and children all ask of you, from doing something for a host who has received you well, and from enriching a nation, by giving it one more citizen. I do not know what this thing is which you call your 'office' but your first duty is to be a man and to be grateful. I do not suggest that you should introduce into your country the ways of Orou, but Orou, your host and friend, begs you to lend yourself to the ways of Tahiti. Whether the ways of Tahiti are better or worse than yours is an easy question to decide. Has the land of your birth more people than it

From *Diderot: Interpreter of Nature*, edited by J. Kemp. Reprinted by permission of International Publishers Co. Inc., copyright © 1943.

can feed? If so your ways are neither worse nor better than ours. But can it feed more than it has? Our ways are better than yours. As to the sense of decency which you offer as objection, I understand you; I agree that I was wrong, and I ask your pardon. I do not want you to injure your health; if you are tired, you must have rest; but I hope that you will not continue to sadden us. See the care you have made appear on all these faces; they fear lest you should have found blemishes on them which merit your disdain. But when it is only the pleasure of doing honour to one of my daughters, amidst her companions and sisters, and of doing a good action, won't that suffice you? Be generous!"

THE ALMONER: It's not that: they are all equally beautiful but my religion! my office!

OROU: They are mine and I offer them to you; they are their own and they give themselves to you. Whatever may be the purity of conscience which the thing 'religion' and the thing 'office' prescribe, you can accept them without scruple. I am not abusing my authority at all; be sure that I know and respect the rights of the individual.

Here the truthful almoner agrees that Providence had never exposed him to such violent temptation. He was young, he became agitated and tormented; he turned his eyes away from the lovely suppliants, and then regarded them again; he raised his hands and eyes to the sky. Thia, the youngest, clasped his knees and said: "Stranger, do not distress my father and mother, do not afflict me. Honour me in the hut, among my own people; raise me to the rank of my sisters, who mock me. Asto, the eldest, already had three children; the second, Palli, has two; but Thia has none at all. Stranger, honest stranger, do not repulse me; make me a mother, make me a child that I can one day lead by the hand, by my side, here in Tahiti; who may be seen held at my breast in nine months' time; one of whom I shall be so proud and who will be part of my dowry when I go from my parents' hut to another's. I shall perhaps be more lucky with you than with our young Tahitians. If you will grant me this favour I shall never forget you; I shall bless you all my life. I shall write your name on my arm and on your son's; we shall pronounce it always with joy. And when you leave these shores, my good wishes will go with you on the seas till you reach your own land."

The candid almoner said that she clasped his knees, and gazed into his eyes so expressively and so touchingly; that she wept; that her father, mother and sisters withdrew; that he remained alone with her, and that, still saying "my religion, my office," he found himself the next morning lying beside the young girl, who overwhelmed him with caresses, and who invited her parents and sisters, when they came to their bed in the morning, to join their gratitude to hers. Asto and Palli, who had withdrawn, returned bringing food, fruits and drink. They kissed their sister and made vows over her. They all ate together.

Then Orou, left alone with the almoner, said to him:

"I see that my daughter is well satisfied with you and I thank you. But would you teach me what is meant by this word 'religion' which you have repeated so many times and so sorrowfully?"

The almoner, after having mused a moment answered: "Who made your hut and the things which furnish it?"

OROU: I did.

THE ALMONER: Well then, we believe that this world and all that it contains is the work of a maker.

OROU: Has he feet, hands and a head then?

THE ALMONER: No.

OROU: Where is his dwelling-place?

THE ALMONER: Everywhere.

OROU: Here too?

THE ALMONER: Here.

OROU: We have never seen him.

THE ALMONER: One doesn't see him.

OROU: That's an indifferent father, then! He must be old, for he will at least be as old as his work.

THE ALMONER: He does not age. He spoke to our ancestors, gave them laws, prescribed the manner in which he wished to be honoured; he ordered a certain behaviour as being good, and he forbade them certain other actions as being wicked.

OROU: I follow you; and one of the actions he forbade them, as wicked, was to lie with a woman or a girl? Why then, did he make two sexes?

THE ALMONER: That they might unite; but with certain requisite conditions, after certain preliminary ceremonies in consequence of which the man belongs to the woman and only to her; and the woman belongs to the man, and only to him.

OROU: For their whole lives?

THE ALMONER: For the whole of their lives.

OROU: So that if it happened that a woman should lie with a man other than her husband, or a husband with another woman

. . . but that couldn't happen. Since the maker is there and this displeases him, he will know how to prevent them doing it.

THE ALMONER: No; he lets them do it, and they sin against the law of God (for it is thus we call the great maker) against the law of the country; and they commit a crime.

OROU: I should be sorry to offend you by what I say, but if you would permit me, I would give you my opinion.

THE ALMONER: Speak.

OROU: I find these singular precepts opposed to nature and contrary to reason, made to multiply crimes and to plague at every moment this old maker, who has made everything, without help of hands, or head, or tools, who is everywhere and is not seen anywhere, who exists to-day and to-morrow and yet is not a day older, who commands and is not obeyed, who can prevent and yet does not do so. Contrary to nature because these precepts suppose that a free, thinking and sentient being can be the property of a being like himself. On what is this law founded? Don't you see that in your country they have confused the thing which has neither consciousness nor thought, nor desire, nor will; which one picks up, puts down, keeps or exchanges, without injury to it, or without its complaining, have confused this with the thing which cannot be exchanged or acquired, which has liberty, will, desire, which can give or refuse itself for a moment or for ever, which laments and suffers, and which cannot become an article of commerce, without its character being forgotten and violence done to its nature; contrary to the general law of existence? In fact, nothing could appear to you more senseless than a precept which refuses to admit that change which is a part of us, which commands a constancy which cannot be found there and which violates the liberty of the male and female by chaining them for ever to each other; more senseless than a fidelity which limits the most capricious of enjoyments to one individual; than an oath of the immutability of two beings made of flesh; and all that in the face of a sky which never for a moment remains the same, in caverns which threaten destruction, below a rock which falls to powder, at the foot of a tree which cracks, on a stone which rocks? Believe me, you have made the condition of man worse than that of animals. I do not know what your great maker may be; but I rejoice that he has never spoken to our forefathers, and I wish that he may never speak to our children; for he might tell them the same foolishness, and they commit the folly of believing it. Yesterday, at supper, you mentioned 'magistrates' and 'priests,' whose authority regulates your conduct; but, tell me, are they the masters of good and evil? Can they make what is just to be unjust, and unjust, just? Does it rest with them to attribute good to harmful actions, and evil to innocent or useful actions? You could not think it, for, at that rate, there would be neither true nor false, good nor bad, beautiful nor ugly; or at any rate only what pleased your great maker, your magistrates and your priests to pronounce so. And from one moment to another you would be obliged to change your ideas and your conduct. One day someone would tell you, on behalf of one of your three masters, to kill, and you would be obliged by your conscience to kill; another day, "steal," and you would have to steal; or "do not eat this fruit" and you would not dare to eat it; "I forbid you this vegetable or animal" and you would take care not to touch them. There is no good thing that could not be forbidden you, and no wickedness that you could not be ordered to do. And what would you be reduced to, if your three masters, disagreeing among themselves, should at once permit, enjoin and forbid you the same thing, as I believe must often happen. Then, to please the priest you must become embroiled with the magistrate; to satisfy the magistrate you must displease the great maker; and to make yourself agreeable to the great maker you must renounce nature. And do you know what will happen then? You will neglect all of them, and you will be neither man, nor citizen, nor pious; you will be nothing; you will be out of favour with all the kinds of authorities, at odds even with yourself, tormented by your heart, persecuted by your enraged masters; and wretched as I saw you yesterday evening when I offered my wife and daughters to you, and you cried out, "But my religion, my office!"

Do you want to know what is good and what is bad in all times and in all places? Hold fast to the nature of things and of actions; to your relations with your fellows; to the influence of your conduct on your individual usefulness and the general good. You are mad if you believe that there is anything, high or low in the universe, which can add to or subtract from the laws of nature. Her eternal will is that good should be preferred to evil, and the general good to the individual good. You may ordain the opposite but you will not be obeyed. You will multiply the number of malefactors and the wretched by fear, punishment and remorse. You will deprave consciences; you will corrupt minds. They will not know what to do or what to avoid. Disturbed in their state of innocence, at ease with crime, they will have lost their guiding star. Answer me sincerely;

in spite of the express orders of your three lawgivers, does a young man, in your country, never lie with a young girl without their permission?

THE ALMONER: I should deceive you if I asserted it.

OROU: Does a woman who has sworn to belong only to her husband never give herself to another man?

THE ALMONER: Nothing is more common.

OROU: Your lawgivers either punish or do not punish; if they punish they are ferocious beasts who fight against nature; if they do not punish, they are imbeciles who have exposed their authority to contempt by an empty prohibition.

THE ALMONER: The culprits who escape the severity of the law are punished by popular condemnation.

OROU: That is to say, justice is exercised through the lack of common sense of the whole nation, and the foolishness of opinion does duty for laws.

THE ALMONER: A girl who has been dishonoured will not find a husband.

OROU: Dishonoured! Why?

THE ALMONER: An unfaithful wife is more or less despised.

OROU: Despised! But why?

THE ALMONER: The young man is called a cowardly seducer.

OROU: A coward, a seducer! But why?

THE ALMONER: The father and mother and child are desolated. The unfaithful husband is a libertine; the betrayed husband shares his wife's shame.

OROU: What a monstrous tissue of extravagances you've just revealed to me! And yet you don't say everything; for as soon as one allows oneself to dispose at pleasure of the ideas of justice and ownership, to take away or to give an arbitrary character to things, to attribute or deny good or evil to certain actions, capriciously, then one can be censorious, vindictive, suspicious, tyrannical, envious, jealous, deceitful. There is spying, quarrelling, cheating and lying; daughters deceive their parents, wives their husbands. Girls, yes, I don't doubt it, will strangle their infants, suspicious fathers will hate and neglect theirs, mothers will leave them and abandon them to their fates. And crime and debauchery will show themselves in all their forms. I know all that as if I had lived among you. It is so, because it must be so; and your society, of which your leader boasts because of its good regulations, will only be a swarm of hypocrites who secretly trample all laws under foot; or of unfortunates who are themselves the instruments of their own suffering in submitting; or of imbeciles in whom prejudices have quite stifled the voice of nature; or of abnormal monsters in whom nature does not protest her rights.

PARADISE LOST

Anatole France

From *Penguin Island*

One day St. Maël was sitting by the seashore on a warm stone that he found. He thought it had been warmed by the sun and he gave thanks to God for it, not knowing that the Devil had been resting on it. The apostle was waiting for the monks of Yvern who had been commissioned to bring a freight of skins and fabrics to clothe the inhabitants of the island of Alca.

Soon he saw a monk called Magis coming ashore and carrying a chest upon his back. This monk enjoyed a great reputation for holiness.

When he had drawn near to the old man he laid the chest on the ground and wiping his forehead with the back of his sleeve, he said:

"Well, father, you wish then to clothe these penguins?"

"Nothing is more needful, my son," said the old man. "Since they have been incorporated into the family of Abraham these penguins share the curse of Eve, and they know that they are naked, a thing of which they were ignorant before. And it is high time to clothe them, for they are losing the down that remained on them after their metamorphosis."

"It is true," said Magis as he cast his eyes over the coast where the penguins were to be seen looking for shrimps, gathering mussels, singing, or sleeping, "they are naked. But do you not think, father, that it would be better to leave them naked? Why clothe them?

From *Penguin Island* by Anatole France, Book II, Chs. 2 and 3; translated by A. V. Evans. Published 1909 by John Lane, The Bodley Head. Reprinted by permission of The Bodley Head and Dodd, Mead & Company, Inc. Copyright 1909 by Dodd, Mead & Company, Inc. Copyright renewed 1937 by A. W. Evans.

When they wear clothes and are under the moral law they will assume an immense pride, a vile hypocrisy, and an excessive cruelty."

"Is it possible, my son," sighed the old man, "that you understand so badly the effects of the moral law to which even the heathen submit?"

"The moral law," answered Magis, "forces men who are beasts to live otherwise than beasts, a thing that doubtless puts a constraint upon them, but that also flatters and reassures them; and as they are proud, cowardly, and covetous of pleasure, they willingly submit to restraints that tickle their vanity and on which they found both their present security and the hope of their future happiness. That is the principle of all morality. . . . But let us not mislead ourselves. My companions are unloading their cargo of stuffs and skins on the island. Think, father, while there is still time! To clothe the penguins is a very serious business. At present when a penguin desires a penguin he knows precisely what he desires and his lust is limited by an exact knowledge of its object. At this moment two or three couples of penguins are making love on the beach. See with what simplicity! No one pays any attention and the actors themselves do not seem to be greatly preoccupied. But when the female penguins are clothed, the male penguin will not form so exact a notion of what it is that attracts him to them. His indeterminate desires will fly out into all sorts of dreams and illusions; in short, father, he will know love and its mad torments. And all the time the female penguins will cast down their eyes and bite their lips, and take on airs as if they kept a treasure under their clothes! . . . what a pity!

"The evil will be endurable as long as these people remain rude and poor; but only wait for a thousand years and you will see, father, with what powerful weapons you have endowed the daughters of Alca. If you will allow me, I can give you some idea of it beforehand. I have some old clothes in this chest. Let us take at hazard one of these female penguins to whom the male penguins give such little thought, and let us dress her as well as we can.

"Here is one coming towards us. She is neither more beautiful nor uglier than the others; she is young. No one looks at her. She strolls indolently along the shore, scratching her back and with her finger at her nose as she walks. You cannot help seeing, father, that she has narrow shoulders, clumsy breasts, a stout figure, and short legs. Her reddish knees pucker at every step she takes, and there is, at each of her joints, what looks like a little monkey's head. Her broad and sinewy feet cling to the rock with their four crooked toes, while the great toes stick up like the heads of two cunning serpents. She begins to walk, all her muscles are engaged in the task, and, when we see them working, we think of her as a machine intended for walking rather than as a machine intended for making love, although visibly she is both, and contains within herself several other pieces of machinery besides. Well, venerable apostle, you will see what I am going to make of her."

With these words the monk, Magis, reached the female penguin in three bounds, lifted her up, carried her in his arms with her hair trailing behind her, and threw her, overcome with fright, at the feet of the holy Maël.

And whilst she wept and begged him to do her no harm, he took a pair of sandals out of his chest and commanded her to put them on.

"Her feet," observed the old man, "will appear smaller when squeezed in by the woollen cords. The soles, being two fingers high, will give an elegant length to her legs and the weight they bear will seem magnified."

As the penguin tied on her sandals she threw a curious look towards the open coffer, and seeing that it was full of jewels and finery, she smiled through her tears.

The monk twisted her hair on the back of her head and covered it with a chaplet of flowers. He encircled her wrist with golden bracelets and making her stand upright, he passed a large linen band beneath her breasts, alleging that her bosom would thereby derive a new dignity and that her sides would be compressed to the greater glory of her hips.

He fixed this band with pins, taking them one by one out of his mouth.

"You can tighten it still more," said the penguin.

When he had, with much care and study, enclosed the soft parts of her bust in this way, he covered her whole body with a rose-coloured tunic which gently followed the lines of her figure.

"Does it hang well?" asked the penguin.

And bending forward with her head on one side and her chin on her shoulder, she kept looking attentively at the appearance of her toilet.

Magis asked her if she did not think the dress a little long, but she answered with assurance that it was not—she would hold it up.

Immediately, taking the back of her skirt in her left hand, she drew it obliquely across her hips, taking care to disclose a glimpse of her heels. Then she went away, walking with short steps and swinging her hips.

She did not turn her head, but as she passed near a stream she glanced out of the corner of her eye at her own reflection.

A male penguin, who met her by chance, stopped in surprise, and retracing his steps began to follow her. As she went along the shore, others coming back from fishing, went up to her, and after looking at her, walked behind her. Those who were lying on the sand got up and joined the rest.

Unceasingly, as she advanced, fresh penguins, descending from the paths of the mountain, coming out of clefts of the rocks, and emerging from the water, added to the size of her retinue.

And all of them, men of ripe age with vigorous shoulders and hairy breasts, agile youths, old men shaking the multitudinous wrinkles of their rosy, and white-haired skins, or dragging their legs thinner and drier than the juniper staff that served them as a third leg, hurried on, panting and emitting an acrid odour and hoarse gasps. Yet she went on peacefully and seemed to see nothing.

"Father," cried Magis, "notice how each one advances with his nose pointed towards the centre of gravity of that young damsel now that the centre is covered by a garment. The sphere inspires the meditations of geometers by the number of its properties. When it proceeds from a physical and living nature it acquires new qualities, and in order that the interest of that figure might be fully revealed to the penguins it was necessary that, ceasing to see it distinctly with their eyes, they should be led to represent it to themselves in their minds. I myself feel at this moment irresistibly attracted towards that penguin. Whether it be because her skirt gives more importance to her hips, and that in its simple magnificence it invests them with a synthetic and general character and allows only the pure idea, the divine principle, of them to be seen, whether this be the cause I cannot say, but I feel that if I embraced her I would hold in my hands the heaven of human pleasure. It is certain that modesty communicates an invincible attraction to women. My uneasiness is so great that it would be vain for me to try to conceal it."

He spoke, and, gathering up his habit, he rushed among the crowd of penguins, pushing, jostling, trampling, and crushing, until he reached the daughter of Alca, whom he seized and suddenly carried in his arms into a cave that had been hollowed out by the sea.

Then the penguins felt as if the sun had gone out. And the holy

Maël knew that the Devil had taken the features of the monk, Magis, in order that he might give clothes to the daughter of Alca. He was troubled in spirit, and his soul was sad. As with slow steps he went towards his hermitage he saw the little penguins of six and seven years of age tightening their waists with belts made of seaweed and walking along the shore to see if anybody would follow them.

.   .   .

The island did not preserve the rugged appearance that it had formerly, when in the midst of floating icebergs it sheltered a population of birds within its rock amphitheatre. Its snow-clad peak had sunk down into a hill from the summit of which one could see the coasts of Armorica eternally covered with mist, and the ocean strewn with sullen reefs like monsters half raised out of its depths.

Its coasts were now very extensive and clearly defined and its shape reminded one of a mulberry leaf. It was suddenly covered with coarse grass, pleasing to the flocks, and with willows, ancient fig-trees, and mighty oaks. This fact is attested by the Venerable Bede and several other authors worthy of credence.

To the north the shore formed a deep bay that in after years became one of the most famous ports in the universe. To the east, along a rocky coast beaten by a foaming sea, there stretched a deserted and fragrant heath. It was the Beach of Shadows, and the inhabitants of the island never ventured on it for fear of the serpents that lodged in the hollows of the rocks and lest they might encounter the souls of the dead who resembled livid flames. To the south, orchards and woods bounded the languid Bay of Divers. On this fortunate shore old Maël built a wooden church and a monastery. To the west, two streams, the Clange and the Surelle, watered the fertile valleys of Dalles and Dombes.

Now one autumn morning, as the blessed Maël was walking in the valley of Clange in company with a monk of Yvern called Bulloch, he saw bands of fierce-looking men loaded with stones passing along the roads. At the same time he heard in all directions cries and complaints mounting up from the valley towards the tranquil sky.

And he said to Bulloch:

"I notice with sadness, my son, that since they became men the inhabitants of this island act with less wisdom than formerly. When they were birds they only quarrelled during the season of their love affairs. But now they dispute all the time; they pick quarrels with each other in summer as well as in winter. How greatly have they fallen from that peaceful majesty which made the assembly of the penguins look like the Senate of a wise republic!

"Look towards Surelle, Bulloch, my son. In yonder pleasant valley a dozen men penguins are busy knocking each other down with the spades and picks that they might employ better in tilling the ground. The women, still more cruel than the men, are tearing their opponents' faces with their nails. Alas! Bulloch, my son, why are they murdering each other in this way?"

"From a spirit of fellowship, father, and through forethought for the future," answered Bulloch. "For man is essentially provident and sociable. Such is his character and it is impossible to imagine it apart from a certain appropriation of things. Those penguins whom you see are dividing the ground among themselves."

"Could they not divide it with less violence?" asked the aged man. "As they fight they exchange invectives and threats. I do not distinguish their words, but they are angry ones, judging from the tone."

"They are accusing one another of theft and encroachment," answered Bulloch. "That is the general sense of their speech."

At that moment the holy Maël clasped his hands and sighed deeply.

"Do you see, my son," he exclaimed, "that madman who with his teeth is biting the nose of the adversary he has overthrown and that other one who is pounding a woman's head with a huge stone?"

"I see them," said Bulloch. "They are creating law; they are founding property; they are establishing the principles of civilization, the basis of society, and the foundations of the State."

"How is that?" asked old Maël.

"By setting bounds to their fields. That is the origin of all government. Your penguins, O Master, are performing the most august of functions. Throughout the ages their work will be consecrated by lawyers, and magistrates will confirm it."

Whilst the monk, Bulloch, was pronouncing these words a big penguin with a fair skin and red hair went down into the valley carrying a trunk of a tree upon his shoulder. He went up to a little penguin who was watering his vegetables in the heat of the sun, and shouted to him:

"Your field is mine!"

And having delivered himself of this stout utterance he brought down his club on the head of the little penguin, who fell dead upon the field that his own hands had tilled.

At this sight the holy Maël shuddered through his whole body and poured forth a flood of tears.

And in a voice stifled by horror and fear he addressed this prayer to heaven:

"O Lord, my God, O thou who didst receive young Abel's sacrifices, thou who didst curse Cain, avenge, O Lord, this innocent penguin sacrificed upon his own field and make the murderer feel the weight of thy arm. Is there a more odious crime, is there a graver offence against thy justice, O Lord, than this murder and this robbery?"

"Take care, father," said Bulloch gently, "that what you call murder and robbery may not really be war and conquest, those sacred foundations of empires, those sources of all human virtues and all human greatness. Reflect, above all, that in blaming the big penguin you are attacking property in its origin and in its source. I shall have no trouble in showing you how. To till the land is one thing, to possess it is another, and these two things must not be confused; as regards ownership the right of the first occupier is uncertain and badly founded. The right of conquest, on the other hand, rests on more solid foundations. It is the only right that receives respect since it is the only one that makes itself respected. The sole and proud origin of property is force. It is born and preserved by force. In that it is august and yields only to a greater force. This is why it is correct to say that he who possesses is noble. And that big red man, when he knocked down a labourer to get possession of his field, founded at that moment a very noble house upon this earth. I congratulate him upon it."

Having thus spoken, Bulloch approached the big penguin, who was leaning upon his club as he stood in the blood-stained furrow:

"Lord Greatauk, dreaded Prince," said he, bowing to the ground, "I come to pay you the homage due to the founder of legitimate power and hereditary wealth. The skull of the vile Penguin you have overthrown will, buried in your field, attest for ever the sacred rights of your posterity over this soil that you have enobled. Blessed be your sons and your sons' sons! They shall be Greatauks, Dukes of Skull, and they shall rule over this island of Alca."

Then raising his voice and turning towards the holy Maël:

"Bless Greatauk, father, for all power comes from God."

Maël remained silent and motionless, with his eyes raised towards heaven; he felt a painful uncertainty in judging the monk Bulloch's doctrine. It was, however, the doctrine destined to prevail in epochs of advanced civilization. Bulloch can be considered as the creator of civil law in Penguinia.

THE LAW OF THE JUNGLE

Rudyard Kipling

"How Fear Came"

The Law of the Jungle—which is by far the oldest law in the world—has arranged for almost every kind of accident that may befall the Jungle-People, till now its code is as perfect as time and custom can make it. If you have read the other stories about Mowgli, you will remember that he spent a great part of his life in the Seeonee Wolf Pack, learning the Law from Baloo the Brown Bear; and it was Baloo who told him, when the boy grew impatient at the constant orders, that the Law was like the giant creeper, because it dropped across every one's back and no one could escape. "When thou hast lived as long as I have, Little Brother, thou wilt see how all the jungle obeys at least one Law. And that will be no pleasant sight," said Baloo.

This talk went in at one ear and out at the other, for a boy who spends his life eating and sleeping does not worry about anything till it actually stares him in the face. But one year Baloo's words came true, and Mowgli saw all the jungle working under one Law.

It began when the winter rains failed almost entirely, and Sahi the Porcupine, meeting Mowgli in a bamboo thicket, told him that the wild yams were drying up. Now everybody knows that Sahi is ridiculously fastidious in his choice of food, and will eat nothing but the very best and ripest. So Mowgli laughed and said: "What is that to me?"

"Not much *now*," said Sahi, rattling his quills in a stiff, uncomfortable way, "but later we shall see. Is there any more diving into the deep rock-pool below the Bee Rocks, Little Brother?"

From *The Jungle Books* by Rudyard Kipling. Reprinted by permission of Mrs. George Bambridge; Doubleday & Company, Inc.; and The Macmillan Company of Canada.

"No. The foolish water is going all away, and I do not wish to break my head," said Mowgli, who was quite sure he knew as much as any five of the Jungle-People put together.

"That is thy loss. A small crack might let in some wisdom." Sahi ducked quickly to prevent Mowgli from pulling his nose-bristles, and Mowgli told Baloo what Sahi had said. Baloo looked very grave, and mumbled half to himself: "If I were alone I would change my hunting-grounds now, before the others began to think. And yet— hunting among strangers ends in fighting—and they might hurt my man-cub. We must wait and see how the *mohwa* blooms."

That spring the *mohwa*-tree, that Baloo was so fond of, never flowered. The greeny, cream-coloured, wax blossoms were heat-killed before they were born, and only a few bad-smelling petals came down when he stood on his hind legs and shook the tree. Then, inch by inch, the untempered heat crept into the heart of the jungle, turning it yellow, brown, and at last black. The green growths in the sides of the ravines burned up to broken wires and curled films of dead stuff; the hidden pools sank down and caked over, keeping the last least footmark on their edges as if it had been cast in iron; the juicy-stemmed creepers fell away from the trees they clung to and died at their feet; the bamboos withered, clanking when the hot winds blew, and the moss peeled off the rocks deep in the jungle, till they were as bare and as hot as the quivering blue boulders in the bed of the stream.

The birds and the Monkey-People went north early in the year, for they knew what was coming, and the deer and the wild pig broke far away into the perished fields of the villages, dying some-times before the eyes of men too weak to kill them. Chil the Kite stayed and grew fat, for there was a great deal of carrion, and eve-ning after evening he brought the news to the beasts, too weak to force their way to fresh hunting-grounds, that the sun was killing the jungle for three days' flight in every direction.

Mowgli, who had never known what real hunger meant, fell back on stale honey, three years old, scraped out of deserted rock-hives—honey black as a sloe, and dusty with dried sugar. He hunted, too, for deep-boring grubs under the bark of the trees, and robbed the wasps of their new broods. All the game in the jungle was no more than skin and bone, and Bagheera could kill thrice in a night and hardly get a full meal. But the want of water was the worst, for though the Jungle-People drink seldom they must drink deep.

And the heat went on and on, and sucked up all the moisture, till at last the main channel of the Wainganga was the only stream that carried a trickle of water between its dead banks. And when Hathi the Wild Elephant, who lives for a hundred years and more, saw a long, lean blue ridge of rock show dry in the very centre of the stream, he knew that he was looking at the Peace Rock, and then and there he lifted up his trunk and proclaimed the Water Truce, as his father before him had proclaimed it fifty years ago. The deer, wild pig, and buffalo took up the cry hoarsely, and Chil the Kite flew in great circles far and wide, whistling and shrieking the warning.

By the Law of the Jungle it is death to kill at the drinking-places when once the Water Truce has been declared. The reason for this is that drinking comes before eating. Every one in the jungle can scramble along somehow when only game is scarce, but water is water, and when there is but one source of supply, all hunting stops while the Jungle-People go there for their needs. In good seasons, when water was plentiful, those who came down to drink at the Wainganga—or anywhere else, for that matter—did so at the risk of their lives, and that risk made no small part of the fascination of the night's doings. To move down so cunningly that never a leaf stirred; to wade knee-deep in the roaring shallows that drown all noise from behind; to drink, looking backward over one shoulder, every muscle ready for the first desperate bound of keen terror; to roll on the sandy margin, and return, wet-muzzled and well plumped out, to the admiring herd, was a thing that all glossy-horned young bucks took a delight in, precisely because they knew that at any moment Bagheera or Shere Khan might leap upon them and bear them down. But now that life-and-death fun was ended, and the Jungle-People came up, starved and weary, to the shrunken river—tiger, bear, deer, buffalo, and pig together—drank the fouled waters, and hung above them, too exhausted to move off.

The deer and pig had tramped all day in search of something better than dried bark and withered leaves. The buffaloes had found no wallows to be cool in, and no green crops to steal. The snakes had left the jungle and come down to the river in the hope of catching a stray frog. They curled round wet stones, and never offered to strike when the snout of a rooting pig dislodged them. The river-turtles had long ago been killed by Bagheera, cleverest of hunters, and the fish had buried themselves deep in the cracked mud. Only the Peace Rock lay across the shallows like a long snake, and the little tired ripples hissed as they dried on its hot side.

It was here that Mowgli came nightly for the cool and the companionship. The most hungry of his enemies would hardly have cared for the boy then. His naked skin made him look more lean and wretched than any of his fellows. His hair was bleached to tow-colour by the sun; his ribs stood out like the ribs of a basket, and the lumps on his knees and elbows, where he was used to track on all fours, gave his shrunken limbs the look of knotted grass-stems. But his eye, under his matted forelock, was cool and quiet, for Bagheera, his adviser in this time of trouble, told him to move quietly, hunt slowly, and never, on any account, to lose his temper.

"It is an evil time," said the black panther, one furnace-hot evening, "but it will go if we can live till the end. Is thy stomach full, man-cub?"

"There is stuff in my stomach, but I get no good of it. Think you, Bagheera, the rains have forgotten us and will never come again?"

"Not I. We shall see the *mohwa* in blossom yet, and the little fawns all fat with new grass. Come down to the Peace Rock and hear the news. On my back, Little Brother."

"This is no time to carry weight. I can still stand alone, but—indeed we be no fatted bullocks, we two."

Bagheera looked along his ragged, dusty flank and whispered: "Last night I killed a bullock under the yoke. So low was I brought that I think I should not have dared to spring if he had been loose. *Wou!*"

Mowgli laughed. "Yes, we are great hunters now," said he. "I am very bold—to eat grubs." And the two came down together through the crackling undergrowth to the river bank and the lace-work of shoals that ran out from it in every direction.

"The water cannot live long," said Baloo, joining them. "Look across! Yonder are trails like the roads of Man."

On the level plain of the farther bank the stiff jungle-grass had died standing, and, dying, had mummied. The beaten tracks of the deer and the pig, all leading towards the river, had striped that colourless plain with dusty gullies driven through the ten-foot grass, and, early as it was, each long avenue was full of first-comers hastening to the water. You could hear the does and fawns coughing in the snuff-like dust.

Up-stream, at the bend of the sluggish pool around the Peace Rock, and warden of the Water Truce, stood Hathi the Wild Elephant, with his sons, gaunt and grey in the moonlight, rocking to and fro—always rocking. Below him a little were the vanguard of the deer; below these, again, the pig and the wild buffalo; and on the opposite bank, where the tall trees came down to the water's edge, was the place set apart for the Eaters of Flesh—the tiger, the wolves, the panther, the bear, and the others.

"We be under one Law, indeed," said Bagheera, wading into the water and looking across at the lines of clicking horns and staring eyes where the deer and the pig pushed each other to and fro. "Good hunting, all of you of my blood," he added, lying down at full length, one flank thrust out of the shallows. And then, between his teeth: "But for that which is the Law it would be *very* good hunting."

The quick-spread ears of the deer caught the last sentence, and a frightened whisper ran along the ranks. "The Truce! Remember the Truce!"

"Peace there, peace!" gurgled Hathi the Wild Elephant. "The Truce holds, Bagheera. This is no time to talk of hunting."

"Who should know better than I?" Bagheera answered, rolling his yellow eyes up-stream. "I am an eater of turtle—a fisher of frogs. *Ngaayah!* Would I could get good from chewing branches!"

"*We* wish so, very greatly," bleated a young fawn, who had only been born that spring, and did not at all like it. Wretched as the Jungle-People were, even Hathi could not help chuckling, while Mowgli, lying on his elbows in the warm water, laughed aloud, and beat up the foam with his feet.

"Well spoken, little bud-horn," Bagheera purred. "When the Truce ends that shall be remembered in thy favour." And he looked keenly through the darkness to make sure of recognizing the fawn again.

Gradually the talk spread up and down the drinking-places. You could hear the scuffling, snorting pig asking for more room, the buffaloes grunting among themselves as they lurched out across the sandbars, and the deer telling pitiful stories of their long footsore searches in quest of food. Now and again they asked some question of the Eaters of Flesh across the river, but all the news was bad, and the roaring hot wind of the jungle came and went, between the rocks and the rattling branches, and scattered twigs and dust on the water.

"The Men-Folk too, they die beside their ploughs," said a young sambur. "I passed three between sunset and night. They lay still, and their bullocks with them. We also shall lie still in a little."

"The river has fallen since last night," said Baloo. "O Hathi, hast thou ever seen the like of this drouth?"

"It will pass, it will pass," said Hathi, squirting water along his back and sides.

"We have one here that cannot endure long," said Baloo, and he looked towards the boy he loved.

"I?" said Mowgli indignantly, sitting up in the water. "I have no long fur to cover my bones, but—but if thy hide were pulled off, Baloo—"

Hathi shook all over at the idea, and Baloo said severely:

"Man-cub, that is not seemly to tell a Teacher of the Law. *Never* have I been seen without my hide."

"Nay, I meant no harm, Baloo, but only that thou art, as it were, like the cocoanut in the husk, and I am the same cocoanut all naked. Now that brown husk of thine—" Mowgli was sitting cross-legged, and explaining things with his forefinger in his usual way, when Bagheera put out a paddy paw and pulled him over back-wards into the water.

"Worse and worse," said the black panther, as the boy rose spluttering. "First, Baloo is to be skinned and now he is a cocoanut. Be careful that he does not do what the ripe cocoanuts do."

"And what is that?" said Mowgli, off his guard for the minute, though that is one of the oldest catches in the jungle.

"Break thy head," said Bagheera quietly, pulling him under again.

"It is not good to make a jest of thy teacher," said the bear, when Mowgli had been ducked for the third time.

"Not good! What would ye have? That naked thing running to and fro makes a monkey-jest of those who have once been good hunters, and pulls the best of us by the whiskers for sport." This was Shere Khan, the Lame Tiger, limping down to the water. He waited a little to enjoy the sensation he made among the deer on the op-posite bank; then he dropped his square, frilled head and began to lap, growling: "The jungle has become a whelping-ground for naked cubs now. Look at me, man-cub!"

Mowgli looked—stared, rather—as insolently as he knew how, and in a minute Shere Khan turned away uneasily. "Man-cub this, and man-cub that," he rumbled, going on with his drink. "The cub is neither man nor cub, or he would have been afraid. Next sea-son I shall have to beg his leave for a drink. *Aurgh!*"

"That may come, too," said Bagheera, looking him steadily between the eyes. "That may come, too. . . . *Faugh*, Shere Khan! What new shame hast thou brought here?"

The Lame Tiger had dipped his chin and jowl in the water, and dark oily streaks were floating from it downstream.

"Man!" said Shere Khan coolly. "I killed an hour since." He went on purring and growling to himself.

The line of beasts shook and wavered to and fro, and a whisper went up that grew to a cry: "Man! Man! He has killed Man!" Then all looked towards Hathi the Wild Elephant, but he seemed not to hear. Hathi never does anything till the time comes, and that is one of the reasons why he lives so long.

"At such a season as this to kill Man! Was there no other game afoot?" said Bagheera scornfully, drawing himself out of the tainted water, and shaking each paw, cat-fashion, as he did so.

"I killed for choice—not for food." The horrified whisper began again, and Hathi's watchful little white eye cocked itself in Shere Khan's direction. "For choice," Shere Khan drawled. "Now come I to drink and make me clean again. Is there any to forbid?"

Bagheera's back began to curve like a bamboo in a high wind, but Hathi lifted up his trunk and spoke quietly.

"Thy kill was from choice?" he asked, and when Hathi asks a question it is best to answer.

"Even so. It was my right and my night. Thou knowest, O Hathi." Shere Kahn spoke almost courteously.

"Yea, I know," Hathi answered. And, after a little silence: "Hast thou drunk thy fill?"

"For to-night, yes."

"Go, then. The river is to drink, and not to defile. None but the Lame Tiger would have boasted of his right at this season when—when we suffer together—Man and Jungle-People alike. Clean or unclean, get to thy lair, Shere Khan!"

The last words rang out like silver trumpets, and Hathi's three sons rolled forward half a pace, though there was no need. Shere Khan slunk away, not daring to growl, for he knew—what every one else knows—that when the last comes to the last Hathi is the master of the jungle.

"What is this right Shere Khan speaks of?" Mowgli whispered in Bagheera's ear. "To kill Man is *always* shameful. The Law says so. And yet Hathi says—"

"Ask him. I do not know, Little Brother. Right or no right, if

Hathi had not spoken I would have taught that lame butcher his lesson. To come to the Peace Rock fresh from a kill of Man—and to boast of it—is a jackal's trick. Besides, he tainted the good water."

Mowgli waited for a minute to pick up his courage, because no one cared to address Hathi directly, and then he cried: "What is Shere Khan's right, O Hathi?" Both banks echoed his words, for all the people of the jungle are intensely curious, and they had just seen something that no one, except Baloo, who looked very thoughtful, seemed to understand.

"It is an old tale," said Hathi, "a tale older than the jungle. Keep silence along the banks, and I will tell that tale."

There was a minute or two of pushing and shouldering among the pigs and the buffalo, and then the leaders of the herds grunted, one after another: "We wait." And Hathi strode forward till he was almost knee-deep in the pool by the Peace Rock. Lean and wrinkled and yellow-tusked through he was, he looked what the jungle held him to be—their master.

"Ye know, children," he began, "that of all things ye most fear Man." There was a mutter of agreement.

"This tale touches thee, Little Brother," said Bagheera to Mowgli.

"I? I am of the pack—a hunter of the Free People," Mowgli answered. "What have I to do with Man?"

"And ye do not know why ye fear Man?" Hathi went on. "This is the reason. In the beginning of the jungle, and none know when that was, we of the jungle walked together, having no fear of one another. In those days there was no drouth, and leaves and flowers and fruit grew on the same tree, and we ate nothing at all except leaves and flowers and grass and fruit and bark."

"I am glad I was not born in those days," said Bagheera. "Bark is only good to sharpen claws."

"And the Lord of the Jungle was Tha, the First of the Elephants. He drew the jungle out of deep waters with his trunk, and where he made furrows in the ground with his tusks, there the rivers ran, and where he struck with his foot, there rose ponds of good water, and when he blew through his trunk—thus—the trees fell. That was the manner in which the jungle was made by Tha, and so the tale was told to me."

"It has not lost fat in the telling," Bagheera whispered, and Mowgli laughed behind his hand.

"In those days there was no corn or melons or pepper or sugar-cane, nor were there any little huts such as ye have all seen. And the

Jungle-People knew nothing of Man, but lived in the jungle together, making one people. But presently they began to dispute over their food, though there was grazing enough for all. They were lazy. Each wished to eat where he lay, as sometimes we may do now when the spring rains are good. Tha, the First of the Elephants, was busy making new jungles and leading the rivers in their beds. He could not walk everywhere, so he made the First of the Tigers the master and the judge of the jungle, to whom the Jungle-People should bring their disputes. In those days the First of the Tigers ate fruit and grass with the others. He was as large as I am, and he was very beautiful, in colour all over like the blossom of the yellow creeper. There was never stripe nor bar upon his hide in those good days when the jungle was new. All the Jungle-People came before him without fear, and his word was the Law of all the jungle. We were then, remember ye, one people. Yet, upon a night, there was a dispute between two bucks—a grazing-quarrel such as ye now try out with the head and the fore feet—and it is said that as the two spoke together before the First of the Tigers lying among the flowers, a buck pushed him with his horns, and the First of the Tigers forgot that he was the master and judge of the jungle, and, leaping upon that buck, broke his neck.

"Till that night never one of us had died, and the First of the Tigers, seeing what he had done, and being made foolish by the scent of the blood, ran away into the Marshes of the North, and we of the jungle, left without a judge, fell to fighting among ourselves. Tha heard the noise of it and came back. And some of us said this and some of us said that, but he saw the dead buck among the flowers, and asked who had killed, and we of the jungle would not tell because the smell of the blood made us foolish, even as that same smell makes us foolish to-day. We ran to and fro in circles, capering and crying out and shaking our heads. So therefore Tha gave an order to the trees that hang low, and to the trailing creepers of the jungle, that they should mark the killer of the buck that he should know him again. And Tha said: 'Who will now be master of the Jungle-People?' Then up leaped the grey ape who lives in the branches, and said: 'I will now be master of the jungle.' At this Tha laughed, and said: 'So be it,' and went away very angry.

"Children, ye know the grey ape. He was then as he is now. At the first he made a wise face for himself, but in a little while he began to scratch and to leap up and down, and when Tha returned he found the grey ape hanging, head down, from a bough, mocking those who stood below; and they mocked him again. And so there was no Law in the jungle—only foolish talk and senseless words.

"Then Tha called us all together and said: 'The first of your masters has brought Death into the jungle, and the second Shame. Now it is time there was a Law, and a Law that ye may not break. Now ye shall know Fear, and when ye have found him ye shall know that he is your master, and the rest shall follow.' Then we of the jungle said: 'What is Fear?' And Tha said: 'Seek till ye find.' So we went up and down the jungle seeking for Fear, and presently the buffaloes—"

"Ugh!" said Mysa, the leader of the buffaloes, from their sand-bank.

"Yes, Mysa, it was the buffaloes. They came back with the news that in a cave in the jungle sat Fear, and that he had no hair, and went upon his hind legs. Then we of the jungle followed the herd till we came to that cave, and Fear stood at the mouth of it, and he was, as the buffaloes had said, hairless, and he walked upon his hinder legs. When he saw us he cried out, and his voice filled us with the fear that we have now, and we ran away, tramping upon and tearing each other because we were afraid. That night, it was told to me, we of the jungle did not lie down together as used to be our custom, but each tribe drew off by itself—the pig with the pig, the deer with the deer; horn to horn, hoof to hoof—like keeping to like, and so lay shaking in the jungle.

"Only the First of the Tigers was not with us, for he was still hidden in the marshes of the North, and when word was brought to him of the Thing we had seen in the cave, he said: 'I will go to this Thing and break his neck.' So he ran all the night till he came to the cave, but the trees and the creepers on his path, remembering the order Tha had given, let down their branches and marked him as he ran, drawing their fingers across his back, his flank, his forehead, and his jowl. Wherever they touched him there was a mark and a stripe upon his yellow hide. *And those stripes do his children wear to this day!* When he came to the cave, Fear, the Hairless One, put out his hand and called him 'the Striped One That Comes by Night,' and the First of the Tigers was afraid of the Hairless One, and ran back to the swamps howling."

Mowgli chuckled quietly here, his chin in the water.

"So loud did he howl that Tha heard him and said: 'What is the sorrow?' And the First of the Tigers, lifting up his muzzle to the new-made sky, which is now so old, said: 'Give me back my power,

O Tha. I am made ashamed before all the jungle, and I have run away from a Hairless One, and he has called me a shameful name.' 'And why?' said Tha. 'Because I am smeared with the mud of the marshes,' said the First of the Tigers. 'Swim, then, and roll on the wet grass, and if it be mud it will surely wash away,' said Tha. And the First of the Tigers swam, and rolled, and rolled, till the jungle ran round and round before his eyes, but not one little bar upon his hide was changed, and Tha, watching him, laughed. Then the First of the Tigers said: 'What have I done that this comes to me?' Tha said: 'Thou hast killed the buck, and thou hast let Death loose in the jungle, and with Death has come Fear, so that the people of the jungle are afraid one of the other as thou art afraid of the Hairless One.' The First of the Tigers said: 'They will never fear me, for I knew them since the beginning.' Tha said: 'Go and see.' And the First of the Tigers ran to and fro, calling aloud to the deer and the pig and the sambur and the porcupine and all the Jungle-Peoples, but they all ran away from him who had been their judge, because they were afraid.

"Then the First of the Tigers came back, his pride was broken in him, and, beating his head upon the ground, he tore up the earth with all his feet and said: 'Remember that I was once the master of the jungle! Do not forget me, O Tha. Let my children remember that I was once without shame or fear!' And Tha said: 'This much will I do, because thou and I together saw the jungle made. For one night of each year it shall be as it was before the buck was killed—for thee and for thy children. In that one night, if ye meet the Hairless One—and his name is Man—ye shall not be afraid of him, but he shall be afraid of you as though ye were judges of the jungle and masters of all things. Show him mercy in that night of his fear, for thou hast known what Fear is.'

"Then the First of the Tigers answered: 'I am content.' But when next he drank he saw the black stripes upon his flank and his side, and he remembered the name that the Hairless One had given him, and he was angry. For a year he lived in the marshes, waiting till Tha should keep his promise. And upon a night when the Jackal of the Moon [the Evening Star] stood clear of the jungle, he felt that his night was upon him, and he went to that cave to meet the Hairless One. Then it happened as Tha promised, for the Hairless One fell down before him and lay along the ground, and the First of the Tigers struck him and broke his back, for he thought that there was but one such a Thing in the jungle, and that he had killed Fear.

Then, nosing above the kill, he heard Tha coming down from the woods of the North, and presently the voice of the First of the Elephants, which is the voice that we hear now—"

The thunder was rolling up and down the dry, scarred hills, but it brought no rain—only heat-lightning that flickered behind the ridges—and Hathi went on:

"*That* was the voice he heard, and it said: 'Is this thy mercy?' The First of the Tigers licked his lips and said: 'What matter? I have killed Fear.' And Tha said: 'O blind and foolish! Thou hast untied the feet of Death, and he will follow thy trail till thou diest. Thou hast taught Man to kill!'

"The First of the Tigers, standing stiffly to his kill, said: 'He is as the buck was. There is no Fear. Now I will judge the Jungle-Peoples once more.'

"And Tha said: 'Never again shall the Jungle-Peoples come to thee. They shall never cross thy trail, nor sleep near thee, nor follow after thee, nor browse by thy lair. Only Fear shall follow thee, and with a blow that thou canst not see shall bid thee wait his pleasure. He shall make the ground to open under thy feet, and the creeper to twist about thy neck, and the tree-trunks to grow together about thee higher than thou canst leap, and at the last he shall take thy hide to wrap his cubs when they are cold. Thou hast shown him no mercy, and none will he show thee.'

"The First of the Tigers was very bold, for his night was still on him, and he said: 'The promise of Tha is the promise of Tha. He will not take away my night?' And Tha said: 'Thy one night is thine, as I have said, but there is a price to pay. Thou hast taught Man to kill, and he is no slow learner.'

"The First of the Tigers said: 'He is here under my foot, where his back is broken. Let the jungle know that I have killed Fear.'

"Then Tha laughed and said: 'Thou hast killed one of many, but thou thyself shalt tell the jungle—for thy night is ended!'

"So the day came, and from the mouth of the cave went out another Hairless One, and he saw the kill in the path, and the First of the Tigers above it, and he took a pointed stick—"

"They throw a thing that cuts now," said Sahi, rustling down the bank, for Sahi was considered uncommonly good eating by the Gonds—they called him Ho-Igoo—and he knew something of the wicked little Gondi axe that whirls across a clearing like a dragon-fly.

"It was a pointed stick, such as they set in the foot of a pit-trap," said Hathi. "And throwing it, he struck the First of the Tigers deep in the flank. Thus it happened as Tha said, for the First of the Tigers ran howling up and down the jungle till he tore out the stick, and all the jungle knew that the Hairless One could strike from far off, and they feared more than before. So it came about that the First of the Tigers taught the Hairless One to kill—and ye know what harm that has since done to all our peoples—through the noose, and the pitfall, and the hidden trap, and the flying stick, and the stinging fly that comes out of white smoke [Hathi meant the rifle], and the Red Flower that drives us into the open. Yet for one night in the year the Hairless One fears the tiger, as Tha promised, and never has the tiger given him cause to be less afraid. Where he finds him, there he kills him, remembering how the First of the Tigers was made ashamed. For the rest, Fear walks up and down the jungle by day and by night."

"*Ahi! Aoo!*" said the deer, thinking of what it all meant to them.

"And only when there is one great Fear over all, as there is now, can we of the jungle lay aside our little fears, and meet together in one place as we do now."

"For one night only does Man fear the tiger?" said Mowgli.

"For one night only," said Hathi.

"But I—but we—but all the jungle knows that Shere Khan kills Man twice and thrice in a moon."

"Even so. *Then* he springs from behind and turns his head aside as he strikes, for he is full of fear. If Man looked at him he would run. But on his night he goes openly down to the village. He walks between the houses and thrusts his head into the doorway, and the men fall on their faces, and there he does his kill. One kill in that night."

"Oh!" said Mowgli to himself, rolling over in the water. "*Now* I see why Shere Khan bade me look at him. He got no good of it, for he could not hold his eyes steady, and—and I certainly did not fall down at his feet. But then I am not a man, being of the Free People."

"*Umm!*" said Bagheera deep in his furry throat. "Does the tiger know his night?"

"Never till the Jackal of the Moon stands clear of the evening mist. Sometimes it falls in the dry summer and sometimes in the wet rains—this one night of the tiger. But for the First of the Tigers this would never have been, nor would any of us have known fear."

The deer grunted sorrowfully, and Bagheera's lips curled in a wicked smile. "Do men know this—tale?" said he.

"None know it except the tigers, and we, the elephants—the children of Tha. Now ye by the pools have heard it, and I have spoken."

Hathi dipped his trunk into the water as a sign that he did not wish to talk.

"But—but—but," said Mowgli, turning to Baloo, "why did not the First of the Tigers continue to eat grass and leaves and trees? He did but break the buck's neck. He did not *eat*. What led him to the hot meat?"

"The trees and the creepers marked him, Little Brother, and made him the striped thing that we see. Never again would he eat their fruit, but from that day he revenged himself upon the deer, and the others, the Eaters of Grass," said Baloo.

"Then *thou* knowest the tale. *Heh?* Why have I never heard?"

"Because the jungle is full of such tales. If I made a beginning there would never be an end to them. Let go my ear, Little Brother."

THE END OF THE STATE OF WAR

James Agee

From *The Bride Comes to Yellow Sky*

YOUNG MAN: Scratchy Wilson's drunk an' he's turned loose with both hands.

Both Mexicans set down their unfinished beers and fade out the rear door. The Drummer views with mystification; nobody pays any attention to him. They're as quick and efficient as a well-rehearsed fire-drill. Jasper and Ed go out the front door and close the window shutters. The young man bolts the rear door. Laura Lee bars the window on her side and goes center, swinging shut one leaf of the plank door. As Jasper and Ed return, Jasper swings the other shut and bars his window and Ed brings from the corner the bar for the main door and helps Laura Lee put it in place. Laura Lee returns to her place behind the bar. In the sudden, solemn, chapel-like gloom, the Drummer is transfixed; his eyes glitter.

DRUMMER: Say, what *is* this?

A silent reaction from the men.

DRUMMER (continuing): Is there going to be a gun-fight?

JASPER (grimly): Dunno if there'll be a fight or not, but there'll be some shootin'—some good shootin'.

YOUNG MAN: Oh, there's a fight just *waitin'* out there in the street, if anyone wants it.

Jasper and Ed nod solemnly.

DRUMMER (to young man): What'd ye say his name was?
ALL: Scratchy Wilson.

The Drummer does a fast multiple take, person-to-person.

DRUMMER: What're you goin' to do?

Grim silence.

DRUMMER (continuing): Does he do this often?

More silence.

DRUMMER (continuing): Can he break down that door?

LAURA LEE: No: he's give that up. But when he comes you'd better lay down on the floor, stranger. He's dead sure to *shoot* at that door, an' there's no tellin' what a stray bullet might do.

The Drummer, keeping a strict eye on the door, begins carefully removing the stocking from his arm.

DRUMMER: Will he kill anybody?

The men laugh low and scornfully.

JASPER: He's out to shoot, an' he's out fer trouble. Don't see no good *experimentin'* with him.

DRUMMER: But what do you *do* in a case like this? What do you do?

YOUNG MAN: Why, he an' Jack Potter—

JASPER AND ED (across him): Jack ain't back yet.

YOUNG MAN (suddenly frightened): *Lordy!*

DRUMMER: Well who's he? What's *he* got to do with it?

YOUNG MAN: He's Marshal.

LAURA LEE: Comes to shootin', he's the only one in town can go up agin him.

> Far off, o.s. we HEAR a wild Texas yell, a shot, another yell. Everyone becomes very still and tense.

DRUMMER (half whispered):   That must be him comin', hey?

> The men look at him in irritation and look away again. They wait, their eyes shining in the gloom. Jasper holds up three fingers. Moving like a ghost, Laura Lee gets out three glasses and the bottle. The Drummer lifts one forlorn finger; she adds another glass. They pour. In unison they snap the drinks down at a gulp and walk to windows to look through chinks. The Drummer quietly puts a coin on the bar. Laura Lee just looks at it, at him, and away.

> He shamefacedly takes back his coin. She silently takes a Winchester from beneath the bar and breaks it.

DRUMMER (whispered):   You goin' to *shoot* him?

> Silence; everyone looks at him bleakly.

LAURA LEE (low):   Not if I can help it. I ain't a good enough shot. Might kill him.

DRUMMER: Well, it'd be pure self defense if you did, wouldn't it?

> No answer.

DRUMMER (continuing):   Well, *wouldn't* it? Good riddance *too, I'd* say.

> Laura Lee closes the breech.

LAURA LEE (low):   Mister, Scratchy Wilson's an old friend. Nobody'd harm a hair of his head if they's any way out—let alone kill him. You see, trouble is, he's a wonder with a gun. Just a wonder. An' he's a terror when he's drunk. So when he goes on the war trail, we hunt our holes—naturally.

DRUMMER: But—why do they allow him—what's he doin' in a town like this?

LAURA LEE: He's the last of the old gang that used to hang out along the river here.

> A silence. Then nearer, but distant, a howl is heard. The Drummer reacts, jittery.

LAURA LEE (continuing): You better come back o' the bar. I kinda fixed it up.

DRUMMER (ashamed): No thanks, I'll—

LAURA LEE (with a peremptory gesture): Come on.

> He does. He squats low in the front angle of the bar and examines, with some relief, the various plates of scrap metal with which she has armored it. O.S., nearer we HEAR another shot and three yowls. There's a shuffling of feet. They look at each other.

MEN (quietly): Here he comes!

> PAN SHOT
> We DOLLY with Laura Lee, carrying her gun, to look through a chink in the shutter, and through the chink see Scratchy round the corner at the far end of the empty street, yelling, a long heavy blue-black revolver in either hand. We HEAR his words, distant, but preternaturally powerful, as he strides to the middle of the street and stops dead, both guns alert, threatening and at bay.

SCRATCHY: *Yaller Sky, hyar I come!*

> MEDIUM SHOT—SCRATCHY
> He holsters a revolver, extracts a pint bottle from his belt, cocks it vertically and drains it, and tosses it high and glittering into the sunlight, in midair; then shoots it into splinters, left-handed, and does a quick 360-degree whirl, drawing both guns, as if against enemies ambushing him from the rear. He raises a small tornado of dust. CUT TO A HEAD CLOSEUP into which he finishes his pivot, glaring. His eyes are glittering, drunk, mad, frightening. He is eaten up with some kind of interior bitter wildness.

SCRATCHY (a low growl): Got ye, ye yaller-bellies!

> PULL DOWN AND AWAY. He gives a lonely Texas yowl; the echoes die. He glares all about him; his eyes, focusing on something O.S., take on sudden purpose.

SCRATCHY (loud): Jack Potter!

> MEDIUM SHOT—WITH STILL CAMERA—POTTER'S HOUSE—FREEZE CLOSER SHOT—SCRATCHY
> trying to adjust his eyes to this oddity.

SCRATCHY (louder): Jack Potter!

> MED. SHOT—POTTER'S HOUSE—AS BEFORE

SCRATCHY'S VOICE (O.S.): You heared me, Jack Potter. Come on out an' face the music. 'Caze it's time to dance.

CLOSE SHOT—SCRATCHY

Dead silence.
He is puzzled.

SCRATCHY: 'Tain't no ways like you Potter, asullin' there in yer house. You ain't no possum. I treated ye fair an' square. I saved it all up for ye, like I told ye. Now you play square with me.

FRANK'S VOICE (o.s., scared):   Hey, Scratchy.

SCRATCHY (puzzled, looking around):   How's that? Who *is* that?

POTTER'S HOUSE—PAST SCRATCHY.

FRANK'S VOICE: Hit's me. Frank.

SCRATCHY: Why don't ye say so. Whar ye at?

FRANK'S VOICE: I'm up yere in the jail.

SCRATCHY: Well *show* yerself! What ye skeered of?

FRANK'S VOICE: You.

SCRATCHY: Me? Shucks. Only man needs to be skeered o' me is Jack Potter, the yaller hound.

FRANK'S VOICE: Jack ain't here, Scratchy.

SCRATCHY: What ye mean he ain't here?

FRANK'S VOICE: He ain't got back yet, that's what I mean. That's what I was tryin' to tell you.

SCRATCHY: Ain't back! Don't gimme none o' that. He come back yesterday when he promised he would.

FRANK'S VOICE: No he didn't.

SCRATCHY: You lie to *me*. Frank Gudger, I'll give ye what *fer*.

He shoots, striking a bar and ringing a musical note.

FRANK'S VOICE: Scratchy! Don't do that! Hit's dangersome.

SCRATCHY: Not if ye keep yer head low it ain't.

FRANK'S VOICE: 'Tis too. Ye can't tell *whar* them bullets'll *re*bound.

SCRATCHY: Don't you dast tell me how to shoot, ye pore wall-eyed woods colt. *Is* Jack Potter back or *ain't* he?

FRANK'S VOICE: No he ain't and that's the honest truth.

SCRATCHY: Don't you *sass me*.

CLOSE SHOT

Scratchy shoots another bar, ringing a different musical note, which is followed by a shattering of glass.

SCRATCHY (continuing):   Is he back?

FRANK'S VOICE: Quit it, Scratchy. Ye done busted my lamp chimbley.

SCRATCHY: *Is* he back or *ain't* he?

FRANK'S VOICE: All right, have it yer own way. He's back if you say so.

SCRATCHY: Well, why didn't you tell me so straight off?

No answer.

SCRATCHY (continuing):   Why don't he come on out then?

FRANK'S VOICE: Reckon he would if he was inside.

SCRATCHY: Oh, he ain't inside, huh?

FRANK'S VOICE: Not that I know of.

SCRATCHY: Well, that leaves just one other place for him to be.

He turns toward the "Weary Gentleman," hikes his trousers, reaches for the bottle which is no longer there.

SCRATCHY (growling and starting):   Dad burn it. Never seed it yet I didn't run out just at the wrong time!

He walks fast past the respectable houses, the churches and so on, and DOLLYING, SHOOTING PAST HIM, we see they all have an unearthly quietness. As he walks, he talks, now to himself, now shouting.

SCRATCHY (continuing):   But that's all right. Just lay low. 'Caze quick as I wet my whistle, I'm gonna show ye some shootin'!

He stops in front of Morgan's house.

SCRATCHY (continuing):   You, Jasper Morgan. Yeah, and that snivellin' woman o' yourn, too! Too dainty to do like ordinary folks. Too high an' mighty! Git yerself a lot o'fancy plumbing, an' ye ain't man enough to clean out yer own cess-pool. "Let Scratchy do it." Ain't nuthin' so low but Scratchy'll do it for the price of a pint.

He glares around for a target. He spies a potted fern suspended from the porch ceiling. He shoots the suspension chain and the whole thing drops to the porch floor with a foomp. There! Clean that up! He turns, Deacon's house is opposite.

SCRATCHY (continuing; a horrible travesty of a sissy voice): *Dea-con!* Oh *Deacon Smee-eed!* (he makes two syllables of Smeed) You home, Deacon? Kin I pay ye a little call? *Most* places in town, ye just *knock* an' walk *in,* but that ain't *good* enough for a *good* man, *is* it, Deacon? Oh *no!* No—*no!* Pay a little call on the Deacon, ye got to shove a 'lectric bell, real special. (a hard shift of tone) All right, Smeed, start singin' them psalms o' yourn. You'll be whangin' 'em on a harp, few mo' minutes, you an' yer missuz, too. Can't stop in right now, I'm a mite too thirsty. But I'll be back, Deacon. Oh, I'll be back. (he studies the house) Here's my callin' card.

He takes careful aim, and

INSERT
Hits the doorbell, so fusing it that it rings continuously. We HEAR a woman scream hysterically.

CLOSE SHOT OF SCRATCHY

SCRATCHY: Ah, quit it. Don't holler 'til yer hurt.

INT. DEACON'S HOUSE—DEACON AND WIFE
Past Deacon and his wife, through the curtained window, we see Scratchy pass.
The Deacon has an arm around his wife. He is trying pathetically to resemble an intrepid doomed frontiersman in an Indian fight.

DEACON: He'll pay for this. By the Almighty, he'll pay dearly. I'm not going to stand for it, I'm simply not going—

MRS. SMEED: Oh hush. For goodness sake, stop that horrid *bell!*

He looks at her, goes into the hallway with wounded dignity, and jerks a wire loose. Just as the bell stops, there is a shot and the stinging SOUND o.s. of the church bell being shot at. The Deacon reacts to this latest outrage.

MEDIUM SHOT—UPWARD—CHURCH BELL—FROM SCRATCHY'S VIEW-POINT
CLOSE SHOT—SHOOTING DOWN—SCRATCHY

looking up at bell, both pleased and angry, and shooting again at the church bell.

SCRATCHY (he bellows):   Come on out and fight if you dast— only you don't dast.

He starts glancing all around; the revolvers in each hand are as sensitive as snakes; the little fingers play in a musician-like way; INTER-CUT with still facades of details of greater stillness; a motionless curtain of machine-made lace with a head dimly silhouetted behind; a drawn shade, with an eye and fingertips visible at the edge.

SCRATCHY (continuing):   Oh no! You know who's *boss* in *this* town. Marcellus T. Wilson, that's who. He ain't fittin' to wipe yer boots on, no-sirree, he's the lowest of the low, but he's boss all the same. 'Caze *this* is a boss (gesturing with a revolver), an' *this* is a boss (another), an' this is the feller that can boss the both of 'em better'n any other man that's left in this wore-out womanizin' country. An' there ain't hardly a man of ye dast *touch* a gun, let alone come up agin a *man* with one. Oh no! Got li'l ole honeybunch to worry about, li'l ole wifey-pifey, all the young 'uns, make ye some easy money runnin' a store, doctorin', psalm-singing, fix ye a purty lawn so Scratchy kin cut it for ye, if ye can't get a Mex cheap enough. Oh, I—(he searches helplessly, then half-says)—hate—I could wipe every one of ye offen the face o' the earth, a-hidin' behind yore women's skirts, ever' respectable last one of ye! Come out an' fight! Come on! Come on! Dad *blast* ye!

He glares all around again. There is no kind of response at all. His attention shifts; his eyes focus on something o.s., he becomes purposeful.

EXT. "WEARY GENTLEMAN" SALOON—BARRICADED—DAY

DOLLY SHOT over Scratchy's shoulder as he advances on door.
CUT TO

MEDIUM CLOSE SHOT—SCRATCHY
He comes to door and hammers on it with gun butt.

SCRATCHY: Laura Lee. (pause) Laura Lee. (pause)

Now he hammers with both revolvers.

SCRATCHY (continuing; yelling):   *Laura Lee!* (no answer) You can't fool me. I know you're there. Open up. I want a drink. (no answer) All I want's a little drink.

Now he hammers harder than ever. Over SOUND of hammering, CUT INSIDE

TO CLOSE SHOTS IN THIS ORDER

CLOSE SHOT—LAURA LEE
low behind bar, her rifle ready if need be, thumb on safety.

CLOSE SHOT—THREE LOCAL MEN
on floor, watching the door fixedly.

CLOSE SHOT—THE DRUMMER
behind the bar, plenty scared.

CLOSE SHOT—BACK TO SCRATCHY
finishing his hammering. He is rather tired. He glares at the door a moment, then:

SCRATCHY: All right then. All right.

He looks around him, sore. He sights a scrap of paper in the dirt, picks it up, and with a vicious and cruel thrust, nails it to the door with a knife. Then he turns his back contemptuously on the saloon, walks to the far side of the street and, spinning quickly and lithely, fires at the sheet of paper.

INSERT
The bullet misses by half an inch.

SCRATCHY AS BEFORE

SCRATCHY: Well, I. Gah . . . gittin' old in yer old age, Scratchy.

He takes careful aim and fires.

INSERT
The bullet splits the haft of the knife; the blade clatters down; the paper follows, fluttering; a hole appears in the door.

CLOSE SHOT—INT. WEARY GENTLEMAN
Jasper is on floor, between a chair and a spittoon. Bullet flicks wood from chair, ricochets with appropriate SOUNDS, puncturing spittoon from which dark liquid oozes. Jasper, with slow horror, looks at it.

FROM SCRATCHY'S VIEWPOINT
the paper finishes settling.

CLOSE SHOT—SCRATCHY
He is satisfied; he turns and starts walking grandly away. Suddenly he cries out:

SCRATCHY: Hey! (and stops and faces the saloon again) Hey, tell Jack Potter to come on out o' there like a man!

REVERSE ANGLE—OVER SCRATCHY
No answer.

SCRATCHY (continuing; yelling):   *Jack!* JACK POTTER?

CLOSE SHOT—INT. SALOON

LAURA LEE: Jack Potter ain't here, Scratchy, an' you know it! 'Cause if he was, he'd be out thar arter ye.

CLOSE SHOT—SCRATCHY
He hesitates, thinks it over.

SCRATCHY (uncertainly): You wouldn't fool me, would ye, Laura Lee?

LAURA LEE'S VOICE (o.s.): I never did, did I?

SCRATCHY: Well don't never you try it. 'Caze I ain't the man'll stand fer it. (suddenly sore) That lyin' no-'count Frank! I'll fix *him!* I'll cook *his* goose!

HE STARTS OUT FAST UP THE STREET—there is the SOUND of a distant train whistle o.s. Over it   DISSOLVE TO

INT. PARLOR CAR—DAY
SOUND of dying wail of whistle o.s. Throughout scene, SOUND of slowing train.

TWO SHOT—POTTER AND BRIDE
Tension and emotion increase in their faces.

POTTER (with desperate finality): Well—

She looks to him anxiously—he meets her eyes briefly and both smile, then lower their eyes pathetically. He gratefully thinks of *something* to do.

POTTER (continuing): Better git down our trunk.

With day-coach reflex, he stands up, reaching for the non-existent baggage rack, realizes his mistake, and pretends he is only tidying his clothes.

PORTER'S VOICE (o.s., loud and glad): Don't you bother, mister—
                                                            CUT TO

CLOSE SHOT—PORTER
grinning.

PORTER (continuing)—: I got it all ready an' waitin'!

FULL SHOT
Some amused heads turn.

BRIDE AND POTTER AS BEFORE
He sits down abashed. Train SOUND is much slower. Their time is short.

POTTER (smiling and wretched): Home at last.
BRIDE (uneasy): Mm-hmm.

A silence.

CLOSE SHOT—POTTER
in real desperation. o.s. SOUND of train bell.

POTTER (sweating; rapidly): Say listen. You ain't goana like me fer this an' I don't blame ye, but I just can't face 'em if we can help it, not right yet. What I want, I want to sorta *sneak* in, if we can git away with it, an' make home without nobody seein' us, an' then study what to do about 'em. I figure we got a chance if we kinda skin along the hind side o' Main Street. We got cover 'til about sixty foot from my door. Would ye do it?

CAMERA PULLS AND PANS into TWO SHOT—POTTER AND BRIDE

BRIDE (fervent): Oh gee, if only they don't ketch us!

POTTER (incredulously grateful): You don't hate me fer it?

BRIDE (with all her heart): *Hate* you?

They look at each other with entirely new love. The train is stopping. They get up fast and leave the shot.   CUT TO

EXT. STATION YELLOW SKY—DAY
As train pulls to a stop, PAN AND DOLLY into CLOSE UP-SHOT of train steps. The Porter descends first and leaves the shot. Potter, with Bride behind and above him, peers anxiously forward along the station platform.

LONG SHOT—HIS VIEWPOINT
The empty platform.

MEDIUM SHOT—PANNING

POTTER (over shoulder): Come on girl. Hurry.

He steps to platform, she follows unassisted. He grabs up both bags and, looking back to her, collides with the untipped, dismayed Porter.

POTTER: Oh.

He sets down bags. A fumbling rush for change. He hands out a coin.

POTTER (continuing): Much obliged.

He picks up bags and starts walking, the Bride alongside.

POTTER: Let's git outa here.

PORTER (across him): Much obliged to *you*, sir.

Potter walks away so fast that she has to hustle to keep alongside.

Both are eagle-eyed—he with anxiety, she with that and with simple interest.

REVERSE ANGLE SHOT
We glimpse an empty segment of street.

BRIDE'S VOICE (o.s.):   Gee, I don't see nobody.

BRIDE AND POTTER AS BEFORE

POTTER: Just the hot time o' day, let's not risk it.

They walk still faster around rear corner of station and out of sight.
CUT TO

CLOSE SHOT—CELL WINDOW IN POTTER'S HOUSE
It is empty; very, very slowly a little mirror rises to eye level above the sill—and jerks down fast.

CLOSE SHOT
between the rear of two buildings toward the vacant Main Street. Potter's head comes CLOSE INTO SHOT, then the Bride's.

POTTER (whispering):   All right.

They dart noiselessly across the gap.

POTTER (continuing):   Good girl.

They laugh, low and sheepish, and steal ahead. CAMERA PANS WITH THEM l. to r.

POTTER (still whispering):   Next corner, dear, an' I can show you our home.

BRIDE (same):   Oh, Jack.

She stops. Her eyes are damp. He stops.

POTTER (whispering):   Sumpin' the matter?

VERY CLOSE SHOT—BRIDE

BRIDE: The way you said that!

POTTER'S VOICE (o.s.):   Said what?

BRIDE (moved):   Our home!

She smiles very shyly. He is moved and says, in a most embarrassed voice:

POTTER: Come on then, girl.—Let's *get* there.

ANOTHER ANGLE

They start walking fast and quiet; we PAN with them, approaching the frame corner of a house.

POTTER (continuing): Now right the next second, you can see it!

They continue. We LEAD THEM slightly as they circle the corner and come face to face with a CLOSE SHOT of SCRATCHY. He is leaning against the wall, just around the corner, reloading. Instantly he drops this revolver, whips the other from its holster, and aims it at Potter's chest.

A deadly silence.

REVERSE ANGLE—OVER SCRATCHY ONTO POTTER AND BRIDE
The Bride grabs Potter's right arm. He drops both bags and exhibits the desperate reflex of a man whose fighting arm has never before been encumbered. He reaches for the gun that is not there. He sweeps her behind him.

CLOSEUP—SCRATCHY

CLOSE SHOT—THE BRIDE

Her face looks crumpled with terror; she gazes at the gun as at an apparitional snake.

CLOSE SHOT—POTTER

He looks up from the gun into Scratchy's eyes.

CLOSE SHOT—THE REVOLVER

CAMERA RISES SLOWLY TO BRING IN SCRATCHY IN EXTREME CLOSEUP. His eyes are cold and mad; his face is almost solemn.

SCRATCHY (almost reproachfully): Tried to sneak up on me. Tried to sneak up on me!

TWO SHOT OF THE MEN—THE BRIDE BEHIND POTTER
Potter makes a slight movement; Scratchy thrusts his revolver venomously forward; CAMERA LUNGES FORWARD CORRESPONDINGLY.

CLOSE SHOT OF SCRATCHY

SCRATCHY (he smiles with a new and quiet ferocity): No, don't ye do it, Jack Potter. Don't you move a finger towards a gun just yet. Don't you bat an eyelash. The time has come fer me to settle with you, so I aim to do it my own way, an' loaf along without no interferin'. So if ye don't want a gun bent on ye, or a third eye right now, just mind what I tell ye.

He slowly raises his revolver to eye level, so that it is pointing a little upward, DEAD INTO THE LENS

CLOSE SHOT—POTTER—PAST GUN
He is looking directly down the barrel. He is not at all a cowardly

man but he is looking directly into the eye of death. Sweat breaks
out on his face.

EXTREME CLOSE SHOT
looking down the pistol barrel.

EXTREME CLOSE SHOT—POTTER
then,

THE BRIDE'S FACE, saying "our home" (without sound) and smiling.

RETURN TO POTTER
His eyes, a little dizzily out of focus, restore to normal.

POTTER (quietly): I ain't got a gun, Scratchy. Honest I ain't.
You'll have to do all the shootin' yerself.

CLOSE SHOT—SCRATCHY—PAST POTTER
He goes livid and steps forward and lashes his weapon to and fro.

SCRATCHY: Don't you tell me you ain't got no gun on you, you
whelp. Don't tell me no lie like that. There ain't a man in Texas ever
seen you without no gun. Don't take me fer no kid.

His eyes blaze with light; his throat works like a pump.

CLOSE SHOT—POTTER—PAST SCRATCHY

POTTER: I ain't takin' you fer no kid. I'm takin' you fer a damned
fool. I tell you I ain't got a gun an' I ain't. If you're gonna shoot me
up, ya better do it now; you'll never get a chance like this again.

PULL AWAY INTO TWO SHOT—Scratchy calms a little.

SCRATCHY (sneering): If you ain't got a gun, why ain't you got
a gun? Been to Sunday school?

POTTER: You know where I been. I been in San Antone. An' I
ain't got a gun because I just got married. An' if I'd thought there
was goin' to be any galoots like you prowlin' around, when I brought
my wife home, I'd a had a gun, an' don't you fergit it.

SCRATCHY (says the word with total, uncomprehending vacancy):
Married?

POTTER: Yes, married. I'm married.

SCRATCHY (a little more comprehension): Married? You mean,
you? (he backs off a pace; the arm and pistol drop) No. (he studies
Potter cagily and shakes his head)

Then literally for the first time, he sees the Bride.

SCRATCHY (continuing): What's that ye got there? Is this the lady?

POTTER: Yes, this is the lady.

A silence.

SCRATCHY: Well, I s'pose it's all off now.

POTTER: It's all off if you say so, Scratchy. You know I didn't make the trouble.

He picks up both valises.

NEW SHOT—SCRATCHY—OVER POTTER
He studies Potter up and down, slowly, incredulously. Then he looks at the ground.

SCRATCHY: Well, I 'low it's off, Jack. (he shakes his head) *Married!*

He looks up with infinite reproach, sadness and solitude. He picks up his fallen revolver. He hefts it and turns both revolvers in his hands, looking at them, then puts them with finality into their holsters. Then he again meets Potter's eyes.

SCRATCHY (continuing; almost inaudibly):   G'bye, Jack.

CLOSE SHOT—POTTER
He begins to comprehend; he is moved.

POTTER: 'Bye, Scratchy.

THE SOCIAL CONTRACT

Jean Giono

From *Joy of Man's Desiring*

Bobi was uneasy about Aurore, and when he entered the house, he looked at once to see if she were there. Neither she nor Madame Hélène. A little later, Madame Hélène arrived, but alone. Then Joséphine entered, with a wisp of oats in her teeth, looking as if there were nothing unusual.

From Chapter 20; translated by K. A. Clarke. Reprinted by permission of the author.

"Here is what I have to say," said Bobi. "First, who has any wheat?"

"What?" said Jacquou. And then: "I have some."

They all said:

"We all have some. Who has wheat? Why, sure, we all have some. Why?"

"Wait, and you'll see," said Bobi. "Have *you* any?"

He had turned to Randoulet.

"I have," said Randoulet.

"He's a liar," said Le Noir, "like a tooth-puller."

"Mind your own business," said Randoulet.

"If I did," said Le Noir, "you'd be in a fine way!"

The master-shepherd's eyes were shining and his mouth bright red as if his words were burning.

Randoulet went: "Bo, bo!" and shrugged his shoulders.

"A hard head, a little pitcher, a saltlick, a mountain of manure, a hazel nut, an animal forehead, and a headache—that's what you are," said Le Noir.

"You ought to talk to your master more respectfully," said Honorine.

"For," said Randoulet, "if ever you talk rough to me, I'll start you out on the long roads, some day or other. Look out for your tongue!"

"Look," said Le Noir, "he hasn't any wheat. This fellow is dying with his mouth open."

"No!" shouted Randoulet.

"We are all right," said Honorine.

"But," said Bobi, "your wheat? On what part of your land have you sown it?"

"I beg your pardon?" said Randoulet.

"Where is your wheat field?"

"You know very well I haven't any."

"Then it is wheat that grows in the air?"

"It is wheat that grows with sous," said Le Noir, "and I can see the time coming when that man is going to say to me: 'Let's go down to the plains with the sheep.' For he will be forced to sell some, maybe to sell all of them, to make sous and to buy flour. For that fellow you see there, who is my boss and who hasn't any fields, that fellow, my fine people, harvests without need of sun or scythe. But do you know what he is harvesting and what he makes his bread of? He makes his bread of his happiness. He has never been so happy as he has been since he got his big flock up in his big meadow. But you'll see that maybe tomorrow, or the day after tomorrow, or next week, he'll say to me: 'Come along, Le Noir, we're going down to the plains.' And he will go and sell everything. Because I have seen what is left in the flour barrel. I know. I am not talking just words. I am not talking to say: 'I have wheat.' *I* am not a liar, I'm not."

Randoulet shrugged his shoulders, but he hung his head.

"You, you have a habit of talking to yourself when you are alone in the fields with your sheep," he said. "Up there, what you say is not important. But there are people here. It isn't necessary to say things that hurt."

"I didn't mean to hurt you."

"Marthe," said Bobi, "just show what you have done with Randoulet's wool."

Marthe said: "Move a little."

Jacquou stepped aside. Marthe lifted the lid of the flour trough. She took out of it the woollen cloth.

"I put it in there," she said, "to dry it a little. But not to bleach it. The wool was as white as snow."

She shook it out. Flour dust filled the four big rays of sunshine that fell from the window.

"Look," said Marthe. "Feel."

The women crowded around her.

"Don't lower the comb," said Barbe, "but strike it a sharp blow on the woof and then, instead of making the 'wheat grain' weave, it will make you the 'rice grain' weave. It is firmer," she added.

"What do you think of it?" said Bobi. "Suppose we were dressed like that?"

"That white," said Jacquou, "isn't practical for going about the land or the stables."

"There is a blackish wool," said Randoulet.

"Yes," said Bobi, "and just the colour of the earth."

"There is the sap of the eglantine," said Jourdan, "if you let it drop into a pot and boil it, it gives a green colour to dye the wool."

"As for that," said Barbe, "you also have the husk of corn that makes a yellow, and ever so many other things."

"We'll find out about them all," said Jourdan.

"But," said Marthe, "you haven't seen yet how this looks on a person. Come here a moment, Zulma."

The piece of cloth was three metres long and two wide.

"Take off your straw crown," said Randoulet.

"Leave it on her," said Honorine.

Marthe covered Zulma's shoulders with the woollen cloth as with a mantle. She draped her figure in the great piece that fell.

"See the shepherdess," she said.

The girl appeared in all her beauty. They could see that she had plump little hands and a round, firm neck. When Marthe dropped the material with her right hand, long folds like trunks of young birches hung down Zulma's figure to the ground. And they saw that she was tall, well formed, broad of hip, healthy, assured, and of striking beauty. She did not move. She dropped her eyes. For the first time, they could see that her cheeks had the pure line of egg shells.

"I cannot . . ." said Madame Hélène.

"What's the matter?"

"I do not know," she said, "I have just seen. I am old. It came like a flash."

Her eyes filled with tears, her lashes were wet.

"That doesn't look like an ordinary woman," said Jacquou softly.

"Let her rest," said Madame Carle.

"She isn't tired," said Honorine.

"Yes, maybe," said Madame Carle, "perhaps that is true."

"What we need," said Bobi, "is to live leisurely. Let us give wheat to Randoulet. He won't have to go down to the plains to exchange his sheep for flour."

"Nobody has ever fed me," said Randoulet.

"You will give us wool," said Bobi.

"Well," said Barbe, "come and see how we work to dress a beautiful girl."

She stood in front of the loom and began to move her arms with that light, precise motion that testified to her long habit of weaving. The cedar uprights moaned, the cloth vibrated dully under the first shocks of the comb, the shuttle hissed, clacked. They had all gathered around, the women close about Barbe so as almost to hinder her, and all eyes went from right to left, and back again, following the shuttle, and all the eyelids blinked each time the comb struck the cloth.

Suddenly they were simply one common body. There were no longer Bobi or Jacquou or Madame Hélène or anyone. There was no longer the lung of one, the heart of another, the leg, the loin, the eye, or the mouth; but all eyes together followed the shuttle, and in all the breasts at the same moment rang the dull blow of the comb as it struck the cloth. The cadence of the warp rods forced their breathing in time with it. Then gradually these beats fused and there was only one beat, and all the lungs breathed together. All eyes were fixed on the shuttle; Bobi's blue eyes, Joséphine's green ones, Marthe's brown, the reddish brown, the grey, another blue, a beautiful deep violet that belonged to Jacquou, a keen, cold one that belonged to Carle's son. And the shuttle carried them along together, right, left, right, left, as if they, at the same time, wove with all those glances, to unite them in one solid body. They were all attached to the shuttle at the same point, at that spot in the cedar shuttle where the polished wood reflected the sun. At one end they were attached there. At the other end the glances were attached to the eyes of Bobi, Jourdan, Marthe, Joséphine, Madame Hélène, Madame Carle, Carle, his son, Honoré, Randoulet, Le Noir.

All eyes moved in unison from right to left, right, left. The muscles that moved the eyes were making the same effort together in all the heads. The particular thoughts in each head were cut at the same time by this regular motion, this regular effort, like straw under the chopper. On this side of the chopper was the handful of straw with all the stems separated from one another, but on the other side of the chopper there was only a confused heap of straw hashed in tiny pieces.

In like manner, on one side of the warp, on the upper side that went from the warp rods to the bar above, on which the stag and the stars were carved, were all the wool threads, each one separate, each with its strength, its colour that at times changed the colour of the thread next to it by some almost imperceptible thing which is the special character of the thread. On the other side of the warp, the under side that went from the warp rod to the beam, was the cloth. It was no longer thread, it was cloth—all the threads gathered and united, and the union of all the subtleties of shades of each thread shimmered in the cloth like the lights of mother-of-pearl in seashells.

Each time the comb struck it was like the thump of a drum. There were reverberations to the very foundations of the house and into the soil of the plateau. Each time Barbe tightened the woof thread, this happened. The ear listened for it. It came, it struck the ear, the blood carried it through the body. But at the same time, it struck in that hollow, in the keel of the ribs beneath the breast, where Joséphine was so sensitive, where Madame Hélène was so sensitive, where Madame Carle suddenly put her hand, saying to herself: "What's the matter with me?" With each blow, she felt at that place a delightful and intoxicating pain, as when one is in a cart and suddenly the horse jerks into a gallop. That spot where Jacquou, Jourdan, Carle, Randoulet, and Le Noir felt as if seized in a grip, where a good many memories awoke in Bobi, where it had only to touch to give Carle's son a desire to turn his head swiftly to look at Zulma, still dressed in the wool cloth, standing apart from the group, alone, in the four rays of the sun that fell from the window.

Barbe wove at the cedar loom that seemed like a living thing.

"Why," said Bobi, "should we each have our little field of wheat? Suppose we had one big field of wheat for everyone, that we'd all sow together and cut together, and that would produce wheat for everybody without our having to say 'my wheat' or 'your field,' and without one of us, the one who gives us the wool, being offended when we give him wheat, since he would have ploughed and sown and reaped and winnowed and threshed and ground and kneaded and baked the wheat of all with us all together as his own wheat?"

"What's that you are saying? What did you say about wheat?" whispered the men.

"Come here."

They gathered around him.

Barbe was tightening the cloth with the shuttle and the rods, and the loom squeaked and groaned.

"Suppose next year," said Bobi, "we made one big field of the best land, whether it belongs to you or to another? First, maybe we could arrange it so that this field will be partly on your land, or on yours, but that isn't definite. The most logical thing is to choose the best land, whether it belongs to you or to you—what difference does that make, since we'd all be working together? And the wheat would belong to us all, and the important thing is that it must be fine."

Through his speech rang the blows of Barbe's comb as it tightened the weave of the cloth, the beautiful woollen cloth, in rice weave, thick and heavy and pure as the snow. The thumps of the dull drum beat on their ears. The blood swept them along with the sound of Bobi's words. The blows struck the warmest and most sensitive places in their breasts where they had hidden their secret hopes and cares.

Jacquou began to speak. He looked at his wife at the loom, his old wife. He would never have believed that she was still so strong, so strong to weave, so powerful in all that she commanded in her earthy old peasant heart. For he remembered the time when he had gone to get her in her village, high up in the blue mountains where the storms are born. They are blue only when you see them from a distance. When you are up there, the earth is the earth, grey as everywhere else, like all earth. Who can tell what makes people come together and go through life together side by side? You can't live alone. There is already the proof if you will only take the trouble to look at it. What had they done? What could they do, Barbe? He cleared his throat from time to time and spoke low, in spite of all his coughings, with a little voice that was drowned by the noise of the loom. Good days, bad days, but surely nothing solid, that is certain, and always the fear that everything would crumble when things go fairly well. But what is certain is that there is nothing solid, and there is always the struggle against fate.

Jourdan and Carle began to talk without waiting for Jacquou to finish. It was a question, in short, of the heart and no longer necessarily a question of mere food, if one might put it thus. The wheat . . .

"What are you saying?" asked Joséphine.

"We are talking about the wheat."

"I heard you say 'heart.'" For some time she had been wanting to talk, too. She had one great desire: to talk so Bobi would hear her.

"The wheat," one said, "they always say that it is the main thing. No, it isn't the main thing. Ah, no, indeed! That is just the point. Of course it is necessary. Of course it is exactly like the air you breathe. If you stop breathing, you can't keep it up a long time or you'll die. If you have nothing more to breathe, you die; we know that. We know the beautiful, great, powerful value of wheat. Who says any different? Nobody. We least of all, because we are the ones who know it best. But it must be exactly like the air we breathe. We ought to use wheat as we use air. We ought to use it without thinking about it, mechanically, involuntarily, like something without value. That is just the way to put it. Exactly that, like something without value, like air. Like something inexhaustible that you take and swallow and there it is, with no value, absolutely like air. Because you would not need to devote so much time to this food that you swallowed, and that was an end to it. I don't say it is not agreeable; certainly I know it is pleasant to eat. It is a joy. That is what makes blood. That counts. But what I mean is that it doesn't count for everything.

"I mean that when one has only one single joy, it is like when one has only one lamp or an only child. Suddenly all might go out, or even, I mean, that a single lamp, although it is lit, sometimes isn't enough if it is all alone in a big room. For the fact is we have many needs and not only the need of wheat. If you consider, look how many things we want which seem important to us, and if someone said to us: 'Give up eating to get them,' we would willingly give up eating. But it is as necessary for us as it is to breathe. And so, let's make it so it doesn't weigh us down, so it isn't hard for us, but very easy, and then we'll have time for all our other needs. When all is said and done, things are simple if you go about them with a good will."

"Yes," said Carle.

There was great approval in Carle. He spoke, he said his say. He agreed. And, at his side, the son nodded, yes, with his head, and even Randoulet, who was listening with a frown, but who was all stirred in the hollow of his breast by the dull blows of the comb that was tightening the weave. He approved too. He heard Jacquou on his other side going on to talk about his dreams, about his marvellous animals, his bulls almost too fine for this world, his cows with their cream-coloured udders, that even talked at times, until one wondered how Jacquou could have imagined them. Their eyes were as big as the bottoms of bottles, and so calm that he could stand in front of them to shave. He talked of them as if it were all true, as if these animals were already there. And yet they were still in his dreams.

But Randoulet understood because he knew what it was to be linked to beasts as with iron bolts and nails. And it was useless to tell him that sometimes one went without eating so as not to do without some other nourishment that one considers at the moment much more necessary. For what was he doing with his sheep, if not that very thing?

"Joy and peace," thought Bobi. "Joy must be tranquil. Joy must be a habit and quite peaceful and calm, and not belligerent and passionate. For I do not say that joy is when one laughs or sings, or even when our pleasure is more than bodily. I say that one is joyful when all the habitual gestures are gestures of joy; when it is a joy to work for one's food; when one is in an atmosphere that one appreciates and loves; when each day, at every moment, at each instant, all is easy and peaceful. When everything that one desires is there." And unfortunately, there was Joséphine; and the sound of the loom and all the voices could be a roar fit to burst one's ears like the roar of the torrent, yet what he heard plainest was the sound of Joséphine's breathing. And the dull blows of the loom could be repeated by the echoes beneath the earth and the foundations of the house, and make the soles of his feet vibrate; what really made him shudder from head to foot was that warm little shock of Joséphine's breath as it struck against his right cheek. And he knew that she was beside him, that she was looking at him with her green eyes. He knew that her mouth was full and hot. He knew that her breasts were just the size of his hollowed hands, that for him she was full of joy, which, when he felt it, was more than a bodily joy. He was aware that henceforth for him joy would not be peaceful. And he stood there fighting and struggling because joy is nothing and is not worth the trouble if it is not abiding.

"We might first . . ." said Bobi.

"Listen."

"Be quiet, Barbe."

"What?" shouted Barbe.

"Stop a minute, we can't hear ourselves talk."

Barbe stopped working.

"This is what we might do," said Bobi. "This year, since it is too late, we will start, if you like, by having a common harvest. We'll cut each field, but we'll tread all the wheat on one threshing floor, on the floor of all and every one of us together. We'll put the grain in a single barn. It will belong neither to one nor to another; like the stag. It will belong to all. As much to Randoulet as to us. And next year we'll choose a field where we'll all sow our wheat together. We'll have a little more time," he said with a grey little smile, "to spend on what we want to do."

Chapter ▊▊

Justice: Obligation
and the Law

Justice has traditionally been defined as that condition whereby every man receives his due. But this is the sort of definition that serves only to facilitate disagreement. It provides no answers, and no procedure for finding answers, to any of the most important questions: What is "due" to this man or that one, or to this or that group of men? What does the government owe to its citizens? What do citizens owe to one another and to "the powers that be"? Do we have only such debts as we willingly acquire (by social contracts like the one described in the first chapter); or are we born in debt (as Socrates argues in the Crito), owing reverence and obedience to parents and magistrates?

These questions have always been the central concerns of political philosophers, but no man who claims to say anything at all about the extraordinary tangle of relations in which we are all caught up can possibly avoid them. And it may be that novelists and dramatists committed to that tangle, committed to situating their characters in specific social settings and relating them to concrete others, have things to tell us about our duties that philosophy by itself cannot impart. Not that they write didactic discourses, for their power as novelists and dramatists depends in large part on their capacity to make the two sides of the harshest contradiction equally plausible, to reveal the circumstances, reasons, passions, and wills that make one choice and its opposite equally human and, sometimes, equally tragic. What we learn from the best writers is not the "true" meaning of justice, but rather what the various meanings mean in human terms; not what choices we ought to make, but what it is to choose.

The crucial setting within which men must decide what is due to whom is the state. For the laws of the state establish our conventional indebtedness—though not necessarily our most profound obligations. The relation between individual and state has been imagined in a great variety of ways (some of these are illustrated in Chapter III) but, by writers concerned with justice, most often in the form of a rough exchange. The state provides security—that most precious Hobbesian commodity—and perhaps also welfare for the whole community. Individual citizens ought then to obey the laws of the state for the sake of the community's security and welfare and, most often, of course, for the sake of their own as well.

Given this paradigm, there are two sorts of conflict likely to occur. First, conflict arises when particular individuals or groups claim that they have not received their equal or fair share of the security and welfare the state supposedly provides. The political authorities may then deny that this is so or argue that an equality of shares is either impossible or undesirable. Most often, they choose the second of these responses; for the misery of the many is generally too obvious to deny and so must be justified—as it is, for example, by Shakespeare's aristocrats in Coriolanus. A second sort of conflict begins when particular individuals or groups announce that they have commitments that take precedence over their obligation to obey the law—alternative obligations to their gods, their family or tribe, or their friends or comrades. The conventional response of the authorities is to deny categorically that this can ever be the case. They insist upon the moral precedence of the state, which is in effect to insist that the worldly peace it brings is the greatest good that men can know. In both these cases justice is at issue, yet the issues are very different. In the first, the justice of the state's distributive system is challenged; the rebels come forward with new ideas about "fair shares" or equality before the law. In the second, the distributive system is accepted but another and presumably higher conception of justice proclaimed; now the rebels deny the precedence of the state and come forward with new ideas about the hierarchy of human values.

In the first scene of Shakespeare's Coriolanus, as the Polish director Jan Kott has suggested, two different conceptions of social structure and economic distribution are revealed as the ideologies of two different social classes. The plebs see the world in the harsh light of class struggle: It is divided into rich and poor, and the suffering of the poor makes the abundance of the rich. The aristocrat Agrippa conceives the state as a functional union, a harmonious organism. Justice is done, he argues, when the powerful and active parts of the body help the poor and the weak parts, which are incapable of helping themselves. But the plebeians reply that the powerful care only to increase their power; their benevolent concern is a fraud. Justice requires a radical redistribution of benefits, which is to say justice requires class war and a triumphant people. It is an old argument, and Shakespeare's sympathies probably lay with the aristocracy. But in Coriolanus he succeeds in making the encounter ambiguous; for once in his plays First and Second Citizen appear in a group that is not a conventional mob, whose members are real men. But the social distance is maintained: The plebs speak in an angry, rough prose; Agrippa in witty and elegant verse.

Shakespeare's citizens form a social class, capable of collective protest. The encounter between a single plebeian and the authority of the state takes a very different course. Victor Hugo's Jean Valjean is a man almost broken in that encounter. He survives not as a citizen, not even as a rebel, but as a criminal. At least, that is how the authorities describe him. He describes himself as a just man, for he has carefully reckoned up his debts and concluded that what he owes the state is—war. Crime represents his private struggle for a redistribution of benefits.

It is not a struggle he is likely to win; yet Jean Valjean's life, for all its suffering, is not a tragedy. We are unlikely to recognize any conflict in his history; we assent too quickly to his moral reckoning. Hugo has composed a classic melodrama. Tragedy only arises when a man's own calculation of his debts and obligations is unsure or problematic, when he must make a choice and cannot, in any easy or conventional sense, choose rightly. Tragedy is the revelation of justice as a potential or an actual contradiction. Thus Sophocles' Antigone is tragic not merely because the heroine's choice involves her death, but also because the opposite choice is a moral possibility. She gives what is due to the gods and to her brother, and this requires her to break the laws of the state. Creon, who enforces those laws, makes the classic case for obedience:

> The worst of evils is to disobey.
> Cities by this are ruined, homes of men
> Made desolate . . .

Antigone is no perfect martyr. If Creon is marked by his blustering authoritarianism, she is revealed as a fanatic. So Sophocles exposes the characteristic defects of these two conceptions of justice: that which pays its due to the laws, that which pays its due to the gods.

We must also give what is due to our friends—and here is yet another source of contradiction and conflict. "If I had to choose between betraying my country and betraying my friend," E. M. Forster has written, "I hope I should have the guts to betray my country." If those were the terms of the choice, it would not, in fact, be so easy. Huck Finn's choice, in the chapter we have selected from Mark Twain's novel, is a rather different one. He must choose between betraying a friend (the great discovery of the chapter is that "Nigger Jim" is a friend) and breaking the laws of his country. And however hard that choice is for him, Twain himself certainly regards it as an obvious one. We must sometimes disobey the law, he suggests, because of other, overriding debts—and also, of course, because the law (in this case the Fugitive Slave Law) is sometimes unjust.

Even when it is unjust, however, men most often obey the law. They obey without caring, or in fear, or innocently, or as saints and martyrs. They obey because the law is there, the embodiment of worldly necessity, proclaimed and enforced by men of substance and worldly wisdom. Billy Budd is innocently obedient; he is also a victim of the men of substance. If Herman Melville's story is a tragedy, it is the tragedy of Captain Vere, who makes an impossible choice and sacrifices Billy for the sake of law and order. Vere is, as it were, a reluctant Creon: Like the Theban king, he honestly believes that cities are ruined (and ships threatened with mutiny) if crimes against the law go unpunished. Billy merely accepts that argument, without hearing it, and dies blessing the man who has sentenced him to death. He is no martyr to the law, for he has made no choice at all; his trust in the captain is a function of his innocence, not of his faith. In a sense, he is uninvolved (though everyone loves him), a stranger here below, "in a world he never made."

A. E. Housman's poem, from which that last line is taken, describes another kind of alienation from the law and another kind of obedience: self-conscious, tough, of the old rather than the new world. Man's justice is foreign to the poet; but since he cannot "fly to Saturn nor to Mercury," he makes his peace. Unlike Billy, he does not bless the authorities, nor does he break the law. His is the voice of the skeptic, denying that he is bound either to obey or to disobey. But what would the poet say if he lived in a world that he had made?

CLASS STRUGGLE

William Shakespeare

From *Coriolanus*

ACT I

Scene 1: [Rome. A street.]

Enter a company of mutinous CITIZENS, *with staves, clubs, and other weapons.*

1. CIT.:   Before we proceed any further, hear me speak.

ALL: Speak, speak.

1. CIT.:   You are all resolved rather to die than to famish?

ALL: Resolved, resolved.

1. CIT.:   First, you know Caius Marcius is chief enemy to the people.

ALL: We know't, we know't.

1. CIT.:   Let us kill him, and we'll have corn at our own price. Is't a verdict?

ALL: No more talking on't; let it be done. Away, away!

2. CIT.:   One word, good citizens.

1. CIT.:   We are accounted poor citizens, the patricians good. What authority surfeits on would relieve us; if they would yield us but the superfluity while it were wholesome, we might guess they relieved us humanely; but they think we are too dear. The leanness that afflicts us, the object of our misery, is as an inventory to particularize their abundance; our sufferance is a gain to them. Let us revenge this with our pikes ere we become rakes; for the gods know I speak this in hunger for bread, not in thirst for revenge.

2. CIT.:   Would you proceed especially against Caius Marcius?

1. CIT.:   Against him first; he's a very dog to the commonalty.

2. CIT.:   Consider you what services he has done for his country?

1. CIT.:   Very well, and could be content to give him good report for't but that he pays himself with being proud.

2. CIT.:   Nay, but speak not maliciously.

1. CIT.:   I say unto you, what he hath done famously he did it to

that end; though soft-conscienced men can be content to say it was for his country, he did it to please his mother and to be partly proud, which he is, even to the altitude of his virtue.

2. CIT.: What he cannot help in his nature you account a vice in him. You must in no way say he is covetous.

1. CIT.: If I must not, I need not be barren of accusations; he hath faults, with surplus, to tire in repetition.

Shouts within.

What shouts are these? The other side o' the city is risen. Why stay we prating here? To the Capitol!

ALL: Come, come.

1. CIT.: Soft! Who comes here?

Enter MENENIUS AGRIPPA.

2. CIT.: Worthy Menenius Agrippa; one that hath always loved the people.

1. CIT.: He's one honest enough; would all the rest were so!

MEN.: What work's, my countrymen, in hand?
Where go you
With bats and clubs? The matter? Speak, I pray you.

1. CIT.: Our business is not unknown to the Senate; they have had inkling this fortnight what we intend to do, which now we'll show 'em in deeds. They say poor suitors have strong breaths; they shall know we have strong arms too.

MEN.: Why, masters, my good friends, mine honest neighbors,
Will you undo yourselves?

1. CIT.: We cannot, sir; we are undone already.

MEN.: I tell you, friends, most charitable care
Have the patricians of you. For your wants,
Your suffering in this dearth, you may as well
Strike at the heaven with your staves as lift them
Against the Roman state, whose course will on
The way it takes, cracking ten thousand curbs
Of more strong link asunder than can ever
Appear in your impediment. For the dearth,
The gods, not the patricians, make it, and
Your knees to them, not arms, must help. Alack,
You are transported by calamity
Thither where more attends you; and you slander
The helms o' the state, who care for you like fathers,
When you curse them as enemies.

1. CIT.:   Care for us! True, indeed! They ne'er cared for us yet. Suffer us to famish, and their storehouses crammed with grain; make edicts for usury, to support usurers; repeal daily any wholesome act established against the rich, and provide more piercing statutes daily to chain up and restrain the poor. If the wars eat us not up, they will; and there's all the love they bear us.

MEN.:   Either you must
Confess yourselves wondrous malicious,
Or be accused of folly. I shall tell you
A pretty tale. It may be you have heard it;
But, since it serves my purpose, I will venture
To stale't a little more.

1. CIT.:   Well, I'll hear it, sir; yet you must not think to fob off our disgrace with a tale. But, an't please you deliver.

MEN.:   There was a time when all the body's members
Rebelled against the belly; thus accused it:
That only like a gulf it did remain
I' the midst o' the body, idle and unactive,
Still cupboarding the viand, never bearing
Like labor with the rest; where the other instruments
Did see and hear, devise, instruct, walk, feel,
And, mutually participate, did minister
Unto the appetite and affection common
Of the whole body. The belly answered—

1. CIT.:   Well, sir, what answer made the belly?

MEN.:   Sir, I shall tell you. With a kind of smile,
Which ne'er came from the lungs, but even thus—
For look you, I may make the belly smile
As well as speak—it tauntingly replied
To the discontented members, the mutinous parts
That envied his receipt; even so most fitly
As you malign our senators for that
They are not such as you.

1. CIT.:   Your belly's answer—What?
The kingly crowned head, the vigilant eye,
The counselor heart, the arm our soldier,
Our steed the leg, the tongue our trumpeter,
With other muniments and petty helps
In this our fabric, if that they—

MEN.:   What then?
Fore me, this fellow speaks. What then? What then?

1. CIT.:   Should by the cormorant belly be restrained,
Who is the sink o' the body—
　　MEN.:   Well, what then?
　　1. CIT.:   The former agents, if they did complain, What could the belly answer.
　　MEN.:   I will tell you;
If you'll bestow a small—of what you have little—
Patience awhile, you'st hear the belly's answer.
　　1. CIT.:   Y'are long about it.
　　MEN.:   Note me this, good friend:
Your most grave belly was deliberate,
Not rash like his accusers, and thus answered.
"True is it, my incorporate friends," quoth he,
"That I receive the general food at first
Which you do live upon; and fit it is,
Because I am the storehouse and the shop
Of the whole body. But, if you do remember,
I send it through the rivers of your blood,
Even to the court, the heart, to the seat o' the brain;
And, through the cranks and offices of man,
The strongest nerves and small inferior veins
From me receive that natural competency
Whereby they live. And though that all at once
You, my good friends"—this says the belly; mark me—
　　1. CIT.:   Ay, sir; well, well.
　　MEN.:   "Though all at once cannot
See what I do deliver out to each,
Yet I can make my audit up, that all
From me do back receive the flour of all,
And leave me but the bran." What say you to't?
　　1. CIT.:   It was an answer. How apply you this?
　　MEN.:   The senators of Rome are this good belly,
And you the mutinous members; for, examine
Their counsels and their cares, digest things rightly
Touching the weal o' the common, you shall find
No public benefit which you receive
But it proceeds or comes from them to you,
And no way from yourselves. What do you think,
You, the great toe of this assembly?
　　1. CIT.:   I the great toe? Why the great toe?
　　MEN.:   For that, being one o' the lowest, basest, poorest,

Of this most wise rebellion, thou goest foremost.
Thou rascal, that art worst in blood to run,
Leadst first to win some vantage.
But make you ready your stiff bats and clubs.
Rome and her rats are at the point of battle;
The one side must have bale.*

THE MAKING OF A CRIMINAL

Victor Hugo

From *Les Misérables*

Toward the middle of the night, Jean Valjean awoke. He belonged
to a poor peasant family of La Brie. In his childhood he had not
been taught to read, and when he was of man's age he was a pruner
at Faverolles. His mother's name was Jeanne Mathieu; his father's,
Jean Valjean or Vlajean,—probably a nickname and a contraction
of *Voilà Jean.* Jean Valjean possessed a pensive but not melancholy
character, which is peculiar to affectionate natures; but altogether
he was a dull, insignificant fellow, at least apparently. He had lost
father and mother when still very young; the latter died of a badly
managed milk-fever; the former, a pruner, like himself, was killed
by a fall from a tree. All that was left Jean Valjean, was a sister
older than himself, a widow with seven children, boys and girls. This
sister brought Jean Valjean up, and so long as her husband was
alive she supported her brother. When the husband died, the
oldest of the seven children was eight years of age, the youngest,
one, while Jean Valjean had just reached his twenty-fifth year; he
took the place of the father, and in his turn supported the sister who
had reared him. This was done simply as a duty, and even rather
roughly, by Jean Valjean; and his youth was thus expended in hard
and ill-paid toil. He was never known to have a sweetheart, for he
had no time for love-making.

At night he came home tired, and ate his soup without a word.
His sister, Mother Jeanne, while he was eating, often took out of

From Book II, Chs. 6 and 7.
* Editors' note: Bale *woe* or *injury.*

his porringer the best part of his meal,—the piece of meat, the slice of bacon, or the heart of the cabbage,—to give to one of her children; he, still eating, bent over the table with his head almost in the soup, and, his long hair falling around his porringer and hiding his eyes, pretended not to see it, and let her do as she pleased. There was at Faverolles, not far from the Valjeans' cottage, on the other side of the lane, a farmer's wife called Marie Claude. The young Valjeans, who were always starving, would sometimes go and borrow a pint of milk, in their mother's name, from Marie Claude, which they drank behind a hedge or in some corner, tearing the jug from each other so eagerly that the little girls spilled the milk over their aprons. Their mother, had she been aware of this fraud, would have severely corrected the delinquents; but Jean Valjean, coarse and rough though he was, paid Marie Claude for the milk behind his sister's back, and the children were not punished.

He earned in the pruning season eighteen sous a day, and besides hired himself out as reaper, labourer, neatheard, and odd man. He did what he could; his sister worked too, but what could she do with seven little children? It was a sad group, which wretchedness gradually enveloped and choked. A hard winter came, Jean had no work, and the family had no bread. No bread,—literally none,—and seven children.

One Sunday evening, Maubert Isabeau, the baker in the church square at Faverolles, was just going to bed when he heard a violent blow on the grated and glazed front of his shop. He ran out in time to see an arm passed through a hole made by a fist through the gratings and window-pane; a hand seized a loaf, and carried it off. Isabeau rushed to the door; the thief ran away at his hardest, but the baker caught him up and stopped him. The thief had thrown away the loaf, but his arm was still bleeding; it was Jean Valjean.

This took place in 1795. Jean Valjean was brought before the courts, charged "with burglary committed with violence at night, in an inhabited house." He had a gun, was a splendid shot, and a bit of a poacher, and this injured him. There is a legitimate prejudice against poachers, for, like smugglers, they trench very closely on brigandage. Still we must remark that there is an abyss between these classes and the hideous assassins of our cities. The poacher lives in the forest; the smuggler in the mountains and on the sea. Cities produce ferocious men because they produce corrupt men. The forest, the mountain, and the sea produce savage men; but, while they develop their fierce side, they do not always destroy their humane side. Jean Valjean was found guilty, and the terms of the code were explicit. There are in our civilization formidable moments; they are those in which penal justice decrees a shipwreck. What a mournful minute is that in which society withdraws and consummates the irreparable abandonment of a thinking being! Jean Valjean was sentenced to five years at the galleys.

On April 22, 1796, men were crying in the streets of Paris the victory of Montenotte, gained by the general-in-chief of the army of Italy, whom the message of the Directory to the Five Hundred of 2 Floréal, year IV., calls Buona-Parte; and on the same day a heavy gang was put in chains at Bicêtre, and Jean Valjean formed part of the gang. A former jailer of the prison, now nearly ninety years of age, perfectly remembers the wretched man who was chained at the end of the fourth line, in the north corner of the courtyard. He was seated on the ground like the rest, and seemed not at all to understand his position, except that it was horrible. It is probable that he also was disentangling something excessive from amidst the vague ideas of an utterly ignorant man. While the bolt of his iron collar was being riveted with heavy hammer-blows behind his head, he wept; tears choked him, and prevented him from speaking, and he could only manage to say from time to time, "I was a pruner at Faverolles." Then, still sobbing, he raised his right hand, and lowered it gradually seven times, as if touching seven heads of unequal height, and from this gesture it could be guessed that, whatever the crime he had committed, he had done it to feed and clothe seven little children.

He started for Toulon, and arrived there after a journey of twenty-seven days in a cart, with a chain on his neck. At Toulon he was dressed in the red jacket. All that had hitherto been his life, even to his name, was effaced. He was no longer Jean Valjean, but No. 24,601. What became of his sister, what became of the seven children? Who troubles himself about that? What becomes of the spray of leaves when the young tree is chopped off at the foot? It is always the same story. These poor living beings, these creatures of God, henceforth without support, guide, or shelter, went off at random, and were gradually lost in that cold fog which swallows up solitary destinies, that mournful gloom in which so many unfortunates disappear during the sombre progress of the human race. They left the country. What had once been the steeple of their village church forgot them; what had once been their hedgerow forgot them; and after a few years' stay in the galleys, Jean Valjean himself forgot them. In that heart where there had once been a wound, there was now a scar; that was all. He only heard of his sister once during the whole time he spent at Toulon; it was, I believe, toward the end of the fourth year of his imprisonment, though I have forgotten in what way the information reached him. She was in Paris, living in the Rue du Gindre, a poor street, near St. Sulpice, and had only one child with her, the youngest, a boy. Where were the other six? Perhaps she did not know herself. Every morning she went to a printing-office, No. 3 Rue du Sabot, where she was a folder and stitcher; she had to be there at six in the morning, long before day-light in winter. In the same house as the printing-office there was a day-school, to which she took the little boy, who was seven years of age; but as she went to work at six and the school did not open till seven, the boy was compelled to wait in the yard for an hour, in winter,—an hour of winter night in the open air. The boy was not allowed to enter the printing-office, because it was said that he would be in the way. The workmen as they passed in the morning saw the poor little fellow seated on the pavement, and often sleeping in the darkness, with his head on his satchel. When it rained, an old woman, the portress, took pity on him; she invited him into her den, where there were only a bed, a spinning-wheel, and two chairs, and the little fellow fell asleep in a corner, nestling up to the cat, to keep him warm. At seven o'clock the school opened and the child went in. This is what Jean Valjean was told. It was a momentary flash, as though a window had suddenly opened upon the destiny of the beings he had loved, and then was closed again; he never heard of them more. Nothing reached him from them; he never saw them again, never met them, and we shall not come across them in the course of this melancholy tale.

Toward the end of this fourth year, Jean Valjean's turn to escape came, and his comrades aided him as they always do in that sorrow-ful place. He escaped, and wandered about the fields at liberty for two days,—if it is liberty to be hunted down; to turn one's head at every moment; to start at the slightest sound; to be afraid of every-thing,—of a smoking chimney, a passing man, a barking dog, a galloping horse, the striking of the hour, of day because people see, of night because they do not see, of the highway, the path, the thicket, and even of sleep. On the evening of the second day he was recaptured; he had not eaten or slept for six-and-thirty hours. The maritime tribunal added three years to his sentence for this crime, which made it eight years. In the sixth year, it was again his turn to escape; he tried, but did not succeed. He was missing at roll-call, the gun was fired, and at night the watchman found him hidden under the keel of a ship that was building, and he resisted the prison guard who seized him. Escape and rebellion; this case, provided for by the special code, was punished by an addition of five years, of which two would be spent in double chains. Thirteen years. In his tenth year his turn came again, and he took advantage of it, but succeeded no better; three years for this new attempt, or sixteen years in all. Finally, I think it was during his thirteenth year, he made a last attempt, and only succeeded in being recaptured in four hours; three years for these four hours, and a total of nineteen years. In October, 1815, he was set free; in 1796 he had gone in for breaking a window and stealing a loaf.

Let us make room for a short parenthesis. This is the second time that, during his study of the penal question and condemnation by the law, the author of this book has come across a loaf as the starting-point of the disaster of a destiny. Claude Gueux stole a loaf, and so did Jean Valjean; and English statistics prove that in London four robberies out of five have hunger for their immediate cause. Jean Valjean entered the galleys sobbing and shuddering; he left them stoically. He entered in despair; he came out gloomy. What had taken place in his soul?

.   .   .

Let us try to tell.

Society must necessarily look at these things, because it creates them. He was, as we have said, an ignorant man, but he was not a fool. The light of nature was kindled within him, and misfortune, which also has its own clear vision, increased the little daylight that existed in his mind. Under the stick and the chain in the dungeon, when at work beneath the torrid sun of the galleys, or when lying on the convict's plank, he reflected. He constituted himself a court, and began by trying himself. He saw that he was not an innocent man unjustly punished. He confessed that he had committed an extreme and blamable action; that the loaf would probably not have been refused him had he asked for it; that in any case it would have been better to wait till he could get it, either from pity or by work; and that it was not a thoroughly unanswerable argument to say, "Can a man wait when he is hungry?" that, in the first place, it is very rare for a man to die literally of hunger; next, that, unhappily or happily, man is so made that he can suffer long and severely, morally and physically, without dying; that hence he should have been patient; that it would have been better for the poor little children; that it was an act of madness for him, a wretched, weak man, violently to collar society and to imagine that a man can escape wretchedness by theft; that in any case, the door by which a man enters infamy is a bad one by which to escape from wretchedness,—and, in short, that he had been in the wrong.

Then he asked himself if he were the only person who had been in the wrong in his fatal history; whether, in the first place, it was not a serious thing that he, a workman, should want for work,—that he, industrious as he was, should want for bread; whether, next, when the fault was committed and confessed, the punishment had not been ferocious and excessive, and if there were not more abuse on the part of the law in the penalty than there was on the side of the culprit in the crime; whether there had not been an excessive weight in one of the scales,—that one in which expiation lies; whether the excess of punishment did not efface the crime, and reverse the situation by making a victim of the culprit, a creditor of the debtor, and definitely placing the right on the side of the man who had violated it; whether this penalty, complicated by successive aggravations for attempts at escape, did not eventually become a sort of attack made by the stronger on the weaker, a crime of society committed on the individual, a crime which was renewed every day, and had lasted for nineteen years? He asked himself if human society could have the right to make its members suffer equally, on one side, from its unreasonable improvidence, on the other, from its pitiless foresight, and to hold a poor man eternally between a want and an excess,—want of work and excess of punishment; whether it were not outrageous that society should thus treat those of its members who were worst endowed in that division of property which is made by chance, and who were consequently most worthy of indulgence?

These questions asked and solved, he passed sentence on society and condemned it—to his hatred. He made it responsible for the fate he was suffering, and said to himself that he would not hesitate to call it to account some day. He declared that there was no equilibrium between the harm he had done and the harm done him; and he came to the conclusion that his punishment was not unjust, but most assuredly iniquitous. Wrath may be wild and absurd; a man may be wrongfully irritated; but he is only indignant when he has some show of reason somewhere. Jean Valjean felt indignant. And then again, human society had never done him aught but harm; he

had only seen its wrathful face, which is called its justice, and which
it shows to those whom it strikes. Men had only laid hands on him
to injure him, and every contact with them had been a blow. Never,
since his infancy, since the time of his mother and his sister, had he
heard a kind word or met a friendly look. From suffering after suffering, he gradually attained to the conviction that life was war, and
that in this war he was the vanquished. As he had no weapon but
his hatred, he resolved to sharpen it in the galleys and to take it
with him when he left.

THE OBLIGATION TO DISOBEY

Sophocles

From *Antigone*

CREON: Where, on what manner, was your captive taken?
SENTINEL: Burying the man, we took her: all is told.
CREON: Art thou advised of this? Is it the truth?
SENTINEL: I say I saw her burying the body,
That you forbade. Is that distinct and clear?
CREON: How was she seen, and taken in the act?
SENTINEL: So it fell out. When I had gone from hence,
With thy loud threats yet sounding in my ears,
We swept off all the dust that hid the limbs,
And to the light stripped bare the clammy corpse,
And on the hill's brow sat, and faced the wind,
Choosing a spot clear of the body's stench.
Roundly we chid each other to the work;
"No sleeping at your post there" was our word.
So did we keep the watch, till in mid-heaven
The sun's bright-burning orb above us hung,
With fierce noon-heat: and now a sudden blast
Swept, and a storm of dust, that vexed the sky
And choked the plain, and all the leaves o' the trees
O' the plain were marred, and the wide heaven it filled:

Translated by Robert Whitelaw.

We with shut eyes the heaven-sent plague endured.
And, when after a long time its force was spent,
We saw this maiden, and a bitter cry
She poured, as of a wailing bird that sees
Her empty nest dismantled of its brood:
So she, when she espied the body bare,
Cried out and wept, and many a grievous curse
Upon their heads invoked by whom 'twas done.
And thirsty dust she sprinkled with her hands,
And lifted up an urn, fair-wrought of brass,
And with thrice-poured libations crowned the dead.
We saw it and we hasted, and at once,
All undismayed, our captive, hemmed her round,
And with the two offences charged her there,
Both first and last. Nothing did she deny,
But made me glad and sorry, owning all.
For to have slipped one's own neck from the noose
Is sweet, yet no one likes to get his friends
In trouble: but my nature is to make
All else of small account, so I am safe.
    CREON: Speak thou, who bendest on the earth thy gaze,
Are these things, which are witnessed, true or false?
    ANTIGONE: Not false, but true: that which he saw, he speaks.
    CREON: So, sirrah, thou art free; go where thou wilt,
Loosed from the burden of this heavy charge.

    (*Exit the* SENTINEL.)

But tell me thou—and let thy speech be brief—
The edict hadst thou heard, which this forbade?
    ANTIGONE: I could not choose but hear what all men heard.
    CREON: And didst thou dare to disobey the law?
    ANTIGONE: Nowise from Zeus, methought, this edict came,
Nor Justice, that abides among the gods
In Hades, who ordained these laws for men.
Nor did I deem *thine* edicts of such force
That they, a mortal's bidding, should o'erride
Unwritten laws, eternal in the heavens.
Not of to-day or yesterday are these,
But live from everlasting, and from whence
They sprang, none knoweth. I would not, for the breach
Of these, through fear of any human pride,

To heaven atone. I knew that I must die:
How else? Without thine edict, that were so.
And if before my time, why, this were gain.
Compassed about with ills, who lives, as I,
Death, to such life as his, must needs be gain.
So is it to me to undergo this doom
No grief at all: but had I left my brother,
My mother's child, unburied where he lay,
Then I had grieved; but now this grieves me not.
Senseless I seem to thee, so doing? Belike
A senseless judgment finds me void of sense.

   CHORUS: How in the child the sternness of the sire
Shows stern, before the storm untaught to bend!

   CREON: Yet know full well that such o'er-stubborn wills
Are broken most of all, as sturdiest steel,
Of an untempered hardness, fresh from forge,
Most surely snapped and shivered should ye see.
Lo how a little curb has strength enough
To tame the restive horse: for to a slave
His masters give no licence to be proud.
Insult on insult heaped! Was't not enough
My promulgated laws to have transgressed,
But, having done it, face to face with me
She boasts of this and glories in the deed?
I surely am the woman, she the man,
If she defies my power, and I submit.
Be she my sister's child, or sprung from one
More near of blood than all my house to me,
Not so shall they escape my direst doom—
She and her sister: for I count her too
Guilty no less of having planned this work.
Go, call her hither: in the house I saw her
Raving ev'n now, nor mistress of her thoughts.
So oft the mind, revolving secret crime,
Makes premature disclosure of its guilt.
But this is hateful, when the guilty one,
Detected, thinks to glorify his fault.

   ANTIGONE: To kill me—wouldst thou more with me than this?

   CREON: This is enough: I do desire no more.

   ANTIGONE: Why dost thou then delay? I have no pleasure
To hear thee speak—have not and would not have:

Nor less distasteful is my speech to thee.
Yet how could I have won myself a praise
More honourable than this, of burying
My brother? This from every voice should win
Approval, might but fear men's lips unseal.
But kings are fortunate—not least in this,
That they may do and speak what things they will.

CREON: All Thebes sees this with other eyes than thine.
ANTIGONE: They see as I, but bate their breath to thee.
CREON: And art thou not ashamed, from them to differ?
ANTIGONE: To reverence a brother is not shameful.
CREON: And was not he who died for Thebes thy brother?
ANTIGONE: One mother bore us, and one sire begat.
CREON: Yet, honouring both, thou dost dishonour him.
ANTIGONE: He in the grave will not subscribe to this.
CREON: How, if no less thou dost revere the guilty?
ANTIGONE: 'Twas not his slave that perished, but his brother.
CREON: The enemy of this land: its champion, he.
ANTIGONE: Yet Death of due observance must not fail.
CREON: Just and unjust urge not an equal claim.
ANTIGONE: Perchance in Hades 'tis a holy deed.
CREON: Hatred, not ev'n in death, converts to love.
ANTIGONE: Not in your hates, but in your loves, I'd share.
CREON: Go to the shades, and, if thou'lt love, love there:
No woman, while I live, shall master me.

.   .   .

CHORUS:
See, thy son Haemon comes hither, of all
Thy children the last. Comes he lamenting
The doom of the maiden, his bride Antigone—
And the frustrated hope of his marriage?

(*Enter* HAEMON.)

CREON: Soon we shall know, better than seers could say.
My son, in anger art thou come to me,
Hearing the sentence, not to be reversed,
Which on thy destined bride I have pronounced?
Or am I still thy friend, do what I may?

HAEMON: Father, I am in thy hand: with thy wise counsels
Thou dost direct me; these I shall obey.
Not rightly should I deem of more account

The winning of a wife than thy good guidance.
   CREON: Be this thy dearest wish and next thy heart,
In all things to uphold thy father's will.
For to this end men crave to see grow up
Obedient children round them in their homes,
Both to requite their enemies with hate,
And render equal honour to their friends.
Whoso begets unprofitable children,
What shall be said of him, but that he gets
Grief for himself, loud laughter for his foes?
Never, my son, let for a woman's sake
Reason give way to sense, but know full well
Cold is the pleasure that he clasps, who woos
An evil woman to his board and bed.
What wounds so deeply as an evil friend?
Count then this maiden as thine enemy,
Loathe her, and give her leave, in that dark world
To which she goes, to marry with another.
For out of all the city since I found
Her only, and her openly, rebellious,
I shall not to the city break my word,
But she shall die. Let her appeal to Zeus,
And sing the sanctity of kindred blood—
What then? If in my own house I shall nurse
Rebellion, how shall strangers not rebel?
He who to his own kith and kin does right,
Will in the state deal righteously with all.
Of such a man I shall not fear to boast,
Well he can rule, and well he would obey,
And in the storm of battle at his post
Firm he would stand, a comrade staunch and true.
But praise from me that man shall never have,
Who either boldly thrusts aside the law
Or takes upon him to instruct his rulers,
Whom, by the state empowered, he should obey,
In little and in much, in right and wrong.
The worst of evils is to disobey.
Cities by this are ruined, homes of men
Made desolate by this; this in the battle
Breaks into headlong rout the wavering line;
The steadfast ranks, the many lives unhurt,

Are to obedience due. We must defend
The government and order of the state,
And not be governed by a wilful girl.
We'll yield our place up, if we must, to men;
To women that we stooped, shall not be said.
  CHORUS: Unless an old man's judgment is at fault,
These words of thine, we deem, are words of wisdom.
  HAEMON: Reason, my father, in the mind of man,
Noblest of all their gifts, the gods implant,
And how to find thy reasoning at fault,
I know not, and to learn I should be loth;
Yet for another it might not be amiss.
But I for thee am vigilant to mark
All that men say, or do, or find to blame.
Thy presence awes the simple citizen
From speaking words that shall not please thine ear,
But I hear what they whisper in the dark,
And how the city for this maid laments,
That of all women she the least deserving
Dies for most glorious deeds a death most cruel,
Who her own brother, fall'n among the slain,
Left not unburied there, to be devoured
By ravening dogs or any bird o' the air:—
"Should not her deed be blazoned all in gold?"
Upon the darkness still such whisper grows.
But I of all possessions that I have
Prize most, my father, thy prosperity.
Welldoing and fair fame of sire to son,
Of son to sire, is noblest ornament.
Cleave not, I pray thee, to this constant mind,
That what thou sayest, and nought beside, is truth.
For men who think that only they are wise,
None eloquent, right-minded none, but they,
Often, when searched, prove empty. 'Tis no shame,
Ev'n if a man be wise, that he should yet
Learn many things, and not hold out too stiffly.
Beside the torrent's course, of trees that bend
Each bough, thou seest, and every twig is safe;
Those that resist are by the roots uptorn.
And ships, that brace with stubborn hardihood
Their mainsheet to the gale, pursue their voyage

Keel-uppermost, their sailors' thwarts reversed.
Cease from thy wrath; be not inexorable:
For if despite my youth I too may think
My thought, I'll say that best it is by far
That men should be all-knowing if they may,
But if—as oft the scale inclines not so—
Why then, by good advice 'tis good to learn.
   CHORUS: What in thy son's speech, king, is seasonable
'Tis fit thou shouldst receive: and thou in his:
For there is reason in the words of both.
   CREON: Shall I, grown grey with age, be taught indeed—
And by this boy—to think what he thinks right?
   HAEMON: Nothing that is not right: though I am young,
Consider not my years, but how I act.
   CREON: Is this thine act—to honour the unruly?
   HAEMON: Wrongdoers, dishonour—outrage, if thou wilt!
   CREON: Hath not this maiden caught this malady?
   HAEMON: The general voice of Thebes says no to that.
   CREON: Shall Thebes prescribe to me how I must govern?
   HAEMON: How all too young art thou in speaking thus!
   CREON: Whose business is't but mine how Thebes is governed?
   HAEMON: A city is none, that to one man belongs.
   CREON: Is it not held, the city is the king's?
   HAEMON: Finely thou'dst rule, alone, a land dispeopled!
   CREON: It seems this boy will plead the woman's cause.
   HAEMON: Woman art thou? my care is all for thee.
   CREON: Shameless—is't right to wrangle with thy father?
   HAEMON: I see that wrong for right thou dost mistake.
   CREON: Do I mistake, to reverence my office?
   HAEMON: What reverence, heaven's honours to contemn?
   CREON: O hateful spirit, ruled by a woman's will!
   HAEMON: To no base service shalt thou prove me bound.
   CREON: Art thou not pleading all the time for her?
   HAEMON: For thee and me, and for the gods below.
   CREON: Thou shalt not marry her, this side the grave.
   HAEMON: If she must die, she shall: but not alone.
   CREON: Art grown so bold, thou dost fly out in threats?
   HAEMON: What threats, to argue with a foolish purpose?
   CREON: Thou'lt rue—unwise—thy wisdom spent on me.
   HAEMON: Thou art my father; or wise I scarce had called thee.
   CREON: Slave—to thy mistress babble, not to me.

HAEMON: Wouldst thou have all the talking for thine own?
CREON: Is't come to this? But, by Olympus yonder,
Know well, thou shalt be sorry for these taunts,
Wherewith thou dost upbraid me. Slaves, what ho!
Bring that abhorrence hither, that she may die,
Now, in her bridegroom's sight, whilst here he stands.
HAEMON: Neither in my sight—imagine no such thing—
Shall she be slain; nor shalt thou from this hour
Look with thine eyes upon my face again:
To friends who love thy madness I commit thee.

(*Exit* HAEMON.)

CHORUS: Suddenly, sire, in anger he is gone:
Young minds grow desperate, by grief distemper'd.
CREON: More than a man let him conceive and do;
He shall not save these maidens from their doom.
CHORUS: Both sisters art thou purposed to destroy?
CREON: Not her whose hands sinned not; thou askest well.
CHORUS: What of the other? how shall she be slain?
CREON: By paths untrodden of men I will conduct her,
And shut her, living in a vault, rock-hewn,
And there, with food, no more than shall suffice
To avert the guilt of murder from the city,
To Hades, the one god whom she reveres,
She, praying not to die, either shall have
Her asking, or shall learn, albeit too late,
That to revere the dead is fruitless toil.

THE CONFLICT OF LOYALTIES

Mark Twain

From *The Adventures of Huckleberry Finn*

We dasn't stop again at any town for days and days; kept right along down the river. We was down south in the warm weather now, and a mighty long ways from home. We began to come to

From Ch. XXXI.

trees with Spanish moss on them, hanging down from the limbs like long, gray beards. It was the first I ever see it growing, and it made the woods look solemn and dismal. So now the frauds reckoned they was out of danger, and they begun to work the villages again.

First they done a lecture on temperance; but they didn't make enough for them both to get drunk on. Then in another village they started a dancing-school; but they didn't know no more how to dance than a kangaroo does; so the first prance they made the general public jumped in and pranced them out of town. Another time they tried to go at yellocution; but they didn't yellocute long till the audience got up and give them a solid good cussing, and made them skip out. They tackled missionarying, and mesmerizing, and doctoring, and telling fortunes, and a little of everything; but they couldn't seem to have no luck. So at last they got just about dead broke, and laid around the raft as she floated along, thinking and thinking, and never saying nothing, by the half a day at a time, and dreadful blue and desperate.

And at last they took a change and begun to lay their heads together in the wigwam and talk low and confidential two or three hours at a time. Jim and me got uneasy. We didn't like the look of it. We judged they was studying up some kind of worse deviltry than ever. We turned it over and over, and at last we made up our minds they was going to break into somebody's house or store, or was going into the counterfeit money business, or something. So then we was pretty scared, and made up an agreement that we wouldn't have nothing in the world to do with such actions, and if we ever got the least show we would give them the cold shake and clear out and leave them behind. Well, early one morning we hid the raft in a good, safe place about two mile below a little bit of a shabby village named Pikesville, and the king he went ashore and told us all to stay hid whilst he went up to town and smelt around to see if anybody had got any wind of the "Royal Nonesuch" there yet. ("House to rob, you *mean*," says I to myself; "and when you get through robbing it you'll come back here and wonder what has become of me and Jim and the raft—and you'll have to take it out in wondering.") And he said if he warn't back by midday the duke and me would know it was all right, and we was to come along.

So we stayed where we was. The duke he fretted and sweated around, and was in a mighty sour way. He scolded us for everything, and we couldn't seem to do nothing right; he found fault with every little thing. Something was a-brewing, sure. I was good and glad when midday come and no king; we could have a change, anyway—and maybe a chance for *the* change on top of it. So me and the duke went up to the village, and hunted around there for the king, and by and by we found him in the back room of a little low doggery, very tight, and a lot of loafers bullyragging him for sport, and he a-cussing and a-threatening with all his might, and so tight he couldn't walk, and couldn't do nothing to them. The duke he begun to abuse him for an old fool, and the king begun to sass back, and the minute they was fairly at it I lit out and shook the reefs out of my hind legs, and spun down the river road like a deer, for I see our chance; and I made up my mind that it would be a long day before they ever see me and Jim again. I got down there all out of breath but loaded up with joy, and sung out:

"Set her loose, Jim; we're all right now!"

But there warn't no answer, and nobody come out of the wigwam. Jim was gone! I set up a shout—and then another—and then another one; and run this way and that in the woods, whooping and screeching; but it warn't no use—old Jim was gone. Then I set down and cried; I couldn't help it. But I couldn't set still long. Pretty soon I went out on the road, trying to think what I better do, and I run across a boy walking, and asked him if he'd seen a strange nigger dressed so and so, and he says:

"Yes."

"Whereabouts?" says I.

"Down to Silas Phelps's place, two mile below here. He's a runaway nigger, and they've got him. Was you looking for him?"

"You bet I ain't! I run across him in the woods about an hour or two ago, and he said if I hollered he'd cut my livers out—and told me to lay down and stay where I was; and I done it. Been there ever since; afeared to come out."

"Well," he says, "you needn't be afeared no more, becuz they've got him. He run off f'm down South, som'ers."

"It's a good job they got him."

"Well, I *reckon!* There's two hundred dollars' reward on him. It's like picking up money out'n the road."

"Yes, it is—and *I* could 'a' had it if I'd been big enough! I see him *first.* Who nailed him?"

"It was an old fellow—a stranger—and he sold out his chance in him for forty dollars, becuz he's got to go up the river and can't wait. Think o' that, now! You bet *I'd* wait, if it was seven year."

"That's me, every time," says I. "But maybe his chance ain't worth no more than that, if he'll sell it so cheap. May be there's something ain't straight about it."

"But it *is*, though—straight as a string. I see the handbill myself. It tells all about him, to a dot—paints him like a picture, and tells the plantations he's frum, below New*rleans*. No-siree-*bob*, they ain't no trouble 'bout *that* speculation, you bet you. Say, gimme a chaw tobacker, won't ye?"

I didn't have none, so he left. I went to the raft, and set down in the wigwam to think. But I couldn't come to nothing. I thought till I wore my head sore, but I couldn't see no way out of the trouble. After all this long journey, and after all we'd done for them scoundrels, here it was all come to nothing, everything all busted up and ruined, because they could have the heart to serve Jim such a trick as that, and make him a slave again all his life, and amongst strangers, too, for forty dirty dollars.

Once I said to myself it would be a thousand times better for Jim to be a slave at home where his family was as long as he'd *got* to be a slave, and so I'd better write a letter to Tom Sawyer and tell him to tell Miss Watson where he was. But I soon give up that notion for two things: she'd be mad and disgusted at his rascality and ungratefulness for leaving her, and so she'd sell him straight down the river again; and if she didn't, everybody naturally despises an ungrateful nigger, and they'd make Jim feel it all the time, and so he'd feel ornery and disgraced. And then think of *me!* It would get all around that Huck Finn helped a nigger to get his freedom; and if I was ever to see anybody from that town again I'd be ready to get down and lick his boots for shame. That's just the way: a person does a low-down thing, and then he don't want to take no consequences of it. Thinks as long as he can hide, it ain't no disgrace. That was my fix exactly. The more I studied about this the more my conscience went to grinding me, and the more wicked and low-down and ornery I got to feeling. And at last, when it hit me all of a sudden that here was the plain hand of Providence slapping me in the face and letting me know my wickedness was being watched all the time from up there in heaven, whilst I was stealing a poor old woman's nigger that hadn't ever done me no harm, and now was showing me there's One that's always on the lookout, and ain't a-going to allow no such miserable doings to go only just so fur and no further, I most dropped in my tracks I was so scared. Well, I tried the best I could to kinder soften it up somehow for myself by saying I was brung up wicked, and so I warn't so much to blame, but something inside of me kept saying, "There was the Sunday-school, you could 'a' gone to it; and if you'd 'a' done it they'd 'a' learnt you there that people that acts as I'd been acting about the nigger goes to everlasting fire."

It made me shiver. And I about made up my mind to pray, and see if I couldn't try to quit being the kind of a boy I was and be better. So I kneeled down. But the words wouldn't come. Why wouldn't they? It warn't no use to try and hide it from Him. Nor from *me*, neither. I knowed very well why they wouldn't come. It was because my heart warn't right; it was because I warn't square; it was because I was playing double. I was letting *on* to give up sin, but away inside of me I was holding on to the biggest one of all. I was trying to make my mouth *say* I would do the right thing and the clean thing, and go and write to that nigger's owner and tell where he was; but deep down in me I knowed it was a lie, and He knowed it. You can't pray a lie—I found that out.

So I was full of trouble, full as I could be; and didn't know what to do. At last I had an idea; and I says, I'll go and write the letter—and *then* see if I can pray. Why, it was astonishing, the way I felt as light as a feather right straight off, and my troubles all gone. So I got a piece of paper and a pencil, all glad and excited, and set down and wrote:

> Miss Watson, your runaway nigger Jim is down here two mile below Pikesville, and Mr. Phelps has got him and he will give him up for the reward if you send.
>
>   HUCK FINN

I felt good and all washed clean of sin for the first time I had ever felt so in my life, and I knowed I could pray now. But I didn't do it straight off, but laid the paper down and set there thinking—thinking how good it was all this happened so, and how near I come to being lost and going to hell. And went on thinking. And got to thinking over our trip down the river; and I see Jim before me all the time: in the day and in the night-time, sometimes moonlight, sometimes storms, and we a-floating along, talking and singing and laughing. But somehow I couldn't seem to strike no places to harden me against him, but only the other kind. I'd see him standing my watch on top of his'n, 'stead of calling me, so I could go on sleeping; and see him how glad he was when I come back out of the fog; and when I come to him again in the swamp, up there where the feud was; and suchlike times; and would always call me honey, and pet me, and do everything he could think of for me, and how good he

always was; and at last I struck the time I saved him by telling the
men we had smallpox aboard, and he was so grateful, and said I was
the best friend old Jim ever had in the world, and the *only* one he's
got now; and then I happened to look around and see that paper.

It was a close place. I took it up, and held it in my hand. I was
a-trembling, because I'd got to decide, forever, betwixt two things,
and I knowed it. I studied a minute, sort of holding my breath, and
then says to myself:

"All right, then, I'll *go* to hell"—and tore it up.

It was awful thoughts and awful words, but they was said. And
I let them stay said; and never thought no more about reforming. I
shoved the whole thing out of my head, and said I would take up
wickedness again, which was in my line, being brung up to it, and
the other warn't. And for a starter I would go to work and steal
Jim out of slavery again; and if I could think up anything worse,
I would do that, too; because as long as I was in, and in for good,
I might as well go the whole hog.

THE RATIONALE OF LAW ENFORCEMENT

Herman Melville

From *Billy Budd*

Now when the foretopman found himself closeted there, as it
were, in the cabin with the captain and Claggart, he was surprised
enough. But it was a surprise unaccompanied by apprehension or
distrust. To an immature nature essentially honest and humane, fore-
warning intimations of subtler danger from one's kind come tardily
if at all. The only thing that took shape in the young sailor's mind
was this: Yes, the captain, I have always thought, looks kindly upon
me. Wonder if he's going to make me his coxswain. I should like that.
And maybe now he is going to ask the master-at-arms about me.

"Shut the door there, sentry," said the commander; "stand without,

Chs. 20–22, 26. Reprinted by permission of the publishers from *Melville's Billy
Budd*, edited by Frederic Barron Freeman, corrected by Elizabeth Treeman,
Harvard University Press, Cambridge, Mass. Copyright 1948, 1956, by the Presi-
dent and Fellows of Harvard College.

and let nobody come in.—Now, Master-at-Arms, tell this man to his face what you told of him to me," and stood prepared to scrutinize the mutually confronting visages.

With the measured step and calm collected air of an asylum physician approaching in the public hall some patient beginning to show indications of a coming paroxysm, Claggart deliberately advanced within short range of Billy, and, mesmerically looking him in the eye, briefly recapitulated the accusation.

Not at first did Billy take it in. When he did, the rose-tan of his cheek looked struck as by white leprosy. He stood like one impaled and gagged. Meanwhile the accuser's eyes removing not as yet from the blue dilated ones, underwent a phenomenal change, their wonted rich violet color blurring into a muddy purple, those lights of human intelligence losing human expression, gelidly protruding like the alien eyes of certain uncatalogued creatures of the deep. The first mesmeric glance was one of serpent fascination; the last was as the hungry lurch of the torpedo-fish.

"Speak, man!" said Captain Vere to the transfixed one, struck by his aspect even more than by Claggart's. "Speak! defend yourself." Which appeal caused but a strange dumb gesturing and gurgling in Billy, amazement at such an accusation so suddenly sprung on inexperienced nonage; this, and, it may be, horror of the accuser, serving to bring out his lurking defect and in this instance for the time intensifying it into a convulsed tongue-tie; while the intent head and entire form straining forward in an agony of ineffectual eagerness to obey the injunction to speak and defend himself, gave an expression to the face like that of a condemned Vestal priestess in the moment of being buried alive, and in the first struggle against suffocation.

Though at the time Captain Vere was quite ignorant of Billy's liability to vocal impediment, he now immediately divined it, since vividly Billy's aspect recalled to him that of a bright young schoolmate of his whom he had once seen struck by much the same startling impotence in the act of eagerly rising in the class to be foremost in response to a testing question put to it by the master. Going close up to the young sailor, and laying a soothing hand on his shoulder, he said: "There is no hurry, my boy. Take your time, take your time." Contrary to the effect intended, these words so fatherly in tone doubtless touching Billy's heart to the quick, prompted yet more violent efforts at utterance—efforts soon ending for the time in confirming the paralysis, and bringing to his face an expression which was as a crucifixion to behold. The next instant, quick as the flame from a discharged cannon at night, his right arm shot out, and Claggart dropped to the deck. Whether intentionally or but owing to the young athlete's superior height, the blow had taken effect full upon the forehead, so shapely and intellectual-looking a feature in the master-at-arms, so that the body fell over lengthwise, like a heavy plank tilted from erectness. A gasp or two, and he lay motionless.

"Fated boy," breathed Captain Vere in tone so low as to be almost a whisper, "what have you done! But here, help me."

The twain raised the felled one from the loins up into a sitting position. The spare form flexibly acquiesced, but inertly. It was like handling a dead snake. They lowered it back. Regaining erectness Captain Vere with one hand covering his face stood to all appearance as impassive as the object at his feet. Was he absorbed in taking in all the bearings of the event and what was best, not only now at once to be done, but also in the sequel? Slowly he uncovered his face, and the effect was as if the moon emerging from eclipse should reappear with quite another aspect than that which had gone into hiding. The father in him, manifested toward Billy thus far in the scene, was replaced by the military disciplinarian. In his official tone he bade the foretopman retire to a stateroom aft (pointing it out) and there remain till thence summoned. This order Billy in silence mechanically obeyed. Then, going to the cabin door where it opened on the quarter-deck, Captain Vere said to the sentry without, "Tell somebody to send Albert here." When the lad appeared his master so contrived it that he should not catch sight of the prone one. "Albert," he said to him, "tell the surgeon I wish to see him. You need not come back till called." When the surgeon entered—a self-poised character of that grave sense and experience that hardly anything could take him aback—Captain Vere advanced to meet him, thus unconsciously intercepting his view of Claggart, and, interrupting the other's wonted ceremonious salutation, said, "Nay, tell me how it is with yonder man," directing his attention to the prostrate one.

The surgeon looked, and for all his self-command, somewhat started at the abrupt revelation. On Claggart's always pallid complexion, thick black blood was now oozing from nostril and ear. To the gazer's professional eye it was unmistakably no living man that he saw.

"Is it so then?" said Captain Vere, intently watching him. "I thought it. But verify it." Whereupon the customary tests confirmed the surgeon's first glance, who now, looking up in unfeigned concern, cast a look of intense inquisitiveness upon his superior. But Captain

Vere, with one hand to his brow, was standing motionless. Suddenly, catching the surgeon's arm convulsively, he exclaimed, pointing down to the body—"It is the divine judgment on Ananias! Look!"

Disturbed by the excited manner he had never before observed in the *Indomitable*'s captain, and as yet wholly ignorant of the affair, the prudent surgeon nevertheless held his peace, only again looking an earnest interrogation as to what it was that had resulted in such a tragedy.

But Captain Vere was now again motionless, standing absorbed in thought. But again starting, he vehemently exclaimed—"Struck dead by an angel of God! Yet the angel must hang!"

At these passionate interjections, mere incoherences to the listener as yet unapprised of the antecedents, the surgeon was profoundly discomposed. But now, as recollecting himself, Captain Vere in less passionate tone briefly related the circumstances leading up to the event.

"But come, we must despatch," he added. "Help me to remove him (meaning the body) to yonder compartment," designating one opposite that where the foretopman remained immured. Anew disturbed by a request that, as implying a desire for secrecy, seemed unaccountably strange to him, there was nothing for the subordinate to do but comply.

"Go now," said Captain Vere with something of his wonted manner—"go now. I shall presently call a drumhead court. Tell the lieutenants what happened, and tell Mr. Mordant," meaning the captain of marines, "and charge them to keep the matter to themselves."

·   ·   ·

Full of disquietude and misgiving, the surgeon left the cabin. Was Captain Vere suddenly affected in his mind, or was it but a transient excitement, brought about by so strange and extraordinary a happening? As to the drumhead court, it struck the surgeon as impolitic, if nothing more. The thing to do, he thought, was to place Billy Budd in confinement and in a way dictated by usage, and postpone further action in so extraordinary a case to such time as they should rejoin the squadron, and then refer it to the admiral. He recalled the unwonted agitation of Captain Vere and his excited exclamations so at variance with his normal manner. Was he unhinged? But assuming that he is, it is not so susceptible of proof. What then can he do? No more trying situation is conceivable than that of an officer subordinate under a captain whom he suspects to be, not mad indeed, but yet not quite unaffected in his intellect. To argue his order to him would be insolence. To resist him would be mutiny.

In obedience to Captain Vere he communicated what had happened to the lieutenants and captain of marines, saying nothing as to the captain's state. They fully shared his own surprise and concern. Like him too they seemed to think that such a matter should be referred to the admiral.

. . .

Who in the rainbow can show the line where the violet tint ends and the orange tint begins? Distinctly we see the difference of the colors, but when exactly does the one first blendingly enter into the other? So with sanity and insanity. In pronounced cases, there is no question about them. But in some supposed cases, in various degrees supposedly less pronounced, to draw the exact line of demarcation few will undertake—though for a fee some professional experts will. There is nothing namable but that some men will undertake to do it for pay.

Whether Captain Vere, as the surgeon professionally and privately surmised, was really the sudden victim of any degree of aberration, one must determine for himself by such light as this narrative may afford.

That the unhappy event which has been narrated could not have happened at a worse juncture was but too true. For it was close on the heel of the suppressed insurrections, an aftertime very critical to naval authority, demanding from every English sea commander two qualities not readily interfusible—prudence and rigor. Moreover, there was something crucial in the case.

In the jugglery of circumstances preceding and attending the event on board the *Indomitable,* and in the light of that martial code whereby it was formally to be judged, innocence and guilt personified in Claggart and Budd in effect changed places. In a legal view the apparent victim of the tragedy was he who had sought to victimize a man blameless; and the indisputable deed of the latter, navally regarded, constituted the most heinous of military crimes. Yet more. The essential right and wrong involved in the matter, the clearer that might be, so much the worse for the responsibility of a loyal sea commander inasmuch as he was not authorized to determine the matter on that primitive basis.

Small wonder then that the *Indomitable*'s captain, though in general a man of rapid decision, felt that circumspectness not less than promptitude was necessary. Until he could decide upon his course, and in each detail, and not only so, but until the concluding measure was upon the point of being enacted, he deemed it advisable, in view of all the circumstances, to guard as much as possible against publicity. Here he may or may not have erred. Certain it is, however, that subsequently in the confidential talk of more than one or two gun rooms and cabins he was not a little criticized by some officers, a fact imputed by his friends and vehemently by his cousin Jack Denton to professional jealousy of "Starry Vere." Some imaginative ground for invidious comment there was. The maintenance of secrecy in the matter, the confining all knowledge of it for a time to the place where the homicide occurred, the quarter-deck cabin—in these particulars lurked some resemblance to the policy adopted in those tragedies of the palace which have occurred more than once in the capital founded by Peter the Barbarian.

The case indeed was such that fain would the *Indomitable*'s captain have deferred taking any action whatever respecting it further than to keep the foretopman a close prisoner till the ship rejoined the squadron and then submitting the matter to the judgment of his admiral.

But a true military officer is in one particular like a true monk. Not with more of self-abnegation will the latter keep his vows of monastic obedience than the former his vows of allegiance to martial duty.

Feeling that unless quick action was taken on it, the deed of the foretopman, so soon as it should be known on the gun decks, would tend to awaken any slumbering embers of the Nore among the crew, a sense of the urgency of the case overruled in Captain Vere every other consideration. But though a conscientious disciplinarian he was no lover of authority for mere authority's sake. Very far was he from embracing opportunities for monopolizing to himself the perils of moral responsibility, none at least that could properly be referred to an official superior or shared with him by his official equals or even subordinates. So thinking, he was glad it would not be at variance with usage to turn the matter over to a summary court of his own officers, reserving to himself as the one on whom the ultimate accountability would rest, the right of maintaining a supervision of it, or formally or informally interposing at need. Accordingly a drumhead court was summarily convened, he electing the individuals composing it, the first lieutenant, the captain of marines, and the sailing master.

In associating an officer of marines with the sea lieutenants in a

case having to do with a sailor, the commander perhaps deviated
from general custom. He was prompted thereto by the circumstance
that he took that soldier to be a judicious person, thoughtful, and not
altogether incapable of grappling with a difficult case unprecedented in his prior experience. Yet even as to him he was not without
some latent misgiving, for withal he was an extremely good-natured
man, an enjoyer of his dinner, a sound sleeper, and inclined to
obesity. A man who though he would always maintain his manhood
in battle might not prove altogether reliable in a moral dilemma involving aught of the tragic. As to the first lieutenant and the sailing
master, Captain Vere could not but be aware that, though honest
natures, of approved gallantry upon occasion, their intelligence was
mostly confined to the matter of active seamanship and the fighting
demands of their profession. The court was held in the same cabin
where the unfortunate affair had taken place. This cabin, the commander's, embraced the entire area under the poop deck. Aft, and
on either side, was a small stateroom, the one room temporarily a
jail and the other a dead-house, and a yet smaller compartment leaving a space between, expanding forward into a goodly oblong of
length coinciding with the ship's beam. A skylight of moderate dimension was overhead, and at each end of the oblong space were
two sashed porthole windows easily convertible back into embra-
sures for short carronades.

All being quickly in readiness, Billy Budd was arraigned, Captain
Vere necessarily appearing as the sole witness in the case, and as
such temporarily sinking his rank, though singularly maintaining it
in a matter apparently trivial, namely, that he testified from the
ship's weather side, with that object having caused the court to sit
on the lee side. Concisely he narrated all that had led up to the
catastrophe, omitting nothing in Claggart's accusation and deposing
as to the manner in which the prisoner had received it. At this testi-
mony the three officers glanced with no little surprise at Billy Budd,
the last man they would have suspected either of the mutinous design
alleged by Claggart or the undeniable deed he himself had done.

The first lieutenant, taking judicial primacy and turning toward
the prisoner, said, "Captain Vere has spoken. Is it or is it not as Captain Vere says?" In response came syllables not so much impeded in
the utterance as might have been anticipated. They were these:
"Captain Vere tells the truth. It is just as Captain Vere says, but it is
not as the master-at-arms said. I have eaten the King's bread and
I am true to the King."

"I believe you, my man," said the witness, his voice indicating a suppressed emotion not otherwise betrayed.

"God will bless you for that, your honor!" not without stammering said Billy, and all but broke down. But immediately was recalled to self-control by another question, to which with the same emotional difficulty of utterance he said, "No, there was no malice between us. I never bore malice against the master-at-arms. I am sorry that he is dead. I did not mean to kill him. Could I have used my tongue I would not have struck him. But he foully lied to my face and in presence of my captain, and I had to say something, and I could only say it with a blow, God help me!"

In the impulsive aboveboard manner of the frank one the court saw confirmed all that was implied in words that just previously had perplexed them, coming as they did from the testifier to the tragedy and promptly following Billy's impassioned disclaimer of mutinous intent—Captain Vere's words, "I believe you, my man."

Next it was asked of him whether he knew of or suspected aught savoring of incipient trouble (meaning mutiny, though the explicit term was avoided) going on in any section of the ship's company.

The reply lingered. This was naturally imputed by the court to the same vocal embarrassment which had retarded or obstructed previous answers. But in main it was otherwise here, the question immediately recalling to Billy's mind the interview with the after-guardsman in the forechains. But an innate repugnance to playing a part at all approaching that of an informer against one's own ship-mates—the same erring sense of uninstructed honor which had stood in the way of his reporting the matter at the time though as a loyal man-of-war-man it was incumbent on him, and failure so to do if charged against him and proven, would have subjected him to the heaviest of penalties—this, with the blind feeling now his, that nothing really was being hatched, prevailed with him. When the answer came it was a negative.

"One question more," said the officer of marines, now first speaking and with a troubled earnestness. "You tell us that what the master-at-arms said against you was a lie. Now why should he have so lied, so maliciously lied, since you declare there was no malice between you?"

At that question unintentionally touching on a spiritual sphere wholly obscure to Billy's thoughts, he was nonplused, evincing a confusion indeed that some observers, such as can readily be imagined, would have construed into involuntary evidence of hidden guilt.

Nevertheless he strove some way to answer, but all at once relinquished the vain endeavor, at the same time turning an appealing glance toward Captain Vere, as deeming him his best helper and friend. Captain Vere, who had been seated for a time, rose to his feet, addressing the interrogator. "The question you put to him comes naturally enough. But how can he rightly answer it? or anybody else? unless indeed it be he who lies within there," designating the compartment where lay the corpse. "But the prone one there will not rise to our summons. In effect, though, as it seems to me, the point you make is hardly material. Quite aside from any conceivable motive actuating the master-at-arms, and irrespective of the provocation to the blow, a martial court must needs in the present case confine its attention to the blow's consequence, which consequence justly is to be deemed not otherwise than as the striker's deed."

This utterance, the full significance of which it was not at all likely that Billy took in, nevertheless caused him to turn a wistful interrogative look toward the speaker, a look in its dumb expressiveness not unlike that which a dog of generous breed might turn upon his master, seeking in his face some elucidation of a previous gesture ambiguous to the canine intelligence. Nor was the same utterance without marked effect upon the three officers, more especially the soldier. Couched in it seemed to them a meaning unanticipated, involving a prejudgment on the speaker's part. It served to augment a mental disturbance previously evident enough.

The soldier once more spoke, in a tone of suggestive dubiety addressing at once his associates and Captain Vere: "Nobody is present —none of the ship's company, I mean—who might shed lateral light, if any is to be had, upon what remains mysterious in this matter."

"That is thoughtfully put," said Captain Vere; "I see your drift. Aye, there is a mystery; but, to use a Scriptural phrase, it is 'a mystery of iniquity,' a matter for psychologic theologians to discuss. But what has a military court to do with it? Not to add that for us any possible investigation of it is cut off by the lasting tongue-tie of—him—in yonder," again designating the mortuary stateroom. "The prisoner's deed—with that alone we have to do."

To this, and particularly the closing reiteration, the marine soldier, knowing not how aptly to reply, sadly abstained from saying aught. The first lieutenant, who at the outset had not unnaturally assumed primacy in the court, now overrulingly instructed by a glance from Captain Vere, a glance more effective than words, resumed that primacy. Turning to the prisoner, "Budd," he said, "and scarce in equable tones, "Budd, if you have aught further to say for yourself, say it now."

Upon this the young sailor turned another quick glance toward Captain Vere; then, as taking a hint from that aspect, a hint confirming his own instinct that silence was now best, replied to the lieutenant "I have said all, sir."

The marine—the same who had been the sentinel without the cabin door at the time that the foretopman, followed by the master-at-arms, entered it—he, standing by the sailor throughout these judicial proceedings, was now directed to take him back to the after compartment originally assigned to the prisoner and his custodian. As the twain disappeared from view, the three officers, as partially liberated from some inward constraint associated with Billy's mere presence, simultaneously stirred in their seats. They exchanged looks of troubled indecision, yet feeling that decide they must and without long delay. As for Captain Vere, he for the time stood unconsciously with his back toward them, apparently in one of his absent fits, gazing out from a sashed porthole to windward upon the monotonous blank of the twilight sea. But the court's silence continuing, broken only at moments by brief consultations in low earnest tones, this seemed to arm him and energize him. Turning, he to-and-fro paced the cabin athwart, in the returning ascent to windward climbing the slant deck in the ship's lee roll, without knowing it symbolizing thus in his action a mind resolute to surmount difficulties even if against primitive instincts strong as the wind and the sea. Presently he came to a stand before the three. After scanning their faces he stood less as mustering his thoughts for expression than as one only deliberating how best to put them to well-meaning men not intellectually mature, men with whom it was necessary to demonstrate certain principles that were axioms to himself. Similar impatience as to talking is perhaps one reason that deters some minds from addressing any popular assemblies.

When speak he did, something both in the substance of what he said and his manner of saying it, showed the influence of unshared studies modifying and tempering the practical training of an active career. This, along with his phraseology now and then, was suggestive of the grounds whereon rested that imputation of a certain pedantry socially alleged against him by certain naval men of wholly practical cast, captains who nevertheless would frankly concede that His Majesty's navy mustered no more efficient officer of their grade than "Starry Vere."

What he said was to this effect: "Hitherto I have been but the witness, little more; and I should hardly think now to take another tone, that of your coadjutor, for the time, did I not perceive in you —at the crisis too—a troubled hesitancy, proceeding, I doubt not, from the clash of military duty with moral scruple—scruple vitalized by compassion. For the compassion, how can I otherwise than share it? But, mindful of paramount obligations, I strive against scruples that may tend to enervate decision. Not, gentlemen, that I hide from myself that the case is an exceptional one. Speculatively regarded, it well might be referred to a jury of casuists. But for us here acting not as casuists or moralists, it is a case practical, and under martial law practically to be dealt with.

"But your scruples: do they move as in a dusk? Challenge them. Make them advance and declare themselves. Come now: do they import something like this: If, mindless of palliating circumstances, we are bound to regard the death of the master-at-arms as the prisoner's deed, then does that deed constitute a capital crime whereof the penalty is a mortal one? But in natural justice is nothing but the prisoner's overt act to be considered? How can we adjudge to summary and shameful death a fellow creature innocent before God, and whom we feel to be so?—Does that state it aright? You sign sad assent. Well, I too feel that, the full force of that. It is Nature. But do these buttons that we wear attest that our allegiance is to Nature? No, to the King. Though the ocean, which is inviolate Nature primeval, though this be the element where we move and have our being as sailors, yet as the King's officers lies our duty in a sphere correspondingly natural? So little is that true that, in receiving our commissions, we in the most important regards ceased to be natural free agents. When war is declared are we, the commissioned fighters, previously consulted? We fight at command. If our judgments approve the war, that is but coincidence. So in other particulars. So now. For suppose condemnation to follow these present proceedings. Would it be so much we ourselves that would condemn as it would be martial law operating through us? For that law and the rigor of it, we are not responsible. Our vowed responsibility is in this: That however pitilessly that law may operate, we nevertheless adhere to it and administer it.

"But the exceptional in the matter moves the hearts within you. Even so too is mine moved. But let not warm hearts betray heads that should be cool. Ashore in a criminal case will an upright judge allow himself off the bench to be waylaid by some tender kinswoman of the accused seeking to touch him with her tearful plea? Well the heart here denotes the feminine in man, is as that piteous woman and, hard though it be, she must here be ruled out."

He paused, earnestly studying them for a moment, then resumed.

"But something in your aspect seems to urge that it is not solely the heart that moves in you, but also the conscience, the private conscience. But tell me whether or not, occupying the position we do, private conscience should not yield to that imperial one formulated in the code under which alone we officially proceed?"

Here the three men moved in their seats, less convinced than agitated by the course of an argument troubling but the more the spontaneous conflict within.

Perceiving which, the speaker paused for a moment, then, abruptly changing his tone, went on.

"To steady us a bit, let us recur to the facts.—In wartime at sea a man-of-war's-man strikes his superior in grade, and the blow kills. Apart from its effect, the blow itself is, according to the Articles of War, a capital crime. Furthermore——"

"Aye, sir," emotionally broke in the officer of marines, "in one sense it was. But surely Budd purposed neither mutiny nor homicide."

"Surely not, my good man. And before a court less arbitrary and more merciful than a martial one that plea would largely extenuate. At the Last Assizes it shall acquit. But how here? We proceed under the law of the Mutiny Act. In feature no child can resemble his father more than that Act resembles in spirit the thing from which it derives—War. In His Majesty's service—in this ship indeed—there are Englishmen forced to fight for the King against their will. Against their conscience, for aught we know. Though as their fellow creatures some of us may appreciate their position, yet as navy officers, what reck we of it? Still less recks the enemy. Our impressed men we would fain cut down in the same swath with our volunteers. As regards the enemy's naval conscripts, some of whom may even share our own abhorrence of the regicidal French Directory, it is the same on our side. War looks but to the frontage, the appearance. And the Mutiny Act, War's child, takes after the father. Budd's intent or nonintent is nothing to the purpose.

"But while, put to it by those anxieties in you which I cannot but respect, I only repeat myself—while thus strangely we prolong proceedings that should be summary—the enemy may be sighted and an engagement result. We must do; and one of two things must we do—condemn or let go."

"Can we not convict and yet mitigate the penalty?" asked the junior lieutenant here speaking, and falteringly, for the first.

"Lieutenant, were that clearly lawful for us under the circumstances, consider the consequences of such clemency. The people" (meaning the ship's company) "have native sense; most of them are familiar with our naval usage and tradition, and how would they take it? Even could you explain to them—which our official position forbids—they, long molded by arbitrary discipline, have not that kind of intelligent responsiveness that might qualify them to comprehend and discriminate. No, to the people the foretopman's deed, however it be worded in the announcement, will be plain homicide committed in a flagrant act of mutiny. What penalty for that should follow, they know. But it does not follow. *Why?* they will ruminate. You know what sailors are. Will they not revert to the recent outbreak at the Nore? Aye. They know the well-founded alarm—the panic it struck throughout England. Your clement sentence they would account pusillanimous. They would think that we flinch, that we are afraid of them—afraid of practicing a lawful rigor singularly demanded at this juncture lest it should provoke new troubles. What shame to us such a conjecture on their part, and how deadly to discipline. You see then, whither, prompted by duty and the law, I steadfastly drive. But I beseech you, my friends, do not take me amiss. I feel as you do for this unfortunate boy. But did he know our hearts, I take him to be of that generous nature that he would feel even for us on whom in this military necessity so heavy a compulsion is laid."

With that, crossing the deck he resumed his place by the sashed porthole, tacitly leaving the three to come to a decision. On the cabin's opposite side the troubled court sat silent. Loyal lieges, plain and practical, though at bottom they dissented from some points Captain Vere had put to them, they were without the faculty, hardly had the inclination, to gainsay one whom they felt to be an earnest man, one, too, not less their superior in mind than in naval rank. But it is not improbable that even such of his words as were not without influence over them, less came home to them than his closing appeal to their instinct as sea officers in the forethought he threw out as to the practical consequences to discipline, considering the unconfirmed tone of the fleet at the time, should a man-of-war's-man's violent killing at sea of a superior in grade be allowed to pass for aught else than a capital crime demanding prompt infliction of the penalty.

Not unlikely they were brought to something more or less akin to that harassed frame of mind which in the year 1842 actuated the commander of the U.S. brig-of-war *Somers* to resolve, under the so-called Articles of War, Articles modeled upon the English Mutiny Act, to resolve upon the execution at sea of a midshipman and two petty officers as mutineers designing the seizure of the brig. Which resolution was carried out though in a time of peace and within not many days sail of home—an act vindicated by a naval court of inquiry subsequently convened ashore. History, and here cited without comment. True, the circumstances on board the *Somers* were different from those on board the *Indomitable*. But the urgency felt, well-warranted or otherwise, was much the same.

Says a writer whom few know, "Forty years after a battle it is easy for a noncombatant to reason about how it ought to have been fought. It is another thing personally and under fire to direct the fighting while involved in the obscuring smoke of it. Much so with respect to other emergencies involving considerations both practical and moral, and when it is imperative promptly to act. The greater the fog the more it imperils the steamer, and speed is put on though at the hazard of running somebody down. Little ween the snug card-players in the cabin of the responsibilities of the sleepless man on the bridge."

In brief, Billy Budd was formally convicted and sentenced to be hung at the yardarm in the early morning watch, it being now night. Otherwise, as is customary in such cases, the sentence would forthwith have been carried out. In wartime, on the field or in the fleet, a mortal punishment decreed by a drumhead court—on the field sometimes decreed by but a nod from the general—follows without delay on the heel of conviction, without appeal.

. . .

The night so luminous on the spar-deck but otherwise on the cavernous ones below, levels so like the tiered galleries in a coal mine—the luminous night passed away. But, like the prophet in the chariot disappearing in heaven and dropping his mantle to Elisha, the withdrawing night transferred its pale robe to the breaking day. A meek shy light appeared in the East, where stretched a diaphanous fleece of white furrowed vapor. That light slowly waxed. Suddenly *eight bells* was struck aft, responded to by one louder metallic

stroke from forward. It was four o'clock in the morning. Instantly
the silver whistles were heard summoning all hands to witness punishment. Up through the great hatchways rimmed with racks of
heavy shot, the watch below came pouring, overspreading with
the watch already on deck the space between the mainmast and
foremast, including that occupied by the capacious launch and the
black booms tiered on either side of it, boat and booms making a
summit of observation for the powder-boys and younger tars. A
different group comprising one watch of topmen leaned over the
rail of that sea-balcony, no small one in a seventy-four, looking
down on the crowd below. Man or boy none spake but in whisper,
and few spake at all. Captain Vere—as before, the central figure
among the assembled commissioned officers—stood nigh the break
of the poop deck facing forward. Just below him on the quarter-
deck the marines in full equipment were drawn up much as at the
scene of the promulgated sentence.

At sea in the old time, the execution by halter of a military sailor
was generally from the foreyard. In the present instance, for special
reasons the mainyard was assigned. Under an arm of that lee yard
the prisoner was presently brought up, the chaplain attending him.
It was noted at the time, and remarked upon afterwards, that in
this final scene the good man evinced little or nothing of the per-
functory. Brief speech indeed he had with the condemned one, but
the genuine Gospel was less on his tongue than in his aspect and
manner toward him. The final preparations personal to the latter
being speedily brought to an end by two boatswain's mates, the
consummation impended. Billy stood facing aft. At the penultimate
moment, his words, his only ones, words wholly unobstructed in the
utterance, were these—"God bless Captain Vere!" Syllables so unanticipated coming from one with the ignominious hemp about his
neck—a conventional felon's benediction directed aft toward the
quarters of honor; syllables, too, delivered in the clear melody of a
singing bird on the point of launching from the twig, had a phenomenal effect, not unenhanced by the rare personal beauty of the
young sailor spiritualized now through late experience so poign-
antly profound.

Without volition as it were, as if indeed the ship's populace were
but the vehicles of some vocal current electric, with one voice from
alow and aloft came a resonant sympathetic echo—"God bless Captain Vere!" And yet at that instant Billy alone must have been in
their hearts, even as he was in their eyes.

At the pronounced words and the spontaneous echo that voluminously rebounded them, Captain Vere, either through stoic self-control or a sort of momentary paralysis induced by emotional shock, stood erectly rigid as a musket in the ship-armorer's rack.

The hull deliberately recovering from the periodic roll to leeward was just regaining an even keel, when the last signal, a preconcerted dumb one, was given. At the same moment it chanced that the vapory fleece hanging low in the East was shot through with a soft glory as of the fleece of the Lamb of God seen in mystical vision, and simultaneously therewith, watched by the wedged mass of upturned faces, Billy ascended, and, ascending, took the full rose of the dawn.

A SKEPTICAL VIEW

A. E. Housman

"The Laws of God, the Laws of Man"

> The laws of God, the laws of man,
> He may keep that will and can;
> Not I: let God and man decree
> Laws for themselves and not for me;
> And if my ways are not as theirs
> Let them mind their own affairs.
> Their deeds I judge and much condemn,
> Yet when did I make laws for them?
> Please yourselves, say I, and they
> Need only look the other way.
> But no, they will not; they must still
> Wrest their neighbour to their will,
> And make me dance as they desire
> With jail and gallows and hell-fire.

And how am I to face the odds
Of man's bedevilment and God's?
I, a stranger and afraid
In a world I never made.

They will be master, right or wrong;
Though both are foolish, both are strong.
And since, my soul, we cannot fly
To Saturn nor to Mercury,
Keep we must, if keep we can,
These foreign laws of God and man.

Chapter III

Authority and Liberty

Like the relationship between obligation and conscience, that between authority and liberty is exceedingly difficult to describe satisfactorily. The perennial conflict between these two fundamental political principles poses sharply the question whether it is indeed possible to have both authority and liberty in the same civil society. At first glance the answer to that question might appear to be simple; but in the end that is not the case.

To see why it is not, we may begin by considering the most typical modern definition of liberty, which comes to us from the English philosopher Thomas Hobbes: to be free is to be unrestrained, not interfered with. In this conception, it is evident, every example of liberty—of being able to do as one wishes—may immediately and equally be an example of nonauthority, of the absence of external restraint: of, in a word, anarchy. And so we are presented with a fearful dilemma, a dilemma over which many of the world's great authors of dramatic and narrative fiction, as well as of political philosophy, have agonized. Presumably there must be some regular authority if civil society is to survive. But how can it be provided without restraining people from doing what they want to do?

Three answers to this question are characteristic both of modern political thought and of modern governments; we may call them the authoritarian, the liberal individualist, and the majoritarian solutions. The first of these, which is associated with

Hobbes himself, resolves our dilemma by redefining it: specifically, by distinguishing between liberty as an occasional blessing of social life and liberty as an organizing social principle. Authority, Hobbes reasons, is necessary; and nearly everyone agrees. But how much authority, and who is to decide, and when? If we leave the answers to these questions up to every individual, then we will still be faced with the prospect of falling into the dreaded state of anarchy. Clearly then, a sovereign is needed to make decisions that will be authoritative for all individuals in the society and thus prevent a return to a condition of jungle warfare. The sovereign, further, must have absolute power; for limited sovereignty denotes an inability to force decisive compromises between contending social forces and is thus but a way station on the road to civil war. Hobbes makes clear that the organization of such an absolute state is not incompatible with the existence of a large amount of personal liberty. But it is liberty granted by the sovereign, not retained as a matter of right.

This authoritarian solution must be extremely unattractive to those reared in the philosophical tradition of Western liberalism; yet there is reason to doubt its general unattractiveness. In a great part of the world authoritarianism has always prevailed, and the principal distinction between various governments has been not whether they were basically authoritarian or liberal, but rather how much liberty an authoritarian government would generously decide to allow to its subjects. Such governments have at times proved to be quite stable, surprisingly so to those who believe in an innate human longing for political liberty. In all cultures, even Western ones, political submissiveness—the willingness to take what is given rather than fight for more, the desire to avoid the complex responsibilities of being a free citizen in a free community—has been observed as a widespread trait. As the Grand Inquisitor puts it in Feodor Dostoevski's The Brothers Karamazov "I tell thee that man is tormented by no greater anxiety than to find some one quickly to whom he can hand over that gift of freedom with which the ill-fated creature is born." (The Grand Inquisitor might well have been describing Diederich Hessling in Heinrich Mann's novel Little Superman; see Chapters VII and IX.) It is a commonplace, indeed, that even revolutions invariably substitute new masters for old. Nor do we have to turn to such pathological cases: Everywhere in the Western democracies themselves significant political participation remains an activity of the few, and decision making is retained in as few hands as possible.

The democrat, however, must still object. For him the basic principle of political organization is liberty, not authority; for the individual and not society is the basic unit of value in his philosophy. But just as authoritarian philosophy tends to deny liberty (as a principle) totally in the end, so does liberal individualism tend to deny authority; in this Hobbes was surely correct. For, the liberal must reason, if one invasion of liberty is acceptable, why not one hundred? Or one million? No ready answer being available—that is, no logical way of defining when an invasion of individual liberty is necessary and when it is gratuitous—one influential branch of liberal thought has argued that as an organizing principle at least, authority must go: "That government is best which governs least."

And yet this solution too does not "solve" anything. In the first place, nations interact with each other and therefore must at the very least have authoritative foreign policies; no one wants to leave this area of political decision making up to individual or group choices. In the second place, no one in fact has ever really believed in the impotent "night watchman" state: The potentiality of the organized state for helping people do together those things they cannot do by themselves is too great and too obvious to be neglected for long. And finally, the basic premise of this solution is logically and factually indefensible. That premise is that liberty consists only in not being hindered by formal governmental authority—as though to be hindered by a corporation, a union, a robber band, or the dominant members of one's local community were somehow not a restraint on one's freedom. Of course, if we could be assured that the leaders of such groups had only reasonable, socially functional desires, we might not mind being subjected to their power rather than the state's—but we have no such assurance. Nor can we consistently make such demands on them. For to be an individualist is to insist that any individual possessing any values is as good as any other; and if we think that someone else's values are antisocial, that is just too bad for us. In other words, if one is to put the liberty of the individual above authority as a principle, one must be prepared to accept whatever individuals will choose to do with their liberty. One must, for example, be prepared to coexist peacefully with such an individual as the narrator of Dostoevski's Notes from Underground, who observes with approval that man has "a passionate love for destruction and chaos" and that "corporal punishment is better than nothing." He is not an easy man to live with; nor are, often, much more ordinary, more rational men.

Thus inevitably—and one can use the word securely because in the civilized world there are no known exceptions to this point —men use the force of government against other men, not necessarily to attack the liberty of those against whom they legislate, but rather to increase the sum total of liberty for all in society. The few are hindered in order that the many may have more freedom. And thus we are thrown back upon the principle of authority and upon the observation that despite their apparent incompatibility, authority and liberty must somehow be reconciled.

At the same time, the reference to few and many suggests a possible way out of the dilemma: the method of liberal democracy and majority rule. This democratic doctrine, which will be instantly familiar to all our readers, holds that authority can in fact be exercised without fear of destroying liberty; but only on the condition that "the people," rather than some absolute ruler external to themselves, are themselves the sovereign that decides which invasions of liberty are to be countenanced and which not.

But the majoritarian solution, which in its pure form merely substitutes the people or their representatives for Hobbes's absolute monarch, also raises as many problems as it solves—problems which are depicted by Henrik Ibsen in his play An Enemy of the People and by D. H. Lawrence in his novel Kangaroo.

The chief of these problems is that majority rule is essentially only a rule of fairness. If in the end political philosophers and constitution-makers can't agree on the circumstances in which authority is rightfully exercised by the collectivity over the individual, they can at least agree that as many individuals as possible should constitute the collectivity in a given instance. A majority has always seemed the irreducible minimum that fairness requires. But a majority is not unanimity; and thus as long as there is social conflict, there is the potential for tyranny even in a democratic society—that is, for rule over individuals which they do not recognize as being in any way just or legitimate. In one of the most powerful passages in political literature Lawrence recreates just such a situation. Drawn inexorably into Lawrence's nightmare world of England during World War I, we see the most democratic polity in the world destroy, step by step, the freedom of Richard Lovat Somers—not because he takes overt action against the interests of his fellow citizens, but simply because, thinking differently from them, he refuses to submerge his own beliefs and personality in theirs. In the end he is driven to say that "never while he lived, again, would he be at the disposal of society." To the complaint that his attitude is destructive of all social order the unavoidable reply is that as long as the possibility of tyranny exists, social order can never be worthy of that unquestioning allegiance which its upholders demand.

That the tyranny of which we write is the work of a majority, or even as in this case a "consensus," is a fact that will placate only those who are willing to sacrifice everything—personal and group interest, conceptions of truth and justice, and individual liberty—to fairness and due process. We can guess, however, that for very few men can mere fair procedure be the only end of social life. As Henrik Ibsen demonstrates, if the sacrifices demanded by majority rule are too great, people will be no more willing to adhere to that rule than they will be to sacrifice their interests and their liberty to any other principle of authority. It would be an exaggeration, certainly, to say that men will not ever adhere to a rule of conduct if it fails to benefit them personally. But let majority rule be too destructive of what they believe, of what they know to be true or right or necessary, and very often, with Dr. Stockmann in An Enemy of the People, they will surrender as he surrenders the principle of majoritarianism altogether.

Of course, Dr. Stockmann and Somers have the courage of their convictions (they also have become fanatics, a fate hard to avoid when one is as socially isolated as they are). Most men, it may be, do not, and will surrender their beliefs under the pressure of a dominating majority—like the editor Hovstad, the printer Aslaksen, and the businessman Kiil. But this fact only adds weight to the views of those who are ultimately dissatisfied with the notion of majority rule, for it is difficult to believe that the world would be better off if that kind of courage were absent from it.

None of the modern prescriptions as to the proper relationship between individual, society, and state, then, is wholly acceptable —not even the theory of liberal democracy. Critics of modern society have from time to time, therefore, been led back to the classical view of this relationship, which is quite different in its way of looking at man and his environment. In the classical polis, which admittedly maintained itself more easily in theory than in practice, the conflict between authority and individual liberty that we have described so far did not really exist, at least not in the form which so frustrates the modern democrat. For individuals in the polis fulfilled themselves only through their membership and participation in the community. As long as he was able to make that contribution to his fellow citizens of which he was capable and receive from them in return that which he needed, it was a relatively unimportant question whether he was subject to external restraint in Hobbes's sense. To be free from governmental authority is only one kind of freedom; the classical alternative—to be free to fulfill oneself in concert with one's neighbors—is another and may be equally satisfying.

The excerpt from Paul Goodman's novel Parents Day presents a brief picture of such a community, fragile and small in scale as all attempts at Utopia must be, yet reaching to a part of the human spirit that none of the modern forms of government are quite capable of tapping. His community is egalitarian, as are all radical versions of the classical polis; the conservative version differs chiefly in being hierarchical and inequalitarian. Whether radical or conservative, however, the classical vision attracts men everywhere through its Utopian promise of making liberty responsible and authority unconstraining.

THE MYSTIQUE OF AUTHORITY

Feodor Dostoevski

"The Grand Inquisitor" *

[Ivan Karamazov speaks:] "My poem is called 'The Grand Inquisitor'; it's a ridiculous thing, but I want to tell it to you."

. . .

"Even this must have a preface—that is, a literary preface," laughed Ivan, "and I am a poor hand at making one. You see, my action takes place in the sixteenth century, and at that time, as you probably learnt at school, it was customary in poetry to bring down heavenly powers on earth. Not to speak of Dante, in France, clerks, as well as the monks in the monasteries, used to give regular performances in which the Madonna, the saints, the angels, Christ, and God Himself were brought on the stage. In those days it was done in all simplicity. In Victor Hugo's 'Notre Dame de Paris' an edifying and gratuitous spectacle was provided for the people in the Hotel de Ville of Paris in the reign of Louis XI in honour of the birth of the dauphin. It was called *Le bon jugement de la très sainte et gracieuse Vierge Marie,* and she appears herself on the stage and pronounces her *bon jugement.* Similar plays, chiefly from the Old Testament, were occasionally performed in Moscow too, up to the times of Peter the Great. But besides plays there were all sorts of legends and ballads scattered about the world, in which the saints and angels and all the powers of Heaven took part when required. In our monasteries the monks busied themselves in translating, copying, and even composing such poems—and even under the Tatars. There is, for instance, one such poem (of course, from the Greek), 'The Wanderings of Our Lady through Hell,' with descriptions as bold as Dante's. Our Lady visits Hell, and the Archangel Michael leads her through the torments. She sees the sinners and

Reprinted with permission of The Macmillan Company and William Heinemann Ltd. from *The Brothers Karamazov* by Feodor Dostoevski, Book V, Ch. 5, translated by Constance Garnett. Printed in Great Britain.

* Editors' note: The Legend of the Grand Inquisitor immediately follows the passage reproduced in Chapter IX of this book.

their punishment. There she sees among others one noteworthy set of sinners in a burning lake; some of them sink to the bottom of the lake so that they can't swim out, and 'these God forgets'—an expression of extraordinary depth and force. And so Our Lady, shocked and weeping, falls before the throne of God and begs for mercy for all in Hell—for all she has seen there, indiscriminately. Her conversation with God is immensely interesting. She beseeches Him, she will not desist, and when God points to the hands and feet of her Son, nailed to the Cross, and asks, 'How can I forgive His tormentors?' she bids all the saints, all the martyrs, all the angels and archangels to fall down with her and pray for mercy on all without distinction. It ends by her winning from God a respite of suffering every year from Good Friday till Trinity day, and the sinners at once raise a cry of thankfulness from Hell, chanting, 'Thou art just, O Lord, in this judgment.' Well, my poem would have been of that kind if it had appeared at that time. He comes on the scene in my poem, but He says nothing, only appears and passes on. Fifteen centuries have passed since He promised to come in His glory, fifteen centuries since His prophet wrote, 'Behold, I come quickly'; 'Of that day and that hour knoweth no man; neither the Son, but the Father,' as He Himself predicted on earth. But humanity awaits him with the same faith and with the same love. Oh, with greater faith, for it is fifteen centuries since man has ceased to see signs from Heaven.

> No signs from Heaven come to-day
> To add to what the heart doth say.

There was nothing left but faith in what the heart doth say. It is true there were many miracles in those days. There were saints who performed miraculous cures; some holy people, according to their biographies, were visited by the Queen of Heaven herself. But the devil did not slumber, and doubts were already arising among men of the truth of these miracles. And just then there appeared in the north of Germany a terrible new heresy. 'A huge star like to a torch' (that is, to a church) 'fell on the sources of the waters and they became bitter.' These heretics began blasphemously denying miracles. But those who remained faithful were all the more ardent in their faith. The tears of humanity rose up to Him as before, awaited His coming, loved Him, hoped for Him, yearned to suffer and die for Him as before. And so many ages mankind had prayed with faith and fervour, 'O Lord our God, hasten Thy coming,' so many

ages called upon Him, that in His infinite mercy He deigned to
come down to His servants. Before that day He had come down,
He had visited some holy men, martyrs and hermits, as is written
in their 'Lives.' Among us, Tyutchev, with absolute faith in the
truth of his words bore witness that

> *Bearing the Cross, in slavish dress,*
> *Weary and worn, the Heavenly King*
> *Our mother, Russia, came to bless,*
> *And through our land went wandering.*

And that certainly was so, I assure you.

"And behold, He deigned to appear for a moment to the people,
to the tortured, suffering people, sunk in iniquity, but loving Him
like children. My story is laid in Spain, in Seville, in the most
terrible time of the Inquisition, when fires were lighted every day
to the glory of God, and 'in the splendid *auto da fé* the wicked
heretics were burnt.' Oh, of course, this was not the coming in which
He will appear according to His promise at the end of time in all
His heavenly glory, and which will be sudden 'as lightning flashing
from east to west.' No, He visited His children only for a moment,
and there where the flames were crackling round the heretics.
In his infinite mercy He came once more among men in that human
shape in which He walked among men for three years fifteen centuries ago. He came down to the 'hot pavement' of the southern
town in which on the day before almost a hundred heretics had,
ad majorem gloriam Dei, been burnt by the cardinal, the Grand
Inquisitor, in a magnificent *auto da fé,* in the presence of the king,
the court, the knights, the cardinals, the most charming ladies of
the court, and the whole population of Seville.

"He came softly, unobserved, and yet, strange to say, every one
recognised Him. That might be one of the best passages in the poem.
I mean, why they recognised Him. The people are irresistibly drawn
to Him, they surround Him, they flock about Him, follow Him. He
moves silently in their midst with a gentle smile of infinite compassion. The sun of love burns in His heart, light and power shine
from His eyes, and their radiance, shed on the people, stirs their
hearts with responsive love. He holds out His hands to them, blesses
them, and a healing virtue comes from contact with Him, even with
His garments. An old man in the crowd, blind from childhood, cries
out, 'O Lord, heal me and I shall see Thee!' and, as it were, scales
fall from his eyes and the blind man sees Him. The crowd weeps

and kisses the earth under His feet. Children throw flowers before Him, sing, and cry hosannah. 'It is He—it is He!' all repeat. 'It must be He, it can be no one but Him!' He stops at the steps of the Seville cathedral at the moment when the weeping mourners are bringing in a little open white coffin. In it lies a child of seven, the only daughter of a prominent citizen. The dead child lies hidden in flowers. 'He will raise your child,' the crowd shouts to the weeping mother. The priest, coming to meet the coffin, looks perplexed, and frowns, but the mother of the dead child throws herself at His feet with a wail. 'If it is Thou, raise my child!' she cries, holding out her hands to Him. The procession halts, the coffin is laid on the steps at His feet. He looks with compassion, and His lips once more softly pronounce, 'Maiden, arise!' and the maiden arises. The little girl sits up in the coffin and looks round, smiling with wide-open wondering eyes, holding a bunch of white roses they had put in her hand.

"There are cries, sobs, confusion among the people, and at that moment the cardinal himself, the Grand Inquisitor, passes by the cathedral. He is an old man, almost ninety, tall and erect, with a withered face and sunken eyes, in which there is still a gleam of light. He is not dressed in his gorgeous cardinal's robes, as he was the day before, when he was burning the enemies of the Roman Church—at that moment he was wearing his coarse, old, monk's cassock. At a distance behind him come his gloomy assistants and slaves and the 'holy guard.' He stops at the sight of the crowd and watches it from a distance. He sees everything; he sees them set the coffin down at His feet, sees the child rise up, and his face darkens. He knits his thick grey brows and his eyes gleam with a sinister fire. He holds out his finger and bids the guards take Him. And such is his power, so completely are the people cowed into submission and trembling obedience to him, that the crowd immediately make way for the guards, and in the midst of deathlike silence they lay hands on Him and lead Him away. The crowd instantly bows down to the earth, like one man, before the old inquisitor. He blesses the people in silence and passes on. The guards lead their prisoner to the close, gloomy vaulted prison in the ancient palace of the Holy Inquisition and shut Him in it. The day passes and is followed by the dark, burning 'breathless' night of Seville. The air is 'fragrant with laurel and lemon.' In the pitch darkness the iron door of the prison is suddenly opened and the Grand Inquisitor himself comes in with a light in his hand. He is alone; the door is closed at once behind him. He stands in the doorway and for a minute or two gazes into His face. At last he goes up slowly, sets the light on the table and speaks.

" 'Is it Thou? Thou?' but receiving no answer, he adds at once, 'Don't answer, be silent. What canst Thou say, indeed? I know too well what Thou wouldst say. And Thou hast no right to add anything to what Thou hadst said of old. Why, then, art Thou come to hinder us? For Thou hast come to hinder us, and Thou knowest that. But dost Thou know what will be to-morrow? I know not who Thou art and care not to know whether it is Thou or only a semblance of Him, but to-morrow I shall condemn Thee and burn Thee at the stake as the worst of heretics. And the very people who have to-day kissed Thy feet, to-morrow at the faintest sign from me will rush to heap up the embers of Thy fire. Knowest Thou that? Yes, maybe Thou knowest it,' he added with thoughtful penetration, never for a moment taking his eyes off the Prisoner."

"I don't quite understand, Ivan. What does it mean?" Alyosha, who had been listening in silence, said with a smile. "Is it simply a wild fantasy, or a mistake on the part of the old man—some impossible *quiproquo?*"

"Take it as the last," said Ivan, laughing, "if you are so corrupted by modern realism and can't stand anything fantastic. If you like it to be a case of mistaken identity, let it be so. It is true," he went on, laughing, "the old man was ninety, and he might well be crazy over his set idea. He might have been struck by the appearance of the Prisoner. It might, in fact, be simply his ravings, the delusion of an old man of ninety, over-excited by the *auto da fé* of a hundred heretics the day before. But does it matter to us after all whether it was a mistake of identity or a wild fantasy? All that matters is that the old man should speak out, should speak openly of what he has thought in silence for ninety years."

"And the Prisoner too is silent? Does He look at him and not say a word?"

"That's inevitable in any case," Ivan laughed again. "The old man has told Him He hasn't the right to add anything to what He has said of old. One may say it is the most fundamental feature of Roman Catholicism, in my opinion at least. 'All has been given by Thee to the Pope,' they say, 'and all, therefore, is still in the Pope's hands, and there is no need for Thee to come now at all. Thou must not meddle for the time, at least.' That's how they speak and write too—the Jesuits, at any rate. I have read it myself in the works of their theologians. 'Hast Thou the right to reveal to us one of the mysteries of that world from which Thou hast come?' my old man asks Him, and answers the question for Him. 'No, Thou hast not; that Thou mayest not add to what has been said of old and mayest not take from men the freedom which Thou didst exalt when Thou wast on earth. Whatsoever Thou revealest anew will encroach on men's freedom of faith; for it will be manifest as a miracle, and the freedom of their faith was dearer to Thee than anything in those days fifteen hundred years ago. Didst Thou not often say then, "I will make you free"? But now Thou hast seen these "free" men,' the old man adds suddenly, with a pensive smile. 'Yes, we've paid dearly for it,' he goes on, looking sternly at Him, 'but at last we have completed that work in Thy name. For fifteen centuries we have been wrestling with Thy freedom, but now it is ended and over for good. Dost Thou not believe that it's over for good? Thou lookest meekly at me and deignest not even to be wroth with me. But let me tell Thee that now, to-day, people are more persuaded than ever that they have perfect freedom, yet they have brought their freedom to us and laid it humbly at our feet. But that has been our doing. Was this what Thou didst? Was this Thy freedom?' "

"I don't understand again," Alyosha broke in. "Is he ironical, is he jesting?"

"Not a bit of it! He claims it as a merit for himself and his Church that at last they have vanquished freedom and have done so to make men happy. 'For now' (he is speaking of the Inquisition, of course) 'for the first time it has become possible to think of the happiness of men. Man was created a rebel; and how can rebels be happy? Thou wast warned,' he says to Him. 'Thou hast had no lack of admonitions and warnings, but Thou didst not listen to those warnings; Thou didst reject the only way by which men might be made happy. But, fortunately, departing Thou didst hand on the work to us. Thou hast promised, Thou hast established by Thy word, Thou hast given to us the right to bind and to unbind, and now, of course, Thou canst not think of taking it away. Why, then, hast Thou come to hinder us?' "

"And what's the meaning of 'no lack of admonitions and warnings'?" asked Alyosha.

"Why, that's the chief part of what the old man must say."

" 'The wise and dread spirit, the spirit of self-destruction and non-existence,' the old man goes on, 'the great spirit talked with Thee in the wilderness, and we are told in the books that he "tempted" Thee. Is that so? And could anything truer be said than what he revealed to Thee in three questions and what Thou didst reject, and what in the books is called "the temptation"? And yet if there has ever been on earth a real stupendous miracle, it took place on that day, on the day of the three temptations. The statement of those three questions was itself the miracle. If it were possible to imagine simply for the sake of argument that those three questions of the dread spirit had perished utterly from the books, and that we had to restore them and to invent them anew, and to do so had gathered together all the wise men of the earth—rulers, chief priests, learned men, philosophers, poets—and had set them the task to invent three questions, such as would not only fit the occasion, but express in three words, three human phrases, the whole future history of the world and of humanity—dost Thou believe that all the wisdom of the earth united could have invented anything in depth and force equal to the three questions which were actually put to Thee then by the wise and mighty spirit in the wilderness? From those questions alone, from the miracle of their statement, we can see that we have here to do not with the fleeting human intelligence, but with the absolute and eternal. For in those three questions the whole subsequent history of mankind is, as it were, brought together into one whole, and foretold, and in them are united all the unsolved historical contradictions of human nature. At the time it could not be so clear, since the future was unknown; but now that fifteen hundred years have passed, we see that everything in those three questions was so justly divined and foretold, and has been so truly fulfilled, that nothing can be added to them or taken from them.

" 'Judge Thyself who was right—Thou or he who questioned Thee then? Remember the first question; its meaning, in other words, was this: "Thou wouldst go into the world, and art going with empty hands, with some promise of freedom which men in their simplicity and their natural unruliness cannot even understand, which they fear and dread—for nothing has ever been more insupportable for a man and a human society than freedom. But seest Thou these stones in this parched and barren wilderness? Turn them into bread, and mankind will run after Thee like a flock of sheep, grateful and obedient, though for ever trembling, lest Thou withdraw Thy hand and deny them Thy bread." But Thou wouldst not deprive man of freedom and didst reject the offer, thinking, what is that freedom worth, if obedience is bought with bread? Thou didst reply that man lives not by bread alone. But dost Thou know that for the sake of that earthly bread the spirit of the earth will rise up against Thee

and will strive with Thee and overcome Thee, and all will follow
him, crying, "Who can compare with this beast? He has given us
fire from heaven!" Dost Thou know that the ages will pass, and
humanity will proclaim by the lips of their sages that there is no
crime, and therefore no sin; there is only hunger? "Feed men, and
then ask of them virtue!" that's what they'll write on the banner,
which they will raise against Thee, and with which they will destroy
Thy temple. Where Thy temple stood will rise a new building; the
terrible tower of Babel will be built again, and though, like the one
of old, it will not be finished, yet Thou mightest have prevented that
new tower and have cut short the sufferings of men for a thousand
years; for they will come back to us after a thousand years of agony
with their tower. They will seek us again, hidden underground in
the catacombs, for we shall be again persecuted and tortured. They
will find us and cry to us, "Feed us, for those who have promised us
fire from heaven haven't given it!" And then we shall finish building
their tower, for he finishes the building who feeds them. And we
alone shall feed them in Thy name, declaring falsely that it is in
Thy name. Oh, never, never can they feed themselves without us!
No science will give them bread so long as they remain free. In the
end they will lay their freedom at our feet, and say to us, "Make us
your slaves, but feed us." They will understand themselves, at last,
that freedom and bread enough for all are inconceivable together,
for never, never will they be able to share between them! They will
be convinced, too, that they can never be free, for they are weak,
vicious, worthless and rebellious. Thou didst promise them the
bread of Heaven, but, I repeat again, can it compare with earthly
bread in the eyes of the weak, ever sinful and ignoble race of man?
And if for the sake of the bread of Heaven thousands and tens of
thousands shall follow Thee, what is to become of the millions and
tens of thousands of millions of creatures who will not have the
strength to forego the earthly bread for the sake of the heavenly?
Or dost Thou care only for the tens of thousands of the great and
strong, while the millions, numerous as the sands of the sea, who are
weak but love Thee, must exist only for the sake of the great and
strong? No, we care for the weak too. They are sinful and rebellious,
but in the end they too will become obedient. They will marvel at
us and look on us as gods, because we are ready to endure the freedom which they have found so dreadful and to rule over them—so
awful it will seem to them to be free. But we shall tell them that we
are Thy servants and rule them in Thy name. We shall deceive them

again, for we will not let Thee come to us again. That deception will be our suffering, for we shall be forced to lie.

"'This is the significance of the first question in the wilderness, and this is what Thou hast rejected for the sake of that freedom which Thou hast exalted above everything. Yet in this question lies hid the great secret of this world. Choosing "bread," Thou wouldst have satisfied the universal and everlasting craving of humanity— to find some one to worship. So long as man remains free he strives for nothing so incessantly and so painfully as to find some one to worship. But man seeks to worship what is established beyond dispute, so that all men would agree at once to worship it. For these pitiful creatures are concerned not only to find what one or the other can worship, but to find something that all would believe in and worship; what is essential is that all may be *together* in it. This craving for *community* of worship is the chief misery of every man individually and of all humanity from the beginning of time. For the sake of common worship they've slain each other with the sword. They have set up gods and challenged one another, "Put away your gods and come and worship ours, or we will kill you and your gods!" And so it will be to the end of the world, even when gods disappear from the earth; they will fall down before idols just the same. Thou didst know, Thou couldst not but have known, this fundamental secret of human nature, but Thou didst reject the one infallible banner which was offered Thee to make all men bow down to Thee alone—the banner of earthly bread; and Thou hast rejected it for the sake of freedom and the bread of Heaven. Behold what Thou didst further. And all again in the name of freedom! I tell Thee that man is tormented by no greater anxiety than to find some one quickly to whom he can hand over that gift of freedom with which the ill-fated creature is born. But only one who can appease their conscience can take over their freedom. In bread there was offered Thee an invincible banner; give bread, and man will worship Thee, for nothing is more certain than bread. But if some one else gains possession of his conscience—oh! then he will cast away Thy bread and follow after him who has ensnared his conscience. In that Thou wast right. For the secret of man's being is not only to live but to have something to live for. Without a stable conception of the object of life, man would not consent to go on living, and would rather destroy himself than remain on earth, though he had bread in abundance. That is true. But what happened? Instead of taking men's freedom from them, Thou didst make it greater than ever!

Didst Thou forget that man prefers peace, and even death, to freedom of choice in the knowledge of good and evil? Nothing is more
seductive for man than his freedom of conscience, but nothing is a
greater cause of suffering. And behold, instead of giving a firm
foundation for setting the conscience of man at rest for ever, Thou
didst choose all that is exceptional, vague and enigmatic; Thou
didst choose what was utterly beyond the strength of men, acting as
though Thou didst not love them at all—Thou who didst come to
give Thy life for them! Instead of taking possession of men's freedom, Thou didst increase it, and burdened the spiritual kingdom of
mankind with its sufferings for ever. Thou didst desire man's free
love, that he should follow Thee freely, enticed and taken captive
by Thee. In place of the rigid ancient law, man must hereafter with
free heart decide for himself what is good and what is evil, having
only Thy image before him as his guide. But didst Thou not know
he would at last reject even Thy image and Thy truth, if he is
weighed down with the fearful burden of free choice? They will
cry aloud at last that the truth is not in Thee, for they could not
have been left in greater confusion and suffering than Thou hast
caused, laying upon them so many cares and unanswerable problems.

" 'So that, in truth, Thou didst Thyself lay the foundation for the
destruction of Thy kingdom, and no one is more to blame for it. Yet
what was offered Thee? There are three powers, three powers alone,
able to conquer and to hold captive for ever the conscience of these
impotent rebels for their happiness—those forces are miracle, mystery
and authority. Thou hast rejected all three and hast set the example
for doing so. When the wise and dread spirit set Thee on the pinnacle of the temple and said to Thee, "If Thou wouldst know whether
Thou art the Son of God then cast Thyself down, for it is written:
the angels shall hold him up lest he fall and bruise himself, and Thou
shalt know then whether Thou art the Son of God and shalt prove
then how great is Thy faith in Thy Father." But Thou didst refuse
and wouldst not cast Thyself down. Oh! of course, Thou didst
proudly and well, like God; but the weak, unruly race of men, are
they gods? Oh, Thou didst know then that in taking one step, in
making one movement to cast Thyself down, Thou wouldst be tempt-
ing God and have lost all Thy faith in Him, and wouldst have been
dashed to pieces against that earth which Thou didst come to save.
And the wise spirit that tempted Thee would have rejoiced. But I
ask again, are there many like Thee? And couldst Thou believe for

one moment that men, too, could face such a temptation? Is the nature of men such, that they can reject miracle, and at the great moments of their life, the moments of their deepest, most agonising spiritual difficulties, cling only to the free verdict of the heart? Oh, Thou didst know that Thy deed would be recorded in books, would be handed down to remote times and the utmost ends of the earth, and Thou didst hope that man, following Thee, would cling to God and not ask for a miracle. But Thou didst not know that when man rejects miracle he rejects God too; for man seeks not so much God as the miraculous. And as man cannot bear to be without the miraculous, he will create new miracles of his own for himself, and will worship deeds of sorcery and witchcraft, though he might be a hundred times over a rebel, heretic and infidel. Thou didst not come down from the Cross when they shouted to Thee, mocking and reviling Thee, "Come down from the cross and we will believe that Thou art He." Thou didst not come down, for again Thou wouldst not enslave man by a miracle, and didst crave faith given freely, not based on miracle. Thou didst crave for free love and not the base raptures of the slave before the might that has overawed him for ever. But Thou didst think too highly of men therein, for they are slaves, of course, though rebellious by nature. Look round and judge; fifteen centuries have passed, look upon them. Whom hast Thou raised up to Thyself? I swear, man is weaker and baser by nature than Thou hast believed him! Can he, can he do what Thou didst? By showing him so much respect, Thou didst, as it were, cease to feel for him, for Thou didst ask far too much from him—Thou who hast loved him more than Thyself! Respecting him less, Thou wouldst have asked less of him. That would have been more like love, for his burden would have been lighter. He is weak and vile. What though he is everywhere now rebelling against our power, and proud of his rebellion? It is the pride of a child and a schoolboy. They are little children rioting and barring out the teacher at school. But their childish delight will end; it will cost them dear. They will cast down temples and drench the earth with blood. But they will see at last, the foolish children, that, though they are rebels, they are impotent rebels, unable to keep up their own rebellion. Bathed in their foolish tears, they will recognise at last that He who created them rebels must have meant to mock at them. They will say this in despair, and their utterance will be a blasphemy which will make them more unhappy still, for man's nature cannot bear blasphemy, and in the end always avenges it on itself. And so unrest, confusion and unhappiness—that is the present lot of man after Thou didst bear so much for their freedom! Thy great prophet tells in vision and in image, that he saw all those who took part in the first resurrection and that there were of each tribe twelve thousand. But if there were so many of them, they must have been not men but gods. They had borne Thy cross, they had endured scores of years in the barren, hungry wilderness, living upon locusts and roots—and Thou mayest indeed point with pride at those children of freedom, of free love, of free and splendid sacrifice for Thy name. But remember that they were only some thousands; and what of the rest? And how are the other weak ones to blame, because they could not endure what the strong have endured? How is the weak soul to blame that it is unable to receive such terrible gifts? Canst Thou have simply come to the elect and for the elect? But if so, it is a mystery and we cannot understand it. And if it is a mystery, we too have a right to preach a mystery, and to teach them that it's not the free judgment of their hearts, not love that matters, but a mystery which they must follow blindly, even against their conscience. So we have done. We have corrected Thy work and have founded it upon *miracle, mystery* and *authority*. And men rejoiced that they were again led like sheep, and that the terrible gift that had brought them such suffering, was, at last, lifted from their hearts. Were we right teaching them this? Speak! Did we not love mankind, so meekly acknowledging their feebleness, lovingly lightening their burden, and permitting their weak nature even sin with our sanction? Why hast Thou come now to hinder us? And why dost Thou look silently and searchingly at me with Thy mild eyes? Be angry. I don't want Thy love, for I love Thee not. And what use is it for me to hide anything from Thee? Don't I know to Whom I am speaking? All that I can say is known to Thee already. And is it for me to conceal from Thee our mystery? Perhaps it is Thy will to hear it from my lips. Listen, then. We are not working with Thee, but with *him*—that is our mystery. It's long —eight centuries—since we have been on *his* side and not on Thine. Just eight centuries ago, we took from him what Thou didst reject with scorn, that last gift he offered Thee, showing Thee all the kingdoms of the earth. We took from him Rome and the sword of Caesar, and proclaimed ourselves sole rulers of the earth, though hitherto we have not been able to complete our work. But whose fault is that? Oh, the work is only beginning, but it has begun. It has long to await completion and the earth has yet much to suffer, but we shall triumph and shall be Caesars, and then we shall plan the universal happiness of man. But Thou mightest have taken even then the sword of Caesar. Why didst Thou reject that last gift? Hadst Thou accepted that last counsel of the mighty spirit, Thou wouldst have accomplished all that man seeks on earth—that is, some one to worship, some one to keep his conscience, and some means of uniting all in one unanimous and harmonious ant-heap, for the craving for universal unity is the third and last anguish of men. Mankind as a whole has always striven to organise a universal state. There have been many great nations with great histories, but the more highly they were developed the more unhappy they were, for they felt more acutely than other people the craving for world-wide union. The great conquerors, Timours and Ghenghis-Khans, whirled like hurricanes over the face of the earth striving to subdue its people, and they too were but the unconscious expression of the same craving for universal unity. Hadst Thou taken the world and Caesar's purple, Thou wouldst have founded the universal state and have given universal peace. For who can rule men if not he who holds their conscience and their bread in his hands? We have taken the sword of Caesar, and in taking it, of course, have rejected Thee and followed *him*. Oh, ages are yet to come of the confusion of free thought, of their science and cannibalism. For having begun to build their tower of Babel without us, they will end, of course, with cannibalism. But then the beast will crawl to us and lick our feet and spatter them with tears of blood. And we shall sit upon the beast and raise the cup, and on it will be written, "Mystery." But then, and only then, the reign of peace and happiness will come for men. Thou art proud of Thine elect, but Thou hast only the elect, while we give rest to all. And besides, how many of those elect, those mighty ones who could become elect, have grown weary waiting for Thee, and have transferred and will transfer the powers of their spirit and the warmth of their heart to the other camp, and end by raising their *free* banner against Thee. Thou didst Thyself lift up that banner. But with us all will be happy and will no more rebel nor destroy one another as under Thy freedom. Oh, we shall persuade them that they will only become free when they renounce their freedom to us and submit to us. And shall we be right or shall we be lying? They will be convinced that we are right, for they will remember the horrors of slavery and confusion to which Thy freedom brought them. Freedom, free thought and science, will lead them into such straits and will bring them face to face with such marvels and insoluble mysteries, that some of them, the fierce and rebellious, will destroy themselves, others, rebellious but weak, will destroy one another, while the rest, weak and unhappy, will crawl fawning to our feet and whine to us: "Yes, you were right, you alone possess His mystery, and we come back to you, save us from ourselves!"

"'Receiving bread from us, they will see clearly that we take the bread made by their hands from them, to give it to them, without any miracle. They will see that we do not change the stones to bread, but in truth they will be more thankful for taking it from our hands than for the bread itself! For they will remember only too well that in old days, without our help, even the bread they made turned to stones in their hands, while since they have come back to us, the very stones have turned to bread in their hands. Too, too well they know the value of complete submission! And until men know that, they will be unhappy. Who is most to blame for their not knowing it, speak? Who scattered the flock and sent it astray on unknown paths? But the flock will come together again and will submit once more, and then it will be once for all. Then we shall give them the quiet humble happiness of weak creatures such as they are by nature. Oh, we shall persuade them at last not to be proud, for Thou didst lift them up and thereby taught them to be proud. We shall show them that they are weak, that they are only pitiful children, but that childlike happiness is the sweetest of all. They will become timid and will look to us and huddle close to us in fear, as chicks to the hen. They will marvel at us and will be awestricken before us, and will be proud at our being so powerful and clever, that we have been able to subdue such a turbulent flock of thousands of millions. They will tremble impotently before our wrath, their minds will grow fearful, they will be quick to shed tears like women and children, but they will be just as ready at a sign from us to pass to laughter and rejoicing, to happy mirth and childish song. Yes, we shall set them to work, but in their leisure hours we shall make their life like a child's game, with children's songs and innocent dance. Oh, we shall allow them even sin, they are weak and helpless, and they will love us like children because we allow them to sin. We shall tell them that every sin will be expiated, if it is done with our permission, that we allow them to sin because we love them, and the punishment for these sins we take upon ourselves. And we shall take it upon ourselves, and they will adore us as their saviours who have taken on themselves their sins before God. And they will have no secrets from us. We shall allow or forbid them to live with their wives and mistresses, to have or not to have children—according to whether they have been obedient or disobedient—and they will submit to us gladly and cheerfully. The most painful secrets of their conscience, all, all they will bring to us, and we shall have an answer for all. And they will be glad to believe our answer, for it will save them from the great anxiety and terrible agony they endure at present in making a free decision for themselves. And all will be happy, all the millions of creatures except the hundred thousand who rule over them. For only we, we who guard the mystery, shall be unhappy. There will be thousands of millions of happy babes, and a hundred thousand sufferers who have taken upon themselves the curse of the knowledge of good and evil. Peacefully they will die, peacefully they will expire in Thy name, and beyond the grave they will find nothing but death. But we shall keep the secret, and for their happiness we shall allure them with the reward of heaven and eternity. Though if there were anything in the other world, it certainly would not be for such as they. It is prophesied that Thou wilt come again in victory, Thou wilt come with Thy chosen, the proud and strong, but we will say that they have only saved themselves, but we have saved all. We are told that the harlot who sits upon the beast, and holds in her hands the *mystery*, shall be put to shame, that the weak will rise up again, and will rend her royal purple and will strip naked her loathsome body. But then I will stand up and point out to Thee the thousand millions of happy children who have known no sin. And we who have taken their sins upon us for their happiness will stand up before Thee and say: "Judge us if Thou canst and darest." Know that I fear Thee not. Know that I too have been in the wilderness, I too have lived on roots and locusts, I too prized the freedom with which Thou hast blessed men, and I too was striving to stand among Thy elect, among the strong and powerful, thirsting "to make up the number." But I awakened and would not serve madness. I turned back and joined the ranks of those *who have corrected Thy work*. I left the proud and went back to the humble, for the happiness of the humble. What I say to Thee will come to pass, and our dominion will be built up. I repeat, to-morrow Thou shalt see that obedient flock who at a sign from me will hasten to heap up the hot cinders about the pile on which I shall burn Thee for coming to hinder us. For if any one has ever deserved our fires, it is Thou. To-morrow I shall burn Thee. *Dixi.*' "

Ivan stopped. He was carried away as he talked and spoke with excitement; when he had finished, he suddenly smiled.

Alyosha had listened in silence; towards the end he was greatly moved and seemed several times on the point of interrupting, but restrained himself. Now his words came with a rush.

"But . . . that's absurd!" he cried, flushing. "Your poem is in praise of Jesus, not in blame of Him—as you meant it to be. And who will believe you about freedom? Is that the way to understand it? That's not the idea of it in the Orthodox Church. . . . That's Rome, and not even the whole of Rome, it's false—those are the worst of the Catholics, the Inquisitors, the Jesuits! . . . And there could not be such a fantastic creature as your inquisitor. What are these sins of mankind they take on themselves? Who are these keepers of the mystery who have taken some curse upon themselves for the happiness of mankind? When have they been seen? We know the Jesuits, they are spoken ill of, but surely they are not what you describe? They are not that at all, not at all. . . . They are simply the Romish army for the earthly sovereignty of the world in the future, with the Pontiff of Rome for Emperor . . . that's their ideal, but there's no sort of mystery or lofty melancholy about it. . . . It's simple lust of power, of filthy earthly gain, of domination—something like a universal serfdom with them as masters—that's all they stand for. They don't even believe in God perhaps. Your suffering inquisitor is a mere fantasy."

"Stay, stay," laughed Ivan, "how hot you are! A fantasy you say, let it be so! Of course it's a fantasy. But allow me to say: do you really think that the Roman Catholic movement of the last centuries is actually nothing but the lust of power, of filthy earthly gain? Is that Father Paissy's teaching?"

"No, no, on the contrary, Father Paissy did once say something rather the same as you . . . but of course it's not the same, not a bit the same," Alyosha hastily corrected himself.

"A precious admission, in spite of your 'not a bit the same.' I ask you why your Jesuits and Inquisitors have united simply for vile material gain? Why can there not be among them one martyr oppressed by great sorrow and loving humanity? You see, only suppose that there was one such man among all those who desire nothing but filthy material gain—if there's only one like my old inquisitor, who had himself eaten roots in the desert and made frenzied efforts to subdue his flesh to make himself free and perfect. But yet all his life he loved humanity, and suddenly his eyes were opened, and he saw that it is no great moral blessedness to attain perfection and freedom, if at the same time one gains the conviction that millions of God's creatures have been created as a mockery, that they will never be capable of using their freedom, that these poor rebels can never turn into giants to complete the tower, that it was not for such geese that the great idealist dreamt his dream of harmony. Seeing all that he turned back and joined—the clever people. Surely that could have happened?"

"Joined whom, what clever people?" cried Alyosha, completely carried away. "They have no such great cleverness and no mysteries and secrets. . . . Perhaps nothing but Atheism, that's all their secret. Your inquisitor does not believe in God, that's his secret!"

"What if it is so! At last you have guessed it. It's perfectly true that that's the whole secret, but isn't that suffering, a least for a man like that, who has wasted his whole life in the desert and yet could not shake off his incurable love of humanity? In his old age he reached the clear conviction that nothing but the advice of the great dread spirit could build up any tolerable sort of life for the feeble, unruly, 'incomplete, empirical creatures created in jest.' And so, convinced of this, he sees that he must follow the counsel of the wise spirit, the dread spirit of death and destruction, and therefore accept lying and deception, and lead men consciously to death and destruction, and yet deceive them all the way so that they may not notice where they are being led, that the poor blind creatures may at least on the way think themselves happy. And note, the deception is in the name of Him in Whose ideal the old man had so fervently believed all his life long. Is not that tragic? And if only one such stood at the head of the whole army 'filled with the lust of power only for the sake of filthy gain'—would not one such be enough to make a tragedy? More than that, one such standing at the head is enough to create the actual leading idea of the Roman Church with all its armies and Jesuits, its highest idea. I tell you frankly that I firmly believe that there has always been such a man among those who stood at the head of the movement. Who knows, there may have been some such even among the Roman Popes. Who knows, perhaps the spirit of that accursed old man who loves mankind so obstinately in his own way, is to be found even now in a whole multitude of such old men, existing not by chance but by agreement, as a secret league formed long ago for the guarding of the mystery, to guard it from the weak and the unhappy, so as to make them happy. No doubt it is so, and so it must be indeed. I fancy that even among the Masons there's something of the same mystery at the bottom, and that that's why the Catholics so detest the Masons as their rivals breaking up the unity of the idea, while it is so essential that there should be one flock and one shepherd. . . . But from the way I defend my idea I might be an author impatient of your criticism. Enough of it."

"You are perhaps a Mason yourself!" broke suddenly from Alyosha. "You don't believe in God," he added, speaking this time very sorrowfully. He fancied besides that his brother was looking at him ironically. "How does your poem end?" he asked, suddenly looking down. "Or was it the end?"

"I meant to end it like this. When the Inquisitor ceased speaking he waited some time for his Prisoner to answer him. His silence weighed down upon him. He saw that the Prisoner had listened intently all the time, looking gently in his face and evidently not wishing to reply. The old man longed for Him to say something, however bitter and terrible. But He suddenly approached the old man in silence and softly kissed him on his bloodless aged lips. That was all His answer. The old man shuddered. His lips moved. He went to the door, opened it, and said to Him: 'Go, and come no more . . . come not at all, never, never!' And he let Him out into the dark alleys of the town. The Prisoner went away."

"And the old man?"

"The kiss glows in his heart, but the old man adheres to his idea."

THE LIMITS OF INDIVIDUALISM

Feodor Dostoevski

From *Notes from Underground*

But these are all golden dreams. Oh, tell me, who was it first announced, who was it first proclaimed, that man only does nasty things because he does not know his own interests; and that if he were enlightened, if his eyes were opened to his real normal interests, man would at once cease to do nasty things, would at once

Reprinted with permission of The Macmillan Company and William Heinemann Ltd. from "Notes from Underground," Chapters VII and IX, by Feodor Dostoevski, translated by Constance Garnett, from *White Nights and Other Stories*. Printed in Great Britain.

become good and noble because, being enlightened and understanding his real advantage, he would see his own advantage in the good and nothing else, and we all know that not one man can, consciously, act against his own interests, consequently, so to say, through necessity, he would begin doing good? Oh, the babe! Oh, the pure, innocent child! Why, in the first place, when in all these thousands of years has there been a time when man has acted only from his own interest? What is to be done with the millions of facts that bear witness that men, *consciously*, that is, fully understanding their real interests, have left them in the background and have rushed headlong on another path, to meet peril and danger, compelled to this course by nobody and by nothing, but, as it were, simply disliking the beaten track, and have obstinately, wilfully, struck out another difficult, absurd way, seeking it almost in the darkness. So, I suppose, this obstinacy and perversity were pleasanter to them than any advantage. . . . Advantage! What is advantage?

And will you take it upon yourself to define with perfect accuracy in what the advantage of man consists? And what if it so happens that a man's advantage, *sometimes*, not only may, but even must, consist in his desiring in certain cases what is harmful to himself and not advantageous. And if so, there can be such a case, the whole principle falls into dust. What do you think—are there such cases? You laugh; laugh away, gentlemen, but only answer me: have man's advantages been reckoned up with perfect certainty? Are there not some which not only have not been included but cannot possibly be included under any classification? You see, you gentlemen have, to the best of my knowledge, taken your whole register of human advantages from the averages of statistical figures and politico-economical formulas. Your advantages are prosperity, wealth, freedom, peace—and so on, and so on. So that the man who should, for instance, go openly and knowingly in opposition to all that list would, to your thinking, and indeed mine too, of course, be an obscurantist or an absolute madman: would not he? But, you know, this is what is surprising: why does it so happen that all these statisticians, sages and lovers of humanity, when they reckon up human advantages invariably leave out one? They don't even take it into their reckoning in the form in which it should be taken, and the whole reckoning depends upon that. It would be no great matter, they would simply have to take it, this advantage, and add it to the list. But the trouble is, that this strange advantage does not fall

under any classification and is not in place in any list. I have a friend
for instance . . . Ech! gentlemen, but of course he is your friend,
too; and indeed there is no one, no one, to whom he is not a friend!

When he prepares for any undertaking this gentleman immediately explains to you, elegantly and clearly, exactly how he must
act in accordance with the laws of reason and truth. What is more,
he will talk to you with excitement and passion of the true normal
interests of man; with irony he will upbraid the short-sighted fools
who do not understand their own interests, nor the true significance
of virtue; and, within a quarter of an hour, without any sudden
outside provocation, but simply through something inside him which
is stronger than all his interests, he will go off on quite a different
tack—that is, act in direct opposition to what he has just been saying
about himself, in opposition to the laws of reason, in opposition to
his own advantage—in fact, in opposition to everything. . . . I warn
you that my friend is a compound personality, and therefore it is
difficult to blame him as an individual. The fact is, gentlemen, it
seems there must really exist something that is dearer to almost
every man than his greatest advantages, or (not to be illogical)
there is a most advantageous advantage (the very one omitted of
which we spoke just now) which is more important and more advantageous than all other advantages, for the sake of which a man if
necessary is ready to act in opposition to all laws; that is, in opposition to reason, honour, peace, prosperity—in fact, in opposition to
all those excellent and useful things if only he can attain that fundamental, most advantageous advantage which is dearer to him than
all. "Yes, but it's advantage all the same," you will retort. But excuse
me, I'll make the point clear, and it is not a case of playing upon
words. What matters is, that this advantage is remarkable from the
very fact that it breaks down all our classifications, and continually
shatters every system constructed by lovers of mankind for the
benefit of mankind. In fact, it upsets everything. But before I mention this advantage to you, I want to compromise myself personally,
and therefore I boldly declare that all these fine systems—all these
theories for explaining to mankind their real normal interests, in
order that inevitably striving to pursue these interests they may at
once become good and noble—are, in my opinion, so far, mere logical
exercises! Yes, logical exercises. Why, to maintain this theory of the
regeneration of mankind by means of the pursuit of his own advantage is to my mind almost the same thing as . . . as to affirm, for
instance, following Buckle, that through civilization mankind be-

comes softer, and consequently less bloodthirsty, and less fitted for warfare.

Logically it does seem to follow from his arguments. But man has such a predilection for systems and abstract deductions that he is ready to distort the truth intentionally, he is ready to deny the evidence of his senses only to justify his logic. I take this example because it is the most glaring instance of it. Only look about you: blood is being spilt in streams, and in the merriest way, as though it were champagne. Take the whole of the nineteenth century in which Buckle lived. Take Napoleon—the Great and also the present one. Take North America—the eternal union. Take the farce of Schleswig-Holstein. . . . And what is it that civilization softens in us? The only gain of civilization for mankind is the greater capacity for variety of sensations—and absolutely nothing more. And through the development of this manysidedness man may come to finding enjoyment in bloodshed. In fact, this has already happened to him. Have you noticed that it is the most civilized gentlemen who have been the subtlest slaughterers, to whom the Attilas and Stenka Razins could not hold a candle, and if they are not so conspicuous as the Attilas and Stenka Razins it is simply because they are so often met with, are so ordinary and have become so familiar to us. In any case civilization has made mankind if not more blood-thirsty, at least more vilely, more loathsomely blood-thirsty. In old days he saw justice in bloodshed and with his conscience at peace exterminated those he thought proper. Now we do think bloodshed abominable and yet we engage in this abomination, and with more energy than ever. Which is worse? Decide that for yourselves.

They say that Cleopatra (excuse an instance from Roman history) was fond of sticking gold pins into her slave-girls' breasts and derived gratification from their screams and writhings. You will say that that was in the comparatively barbarous times; that these are barbarous times too, because also, comparatively speaking, pins are stuck in even now; that though man has now learned to see more clearly than in barbarous ages, he is still far from having learnt to act as reason and science would dictate. But yet you are fully convinced that he will be sure to learn when he gets rid of certain old bad habits, and when common sense and science have completely re-educated human nature and turned it in a normal direction. You are confident that then man will cease from *intentional* error and will, so to say, be compelled not to want to set his will against his normal interests. That is not all; then, you say, science itself will teach man (though to my mind it's a superfluous luxury) that he never has really had any caprice or will of his own, and that he himself is something of the nature of a piano-key or the stop of an organ, and that there are, besides, things called the laws of nature; so that everything he does is not done by his willing it, but is done of itself, by the laws of nature. Consequently we have only to discover these laws of nature, and man will no longer have to answer for his actions and life will become exceedingly easy for him. All human actions will then, of course, be tabulated according to these laws, mathematically, like tables of logarithms up to 108,000, and entered in an index; or, better still, there would be published certain edifying works of the nature of encyclopaedic lexicons, in which everything will be so clearly calculated and explained that there will be no more incidents or adventures in the world.

Then—this is all what you say—new economic relations will be established, all ready-made and worked out with mathematical exactitude, so that every possible question will vanish in the twinkling of an eye, simply because every possible answer to it will be provided. Then the "Palace of Crystal" will be built. Then . . . In fact, those will be halcyon days. Of course there is no guaranteeing (this is my comment) that it will not be, for instance, frightfully dull then (for what will one have to do when everything will be calculated and tabulated?), but on the other hand everything will be extraordinarily rational. Of course boredom may lead you to anything. It is boredom sets one sticking golden pins into people, but all that would not matter. What is bad (this is my comment again) is that I dare say people will be thankful for the gold pins then. Man is stupid, you know, phenomenally stupid; or rather he is not at all stupid, but he is so ungrateful that you could not find another like him in all creation. I, for instance, would not be in the least surprised if all of a sudden, apropos of nothing, in the midst of general prosperity a gentleman with an ignoble, or rather with a reactionary and ironical, countenance were to arise and, putting his arms akimbo, say to us all: "I say, gentlemen, hadn't we better kick over the whole show and scatter rationalism to the winds, simply to send these logarithms to the devil, and to enable us to live once more at our own sweet foolish will!" That again would not matter; but what is annoying is that he would be sure to find followers—such is the nature of man. And all that for the most foolish reason, which, one would think, was hardly worth mentioning: that is, that man everywhere and at all times, whoever he may be, has preferred to act as he chose and not in the least as his reason and advantage dictated. And one may choose what is contrary to one's own interests, and sometimes one *positively ought* (that is my idea). One's own free unfettered choice, one's own caprice—however wild it may be, one's own fancy worked up at times to frenzy—is that very "most advantageous advantage" which we have overlooked, which comes under no classification and against which all systems and theories are continually being shattered to atoms. And how do these wiseacres know that man wants a normal, a virtuous choice? What has made them conceive that man must want a rationally advantageous choice? What man wants is simply *independent* choice, whatever that independence may cost and wherever it may lead. And choice, of course, the devil only knows what choice . . .

. . .

Gentlemen, I am joking, and I know myself that my jokes are not brilliant, but you know one can't take everything as a joke. I am, perhaps, jesting against the grain. Gentlemen, I am tormented by questions; answer them for me. You, for instance, want to cure men of their old habits and reform their will in accordance with science and good sense. But how do you know, not only that it is possible, but also that it is *desirable*, to reform man in that way? And what leads you to the conclusion that man's inclinations *need* reforming? In short, how do you know that such a reformation will be a benefit to man? And to go to the root of the matter, why are you so positively convinced that not to act against his real normal interests guaranteed by the conclusions of reason and arithmetic is certainly always advantageous for man and must always be a law for mankind? So far, you know, this is only your supposition. It may be the law of logic, but not the law of humanity. You think, gentlemen, perhaps that I am mad? Allow me to defend myself. I agree that man is pre-eminently a creative animal, predestined to strive consciously for an object and to engage in engineering—that is, incessantly and eternally to make new roads, *wherever they may lead*. But the reason why he wants sometimes to go off at a tangent may just be that he is *predestined* to make the road, and perhaps, too, that however stupid the "direct" practical man may be, the thought sometimes will occur to him that the road almost always does lead *somewhere*, and that the destination it leads to is less important than the process of making it, and that the chief thing is to save the well-conducted child from despising engineering, and so giving way to the fatal idleness, which, as we all know, is the mother of all the vices. Man likes to make roads and to create, that is a fact beyond dispute. But why has he such a passionate love for destruction and chaos also? Tell me that! But on that point I want to say a couple of words myself. May it not be that he loves chaos and destruction (there can be no disputing that he does sometimes love it) because he is instinctively afraid of attaining his object and completing the edifice he is constructing? Who knows, perhaps he only loves that edifice from a distance, and is by no means in love with it at close quarters; perhaps he only loves building it and does not want to live in it, but will leave it, when completed, for the use of *les animaux domestiques*—such as the ants, the sheep, and so on. Now the ants have quite a different taste. They have a marvellous edifice of that pattern which endures for ever—the ant-heap.

With the ant-heap the respectable race of ants began and with the ant-heap they will probably end, which does the greatest credit to their perseverance and good sense. But man is a frivolous and incongruous creature, and perhaps, like a chess-player, loves the process of the game, not the end of it. And who knows (there is no saying with certainty), perhaps the only goal on earth to which mankind is striving lies in this incessant process of attaining in other words, in life itself, and not in the thing to be attained, which must always be expressed as a formula, as positive as twice two makes four, and such positiveness is not life, gentlemen, but is the beginning of death. Anyway, man has always been afraid of this mathematical certainty, and I am afraid of it now. Granted that man does nothing but seek that mathematical certainty, he traverses oceans, sacrifices his life in the quest, but to succeed, really to find it, he dreads, I assure you. He feels that when he has found it there will be nothing for him to look for. When workmen have finished their work they do at least receive their pay, they go to the tavern, then they are taken to the police-station—and there is occupation for a week. But where can man go? Anyway, one can observe a certain awkwardness about him when he has attained such objects. He loves the process of attaining, but does not quite like to have attained, and that, of course, is very absurd. In fact, man is a comical creature; there seems to be a kind of jest in it all. But yet mathematical certainty is, after all, something insufferable. Twice two makes four seems to me simply a piece of insolence. Twice two makes four is a pert coxcomb who stands with arms akimbo barring your path and spitting. I admit that twice two makes four is an excellent thing, but if we are to give everything its due, twice two makes five is sometimes a very charming thing too.

And why are you so firmly, so triumphantly, convinced that only the normal and the positive—in other words, only what is conducive to welfare—is for the advantage of man? Is not reason in error as regards advantage? Does not man, perhaps, love something besides well-being? Perhaps he is just as fond of suffering? Perhaps suffering is just as great a benefit to him as well-being? Man is sometimes extraordinarily, passionately, in love with suffering, and that is a fact. There is no need to appeal to universal history to prove that; only ask yourself, if you are a man and have lived at all. As far as my personal opinion is concerned, to care only for well-being seems to me positively ill-bred. Whether it's good or bad, it is sometimes very pleasant, too, to smash things. I hold no brief for suffering nor for well-being either. I am standing for . . . my caprice, and for its being guaranteed to me when necessary. Suffering would be out of place in vaudevilles, for instance: I know that. In the "Palace of Crystal" it is unthinkable; suffering means doubt, negation, and what would be the good of a "palace of crystal" if there could be any doubt about it? And yet I think man will never renounce real suffering, that is, destruction and chaos. Why, suffering is the sole origin of consciousness. Though I did lay it down at the beginning that consciousness is the greatest misfortune for man, yet I know man prizes it and would not give it up for any satisfaction. Consciousness, for instance, is infinitely superior to twice two makes four. Once you have mathematical certainty there is nothing left to do or to understand. There will be nothing left but to bottle up your five senses and plunge into contemplation. While if you stick to consciousness, even though the same result is attained, you can at least flog yourself at times, and that will, at any rate, liven you up. Reactionary as it is, corporal punishment is better than nothing.

THE PROBLEM OF MAJORITY RULE

Henrik Ibsen

From *An Enemy of the People*

ACT II

. . .

HOVSTAD: Have you heard from the Mayor yet?

DR. STOCKMANN: Not yet. He is coming here later.

HOVSTAD: I have given the matter a great deal of thought since last night.

DR. STOCKMANN: Well?

HOVSTAD: From your point of view, as a doctor and a man of science, this affair of the water-supply is an isolated matter. I mean, you do not realise that it involves a great many other things.

DR. STOCKMANN: How, do you mean?—Let us sit down, my dear fellow. No, sit here on the couch. (HOVSTAD sits down on the couch, DR. STOCKMANN on a chair on the other side of the table.) Now then. You mean that——?

HOVSTAD: You said yesterday that the pollution of the water was due to impurities in the soil.

DR. STOCKMANN: Yes, unquestionably it is due to that poisonous morass up at Mölledal.

HOVSTAD: Begging your pardon, doctor, I fancy it is due to quite another morass altogether.

DR. STOCKMANN: What morass?

HOVSTAD: The morass that the whole life of our town is built on and is rotting in.

DR. STOCKMANN: What the deuce are you driving at, Hovstad?

HOVSTAD: The whole of the town's interests have, little by little, got into the hands of a pack of officials.

DR. STOCKMANN: Oh, come!—they are not all officials.

From Acts II, III, and IV. From *Ghosts, An Enemy of the People, The Warriors at Helgeland* by Henrik Ibsen. Translated by R. Farquharson Sharp. Everyman's Library Edition. Reprinted by permission of E. P. Dutton & Co., Inc., and J. M. Dent & Sons Ltd.: Publishers.

HOVSTAD: No, but those that are not officials are at any rate the officials' friends and adherents; it is the wealthy folk, the old families in the town, that have got us entirely in their hands.

DR. STOCKMANN: Yes, but after all they are men of ability and knowledge.

HOVSTAD: Did they show any ability or knowledge when they laid the conduit-pipes where they are now?

DR. STOCKMANN: No, of course that was a great piece of stupidity on their part. But that is going to be set right now.

HOVSTAD: Do you think that will be all such plain sailing?

DR. STOCKMANN: Plain sailing or no, it has got to be done, anyway.

HOVSTAD: Yes, provided the press takes up the question.

DR. STOCKMANN: I don't think that will be necessary, my dear fellow, I am certain my brother——

HOVSTAD: Excuse me, Doctor; I feel bound to tell you I am inclined to take the matter up.

DR. STOCKMANN: In the paper?

HOVSTAD: Yes. When I took over the "People's Messenger" my idea was to break up this ring of self-opinionated old fossils who had got hold of all the influence.

DR. STOCKMANN: But you know you told me yourself what the result had been; you nearly ruined your paper.

HOVSTAD: Yes, at the time we were obliged to climb down a peg or two, it is quite true; because there was a danger of the whole project of the Baths coming to nothing if they failed us. But now the scheme has been carried through, and we can dispense with these grand gentlemen.

DR. STOCKMANN: Dispense with them, yes; but we owe them a great debt of gratitude.

HOVSTAD: That shall be recognised ungrudgingly. But a journalist of my democratic tendencies cannot let such an opportunity as this slip. The bubble of official infallibility must be pricked. This superstition must be destroyed, like any other.

DR. STOCKMANN: I am whole-heartedly with you in that, Mr. Hovstad; if it is a superstition, away with it!

HOVSTAD: I should be very reluctant to bring the Mayor into it, because he is your brother. But I am sure you will agree with me that truth should be the first consideration.

DR. STOCKMANN: That goes without saying. (*With sudden emphasis.*) Yes, but—but——

HOVSTAD: You must not misjudge me. I am neither more self-interested nor more ambitious than most men.

DR. STOCKMANN: My dear fellow—who suggests anything of the kind?

HOVSTAD: I am of humble origin, as you know; and that has given me opportunities of knowing what is the most crying need in the humbler ranks of life. It is that they should be allowed some part in the direction of public affairs, Doctor. That is what will develop their faculties and intelligence and self-respect——

DR. STOCKMANN: I quite appreciate that.

HOVSTAD: Yes—and in my opinion a journalist incurs a heavy responsibility if he neglects a favourable opportunity of emancipating the masses—the humble and oppressed. I know well enough that in exalted circles I shall be called an agitator, and all that sort of thing; but they may call what they like. If only my conscience doesn't reproach me, then——

DR. STOCKMANN: Quite right! Quite right, Mr. Hovstad. But all the same—devil take it! (A knock is heard at the door.) Come in!

ASLAKSEN appears at the door. He is poorly but decently dressed, in black, with a slightly crumpled white neckcloth; he wears gloves and has a felt hat in his hand.

ASLAKSEN (bowing):   Excuse my taking the liberty, Doctor——

DR. STOCKMANN (getting up):   Ah, it is you, Aslaksen!

ASLAKSEN: Yes, Doctor.

HOVSTAD (standing up):   Is it me you want, Aslaksen?

ASLAKSEN: No; I didn't know I should find you here. No, it was the Doctor I——

DR. STOCKMANN: I am quite at your service. What is it?

ASLAKSEN: Is what I heard from Mr. Billing true, sir—that you mean to improve our water-supply?

DR. STOCKMANN: Yes, for the Baths.

ASLAKSEN: Quite so, I understand. Well, I have come to say that I will back that up by every means in my power.

HOVSTAD (to the DOCTOR):   You see!

DR. STOCKMANN: I shall be very grateful to you, but——

ASLAKSEN: Because it may be no bad thing to have us small tradesmen at your back. We form, as it were, a compact majority in the town—if we choose. And it is always a good thing to have the majority with you, Doctor.

DR. STOCKMANN: That is undeniably true; but I confess I don't see why such unusual precautions should be necessary in this case. It seems to me that such a plain, straightforward thing——

ASLAKSEN: Oh, it may be very desirable, all the same. I know our local authorities so well; officials are not generally very ready to act on proposals that come from other people. That is why I think it would not be at all amiss if we made a little demonstration.

HOVSTAD: That's right.

DR. STOCKMANN: Demonstration, did you say? What on earth are you going to make a demonstration about?

ASLAKSEN: We shall proceed with the greatest moderation, Doctor. Moderation is always my aim; it is the greatest virtue in a citizen—at least, I think so.

DR. STOCKMANN: It is well known to be a characteristic of yours, Mr. Aslaksen.

ASLAKSEN: Yes, I think I may pride myself on that. And this matter of the water-supply is of the greatest importance to us small tradesmen. The Baths promise to be a regular gold-mine for the town. We shall all make our living out of them, especially those of us who are householders. That is why we will back up the project as strongly as possible. And as I am at present Chairman of the House-holders' Association——

DR. STOCKMANN: Yes——?

ASLAKSEN: And, what is more, local secretary of the Temperance Society—you know, sir, I suppose, that I am a worker in the temperance cause?

DR. STOCKMANN: Of course, of course.

ASLAKSEN: Well, you can understand that I come into contact with a great many people. And as I have the reputation of a temperate and law-abiding citizen—like yourself, Doctor—I have a certain influence in the town, a little bit of power, if I may be allowed to say so.

DR. STOCKMANN: I know that quite well, Mr. Aslaksen.

ASLAKSEN: So you see it would be an easy matter for me to set on foot some testimonial, if necessary.

DR. STOCKMANN: A testimonial?

ASLAKSEN: Yes, some kind of an address of thanks from the townsmen for your share in a matter of such importance to the community. I need scarcely say that it would have to be drawn up with the greatest regard to moderation, so as not to offend the authorities —who, after all, have the reins in their hands. If we pay strict attention to that, no one can take it amiss, I should think!

HOVSTAD: Well, and even supposing they didn't like it——

ASLAKSEN: No, no, no; there must be no discourtesy to the authorities, Mr. Hovstad. It is no use falling foul of those upon whom our welfare so closely depends. I have done that in my time, and no good ever comes of it. But no one can take exception to a reasonable and frank expression of a citizen's views.

DR. STOCKMANN (shaking him by the hand): I can't tell you, dear Mr. Aslaksen, how extremely pleased I am to find such hearty support among my fellow-citizens. I am delighted—delighted! Now, you will take a small glass of sherry, eh?

ASLAKSEN: No, thank you; I never drink alcohol of that kind.

DR. STOCKMANN: Well, what do you say to a glass of beer, then?

ASLAKSEN: Nor that either, thank you, Doctor. I never drink anything as early as this. I am going into town now to talk this over with one or two householders, and prepare the ground.

DR. STOCKMANN: It is tremendously kind of you, Mr. Aslaksen; but I really cannot understand the necessity for all these precautions. It seems to me that the thing should go of itself.

ASLAKSEN: The authorities are somewhat slow to move, Doctor. Far be it from me to seem to blame them——

HOVSTAD: We are going to stir them up in the paper tomorrow, Aslaksen.

ASLAKSEN: But not violently, I trust, Mr. Hovstad. Proceed with moderation, or you will do nothing with them. You may take my advice; I have gathered my experience in the school of life. Well, I must say good-bye, Doctor. You know now that we small tradesmen are at your back at all events, like a solid wall. You have the compact majority on your side, Doctor.

DR. STOCKMANN: I am very much obliged, dear Mr. Aslaksen. (Shakes hands with him.) Good-bye, good-bye.

ASLAKSEN: Are you going my way, towards the printing-office, Mr. Hovstad?

HOVSTAD: I will come later; I have something to settle up first.

ASLAKSEN: Very well.

Bows and goes out; STOCKMANN follows him into the hall.

HOVSTAD (as STOCKMANN comes in again): Well, what do you think of that, Doctor? Don't you think it is high time we stirred a little life into all this slackness and vacillation and cowardice?

DR. STOCKMANN: Are you referring to Aslaksen?

HOVSTAD: Yes, I am. He is one of those who are floundering in a bog—decent enough fellow though he may be, otherwise. And most of the people here are in just the same case—see-sawing and edging first to one side and then to the other, so overcome with caution and scruple that they never dare to take any decided step.

DR. STOCKMANN: Yes, but Aslaksen seemed to me so thoroughly well-intentioned.

HOVSTAD: There is one thing I esteem higher than that; and that is for a man to be self-reliant and sure of himself.

DR. STOCKMANN: I think you are perfectly right there.

HOVSTAD: That is why I want to seize this opportunity, and try if I cannot manage to put a little virility into these well-intentioned people for once. The idol of Authority must be shattered in this town. This gross and inexcusable blunder about the water-supply must be brought home to the mind of every municipal voter.

DR. STOCKMANN: Very well; if you are of opinion that it is for the good of the community, so be it. But not until I have had a talk with my brother.

HOVSTAD: Anyway, I will get a leading article ready; and if the Mayor refuses to take the matter up——

DR. STOCKMANN: How can you suppose such a thing possible?

HOVSTAD: It is conceivable. And in that case——

DR. STOCKMANN: In that case I promise you——. Look here, in that case you may print my report—every word of it.

HOVSTAD: May I? Have I your word for it?

DR. STOCKMANN (giving him the MS.):   Here it is; take it with you. It can do no harm for you to read it through, and you can give it me back later on.

HOVSTAD: Good, good! That is what I will do. And now good-bye, Doctor.

·   ·   ·

ACT III

ASLAKSEN: I say—Mr. Hovstad——

HOVSTAD: Well, well!—what is it?

ASLAKSEN: The Mayor is outside in the printing-room.

HOVSTAD: The Mayor, did you say?

ASLAKSEN: Yes, he wants to speak to you. He came in by the back door—didn't want to be seen, you understand.

HOVSTAD: What can he want? Wait a bit—I will go myself. (Goes to the door of the printing-room, opens it, bows and invites PETER STOCKMANN * in.) Just see, Aslaksen, that no one——

ASLAKSEN: Quite so.

Goes into the printing-room.

PETER STOCKMANN: You did not expect to see me here, Mr. Hovstad?

HOVSTAD: No, I confess I did not.

PETER STOCKMANN (looking round):   You are very snug in here—very nice indeed.

HOVSTAD: Oh——

PETER STOCKMANN: And here I come, without any notice, to take up your time!

HOVSTAD: By all means, Mr. Mayor. I am at your service. But let me relieve you of your——(takes STOCKMANN's hat and stick and puts them on a chair). Won't you sit down?

PETER STOCKMANN (sitting down by the table):   Thank you. (HOVSTAD sits down.) I have had an extremely annoying experience to-day, Mr. Hovstad.

HOVSTAD: Really? Ah well, I expect with all the various business you have to attend to——

PETER STOCKMANN: The Medical Officer of the Baths is responsible for what happened to-day.

HOVSTAD: Indeed? The Doctor?

PETER STOCKMANN: He has addressed a kind of report to the Baths Committee on the subject of certain supposed defects in the Baths.

HOVSTAD: Has he indeed?

PETER STOCKMANN: Yes—has he not told you? I thought he said——

HOVSTAD: Ah, yes—it is true he did mention something about——

ASLAKSEN (coming from the printing-room):   I ought to have that copy——

HOVSTAD (angrily):   Ahem!—there it is on the desk.

ASLAKSEN (taking it):   Right.

PETER STOCKMANN: But look there—that is the thing I was speaking of!

ASLAKSEN: Yes, that is the Doctor's article, Mr. Mayor.

HOVSTAD: Oh, is *that* what you were speaking about?

* Editors' note: Dr. Stockmann's brother.

PETER STOCKMANN: Yes, that is it. What do you think of it?

HOVSTAD: Oh, I am only a layman—and I have only taken a very cursory glance at it.

PETER STOCKMANN: But you are going to print it?

HOVSTAD: I cannot very well refuse a distinguished man——

ASLAKSEN: I have nothing to do with editing the paper, Mr. Mayor——

PETER STOCKMANN: I understand.

ASLAKSEN: I merely print what is put into my hands.

PETER STOCKMANN: Quite so.

ASLAKSEN: And so I must——

Moves off towards the printing-room.

PETER STOCKMANN: No, but wait a moment, Mr. Aslaksen. You will allow me, Mr. Hovstad?

HOVSTAD: If you please, Mr. Mayor.

PETER STOCKMANN: You are a discreet and thoughtful man, Mr. Aslaksen.

ASLAKSEN: I am delighted to hear you think so, sir.

PETER STOCKMANN: And a man of very considerable influence.

ASLAKSEN: Chiefly among the small tradesmen, sir.

PETER STOCKMANN: The small tax-payers are the majority—here as everywhere else.

ASLAKSEN: That is true.

PETER STOCKMANN: And I have no doubt you know the general trend of opinion among them, don't you?

ASLAKSEN: Yes, I think I may say I do, Mr. Mayor.

PETER STOCKMANN: Yes. Well, since there is such a praiseworthy spirit of self-sacrifice among the less wealthy citizens of our town——

ASLAKSEN: What?

HOVSTAD: Self-sacrifice?

PETER STOCKMANN: It is pleasing evidence of a public-spirited feeling, extremely pleasing evidence. I might almost say I hardly expected it. But you have a closer knowledge of public opinion than I.

ASLAKSEN: But, Mr. Mayor——

PETER STOCKMANN: And indeed it is no small sacrifice that the town is going to make.

HOVSTAD: The town?

ASLAKSEN: But I don't understand. Is it the Baths——

PETER STOCKMANN: At a provisional estimate, the alterations that the Medical Officer asserts to be desirable will cost somewhere about twenty thousand pounds.

ASLAKSEN: That is a lot of money, but——

PETER STOCKMANN: Of course it will be necessary to raise a municipal loan.

HOVSTAD (getting up):   Surely you never meant that the town must pay——?

ASLAKSEN: Do you mean that it must come out of the municipal funds?—out of the ill-filled pockets of the small tradesmen?

PETER STOCKMANN: Well, my dear Mr. Aslaksen, where else is the money to come from?

ASLAKSEN: The gentlemen who own the Baths ought to provide that.

PETER STOCKMANN: The proprietors of the Baths are not in a position to incur any further expense.

ASLAKSEN: Is that absolutely certain, Mr. Mayor?

PETER STOCKMANN: I have satisfied myself that it is so. If the town wants these very extensive alterations, it will have to pay for them.

ASLAKSEN: But, damn it all—I beg your pardon—this is quite another matter, Mr. Hovstad!

HOVSTAD: It is, indeed.

PETER STOCKMANN: The most fatal part of it is that we shall be obliged to shut the Baths for a couple of years.

HOVSTAD: Shut them? Shut them altogether?

ASLAKSEN: For two years?

PETER STOCKMANN: Yes, the work will take as long as that—at least.

ASLAKSEN: I'm damned if we will stand that, Mr. Mayor! What are we householders to live upon in the meantime?

PETER STOCKMANN: Unfortunately, that is an extremely difficult question to answer, Mr. Aslaksen. But what would you have us do? Do you suppose we shall have a single visitor in the town, if we go about proclaiming that our water is polluted, that we are living over a plague spot, that the entire town——

ASLAKSEN: And the whole thing is merely imagination?

PETER STOCKMANN: With the best will in the world, I have not been able to come to any other conclusion.

ASLAKSEN: Well then I must say it is absolutely unjustifiable of Dr. Stockmann—I beg your pardon, Mr. Mayor——

PETER STOCKMANN: What you say is lamentably true, Mr.

Aslaksen. My brother has, unfortunately, always been a headstrong man.

ASLAKSEN: After this, do you mean to give him your support, Mr. Hovstad?

HOVSTAD: Can you suppose for a moment that I——?

PETER STOCKMANN: I have drawn up a short *résumé* of the situation as it appears from a reasonable man's point of view. In it I have indicated how certain possible defects might suitably be remedied without outrunning the resources of the Baths Committee.

HOVSTAD: Have you got it with you, Mr. Mayor?

PETER STOCKMANN (fumbling in his pocket):   Yes, I brought it with me in case you should——

ASLAKSEN: Good Lord, there he is!

PETER STOCKMANN: Who? My brother?

HOVSTAD: Where? Where?

ASLAKSEN: He has just gone through the printing-room.

PETER STOCKMANN: How unlucky! I don't want to meet him here, and I had still several things to speak to you about.

HOVSTAD (pointing to the door on the right):   Go in there for the present.

PETER STOCKMANN: But——?

HOVSTAD: You will only find Billing in there.

ASLAKSEN: Quick, quick, Mr. Mayor—he is just coming.

PETER STOCKMANN: Yes, very well; but see that you get rid of him quickly.

.   .   .

DR. STOCKMANN has put on the Mayor's hat and taken his stick in his hand. He goes up to the door, opens it and stands with his hand to his hat at the salute. PETER STOCKMANN comes in red with anger. BILLING follows him.

PETER STOCKMANN: What does this tomfoolery mean?

DR. STOCKMANN: Be respectful, my good Peter. I am the chief authority in the town now.

Walks up and down.

MRS. STOCKMANN (almost in tears):   Really, Thomas!

PETER STOCKMANN (following him about):   Give me my hat and stick.

DR. STOCKMANN (in the same tone as before):   If you are chief constable, let me tell you that I am the Mayor—I am the master of the whole town, please understand!

PETER STOCKMANN: Take off my hat, I tell you. Remember it is part of an official uniform.

DR. STOCKMANN: Pooh! Do you think the newly awakened lion-hearted people are going to be frightened by an official hat? There is going to be a revolution in the town to-morrow, let me tell you. You thought you could turn me out; but now I shall turn you out—turn you out of all your various offices. Do you think I cannot? Listen to me. I have triumphant social forces behind me. Hovstad and Billing will thunder in the "People's Messenger," and Aslaksen will take the field at the head of the whole Householders' Association——

ASLAKSEN: That I won't, Doctor.

DR. STOCKMANN: Of course you will——

PETER STOCKMANN: Ah!—may I ask then if Mr. Hovstad intends to join this agitation?

HOVSTAD: No, Mr. Mayor.

ASLAKSEN: No, Mr. Hovstad is not such a fool as to go and ruin his paper and himself for the sake of an imaginary grievance.

DR. STOCKMANN (looking round him):   What does this mean?

HOVSTAD: You have represented your case in a false light, Doctor, and therefore I am unable to give you my support.

BILLING: And after what the Mayor was so kind as to tell me just now, I——

DR. STOCKMANN: A false light! Leave that part of it to me. Only print my article; I am quite capable of defending it.

HOVSTAD: I am not going to print it. I cannot and will not and dare not print it.

DR. STOCKMANN: You dare not? What nonsense!—you are the editor; and an editor controls his paper, I suppose!

ASLAKSEN: No, it is the subscribers, Doctor.

PETER STOCKMANN: Fortunately, yes.

ASLAKSEN: It is public opinion—the enlightened public—house-holders and people of that kind; they control the newspapers.

DR. STOCKMANN (composedly):   And I have all these influences against me?

ASLAKSEN: Yes, you have. It would mean the absolute ruin of the community if your article were to appear.

DR. STOCKMANN: Indeed.

PETER STOCKMANN: My hat and stick, if you please. (DR. STOCK-MANN takes off the hat and lays it on the table with the stick.

PETER STOCKMANN takes them up.) Your authority as mayor has come to an untimely end.

DR. STOCKMANN: We have not got to the end yet. (To HOVSTAD.) Then it is quite impossible for you to print my article in the "People's Messenger"?

HOVSTAD: Quite impossible—out of regard for your family as well.

MRS. STOCKMANN: You need not concern yourself about his family, thank you, Mr. Hovstad.

PETER STOCKMANN (taking a paper from his pocket):   It will be sufficient, for the guidance of the public, if this appears. It is an official statement. May I trouble you?

HOVSTAD (taking the paper):   Certainly; I will see that it is printed.

DR. STOCKMANN: But not mine. Do you imagine that you can silence me and stifle the truth! You will not find it so easy as you suppose. Mr. Aslaksen, kindly take my manuscript at once and print it as a pamphlet—at my expense. I will have four hundred copies—no, five—six hundred.

ASLAKSEN: If you offered me its weight in gold, I could not lend my press for any such purpose, Doctor. It would be flying in the face of public opinion. You will not get it printed anywhere in the town.

DR. STOCKMANN: Then give it me back.

HOVSTAD (giving him the MS.):   Here it is.

DR. STOCKMANN (taking his hat and stick):   It shall be made public all the same. I will read it out at a mass meeting of the townspeople. All my fellow-citizens shall hear the voice of truth!

PETER STOCKMANN: You will not find any public body in the town that will give you the use of their hall for such a purpose.

ASLAKSEN: Not a single one, I am certain.

BILLING: No, I'm damned if you will find one.

MRS. STOCKMANN: But this is too shameful! Why should every one turn against you like that?

DR. STOCKMANN (angrily):   I will tell you why. It is because all the men in this town are old women—like you; they all think of nothing but their families, and never of the community.

MRS. STOCKMANN (putting her arm into his):   Then I will show them that an—an old woman can be a man for once. I am going to stand by you, Thomas!

DR. STOCKMANN: Bravely said, Katherine! It shall be made public—as I am a living soul! If I can't hire a hall, I shall hire a drum, and parade the town with it and read it at every street-corner.

PETER STOCKMANN: You are surely not such an arrant fool as that!

DR. STOCKMANN: Yes, I am.

ASLAKSEN: You won't find a single man in the whole town to go with you.

BILLING: No, I'm damned if you will.

· · ·

ACT IV *

1ST CITIZEN (meeting another): Hullo, Lamstad! You here too?

2ND CITIZEN: I go to every public meeting, I do.

3RD CITIZEN: Brought your whistle too, I expect!

2ND CITIZEN: I should think so. Haven't you?

3RD CITIZEN: Rather! And old Evensen said he was going to bring a cow-horn, he did.

2ND CITIZEN: Good old Evensen!

Laughter among the crowd.

4TH CITIZEN (coming up to them): I say, tell me what is going on here to-night.

2ND CITIZEN: Dr. Stockmann is going to deliver an address attacking the Mayor.

4TH CITIZEN: But the Mayor is his brother.

1ST CITIZEN: That doesn't matter; Dr. Stockmann's not the chap to be afraid.

3RD CITIZEN: But he is in the wrong; it said so in the "People's Messenger."

2ND CITIZEN: Yes, I expect he must be in the wrong this time, because neither the Householders' Association nor the Citizens' Club would lend him their hall for his meeting.

1ST CITIZEN: He couldn't even get the loan of the hall at the Baths.

2ND CITIZEN: No, I should think not.

A MAN IN ANOTHER PART OF THE CROWD: I say—who are we to back up in this?

* Editors' note: The townspeople meet at the home of Captain Horster, a friend of Dr. Stockmann's.

ANOTHER MAN, BESIDE HIM: Watch Aslaksen, and do as he does.

BILLING (pushing his way through the crowd, with a writing-case under his arm):   Excuse me, gentlemen—do you mind letting me through? I am reporting for the "People's Messenger." Thank you very much!

He sits down at the table on the left.

A WORKMAN: Who was that?

SECOND WORKMAN: Don't you know him? It's Billing, who writes for Aslaksen's paper.

> CAPTAIN HORSTER brings in MRS. STOCKMANN and PETRA through the door on the right. EJLIF and MORTEN follow them in.

HORSTER: I thought you might all sit here; you can slip out easily from here, if things get too lively.

MRS. STOCKMANN: Do you think there will be a disturbance?

HORSTER: One can never tell—with such a crowd. But sit down, and don't be uneasy.

MRS. STOCKMANN (sitting down):   It was extremely kind of you to offer my husband the room.

HORSTER: Well, if nobody else would——

PETRA (who has sat down beside her mother):   And it was a plucky thing to do, Captain Horster.

HORSTER: Oh, it is not such a great matter as all that.

> HOVSTAD and ASLAKSEN make their way through the crowd.

ASLAKSEN (going up to HORSTER):   Has the Doctor not come yet?

HORSTER: He is waiting in the next room.

Movement in the crowd by the door at the back.

HOVSTAD: Look—here comes the Mayor!

BILLING: Yes, I'm damned if he hasn't come after all!

> PETER STOCKMANN makes his way gradually through the crowd, bows courteously and takes up a position by the wall on the left. Shortly afterwards DR. STOCKMANN comes in by the right-hand door. He is dressed in a black frock-coat, with a white tie. There is a little feeble applause, which is hushed down. Silence is obtained.

DR. STOCKMANN (in an undertone):   How do you feel, Katherine?

MRS. STOCKMANN: All right, thank you. (Lowering her voice.) Be sure not to lose your temper, Thomas.

DR. STOCKMANN: Oh, I know how to control myself. (Looks at

his watch, steps on to the platform and bows.) It is a quarter past—
so I will begin.

> Takes his MS. out of his pocket.

ASLAKSEN: I think we ought to elect a chairman first.

DR. STOCKMANN: No, it is quite unnecessary.

SOME OF THE CROWD: Yes—yes!

PETER STOCKMANN: I certainly think, too, that we ought to have
a chairman.

DR. STOCKMANN: But I have called this meeting to deliver a lecture, Peter.

PETER STOCKMANN: Dr. Stockmann's lecture may possibly lead
to a considerable conflict of opinion.

VOICES IN THE CROWD: A chairman! A chairman!

HOVSTAD: The general wish of the meeting seems to be that a
chairman should be elected.

DR. STOCKMANN (restraining himself):   Very well—let the meeting have its way.

ASLAKSEN: Will the Mayor be good enough to undertake the
task?

THREE MEN (clapping their hands):   Bravo! Bravo!

PETER STOCKMANN: For various reasons, which you will easily
understand, I must beg to be excused. But fortunately we have
amongst us a man who I think will be acceptable to you all. I refer
to the President of the Householders' Association, Mr. Aslaksen.

SEVERAL VOICES: Yes—Aslaksen! Bravo Aslaksen!

> DR. STOCKMANN takes up his MS. and walks up and down the plat-
> form.

ASLAKSEN: Since my fellow-citizens choose to entrust me with
this duty, I cannot refuse.

> Loud applause. ASLAKSEN mounts the platform.

BILLING (writing):   "Mr. Aslaksen was elected with enthusiasm."

ASLAKSEN: And now, as I am in this position, I should like to say
a few brief words. I am a quiet and peaceable man, who believes
in discreet moderation, and—and—in moderate discretion. All my
friends can bear witness to that.

SEVERAL VOICES: That's right! That's right, Aslaksen!

ASLAKSEN: I have learnt in the school of life and experience that
moderation is the most valuable virtue a citizen can possess——

PETER STOCKMANN: Hear, hear!

ASLAKSEN: ——and moreover that discretion and moderation are what enable a man to be of most service to the community. I would therefore suggest to our esteemed fellow-citizen, who has called this meeting, that he should strive to keep strictly within the bounds of moderation.

A MAN BY THE DOOR: Three cheers for the Moderation Society!

A VOICE: Shame!

SEVERAL VOICES: Sh!—Sh!

ASLAKSEN: No interruptions, gentlemen, please! Does anyone wish to make any remarks?

PETER STOCKMANN: Mr. Chairman.

ASLAKSEN: The Mayor will address the meeting.

PETER STOCKMANN: In consideration of the close relationship in which, as you all know, I stand to the present Medical Officer of the Baths, I should have preferred not to speak this evening. But my official position with regard to the Baths and my solicitude for the vital interests of the town compel me to bring forward a motion. I venture to presume that there is not a single one of our citizens present who considers it desirable that unreliable and exaggerated accounts of the sanitary condition of the Baths and the town should be spread abroad.

SEVERAL VOICES: No, no! Certainly not! We protest against it!

PETER STOCKMANN: Therefore I should like to propose that the meeting should not permit the Medical Officer either to read or to comment on his proposed lecture.

DR. STOCKMANN (impatiently): Not permit——! What the devil——!

MRS. STOCKMANN (coughing): Ahem!—ahem!

DR. STOCKMANN (collecting himself): Very well. Go ahead!

PETER STOCKMANN: In my communication to the "People's Messenger," I have put the essential facts before the public in such a way that every fair-minded citizen can easily form his own opinion. From it you will see that the main result of the Medical Officer's proposals—apart from their constituting a vote of censure on the leading men of the town—would be to saddle the ratepayers with an unnecessary expenditure of at least some thousands of pounds.

Sounds of disapproval among the audience, and some cat-calls.

ASLAKSEN (ringing his bell): Silence, please, gentlemen. I beg to support the Mayor's motion. I quite agree with him that there is something behind this agitation started by the Doctor. He talks about the Baths; but it is a revolution he is aiming at—he wants to get the administration and the town put into new hands. No one doubts the honesty of the Doctor's intentions—no one will suggest that there can be any two opinions as to that. I myself am a believer in self-government for the people, provided it does not fall too heavily on the ratepayers. But that would be the case here; and that is why I will see Dr. Stockmann damned—I beg your pardon—before I go with him in the matter. You can pay too dearly for a thing sometimes; that is my opinion.

Loud applause on all sides.

HOVSTAD: I, too, feel called upon to explain my position. Dr. Stockmann's agitation appeared to be gaining a certain amount of sympathy at first, so I supported it as impartially as I could. But presently we had reason to suspect that we had allowed ourselves to be misled by misrepresentation of the state of affairs——

DR. STOCKMANN: Misrepresentation——!

HOVSTAD: Well, let us say a not entirely trustworthy representation. The Mayor's statement has proved that. I hope no one here has any doubt as to my liberal principles; the attitude of the "People's Messenger" towards important political questions is well known to every one. But the advice of experienced and thoughtful men has convinced me that in purely local matters a newspaper ought to proceed with a certain caution.

ASLAKSEN: I entirely agree with the speaker.

HOVSTAD: And, in the matter before us, it is now an undoubted fact that Dr. Stockmann has public opinion against him. Now, what is an editor's first and most obvious duty, gentlemen? Is it not to work in harmony with his readers? Has he not received a sort of tacit mandate to work persistently and assiduously for the welfare of those whose opinions he represents? Or is it possible I am mistaken in that?

VOICES FROM THE CROWD: No, no! You are quite right!

HOVSTAD: It has cost me a severe struggle to break with a man in whose house I have been lately a frequent guest—a man who till to-day has been able to pride himself on the undivided goodwill of his fellow-citizens—a man whose only, or at all events whose essential, failing is that he is swayed by his heart rather than his head.

A FEW SCATTERED VOICES: That is true! Bravo, Stockmann!

HOVSTAD: But my duty to the community obliged me to break

with him. And there is another consideration that impels me to oppose him, and, as far as possible, to arrest him on the perilous course he has adopted; that is, consideration for his family——

DR. STOCKMANN: Please stick to the water-supply and drainage!

HOVSTAD: ——consideration, I repeat, for his wife and his children for whom he has made no provision.

MORTEN: Is that us, mother?

MRS. STOCKMANN: Hush!

ASLAKSEN: I will now put the Mayor's proposition to the vote.

DR. STOCKMANN: There is no necessity! To-night I have no intention of dealing with all that filth down at the Baths. No; I have something quite different to say to you.

PETER STOCKMANN (aside): What is coming now?

A DRUNKEN MAN (by the entrance door): I am a ratepayer! And therefore I have a right to speak too! And my entire—firm—inconceivable opinion is——

A NUMBER OF VOICES: Be quiet, at the back there!

OTHERS: He is drunk! Turn him out!

They turn him out.

DR. STOCKMANN: Am I allowed to speak?

ASLAKSEN (ringing his bell): Dr. Stockmann will address the meeting.

DR. STOCKMANN: I should like to have seen anyone, a few days ago, dare to attempt to silence me as has been done to-night! I would have defended my sacred rights as a man, like a lion! But now it is all one to me; I have something of even weightier importance to say to you.

The crowd presses nearer to him, MORTEN KIIL conspicuous among them.

DR. STOCKMANN (continuing): I have thought and pondered a great deal, these last few days—pondered over such a variety of things that in the end my head seemed too full to hold them——

PETER STOCKMANN (with a cough): Ahem!

DR. STOCKMANN: ——but I got them clear in my mind at last, and then I saw the whole situation lucidly. And that is why I am standing here to-night. I have a great revelation to make to you, my fellow-citizens! I will impart to you a discovery of a far wider scope than the trifling matter that our water-supply is poisoned and our medicinal Baths are standing on pestiferous soil.

A NUMBER OF VOICES (shouting): Don't talk about the Baths! We won't hear you! None of that!

DR. STOCKMANN: I have already told you that what I want to speak about is the great discovery I have made lately—the discovery that all the sources of our *moral* life are poisoned and that the whole fabric of our civic community is founded on the pestiferous soil of falsehood.

VOICES OF DISCONCERTED CITIZENS: What is that he says?

PETER STOCKMANN: Such an insinuation——!

ASLAKSEN (with his hand on his bell): I call upon the speaker to moderate his language.

DR. STOCKMANN: I have always loved my native town as a man only can love the home of his youthful days. I was not old when I went away from here; and exile, longing and memories cast, as it were, an additional halo over both the town and its inhabitants. (Some clapping and applause.) And there I stayed, for many years, in a horrible hole far away up north. When I came into contact with some of the people that lived scattered about among the rocks, I often thought it would have been more service to the poor half-starved creatures if a veterinary doctor had been sent up there, instead of a man like me.

Murmurs among the crowd.

BILLING (laying down his pen): I'm damned if I have ever heard——!

HOVSTAD: It is an insult to a respectable population!

DR. STOCKMANN: Wait a bit! I do not think anyone will charge me with having forgotten my native town up there. I was like one of the eider-ducks brooding on its nest, and what I hatched was—the plans for these Baths. (Applause and protests.) And then when fate at last decreed for me the great happiness of coming home again—I assure you, gentlemen, I thought I had nothing more in the world to wish for. Or rather, there was one thing I wished for—eagerly, untiringly, ardently—and that was to be able to be of service to my native town and the good of the community.

PETER STOCKMANN (looking at the ceiling): You chose a strange way of doing it—ahem!

DR. STOCKMANN: And so, with my eyes blinded to the real facts, I revelled in happiness. But yesterday morning—no, to be precise, it was yesterday afternoon—the eyes of my mind were opened wide, and the first thing I realised was the colossal stupidity of the authorities——

> Uproar, shouts and laughter. MRS. STOCKMANN coughs persistently.

PETER STOCKMANN: Mr. Chairman!

ASLAKSEN (ringing his bell):   By virtue of my authority——!

DR. STOCKMANN: It is a petty thing to catch me up on a word, Mr. Aslaksen. What I mean is only that I got scent of the unbelievable piggishness our leading men had been responsible for down at the Baths. I can't stand leading men at any price!—I have had enough of such people in my time. They are like billy-goats in a young plantation; they do mischief everywhere. They stand in a free man's way, whichever way he turns, and what I should like best would be to see them exterminated like any other vermin——

> Uproar.

PETER STOCKMANN: Mr. Chairman, can we allow such expressions to pass?

ASLAKSEN (with his hand on his bell):   Doctor——!

DR. STOCKMANN: I cannot understand how it is that I have only now acquired a clear conception of what these gentry are, when I had almost daily before my eyes in this town such an excellent specimen of them—my brother Peter—slow-witted and hide-bound in prejudice——

> Laughter, uproar and hisses. MRS. STOCKMANN sits coughing assiduously. ASLAKSEN rings his bell violently.

THE DRUNKEN MAN (who has got in again):   Is it me he is talking about? My name's Petersen, all right—but devil take me if I——

ANGRY VOICES: Turn out that drunken man! Turn him out.

> He is turned out again.

PETER STOCKMANN: Who was that person?

1ST CITIZEN: I don't know who he is, Mr. Mayor.

2ND CITIZEN: He doesn't belong here.

3RD CITIZEN: I expect he is a navvy from over at (the rest is inaudible).

ASLAKSEN: He had obviously had too much beer—Proceed, Doctor; but please strive to be moderate in your language.

DR. STOCKMANN: Very well, gentlemen, I will say no more about our leading men. And if anyone imagines, from what I have just said, that my object is to attack these people this evening, he is wrong—absolutely wide of the mark. For I cherish the comforting conviction that these parasites—all these venerable relics of a dying school of thought—are most admirably paving the way for their own extinction; they need no doctor's help to hasten their end. Nor is it folk of that kind who constitute the most pressing danger to the community. It is not they who are most instrumental in poisoning the sources of our moral life and infecting the ground on which we stand. It is not they who are the most dangerous enemies of truth and freedom amongst us.

SHOUTS FROM ALL SIDES: Who then? Who is it? Name! Name!

DR. STOCKMANN: You may depend upon it I shall name them! That is precisely the great discovery I made yesterday. (Raises his voice.) The most dangerous enemy of truth and freedom amongst us is the compact majority—yes, the damned compact Liberal majority—that is it! Now you know!

> Tremendous uproar. Most of the crowd are shouting, stamping and hissing. Some of the older men among them exchange stolen glances and seem to be enjoying themselves. MRS. STOCKMANN gets up, looking anxious. EJLIF and MORTEN advance threateningly upon some schoolboys who are playing pranks. ASLAKSEN rings his bell and begs for silence. HOVSTAD and BILLING both talk at once, but are inaudible. At last quiet is restored.

ASLAKSEN: As chairman, I call upon the speaker to withdraw the ill-considered expressions he has just used.

DR. STOCKMANN: Never, Mr. Aslaksen! It is the majority in our community that denies me my freedom and seeks to prevent my speaking the truth.

HOVSTAD: The majority always has right on its side.

BILLING: And truth too, by God!

DR. STOCKMANN: The majority *never* has right on its side. Never, I say! That is one of these social lies against which an independent, intelligent man must wage war. Who is it that constitute the majority of the population in a country? Is it the clever folk or the stupid? I don't imagine you will dispute the fact that at present the stupid people are in an absolutely overwhelming majority all the world over. But, good Lord!—you can never pretend that it is right that the stupid folk should govern the clever ones! (Uproar and cries.) Oh, yes—you can shout me down, I know! but you cannot answer me. The majority has *might* on its side—unfortunately; but *right* it has *not*. I am in the right—I and a few other scattered individuals. The minority is always in the right.

Renewed uproar.

HOVSTAD: Aha!—so Dr. Stockmann has become an aristocrat since the day before yesterday!

DR. STOCKMANN: I have already said that I don't intend to waste a word on the puny, narrow-chested, short-winded crew whom we are leaving astern. Pulsating life no longer concerns itself with them. I am thinking of the few, the scattered few amongst us, who have absorbed new and vigorous truths. Such men stand, as it were, at the outposts, so far ahead that the compact majority has not yet been able to come up with them; and there they are fighting for truths that are too newly-born into the world of consciousness to have any considerable number of people on their side as yet.

HOVSTAD: So the Doctor is a revolutionary now!

DR. STOCKMANN: Good heavens—of course I am, Mr. Hovstad! I propose to raise a revolution against the lie that the majority has the monopoly of the truth. What sort of truths are they that the majority usually supports? They are truths that are of such advanced age that they are beginning to break up. And if a truth is as old as that, it is also in a fair way to become a lie, gentlemen. (Laughter and mocking cries.) Yes, believe me or not, as you like; but truths are by no means as long-lived as Methuselah—as some folks imagine. A normally constituted truth lives, let us say, as a rule seventeen or eighteen, or at most twenty years; seldom longer. But truths as aged as that are always worn frightfully thin, and nevertheless it is only then that the majority recognises them and recommends them to the community as wholesome moral nourishment. There is no great nutritive value in that sort of fare, I can assure you; and, as a doctor, I ought to know. These "majority truths" are like last year's cured meat—like rancid, tainted ham; and they are the origin of the moral scurvy that is rampant in our communities.

ASLAKSEN: It appears to me that the speaker is wandering a long way from his subject.

PETER STOCKMANN: I quite agree with the Chairman.

DR. STOCKMANN: Have you gone clean out of your senses, Peter? I am sticking as closely to my subject as I can; for my subject is precisely this, that it is the masses, the majority—this infernal compact majority—that poisons the sources of our moral life and infects the ground we stand on.

HOVSTAD: And all this because the great, broad-minded majority of the people is prudent enough to show deference only to well-ascertained and well-approved truths?

DR. STOCKMANN: Ah, my good Mr. Hovstad, don't talk nonsense about well-ascertained truths! The truths of which the masses now approve are the very truths that the fighters at the outposts held to in the days of our grandfathers. We fighters at the outposts now-adays no longer approve of them; and I do not believe there is any other well-ascertained truth except this, that no community can live a healthy life if it is nourished only on such old marrowless truths.

HOVSTAD: But instead of standing there using vague generalities, it would be interesting if you would tell us what these old marrow-less truths are, that we are nourished on.

Applause from many quarters.

DR. STOCKMANN: Oh, I could give you a whole string of such abominations; but to begin with I will confine myself to one well-approved truth, which at bottom is a foul lie, but upon which never-theless Mr. Hovstad and the "People's Messenger" and all the "Mes-sengers'" supporters are nourished.

HOVSTAD: And that is——?

DR. STOCKMANN: That is, the doctrine you have inherited from your forefathers and proclaim thoughtlessly far and wide—the doc-trine that the public, the crowd, the masses are the essential part of the population—that they constitute the People—that the common folk, the ignorant and incomplete element in the community, have the same right to pronounce judgment and to approve, to direct and to govern, as the isolated, intellectually superior personalities in it.

BILLING: Well, damn me if ever I——

HOVSTAD (at the same time, shouting out): Fellow-citizens, take good note of that!

A NUMBER OF VOICES (angrily): Oho!—we are not the People! Only the superior folks are to govern, are they!

A WORKMAN: Turn the fellow out, for talking such rubbish!

ANOTHER: Out with him!

ANOTHER (calling out): Blow your horn, Evensen!

A horn is blown loudly, amidst hisses and an angry uproar.

DR. STOCKMANN (when the noise has somewhat abated): Be reasonable! Can't you stand hearing the voice of truth for once?

I don't in the least expect you to agree with me all at once; but I must say I did expect Mr. Hovstad to admit I was right, when he had recovered his composure a little. He claims to be a free-thinker——

VOICES (in murmurs of astonishment):   Freethinker, did he say? Is Hovstad a freethinker?

HOVSTAD (shouting):   Prove it, Dr. Stockmann! When have I said so in print?

DR. STOCKMANN (reflecting):   No, confound it, you are right!— you have never had the courage to. Well, I won't put you in a hole, Mr. Hovstad. Let us say it is I that am the freethinker, then. I am going to prove to you, scientifically, that the "People's Messenger" leads you by the nose in a shameful manner when it tells you that you—that the common people, the crowd, the masses are the real essence of the People. That is only a newspaper lie, I tell you! The common people are nothing more than the raw material of which a People is made. (Groans, laughter and uproar.) Well, isn't that the case? Isn't there an enormous difference between a well-bred and an ill-bred strain of animals? Take, for instance, a common barn-door hen. What sort of eating do you get from a shrivelled up old scrag of a fowl like that? Not much, do you! And what sort of eggs does it lay? A fairly good crow or a raven can lay pretty nearly as good an egg. But take a well-bred Spanish or Japanese hen, or a good pheasant or a turkey—then you will see the difference. Or take the case of dogs, with whom we humans are on such intimate terms. Think first of an ordinary common cur—I mean one of the horrible, coarse-haired, low-bred curs that do nothing but run about the streets and befoul the walls of the houses. Compare one of these curs with a poodle whose sires for many generations have been bred in a gentleman's house, where they have had the best of food and had the opportunity of hearing soft voices and music. Do you not think that the poodle's brain is developed to quite a different degree from that of the cur? Of course it is. It is puppies of well-bred poodles like that, that showmen train to do incredibly clever tricks—things that a common cur could never learn to do even if it stood on its head.

Uproar and mocking cries.

A CITIZEN (calls out):   Are you going to make out we are dogs, now?

ANOTHER CITIZEN: We are not animals, Doctor!

DR. STOCKMANN: Yes, but, bless my soul, we *are*, my friend! It is true we are the finest animals anyone could wish for; but, even amongst us, exceptionally fine animals are rare. There is a tremendous difference between poodle-men and cur-men. And the amusing part of it is, that Mr. Hovstad quite agrees with me as long as it is a question of four-footed animals——

HOVSTAD: Yes, it is true enough as far as they are concerned.

DR. STOCKMANN: Very well. But as soon as I extend the principle and apply it to two-legged animals, Mr. Hovstad stops short. He no longer dares to think independently, or to pursue his ideas to their logical conclusion; so he turns the whole theory upside down and proclaims in the "People's Messenger" that it is the barn-door hens and street curs that are the finest specimens in the menagerie. But that is always the way, as long as a man retains the traces of common origin and has not worked his way up to intellectual distinction.

HOVSTAD: I lay no claim to any sort of distinction. I am the son of humble countryfolk, and I am proud that the stock I come from is rooted deep among the common people he insults.

VOICES: Bravo, Hovstad! Bravo! Bravo!

DR. STOCKMANN: The kind of common people I mean are not only to be found low down in the social scale; they crawl and swarm all around us—even in the highest social positions. You have only to look at your own fine, distinguished Mayor! My brother Peter is every bit as plebeian as anyone that walks in two shoes——

Laughter and hisses.

PETER STOCKMANN: I protest against personal allusions of this kind.

DR. STOCKMANN (imperturbably): ——and that, not because he is, like myself, descended from some old rascal of a pirate from Pomerania or thereabouts—because that is who we are descended from——

PETER STOCKMANN: An absurd legend. I deny it!

DR. STOCKMANN: ——but because he thinks what his superiors think and holds the same opinions as they. People who do that are, intellectually speaking, common people; and that is why my magnificent brother Peter is in reality so very far from any distinction —and consequently also so far from being liberal-minded.

PETER STOCKMANN: Mr. Chairman——!

HOVSTAD: So it is only the distinguished men that are liberal-minded in this country? We are learning something quite new!

Laughter.

DR. STOCKMANN: Yes, that is part of my new discovery too. And another part of it is that broad-mindedness is almost precisely the same thing as morality. That is why I maintain that it is absolutely inexcusable in the "People's Messenger" to proclaim, day in and day out, the false doctrine that it is the masses, the crowd, the compact majority that have the monopoly of broad-mindedness and morality—and that vice and corruption and every kind of intellectual depravity are the result of culture, just as all the filth that is draining into our Baths is the result of the tanneries up at Mölledal! (*Uproar and interruptions.* DR. STOCKMANN *is undisturbed, and goes on, carried away by his ardour, with a smile.*) And yet this same "People's Messenger" can go on preaching that the masses ought to be elevated to higher conditions of life! But, bless my soul, if the "Messenger's" teaching is to be depended upon, this very raising up the masses would mean nothing more or less than setting them straightway upon the paths of depravity! Happily the theory that culture demoralises is only an old falsehood that our forefathers believed in and we have inherited. No, it is ignorance, poverty, ugly conditions of life that do the devil's work! In a house which does not get aired and swept every day—my wife Katherine maintains that the floor ought to be scrubbed as well, but that is a debatable question—in such a house, let me tell you, people will lose within two or three years the power of thinking or acting in a moral manner. Lack of oxygen weakens the conscience. And there must be a plentiful lack of oxygen in very many houses in this town, I should think, judging from the fact that the whole compact majority can be unconscientious enough to wish to build the town's prosperity on a quagmire of falsehood and deceit.

ASLAKSEN: We cannot allow such a grave accusation to be flung at a citizen community.

A CITIZEN: I move that the Chairman direct the speaker to sit down.

VOICES (angrily): Hear, hear! Quite right! Make him sit down!

DR. STOCKMANN (losing his self-control): Then I will go and shout the truth at every street corner! I will write it in other towns' newspapers! The whole country shall know what is going on here!

HOVSTAD: It almost seems as if Dr. Stockmann's intention were to ruin the town.

DR. STOCKMANN: Yes, my native town is so dear to me that I would rather ruin it than see it flourishing upon a lie.

ASLAKSEN: This is really serious.

> Uproar and cat-calls. MRS. STOCKMANN coughs, but to no purpose; her husband does not listen to her any longer.

HOVSTAD (shouting above the din):   A man must be a public enemy to wish to ruin a whole community!

DR. STOCKMANN (with growing fervour):   What does the destruction of a community matter, if it lives on lies! It ought to be razed to the ground, I tell you! All who live by lies ought to be exterminated like vermin! You will end by infecting the whole country; you will bring about such a state of things that the whole country will deserve to be ruined. And if things come to that pass, I shall say from the bottom of my heart: Let the whole country perish, let all these people be exterminated!

VOICES FROM THE CROWD: That is talking like an out-and-out enemy of the people!

BILLING: There sounded the voice of the people, by all that's holy!

THE WHOLE CROWD (shouting):   Yes, yes! He is an enemy of the people! He hates his country! He hates his own people!

ASLAKSEN: Both as a citizen and as an individual, I am profoundly disturbed by what we have had to listen to. Dr. Stockmann has shown himself in a light I should never have dreamed of. I am unhappily obliged to subscribe to the opinion which I have just heard my estimable fellow-citizens utter; and I propose that we should give expression to that opinion in a resolution. I propose a resolution as follows: "This meeting declares that it considers Dr. Thomas Stockmann, Medical Officer of the Baths, to be an enemy of the people."

> A storm of cheers and applause. A number of men surround the DOCTOR and hiss him. MRS. STOCKMANN and PETRA have got up from their seats. MORTEN and EJLIF are fighting the other school-boys for hissing; some of their elders separate them.

DR. STOCKMANN (to the men who are hissing him):   Oh, you fools! I tell you that——

ASLAKSEN (ringing his bell):   We cannot hear you now, Doctor. A formal vote is about to be taken; but, out of regard for personal feelings, it shall be by ballot and not verbal. Have you any clean paper, Mr. Billing?

BILLING: I have both blue and white here.

ASLAKSEN (going to him):   That will do nicely; we shall get on more quickly that way. Cut it up into small strips—yes, that's it. (To the meeting.) Blue means no; white means yes. I will come round myself and collect votes.

> PETER STOCKMANN leaves the hall. ASLAKSEN and one or two others go round the room with the slips of paper in their hats.

1ST CITIZEN (to HOVSTAD):   I say, what has come to the Doctor? What are we to think of it?

HOVSTAD: Oh, you know how headstrong he is.

2ND CITIZEN (to BILLING):   Billing, you go to their house—have you ever noticed if the fellow drinks?

BILLING: Well I'm hanged if I know what to say. There are always spirits on the table when you go.

3RD CITIZEN: I rather think he goes quite off his head sometimes.

1ST CITIZEN: I wonder if there is any madness in his family?

BILLING: I shouldn't wonder if there were.

4TH CITIZEN: No, it is nothing more than sheer malice; he wants to get even with somebody for something or other.

BILLING: Well certainly he suggested a rise in his salary on one occasion lately, and did not get it.

THE CITIZENS (together):   Ah!—then it is easy to understand how it is!

THE DRUNKEN MAN (who has got amongst the audience again): I want a blue one, I do! And I want a white one too!

VOICES: It's that drunken chap again! Turn him out!

MORTEN KIIL (going up to DR. STOCKMANN):   Well, Stockmann, do you see what these monkey tricks of yours lead to?

DR. STOCKMANN: I have done my duty.

MORTEN KIIL: What was that you said about the tanneries at Mölledal?

DR. STOCKMANN: You heard well enough. I said they were the source of all the filth.

MORTEN KIIL: My tannery too?

DR. STOCKMANN: Unfortunately your tannery is by far the worst.

MORTEN KIIL: Are you going to put that in the papers?

DR. STOCKMANN: I shall conceal nothing.

MORTEN KIIL: That may cost you dear, Stockmann.

> Goes out.

A STOUT MAN (going up to CAPTAIN HORSTER, without taking any notice of the ladies): Well, Captain, so you lend your house to enemies of the people?

HORSTER: I imagine I can do what I like with my own possessions, Mr. Vik.

THE STOUT MAN: Then you can have no objection to my doing the same with mine.

HORSTER: What do you mean, sir?

THE STOUT MAN: You shall hear from me in the morning.

Turns his back on him and moves off.

PETRA: Was that not your owner, Captain Horster?

HORSTER: Yes, that was Mr. Vik the ship-owner.

ASLAKSEN (with the voting-papers in his hands, gets up on to the platform and rings his bell): Gentlemen, allow me to announce the result. By the votes of every one here except one person——

A YOUNG MAN: That is the drunk chap!

ASLAKSEN: By the votes of every one here except a tipsy man, this meeting of citizens declares Dr. Thomas Stockmann to be an enemy of the people. (Shouts and applause.) Three cheers for our ancient and honourable citizen community! (Renewed applause.) Three cheers for our able and energetic Mayor, who has so loyally suppressed the promptings of family feeling! (Cheers.) The meeting is dissolved.

MAJORITY TYRANNY

D. H. Lawrence

"The Nightmare"

Also from London occasionally a young man came down and stayed at the inn in the church town, some young friend of Somers who hated the army and the Government and was generally discontented, and so fitfully came as an adherent to Richard Lovat.

From Ch. XII of *Kangaroo* by D. H. Lawrence. Copyright 1923 by Thomas B. Seltzer, Inc., 1951 by Frieda Lawrence. Reprinted by permission of The Viking Press, Inc.

One of these was James Sharpe, a young Edinburgh man with a moderate income of his own, interested in music. Sharpe was hardly more than a lad—but he was the type of lowland Scotsman who is half an artist, not more, and so can never get on in the ordinary respectable life, rebels against it all the time, and yet can never get away from it or free himself from its dictates.

Sharpe had taken a house farther along the coast, brought his piano down from London and sufficient furniture and a house-keeper, and insisted, like a morose bird, that he wanted to be alone. But he wasn't really morose, and he didn't want really to be alone. His old house, rather ramshackle, stood back a little way from the cliffs, where the moor came down savagely to the sea, past a de-serted tin-mine. It was lonely, wild, and in a savage way, poetic enough. Here Sharpe installed himself for the moment: to be alone with his music and his general discontent.

Of course he excited the wildest comments. He had window curtains of different colours, so of course, *here* was plain signal-ling to the German submarines. Spies, the lot of them. When still another young man of the same set came and took a bungalow on the moor, West Cornwall decided that it was being delivered straight into German hands. Not that West Cornwall would really have minded that so terribly. No; it wasn't that it feared the Ger-mans. It was that it hated the sight of these recalcitrant young men. And Somers the instigator, the arch-spy, the responsible little swine with his beard.

Somers, meanwhile, began to chuckle a bit to himself. After all he was getting the better of the military *canaille. Canaille! Canaglia! Schweinerei!* He loathed them in all the languages he could lay his tongue to.

So Somers and Harriet went to stay a week-end with Sharpe at Trevenna, as the house was called. Sharpe was a C 2* man on perpetual tenterhooks. He had decided that if ever *he* were sum-moned to serve, he would just disappear. The Somers drove over, only three or four miles, on the Saturday afternoon and the three wandered on the moor and down the cliff. No one was in sight. But how many pairs of eyes were watching, who knows? Sharpe lighting a cigarette for Harriet was an indication of untold im-morality.

Evening came, the lamps were lit, and the incriminating curtains

* Editors' note: This and similar references are to English draft classifications during World War I.

carefully drawn. The three sat before the fire in the long music-room, and tried to be cosy and jolly. But there was something wrong with the mood. After dinner it was even worse. Harriet curled herself up on the sofa with a cigarette, Sharpe spread himself in profound melancholy in his big chair, Somers sat back, near the window. They talked in occasional snatches, in mockery of the enemy that surrounded them. Then Somers sang to himself, in an irritating way, one German folksong after another, not in a songful, but in a defiant way.

"*Annchen von Tharau*"—"*Schatz, mein Schatz, reite nicht so weit von mir.*" "*Zu Strasburg auf der Schanz, da fiel mein Unglück ein.*" This went on till Sharpe asked him to stop.

And in the silence, the tense and irritable silence that followed, came a loud bang. All got up in alarm, and followed Sharpe through the dining-room to the small entrance-room, where a dim light was burning. A lieutenant and three sordid men in the dark behind him, one with a lantern.

"Mr. Sharpe?" the authoritative, and absolutely-in-the-right voice of the puppy lieutenant.

Sharpe took his pipe from his mouth and said laconically, "Yes."

"You've a light burning in your window facing the sea."

"I think not. There is only one window, and that's on the passage where I never go, upstairs."

"A light was showing from that window ten minutes ago."

"I don't think it can have been."

"It was." And the stern, puppy lieutenant turned to his followers, who clustered there in the dark.

"Yes, there was a light there ten minutes since," chimed the followers.

"I don't see how it's possible," persisted Sharpe.

"Oh, well—there is sufficient evidence that it was. What other persons have you in the house——" and this officer and gentleman stepped into the room, followed by his three Cornish weeds, one of whom had fallen into a ditch in his assiduous serving of his country, and was a sorry sight. Of course Harriet saw chiefly him, and had to laugh.

"There's Mrs. Waugh, the housekeeper—but she's in bed."

The party now stood and eyed one another—the lieutenant with his three sorry braves on one hand, Sharpe, Somers, and Harriet in an old dress of soft silk on the other.

"Well, Mr. Sharpe, the light was seen."

"I don't see how it was possible. We've none of us been upstairs, and Mrs. Waugh has been in bed for half an hour."

"Is there a curtain to the passage window?" put in Somers quietly. He had helped Sharpe in setting up house.

"I don't believe there is," said Sharpe. "I forgot all about it, as it wasn't in a room, and I never go to that side of the house. Even Mrs. Waugh is supposed to go up the kitchen stairs, and so she doesn't have to pass it."

"She must have gone across with a candle as she went to bed," said Somers.

But the lieutenant didn't like being pushed into unimportance while these young men so quietly and naturally spoke together, excluding him as if he were an inferior: which they meant to do.

"You have an uncurtained window overlooking the sea, Mr. Sharpe?" he said, in his military counter-jumping voice.

"You'll have to put a curtain to it to-morrow," said Somers to Sharpe.

"What is your name?" chimed the lieutenant.

"Somers—I wasn't speaking to you," said Richard coldly. And then to Sharpe, with a note of contempt: "That's what it is. Mrs. Waugh must just have passed with a candle."

There was a silence. The wonderful watchers did not contradict.

"Yes, I suppose that's it," said Sharpe, fretfully.

"We'll put a curtain up to-morrow," said Somers.

The lieutenant would have liked to search the house. He would have liked to destroy its privacy. He glanced down to the music-room. But Harriet, so obviously a lady, even if a hateful one; and Somers with his pale look of derision; and Sharpe so impassive with his pipe; and the weedy watchers in the background, knowing just how it all was, and almost ready to take sides with the "gentleman" against the officer: they were too much for the lieutenant.

"Well, the light was there, Mr. Sharpe. Distinctly visible from the sea," and he turned to his followers for confirmation.

"Oh, yes, a light plain enough," said the one who had fallen into a ditch, and wanted a bit of his own back.

"A candle!" said Sharpe, with his queer, musical note of derision and fretfulness. "A candle just passing——"

"You have an uncurtained window to the sea, and lights were showing. I shall have to report this to headquarters. Perhaps if you write and apologise to Major Caerlyon it may be passed over, if nothing of the like occurs again——"

So they departed, and the three went back to their room, fuming
with rage and mockery. They mocked the appearance and voice of
the lieutenant, the appearance of the weeds, and Harriet rejoiced
over the one who had fallen into a ditch. This regardless of the fact
that they knew that some of the watchers were lying listening in
the gorse bushes under the windows and had been lying there all
the evening.

"Shall you write and apologise?" said Somers.

"Apologise! No!" replied Sharpe, with peevish contempt.

Harriet and Somers went back home on the Monday. On the
Tuesday appeared Sharpe; the police had been and left him a summons to appear at the market town, charged under the Defence of
the Realm Act.

"I suppose you'll have to go," said Somers.

"Oh, I shall go," said he.

They waited for the day. In the afternoon Sharpe came with a
white face and tears of rage and mortification in his eyes. The
magistrate had told him he ought to be serving his country, and not
causing mischief and skulking in an out-of-the-way corner. And
had fined him twenty pounds.

"*I* shan't pay it," cried Sharpe.

"Your mother will," said Somers.

And so it was. What was the good of putting oneself in their
power in *any* way, if it could be avoided?

So the lower fields were cleared of corn, and they started on the
two big fields above on the moors. Sharpe cycled over to say a
farmer had asked *him* to go and help at Westyr; and for once he
had gone; but he felt spiteful to Somers for letting him in for this.

But Somers was very fond of the family at Buryan Farm, and he
loved working with John Thomas and the girls. John Thomas was a
year or two older than Somers, and at this time his dearest friend.
And so he loved working all day among the corn beyond the high-
road, with the savage moors all round, and the hill with its pre-
Christian granite rocks rising like a great dark pyramid on the left,
the sea in front. Sometimes a great airship hung over the sea,
watching for submarines. The work stopped in the field, and the
men watched. Then it went on again, and the wagon rocked slowly
down the wild, granite road, rocked like a ship past Harriet's
sunken cottage. But Somers stayed above all day, loading or picking, or resting, talking in the intervals with John Thomas, who
loved a half-philosophical, mystical talking about the sun, and the

moon, the mysterious powers of the moon at night, and the mysterious change in man with the change of season, and the mysterious effects of sex on a man. So they talked, lying in the bracken or on the heather as they waited for a wain. Or one of the girls came with dinner in a huge basket, and they ate all together, so happy with the moors and the sky and touch of autumn. Somers loved these people. He loved the sensitiveness of their intelligence. They were not educated. But they had an endless curiosity about the world, and an endless interest in what was *right*.

"Now do you think it's right, Mr. Somers?" The times that Somers heard that question, from the girls, from Arthur, from John Thomas. They spoke in the quick Cornish way, with the West Cornish accent. Sometimes it was:

"Now do'ee think it right?"

And with their black eyes they watched the ethical issue in his face. Queer it was. Right and wrong was not fixed for them as for the English. There was still a mystery for them in what was right and what was wrong. Only one thing was wrong—any sort of *physical* compulsion or hurt. That they were sure of. But as for the rest of behaviour—it was all a flux. They had none of the ethics of chivalry or of love.

Sometimes Harriet came also to tea: but not often. They loved her to come: and yet were a little uneasy when she was there. Harriet was so definitely a lady. She liked them all. But it was a bit *noli me tangere*, with her. Somers was so *very* intimate with them. She couldn't be. And the girls said, "Mrs. Somers don't mix in wi' the likes o' we like Mr. Somers do." Yet they were always very pleased when Harriet came.

Poor Harriet spent many lonely days in the cottage. Richard was not interested in her now. He was only interested in John Thomas and the farm people, and he was growing more like a labourer every day. And the farm people didn't mind how long *she* was left alone, at night too, in that lonely little cottage and with all the tension of fear upon her. Because she felt that it was *she* whom these authorities, these English, hated even more than Somers. Because she made them feel she despised them. And as they were really rather despicable, they hated her at sight, her beauty, her reckless pride, her touch of derision. But Richard—even he neglected her and hated her. She was driven back on herself like a fury. And many a bitter fight they had, he and she.

The days grew shorter before the corn was all down from the

moors. Sometimes Somers alone lay on the sheaves, waiting for the last wain to come to be loaded, while the others were down milking. And then the Cornish night would gradually come down upon the dark, shaggy moors, that were like the fur of some beast, and upon the pale-grey granite masses, so ancient and Druidical, suggesting blood-sacrifice. And as Somers sat there on the sheaves in the under-dark, seeing the light swim above the sea, he felt he was over the border, in another world. Over the border, in that twilight, awesome world of the previous Celts. The spirit of the ancient, pre-Christian world, which lingers still in the truly Celtic places, he could feel it invade him in the savage dusk, making him savage too, and at the same time, strangely sensitive and subtle, understanding the mystery of blood-sacrifice: to sacrifice one's victim, and let the blood run to the fire, there beyond the gorse upon the old grey granite: and at the same time to understand most sensitively the dark flicker of animal life about him, even in a bat, even in the writhing of a maggot in a dead rabbit. Writhe then, Life, he seemed to say to the things—and he no longer saw its sickeningness.

The old Celtic countries have never had our Latin-Teutonic consciousness, never will have. They have never been Christian, in the blue-eyed, or even in the truly Roman, Latin sense of the word. But they have been overlaid by our consciousness and our civilisation, smouldering underneath in a slow, eternal fire, that you can never put out till it burns itself out.

And this autumn Richard Lovat seemed to drift back. He had a passion, a profound nostalgia for the place. He could feel himself metamorphosing. He no longer wanted to struggle consciously along, a thought adventurer. He preferred to drift into a sort of blood-darkness, to take up in his veins again the savage vibrations that still lingered round the secret rocks, the place of the pre-Christian human sacrifice. Human sacrifice! He could feel his dark, blood-consciousness tingle to it again, the desire of it, the mystery of it. Old presences, old awful presences round the black moor-edge, in the thick dusk, as the sky of light was pushed pulsing upwards, away. Then an owl would fly and hoot, and Richard lay with his soul departed back, back into the blood-sacrificial pre-world, and the sun-mystery, and the moon-power, and the mistletoe on the tree, away from his own white world, his own white, conscious day. Away from the burden of intensive mental consciousness. Back, back into semi-dark, the half-conscious, the *clair-obscur*, where consciousness pulsed as a passional vibration, not as mind-knowledge.

Then would come John Thomas with the wain, and the two men would linger putting up the sheaves, linger, talking, till the dark, talking of the half-mystical things with which they both were filled. John Thomas, with his nervous ways and his quick brown eyes, was full of fear: fear of the unseen, fear of the unknown malevolencies, above all, fear of death. So they would talk of death, and the powers of death. And the farmer, in a non-mental way, understood, understood even more than Somers.

And then in the first dark they went down the hill with the wain, to part at the cottage door. And to Harriet, with her pure Teutonic consciousness, John Thomas' greeting would sound like a jeer, as he called to her. And Somers seemed to come home like an enemy, like an enemy, with that look on his face, and that pregnant malevolency of Cornwall investing him. It was a bitter time, to Harriet. Yet glamorous too.

Autumn drew on, corn-harvest was over, it was October. John Thomas drove every Thursday over the moors to market—a two-hours' drive. To-day Somers would go with him—and Ann the sister also, to do some shopping. It was a lovely October morning. They passed the stony little huddle of the church town, and on up the hill, where the great granite boulders shoved out of the land, and the barrenness was ancient and inviolable. They could see the gulls under the big cliffs beyond—and there was a buzzard circling over the marshy place below church town. A Cornish, magic morning. John Thomas and Somers were walking up the hill, leaving the reins to Ann, seated high in the trap.

"One day, when the war ends, before long," said Somers as they climbed behind the trap in the sun, past the still-flickering gorse-bushes, "we will go far across the sea—to Mexico, to Australia—and try living there. You must come too, and we will have a farm."

"Me!" said John Thomas. "Why, however should I come?"

"Why not?"

But the Cornishman smiled with that peculiar sceptical smile.

They reached town at length, over the moors and down the long hill. John Thomas was always late. Somers went about doing his shopping—and then met Ann at an eating-house. John Thomas was to have been there too. But he failed them. Somers walked about the Cornish seaport—he knew it now—and by sight he too was known, and execrated. Yet the tradespeople were always so pleasant and courteous to him. And it was such a sunny day.

The town was buzzing with a story. Two German submarine

officers had come into the town, dressed in clothes they had taken from an English ship they had sunk. They had stayed a night at the Mounts Bay Hotel. And two days later they had told the story to some fisherman whose fishing-boat they stopped. They had shown the incredulous fisherman the hotel bill. Then they had sunk the fishing-boat, sending the three fishermen ashore in the row-boat.

John Thomas, the chatterbox, should have been at the stables at five. He was an endless gossip, never by any chance punctual. Somers and Ann waited till six—all the farmers drove out home, theirs was the last trap.

"Buryan's trap—always the last," said the ostler.

It became dark—the shops were all closing—it was night. And now the town, so busy at noon and all the afternoon, seemed cold, stony, deserted, with the wind blowing down its steep street. Nearly seven, and still no John Thomas. Ann was furious, but she knew him. Somers was more quiet: but he knew that this was a sort of deliberate insult on John Thomas' part, and that he must never trust him again.

It was well after seven when the fellow came—smiling with subtle malevolence and excusing himself so easily.

"I shall never come with you again," said Somers quietly.

"I should think not, Mr. Somers," cried Ann.

It was a two-hours' drive home—a long climb to the dark stretch of the moors—then across the moors in the cold of the night, to the steep, cliff-like descent on the north, where church town lay, and the sea beyond. As they drew near to the north descent, the home face, and the darkness was below them, Somers suddenly said:

"I don't think I shall ever drive this way again."

"Don't you? Why, what makes you say that?" cried the facile John Thomas.

Past nine o'clock as they came down the rocky road and saw the yellow curtain of the cottage glowing. Poor Harriet. Somers was stiff with cold as he rose to jump down.

"I'll come down for my parcels later," he said. Easier to take them out at the farm, and he must fetch the milk.

Harriet opened the door.

"At last you've come," she said. "Something has happened, Lovat!" One of John Thomas' sisters came out too—she had come up with Mr. Somers out of sympathy.

"What?" he said. And up came all the fear.

It was evident Harriet had had a bad shock. She had walked in the afternoon across to Sharpe's place, three miles away: and had got back just at nightfall, expecting Somers home by seven. She had left the doors unlocked, as they usually did. The moment she came in, in the dusk, she knew something had happened. She made a light, and looked round. Things were disturbed. She looked in her little treasure-boxes—everything there, but moved. She looked in the drawers—everything turned upside down. The whole house ransacked, searched.

A terrible fear came over her. She knew she was antagonistic to the government people: in her soul she hated the fixed society with its barrenness and its barren laws. She had always been afraid—always shrunk from the sight of a policeman, as if she were guilty of heaven knows what. And now the horror had happened: all the black animosity of authority was encompassing her. The unknown of it: and the horror.

She fled down to the farm. Yes, three men had come, asking for Mr. and Mrs. Somers. They had told the one who came to the farm that Mr. Somers had driven to town, and Mrs. Somers they had seen going across the fields to church town. Then the men had gone up to the cottage again, and gone inside.

"And they've searched everything—everything," said Harriet, shocked right through with awful fear.

"Well, there was nothing to find. They must have been disappointed," said Richard.

But it was a shock to him also: great consternation at the farm.

"It must have been something connected with Sharpe—it must have been that," said Somers, trying to reassure himself.

"Thank goodness the house was so clean and tidy," said Harriet. But it was a last blow to her.

What had they taken? They had not touched Somers' papers. But they had been through his pockets—they had taken the few loose letters from the pocket of his day-jacket—they had taken a book—and a sort of note-book with scraps of notes for essays in it—and his address-book—yes, a few things like that.

"But it'll be nothing. It'll be something to do with Sharpe's brother."

But he felt sick and sullen, and wouldn't get up early in the morning. Harriet was more prepared. She was down, dressed and tidy, making the breakfast. It was eight o'clock in the morning. Suddenly Somers heard her call:

"Lovat, they're here. Get up."

He heard the dread in her voice, and sprang into his clothes and came downstairs: a young officer, the burly police-sergeant, and two other loutish-looking men. Somers came down without a collar.

"I have here a warrant to search your house," said the young officer.

"But you searched it yesterday, didn't you?" cried Harriet.

The young officer looked at her coldly, without replying. He read the search-warrant, and the two lout detectives, in civilian clothes, began to nose round.

"And the police-sergeant will read this order to you."

Somers, white and very still, spoke no word, but waited. Then the police-sergeant, in rather stumbling fashion, began to read an order from the military authorities that Richard Lovat Somers, and Harriet Emma Marianna Johanna Somers, of Trevetham Cottage, etc., should leave the county of Cornwall within the space of three days. And further, within the space of twenty-four hours of their arrival in any place they must report themselves at the police station of the said place, giving their address. And they were forbidden to enter any part of the area of Cornwall, etc., etc., etc.

Somers listened in silence.

"But why?" cried Harriet. "Why. What have we done?"

"I can't say what you have done," said the young officer in a cold tone, "but it must be something sufficiently serious. They don't send out these orders for nothing."

"But what is it then? What is it? *I* don't know what we've done. Have we no right to know what you accuse us of?"

"No, you have no right to know anything further than what is said in the order." And he folded up the said official foolscap, and handed it officially to Somers. Richard silently took it and read it again.

"But it's monstrous! What have they against us? We live here simply—we do nothing at all that they can charge us with. What have we done?" cried Harriet.

"I don't know what you've done. But we can take no risks in these times—and evidently there is a risk in leaving you here."

"But I should like to know *what?*" cried Harriet.

"That I cannot tell you."

"But do you *know?*" woman-like, she persisted.

"No, I don't even know," he replied coldly.

Harriet broke into a few tears of fright, fear, and chagrin.

"Have we no rights at all?" she cried, furious.

"Be quiet," said Richard to her.

"Yes. It is your duty to serve your country, if it is your country, by every means in your power. If you choose to put yourself under suspicion——"

"Suspicion of what?"

"I tell you, I do not know, and could not tell you even if I did know."

The foul, loutish detectives meanwhile were fumbling around, taking the books off the shelves and looking inside the clock. Somers watched them with a cold eye.

"Is this yours?" said one of the louts, producing a book with queer diagrams.

"Yes, it's a botany notebook," said Somers coldly.

The man secured it.

"He can learn the structure of moulds and parasites," said Richard bitterly to Harriet.

"The house is all open, the men can search everything?" asked the officer coldly.

"You know it is," said Somers. "You tried yesterday while we were out." Then he asked, "Who is responsible for this? Whom can I write to?"

"You can write to Major Witham, Headquarters, Southern Division, Salisbury, if it will do any good," was the answer.

There was a pause. Somers wrote it down: not in his address book because that was gone.

"And one is treated like this for nothing," cried Harriet, again in tears. "For nothing, but just because I wasn't born English. Yet one has married an Englishman, and they don't let one live anywhere but in England."

"It is more than that. It is more than the fact that you are not English born," said the officer.

"Then what? What?" she cried.

He refused to answer this time. The police-sergeant looked on with troubled blue eyes.

"Nothing. It's nothing but that, because it *can't* be," wept Harriet. "It can't be anything else, because we've never done anything else. Just because one wasn't born in England—as if one could help that. And to be persecuted like this, for nothing, for nothing else. And not even openly accused! Not even that." She wiped her tears, half enjoying it now. The police-sergeant looked into the road. One of the louts clumped downstairs and began to look once more among the books.

"That'll do here!" said the officer quietly to the detective lout. But the detective lout wasn't going to be ordered, and persisted.

"This your sketch-book, Mr. Somers?" said the lout.

"No, those are Lady Hermione Rogers' sketches," said Somers, with derision. And the lout stuffed the book back.

"And why don't they let us go away?" cried Harriet. "Why don't they let us go to America? We don't *want* to be here if we are a nuisance. We want to go right away. Why won't they even let us do that!" She was all tear-marked now.

"They must have their reasons," said the young officer, who was getting more and more uncomfortable. He again tried to hurry up the detective lout. But they were enjoying nosing round among other people's privacies.

"And what'll happen to us if we don't go, if we just stay?" said Harriet, being altogether a female.

"You'd better not try," said the young man grimly, so utterly confident in the absoluteness of the powers and the rightness he represented. And Somers would have liked to hit him across the mouth for that.

"Hold your tongue, Harriet," he said, turning on her fiercely. "You've said enough now. Be still, and let them do what they like, since they've the power to do it."

And Harriet was silent. And in the silence only the louts rummaging among the linen, and one looking into the bread-tin and into the tea-caddy. Somers watched them with a cold eye, and that queer slight lifting of his nose, rather like a dog when it shows disgust. And the officer again tried to hurry the louts, in his low tone of command, which had so little effect.

"Where do you intend to go?" said the officer to Somers.

"Oh, just to London," said Somers, who did not feel communicative.

"I suppose they will send the things back that they take?" he said, indicating the louts.

"I should think so—anything that is not evidence."

The louts were drawing to an end: it was nearly over.

"Of course this has nothing to do with me: I have to obey orders, no matter what they are," said the young officer, half apologising.

Somers just looked at him, but did not answer. His face was pale and still and distant, unconscious that the other people were real human beings. To him they were not: they were just *things*, obeying orders. And his eyes showed that. The young officer wanted to get out.

At last it was over: the louts had collected a very few trifles. The officer saw them on to the road, bade them good-morning, and got out of the house as quick as he could.

"Good-morning, sir! Good-morning, mam!" said the police-sergeant in tones of sympathy.

Yes, it was over. Harriet and Lovat looked at one another in silent consternation.

"Well, we must just go," she said.

"Oh yes," he replied.

And she studied the insolent notice to quit the area of Cornwall. In her heart of hearts she was not sorry to quit it. It had become too painful.

In a minute up came one of the farm girls to hear the news: then later Somers went down. Arthur, the boy, had heard the officer say to the police-sergeant as he went up the hill:

"Well, that's a job I'd rather not have had to do."

Harriet was alternately bitter and mocking: but badly shocked. Somers had had in his pocket the words of one of the Hebridean folk songs which Sharpe had brought down, and which they all thought so wonderful. On a bit of paper in his jacket pocket, the words which have no meaning in any language apparently, but are just vocal, almost animal sounds: the Seal Woman's Song—this they had taken.

> "Ver mi hiu—ravo na la vo—
> Ver mi hiu—ravo hovo i—
> Ver mi hiu—ravo na la vo—an catal—
> Traum—san jechar——"

What would the investigation make of this? What, oh, what? Harriet loved to think of it. Somers really expected to be examined under torture, to make him confess. The only obvious word—Traum—pure German.

The day was Friday: they must leave on Monday by the Great Western express. Started a bitter rush of packing. Somers, so sick of things, had a great fire of all his old manuscripts. They decided to leave the house as it was, the books on the shelves, to take only their personal belongings. For Somers was determined to come back. Until he had made up his mind to this, he felt paralysed. He loved the place so much. Ever since the conscription suspense began he had said to himself, when he walked up the wild, little road from his cottage to the moor: shall I see the foxgloves come out? If only I can stay till the foxgloves come. And he had seen the foxgloves come. Then it was the heather—would he see the heather? And then the primroses in the hollow down to the sea: the tufts and tufts of primroses, where the fox stood and looked at him.

Lately, however, he had begun to feel secure, as if he had sunk some of himself into the earth there, and were rooted for ever. His very soul seemed to have sunk into that Cornwall, that wild place under the moors. And now he must tear himself out. He was quite paralysed, could scarcely move. And at the farm they all looked at him with blank faces. He went back to the cottage to burn more manuscripts and pack up.

And then, like a revelation, he decided he would come back. He would use all his strength, put himself against all the authorities, and in a month or two he would come back. Before the snowdrops came in the farm garden.

"I shall be back in a month or two—three months," he said to everybody, and they looked at him.

But John Thomas said to him:

"You remember you said you would never drive to town again. Eh?" And in the black, bright eyes Somers saw that it was so. Yet he persisted.

"It only meant not yet awhile."

On the Monday morning he went down to say good-bye at the farm. It was a bitter moment, he was so much attached to them. And they to him. He could not bear to go. Only one was not there—the Uncle James. Many a time Somers wondered why Uncle James had gone down the fields, so as not to say good-bye.

John Thomas was driving them down in the trap—Arthur had taken the gig luggage in the cart. The family at the farm did everything they could. Somers never forgot that while he and Harriet were slaving, on the Sunday, to get things packed, John Thomas came up with their dinners, from the farm Sunday dinner.

It was a lovely, lovely morning as they drove across the hill-slopes above the sea: Harriet and Somers and John Thomas. In spite of themselves they felt cheerful. It seemed like an adventure.

"I don't know," said John Thomas, "but I feel in myself as if it was all going to turn out for the best." And he smiled in his bright, wondering way.

"So do I," cried Harriet. "As if we were going to be more free."

"As if we were setting out on a long adventure," said Somers.

They drove through the town, where, of course, they were marked people. But it was curious how little they cared, how indifferent they felt to everybody.

At the station Somers bade good-bye to John Thomas, with whom he had been such friends.

"Well, I wonder when we shall see each other again," said the young farmer.

"Soon. We will *make* it soon," said Somers. "We will *make* it soon. And you can come to London to see us."

"Well—if I can manage it—there's nothing would please me better," replied the other. But even as he said it, Somers was thinking of the evening in town, when he and Ann had been kept waiting so long. And he knew he would not see John Thomas again soon.

During the long journey up to London, Somers sat facing Harriet, quite still. The train was full: soldiers and sailors from Plymouth. One naval man talked to Harriet: bitter like all the rest. As soon as a man began to talk seriously, it was in bitterness. But many were beginning to make a mock of their own feelings even. Songs like "Good-byeeee" had taken the place of "Bluebells," and marked the change.

But Somers sat there feeling he had been killed: perfectly still, and pale, in a kind of after death, feeling he had been killed. He had always *believed* so in everything—society, love, friends. This was one of his serious deaths in belief. So he sat with his immobile face of a crucified Christ who makes no complaint, only broods silently and alone, remote. This face distressed Harriet horribly. It made her feel lost and shipwrecked, as if her heart was destined to break also. And she was in rather good spirits really. Her horror had been that she would be interned in one of the horrible camps, away from Somers. She had far less belief than he in the goodness of mankind. And she was rather relieved to get out of Cornwall. She had felt herself under a pressure there, long suffering. That very pressure he had loved so much. And so, while his still, fixed, crucified face distressed her horribly, at the same time it made her angry. What did he want to look like that for? Why didn't he show fight?

They came to London, and he tried taxi after taxi before he could get one to take them up to Hampstead. He had written to a staunch friend, and asked her to wire if she would receive them for a day or two. She wired that she would. So they went to her house. She was a little delicate lady who reminded Somers of his mother, though she was younger than his mother would have been. She and her husband had been friends of William Morris in those busy days of incipient Fabianism. Now her husband was sick, and she lived with him and a nurse and her grown-up daughter in a little old house in Hampstead.

Mrs. Redburn was frightened, receiving the tainted Somers. But she had pluck. Everybody in London was frightened at this time, everybody who was not a rabid and disgusting so-called patriot. It was a reign of terror. Mrs. Redburn was a staunch little soul, but she was bewildered: and she was frightened. They did such horrible things to you, the authorities. Poor tiny Hattie, with her cameo face, like a wise child, and her grey, bobbed hair. Such a frail little thing to have gone sailing these seas of ideas, and to suffer the awful breakdown of her husband. A tiny little woman with grey, bobbed hair and wide, unyielding eyes. She had three great children. It all seemed a joke and a tragedy mixed to her. And now the war. She was just bewildered, and would not live long. Poor, frail, tiny Hattie, receiving the Somers into her still, tiny old house. Both Richard and Harriet loved her. He had pledged himself, in some queer way, to keep a place in his heart for her for ever, even when she was dead. Which he did.

But he suffered from London. It was cold, heavy, foggy weather, and he pined for his cottage, the granite-strewn, gorse-grown slope from the moors to the sea. He could not bear Hampstead Heath now. In his eyes he saw the farm below—grey, naked, stony, with the big, pale-roofed new barn—and the network of dark green fields with the pale-grey walls—and the gorse and the sea. Torture of nostalgia. He craved to be back, his soul was there. He wrote passionately to John Thomas.

Richard and Harriet went to a police station for the first time in their lives. They went and reported themselves. The police at the station knew nothing about them and said they needn't have come. But next day a great policeman thumping at Hattie's door, and were some people called Somers staying there? It was explained to the policeman that they had already reported—but he knew nothing of it.

Somers wanted as quickly as possible to find rooms, to take the burden from Hattie. The American wife of an English friend, a poet serving in the army, offered her rooms in Mecklenburgh Square, and the third day after their arrival in London Somers and Harriet moved there: very grateful indeed to the American girl. They had no money. But the young woman tossed the rooms to them, and food and fuel, with a wild free hand. She was beautiful, reckless, one of the poetesses whose poetry Richard feared and wondered over.

Started a new life: anguish of nostalgia for Cornwall, from Somers. Wandering in the King's Cross Road or Theobald's Road, seeing his cottage and the road going up to the moors. He wrote twice to the headquarters at Salisbury insisting on being allowed to return. Came a reply, this could not be permitted. Then one day a man called and left a book and the little bundle of papers—a handful only—which the detectives had confiscated. A poor little show. Even the scrap of paper with *Ver mi hiu*. Again Somers wrote—but to no effect. Came a letter from John Thomas describing events in the west—the last Somers ever had from his friend.

Then Sharpe came up to London: it was too lonely down there. And they had some gay evenings. Many people came to see Somers. But Sharpe said to him:

"They're watching you still. There were two policemen near the door watching who came in."

There was an atmosphere of terror all through London, as under the Czar when no man dared open his mouth. Only this time it was the lowest orders of mankind spying on the upper orders, to drag them down.

One evening there was a gorgeous commotion in Somers' rooms, four poets and three non-poets, all fighting out poetry: a splendid time. Somers ran down the stairs in the black dark—no lights in the hall—to open the door. He opened quickly—three policemen in the porch. They slipped out before they could be spoken to.

Harriet and Somers had reported at Bow Street—wonderful how little heed the police took of them. Somers could tell how the civil police loathed being under the military orders.

But watched and followed he knew he was. After two months the American friend needed her rooms. The Somers transferred to Kensington, to a flat belonging to Sharpe's mother. Again many friends came. One evening Sharpe was called out from the drawing-room: detectives in the hall enquiring about Somers, where he got his money from, etc., etc., such clowns, louts, mongrels of detectives. Even Sharpe laughed in their faces: such *canaille*. At the same time detectives inquiring for them at the old address: though they had reported the change. Such a confusion in the official mind!

It was becoming impossible. Somers wrote bitterly to friends who had been all-influential till lately, but whom the *canaille* were now trying to taint also. And then he and Harriet moved to a little cottage he rented from his dear Hattie, in Oxfordshire. Once more they reported to the police in the market-town: once more the police sympathetic.

"I will report no more," said Somers.

But still he knew he was being watched all the time. Strange men questioning the cottage woman next door, as to all his doings. He began to *feel* a criminal. A sense of guilt, of self-horror began to grow up in him. He saw himself set apart from mankind, a Cain, or worse. Though of course he had committed no murder. But what might he not have done? A leper, a criminal! The foul, dense, carrion-eating mob were trying to set their teeth in him. Which meant mortification and death.

It was Christmas—winter—very cold. He and Harriet were very poor. Then he became ill. He lay in the tiny bedroom looking at the wintry sky and the deep, thatched roof of the cottage beyond. Sick. But then his soul revived. "No," he said to himself. "No. Whatever I do or have done, I am not wrong. Even if I commit what they call a crime, why should I accept *their* condemnation or verdict. Whatever I do, I do of my own responsible self. I refuse their imputations. I despise them. They are *canaille*, carrion-eating, filthy-mouthed *canaille*, like dead-men-devouring jackals. I wish to God I could kill them. I wish I had power to blight them, to slay them with a blight, slay them in thousands and thousands. I wish to God I could kill them off, the masses of *canaille*. Would they make me feel in the wrong? Would they? They shall not. Never. I will watch that they never set their unclean teeth in me, for a bite is blood-poisoning. But fear them! Feel in the wrong because of them? Never. Not if I were Cain several times over, and had killed several brothers and sisters as well. Not if I had committed all the crimes in their calendar. I will not be put in the wrong by them, God knows I will not. And I will report myself no more at their police-stations."

So, whenever the feeling of terror came over him, the feeling of being marked out, branded, a criminal marked out by society, marked out for annihilation, he pulled himself together, saying to himself:

"I am letting them make me feel in the wrong. I am degrading myself by feeling guilty, marked out, and I have convulsions of fear. But I am *not* wrong. I have done no wrong, whatever I have done. That is, no wrong that society has to do with. Whatever wrongs I have done are my own, and private between myself and the other person. One may be wrong, yes, one is often wrong. But not for *them* to judge. For my own soul only to judge. Let me know them for human filth, all these pullers-down, and let me watch them, as I would watch a reeking hyena, but never fear them. Let me watch them, to keep them at bay. But let me never admit for one single moment that *they* may be *my* judges. That, never. I have judged them: they are *canaille*. I am a man, and I abide by my own soul. Never shall they have a chance of judging me."

So he discovered the great secret: to stand alone as his own judge of himself absolutely. He took his stand absolutely on his own judgment of himself. Then, the mongrel-mouthed world would say and do what it liked. This is the greatest secret of behaviour: to stand alone, and judge oneself from the deeps of one's own soul. And then, to know, to hear what the others say and think: to refer their judgment to the touchstone of one's own soul-judgment. To fear one's own inward soul, and never to fear the outside world, nay, not even one single person, nor even fifty million persons.

To learn to be afraid of nothing but one's own deepest soul: but to keep a sharp eye on the millions of the others. Somers would say to himself: "There are fifty million people in Great Britain, and they would nearly all be against me. Let them."

So a period of quiet followed. Somers got no answers to his letters to John Thomas: it was like the evening when he had been kept waiting. The man was scared. It was an end.

And the authorities still would allow of no return to Cornwall. So let that be an end too. He wrote for his books and household linen to be sent up, the rest could be sold.

Bitter, in Oxfordshire, to unpack the things he had loved so dearly in Cornwall. Life would never be quite the same again. Then let it be otherwise. He hardened his heart and his soul.

It was a lovely spring: and here, in the heart of England— Shakespeare's England—there was a sweetness and a humanness that he had never known before. The people were friendly and unsuspicious, though they knew all about the trouble. The police too were delicate and kindly. It was a human world once more, human and lovely: though the gangs of woodmen were cutting down the trees, baring the beautiful spring woods, making logs for trench-props.

And there was always the suspense of being once more called up for military service. "But surely," thought Somers, "if I am so vile they will be glad to leave me alone."

Spring passed on. Somers' sisters were alone, their husbands at the war. His younger sister took a cottage for him in their own bleak Derbyshire. And so he returned, after six years, to his own country. A bitter stranger too, he felt. It was northern, and the industrial spirit was permeated through everything: the alien spirit of coal and iron. People living for coal and iron, nothing else. What good was it all?

This time he would not go to the police-station to report. So one day a police-inspector called. But he was a kindly man, and a little bitter too. Strange that among the civil police, everyone that Somers met was kindly and understanding. But the so-called, brand-new military, they were insolent jackanapes, especially the stay-at-home military who had all the authority in England.

In September, on his birthday, came the third summons: On His Majesty's Service. His Majesty's Service, God help us! Somers was bidden present himself at Derby on a certain date, to join the colours. He replied, "If I am turned out of my home, and forbidden to enter the area of Cornwall: if I am forced to report myself to the police wherever I go, and am treated like a criminal, you surely cannot wish me to present myself to join the colours."

There was an interval: much correspondence with Bodmin, where they seemed to have forgotten him again. Then he received a notice that he was to present himself as ordered.

What else was there to do? But he was growing devilish inside himself. However, he went: and Harriet accompanied him to the town. The recruiting place was a sort of big Sunday School—you went down a little flight of steps from the road. In a smallish ante-room like a basement he sat on a form and waited while all his papers were filed. Beside him sat a big collier, about as old as himself. And the man's face was a study of anger and devilishness growing under humiliation. After an hour's waiting Somers was called. He stripped as usual, but this time was told to put on his jacket over his complete nakedness.

And so—he was shown into a high, long school-room with various sections down one side—bits of screens where various doctor-fellows were performing—and opposite, a long writing-table where clerks and old military buffers in uniform sat in power: the clerks dutifully scribbling, glad to be in a safe job, no doubt, the old military buffers staring about. Near this Judgment-Day table a fire was burning, and there was a bench where two naked men sat ignominiously waiting, trying to cover their nakedness a little with their jackets, but too much upset to care really.

"Good God!" thought Somers. "Naked civilised men in their Sunday jackets and nothing else make the most heaven-forsaken sight I have ever seen."

The big stark-naked collier was being measured: a big, gaunt, naked figure, with a gruesome sort of nudity. "Oh, God, oh God," thought Somers, "why do the animals none of them look like this? It doesn't look like life, like a living creature's figure. It is gruesome, with no life-meaning."

In another section a youth of about twenty-five, stark naked too, was throwing out his chest while a chit of a doctor-fellow felt him between the legs. This naked young fellow evidently thought himself an athlete, and that he must make a good impression, so he threw his head up in a would-be noble attitude, and coughed bravely when the doctor-buffoon said cough! Like a piece of furniture waiting to be sat on, the athletic young man looked.

Across the room the military buffers looked on at the operetta; occasionally a joke, incomprehensible, at the expense of the naked, was called across from the military papas to the fellows who may have been doctors. The place was full of an indescribable tone of jeering, gibing shamelessness. Somers stood in his street jacket and thin legs and beard—a sight enough for any gods—and waited his turn. Then he took off the jacket and was cleanly naked, and stood to be measured and weighed—being moved about like a block of meat, in the atmosphere of corrosive derision.

Then he was sent to the next section for eye-tests, and jokes were called across the room. Then after a time to the next section, where he was made to hop on one foot—then on the other foot—bend over —and so on: apparently to see if he had any physical deformity.

In due course to the next section where a fool of a little fellow, surely no doctor, eyed him up and down and said:

"Anything to complain of?"

"Yes," said Somers. "I've had pneumonia three times and been threatened with consumption."

"Oh. Go over there then."

So in his stalky, ignominious nakedness he was sent over to another section, where an elderly fool turned his back on him for ten minutes, before looking round and saying:

"Yes. What have you to say?"

Somers repeated.

"When did you have pneumonia?"

Somers answered—he could hardly speak, he was in such a fury of rage and humiliation.

"What doctor said you were threatened with consumption? Give his name." This in a tone of sneering scepticism.

The whole room was watching and listening. Somers knew his appearance had been anticipated, and they wanted to count him out. But he kept his head. The elderly fellow then proceeded to listen to his heart and lungs with a stethoscope, jabbing the end of the instrument against the flesh as if he wished to make a pattern on it. Somers kept a set face. He knew what he was out against, and he just hated and despised them all.

The fellow at length threw the stethoscope aside as if he were throwing Somers aside, and went to write. Somers stood still, with a set face, and waited.

Then he was sent to the next section, and the stethoscoping doctor strolled over to the great judgment table. In the final section was a young puppy, like a chemist's assistant, who made most of the jokes. Jokes were all the time passing across the room—but Somers had the faculty of becoming quite deaf to anything that might disturb his equanimity.

The chemist-assistant puppy looked him up and down with a small grin as if to say, "Law-lummy, what a sight of a human scarecrow!" Somers looked him back again, under lowered lids, and the puppy left off joking for the moment. He told Somers to take up other attitudes. Then he came forward close to him, right till their bodies almost touched, the one in a navy blue serge, holding back a little as if from the contagion of the naked one. He put his hand beween Somers' legs, and pressed it upwards, under the genitals. Somers felt his eyes going black.

"Cough," said the puppy. He coughed.

"Again," said the puppy. He made a noise in his throat, then turned aside in disgust.

"Turn round," said the puppy. "Face the other way."

Somers turned and faced the shameful monkey-faces at the long table. So, he had his back to the tall window: and the puppy stood plumb behind him.

"Put your feet apart."

He put his feet apart.

"Bend forward—further—further——"

Somers bent forward, lower, and realised that the puppy was standing aloof behind him to look into his anus. And that this was the source of the wonderful jesting that went on all the time.

"That will do. Get your jacket and go over there."

Somers put on his jacket and went and sat on the form that was placed endwise at the side of the fire, facing the side of the judgment table. The big, gaunt collier was still being fooled. He apparently was not very intelligent, and didn't know what they meant when they told him to bend forward. Instead of bending with stiff knees—not knowing at all what they wanted—he crouched down, squatting on his heels as colliers do. And the doctor puppy, amid the hugest amusement, had to start him over again. So the game went on, and Somers watched them all.

The collier was terrible to him. He had a sort of Irish face with a short nose and a thin black head. This snub-nose face had gone quite blank with a ghastly voidness, void of intelligence, bewildered and blind. It was as if the big, ugly, powerful body could not *obey* words any more. Oh God, such an ugly body—not as if it belonged to a living creature.

Somers kept himself hard and in command, face set, eyes watchful. He felt his cup had been filled now. He watched these buffoons in this great room, as he sat there naked save for his jacket, and he felt that from his heart, from his spine went out vibrations that should annihilate them—blot them out, the *canaille*, stamp them into the mud they belonged to.

He was called at length to the table.

"What is your name?" asked one of the old parties. Somers looked at him.

"Somers," he said, in a very low tone.

"Somers—Richard Lovat?" with an indescribable sneer.

Richard Lovat realised that they had got their knife into him. So! He had his knife in them, and it would strike deeper at last.

"You describe yourself as a writer."

He did not answer.

"A writer of what?"—with a perfect sneer.

"Books—essays."

The old buffer went on writing. Oh, yes, they intended to make him feel they had got their knife into him. They would have his beard off, too! But would they! He stood there with his ridiculous thin legs, in his ridiculous jacket, but he did not feel a fool. Oh, God, no. The white composure of his face, the slight lifting of his nose, like a dog's disgust, the heavy unshakeable watchfulness of his eyes brought even the judgment table to silence: even the puppy doctors. It was not till he was walking out of the room, with his jacket about his thin legs, and his beard in front of him, that they lifted their heads for a final jeer.

He dressed and waited for his card. It was Saturday morning, and he was almost the last man to be examined. He wondered what instructions they had had about him. Oh, foul dogs. But they were very close on him now, very close. They were grinning very close behind him, like hyenas just going to bite. Yes, they were running him to earth. They had exposed all his nakedness to gibes. And they were pining, almost whimpering to give the last grab at him, and haul him to earth, a victim. Finished!

But not yet! Oh, no, not yet. Not yet, not now, nor ever. Not while life was life, should they lay hold of him. Never again. Never would he be touched again. And because they had handled his private parts, and looked into them, their eyes should burst and their hands should wither and their hearts should rot. So he cursed them in his blood, with an unremitting curse, as he waited.

They gave him his card: C 2. Fit for non-military service. He knew what they would like to make him do. They would like to seize him and compel him to empty latrines in some camp. They had that in mind for him. But he had other things in mind.

He went out into accursed Derby, to Harriet. She was reassured again. But he was not. He hated the Midlands now, he hated the North. They were viler than the South, even than Cornwall. They had a universal desire to take life and down it: these horrible machine people, these iron and coal people. They wanted to set their foot absolutely on life, grind it down, and be masters. Masters, as they were of the foul machines. Masters of life, as they were masters of steam-power and electric-power and above all, of money-power. Masters of money-power, with an obscene hatred of life, true spontaneous life.

Another flight. He was determined not to stop in the Derby Military Area. He would move one stage out of their grip, at least. So he and Harriet prepared to go back with their trunks to the Oxfordshire cottage, which they loved. He would not report, nor give any sign of himself. Fortunately in the village everybody was slack and friendly.

Derby had been a crisis. He would obey no more: not one more stride. If they summoned him he would disappear: or find some means of fighting them. But no more obedience: no more presenting himself when called up. By God, no! Never while he lived, again, would he be at the disposal of society.

Emily Dickinson

"Much Madness"

> Much madness is divinest sense
> To a discerning eye;
> Much sense the starkest madness.
> 'Tis the majority
> In this, as all, prevails.
> Assent, and you are sane;
> Demur,—you're straightway dangerous,
> And handled with a chain.

THE POLITICS OF UTOPIA

Paul Goodman

From *Parents Day*

At the Staff Meeting, the principal discussion turned on whether or not Donald Torgesson should be permitted to go home during the weekend to visit his mother. He was in the Second Group, and their teacher was Caroline Brandywine, a plain colorless young woman.

In meticulous detail Caroline explained the situation in the Second Group. When somebody went home, the little clique, the two Jimmies and Steve, began masturbating, and they tortured the children in Group I. . . . Donald had a good relationship with his mother, but then he himself was thrown off when he returned, and

Reprinted by permission of the author.

boasted, this hurt; but if she would put it up to him not to boast because it hurt the others' feelings, he would be sensitive and intelligent enough to cooperate. This would have the effect of deepening his understanding of the social group. But it was too much to ask of him to sacrifice the trip altogether. On the other hand, some, especially Shirley, brightened up when Donny came back and boasted.

Caroline's explanations were interminable not because anything was petty or irrelevant, but because taken as a whole they did not add up to a conclusion nor even to a dilemma. They had the ring of primary experience, either the infinity of creative possibility or the impassable morass of the facts of life (one could not tell which) . . .

I sat on the edge of my chair, enthralled by the concern of so many, more or less wise and expert, for an individual child, an individual act of an individual child. Being new, I had resolved to say nothing. I was sensitive of my importance and sensitive of my immodesty. The result of deciding to hold my peace in any eventuality was that the room buzzed about me and, sitting on the edge of the chair, I had a painful crick in the neck. . . .

Lawrence Dixon rubbed his palms wildly and sprang up and began to prowl. I looked at him in disgust. "In such a case," he giggled, "we cannot penalize happiness! Young Torgesson has a good relationship with his mother. That's his good luck. We must support the positive side. We cannot afford to quench radiance. It shines far. Shirley Thomas is made happy by it in turn. Do you want to reduce excellence to the level of misery? Hm. Hm.

"Furthermore, this happens after every Parents Day." He unaccountably giggled. "It takes a week before they settle down. I say, Good! Excellent! We do not want the troubles kept under. Let them out! It is an invaluable opportunity. What's more trouble for us in the short run is better for them in the long run. We have to live in the world we make, we and our children's children."

This astonishing speeech, full of the creator spirit, raised me to a glow of glory. "Yes! yes!" I wheezed. The others were more accustomed to Dixon's high style.

To me it was an infallible sign if a person said one true thing, for nothing comes from nothing, and the proposition, "we must not penalize happiness," was true. I gave my allegiance to Dixon. But what the devil was he giggling about?

"It's very well," said Caroline dissatisfied. "But I have only two hands, even if I weigh 130 pounds."

"You take out your aggressions on the children," said Dixon.

"Lawrence!" cried some one, shocked.

"That's the meanest remark you ever made to me, Lawrence Dixon," said Caroline. "You could have said it in private."

"I'm sorry," said Dixon, confused.

Bernardine brought cups and a pitcher of tea and at once everything became sociable. I was bewildered.

"What was the decision about Donny?" I asked Dolly Homers. "Is there no vote?"

"Vote? If there's a difference of opinion, it's permissive."

"Permissive to whom?"

"To Donny, of course."

"Ah. Does Dixon always carry?"

"No. But he's usually right. You'll see."

—I was not so sure. He spoke too close to my own sentiments, and my sentiments were suspect to me. Nevertheless, I was suffused with joy and pride at what seemed to me to be the big fact: that there was no vote! because all of us wanted, in a well-intentioned way, to reach unanimity. The aim of the discussion was to conjure up the good idea that all would spontaneously assent to. That there was this aim proved that there was a basis of mutual love.

"It is a beautiful meeting," I said, moved, to Mark Anders. "I never sat at a more beautiful meeting."

Chapter IV

Ends and Means

In general, problems of political action are not easily resolved by a simple intellectual formula. This proposition is especially true with regard to the age-old problem of ends and means—the basic problem of choice, and thus of action, in political life.

Two common solutions to that problem are these: (1) The ends justify the means. This broad statement is usually associated with the name of Machiavelli; yet warrant for it can be found as well in the Biblical injunction, "By their fruits shall ye know them." (2) The ends never justify the means, if the means are evil: a statement associated with the doctrine of pacifism and with the practices of some Christian sects and some Eastern religions. Neither of these simple answers is, unfortunately, wholly satisfactory. This is demonstrated dramatically by Arthur Koestler in his imagined dialogue between the old Bolshevik Rubashov and his interrogator Ivanov, who wishes him, "for the good of the Party," to confess to crimes he never committed. Most of the dilemmas one faces in trying to justify one or the other of these conflicting philosophies of choice are confronted by Koestler; we mention some of them here, more prosaically, by way of introduction to this topic.

If, to begin with, it is literally true that the ends justify the means, then, as Ivan Karamazov asserts (see Chapter IX), anything goes, nothing is forbidden, and neither law nor morality can be truly legitimate. Perhaps one cannot argue with this position on logical grounds—one cannot "prove" it is false, because it is not clear how ethical doctrines can be proved either true or false. But it is possible to point out the consequences of such a doctrine; and when confronted with these, very few thinkers or actors in history (Machiavelli not excluded) have been willing to uphold such a philosophy as consistently as Ivanov—to dispense with Thou shalt not's completely. Most people, in conversation as well as in writing, prove in the end to have at least some minimal conception of things that simply should not be done, as is true even of Hoederer, the committed Communist Party leader in Jean-Paul Sartre's Dirty Hands. This suggests that, paradoxically, a doctrine which is justified on the basis chiefly of its practicality is itself ultimately impractical—that is, most people cannot live by it.

In addition, there are some grave theoretical problems with what seems at first glance to be an uncomplicated belief. Who, for example, is to judge whether and on what grounds ends themselves are worthy, or how their value is established? Every man for himself? The result surely would be a chaos of might makes right, such as is described in Hobbes's picture of the state of nature—but no other obvious answer presents itself. Furthermore, we can never be sure, being fallible, that the ends we seek are really destined to be brought into being; nor can we be sure that when we achieve them they will be as we thought they would be. For it is a truism by now that means mold ends as well as lead to them; that in fact the two concepts are not easily separable; that sometimes in the heat of action our means become our ends; that at other times "ends" for which the most awesome sacrifices were made turn out to have been merely "means" to some still higher and unattained "end." In fact, then, the doctrine that the end justifies the means is both psychologically and theoretically unsophisticated, raises as many problems for action as it solves, and is an unsatisfactory answer to the question, How are we to behave in making political choices?

On the other hand, to say the ends never justify the means if the means are evil is, quite evidently, as Ivanov points out to Rubashov, to turn the field of effective political action over to those who have no such scruples. Such a total renunciation of the desire to be effective—a position supported by Koestler himself in a later essay titled "The Yogi and the Commissar"—can certainly be justified, but only to saints, or to those whose relationship to life is much more otherworldly than is common in the modern world. Thus this position too is unlikely to be adhered to consistently in thought or action.

And like the "Machiavellian" position, furthermore, it also leads to theoretical difficulties. For the question has to be asked, Why must certain means be eschewed? If the answer is because they inevitably lead to evil results, then we have made a testable factual statement rather than taken a stand on principle—and it is a statement that most students of history would consider absurd. However, if we decry certain means because they are in principle intolerable no matter what results they lead to, we are really saying that the avoidance of such acts is itself an end, and we must now ask whether this end justifies the means necessary to achieve it. As Hoederer forcefully asks, does Hugo's personal desire for moral purity justify a refusal to work for the political power that his comrades value more highly? Or, to take another example subtly suggested by William Carlos Williams' short story "The Use of Force," does the "end" of nonparticipation in violence justify the refusal to come to the aid of someone to whom one has obligations? Once again we are left without a satisfactory guide in answering the question, How should we behave?

Discussions in political philosophy and philosophy generally have advanced very little on this subject over the centuries. Certain criteria for a sensible discussion of whether specific means of action are justified by the ends sought are easily imaginable and can be used to expose a really indefensible argument in favor of a given choice. Thus we always want to know something about the proximity or remoteness of the supposed ends with regard to the immediate action designed to bring them into being and about the probability that our actions will produce side-effects detrimental to other ends that we value highly. (The reader may feel that Bertolt Brecht in his poem "To Posterity" does not explore these questions to a satisfactory degree.) We also want to know something about the reasonableness of our valuations and perceptions—whether, that is, in a given situation we really need to accomplish the end in question as badly as we say we do —and about the likelihood that the means we choose will (as does capital punishment, for example) close down the possibility of later choosing alternative courses of action. It is sometimes said of this kind of situation that we lose control over the course of events, so that "violence begets further violence" or as in the case of Robert Penn Warren's All the King's Men, corruption begets further corruption. In addition, it is important to know the extent to which all less drastic channels of action have been realistically explored and if we are violating some general rule of conduct, the scope and importance of the rule violated.

These criteria, however, are exceedingly vague. In all our calculations, therefore, a large area of uncertainty remains, within which we are rarely able to prove to the satisfaction of everyone that a given end does or does not justify a given means. It is this grey area that the selections we have chosen here are meant to illuminate. Sartre on the ambiguous motives and rationales of political choice; Brecht on the claims of the future against the present; Yeats on revolutionary nationalism; Williams on the use of force; Warren on corruption—all explore different aspects of this fundamental problem in political philosophy.*

Two phrases stand out from among all these selections, in that they graphically illustrate how two-sided are all our techniques of governance and change: Yeats' "A terrible beauty is born" and Warren's "You're leaving me all alone with the sons-of-bitches." Anyone who could tell us definitively whether to judge those Irishmen and Irishwomen who led the Easter rising against English rule by the beauty or the terror that they wrought, or whether the morally upright Hugh Miller in All the King's Men should or should not be willing to work with "the sons-of-bitches," would be making a contribution of unparalleled magnitude to political philosophy.

* The reader should remember also that just as the perennial themes of political thought are always intermingled, so too must be the categories in which we have placed our selections. Thus there are important treatments of the ends-means problem to be found throughout this reader, among them the two selections from Dostoevski's *The Brothers Karamazov*, Isaac Babel's short story "Gedali," and in particular the excerpt on violence from Ramon Sender's *Seven Red Sundays* (the last two selections will be found in Chapter V, "Revolution").

THE NEW MACHIAVELLI

Arthur Koestler

From *Darkness at Noon*

He groaned in his sleep; the dream of his first arrest had come back; his hand, hanging slackly from the bed, strained for the sleeve of his dressing-gown; he waited for the blow to hit him at last, but it did not come.

Instead, he woke up, because the electric light in his cell was turned on suddenly. A figure stood next to his bed, looking at him. Rubashov could hardly have slept a quarter of an hour, but after that dream he always needed several minutes to find himself again. He blinked in the bright light, his mind worked laboriously through the habitual hypotheses, as though he were carrying out an unconscious ritual. He was in a cell; but not in the enemy country—that was only dreamed. So he was free—but the colour-print of No. 1 hanging over his bed was lacking, and over there stood the bucket. Besides, Ivanov was standing at his bedside and blowing cigarette smoke into his face. Was that also dreamed? No, Ivanov was real, the bucket was real. He was in his own country, but it had become an enemy country; and Ivanov, who had been his friend, had now also become an enemy; and the whimpering of Arlova was not a dream either. But no, it had not been Arlova, but Bogrov, who had been dragged past like a wax-doll; Comrade Bogrov, faithful unto the grave; and he had called out his name; that was not dreamed. Arlova, on the other hand, had said: "You can do whatever you like with me. . . ."

"Do you feel ill?" asked Ivanov.

Rubashov blinked at him, blinded by the light. "Give me my dressing-gown," he said.

Ivanov watched him. The right side of Rubashov's face was swollen. "Would you like some brandy?" Ivanov asked. Without waiting for a reply, he hobbled to the spy-hole and called out something into the corridor. Rubashov's eyes followed him, blinking. His dazedness would not go. He was awake, but he saw, heard and thought in a mist.

"Have you been arrested too?" he asked.

"No," said Ivanov quietly. "I only came to visit you. I think you have a temperature."

"Give me a cigarette," said Rubashov. He inhaled deeply once or twice, and his gaze became clearer. He lay down again, smoking, and looked at the ceiling. The cell door opened; the warder brought a bottle of brandy and a glass. This time it was not the old man, but a lean youth in uniform, with steel-rimmed spectacles. He saluted Ivanov, handed the brandy and glass over to him and shut the door from outside. One heard his steps receding down the corridor.

Ivanov sat down on the edge of Rubashov's bunk and filled the glass. "Drink," he said. Rubashov emptied the glass. The mistiness in his head cleared, events and persons—his first and second imprisonment, Arlova, Bogrov, Ivanov—arranged themselves in time and space.

"Are you in pain?" asked Ivanov.

"No," said Rubashov. The only thing he did not yet understand was what Ivanov was doing in his cell.

"Your cheek is badly swollen. Probably you also have a temperature."

Rubashov stood up from the bunk, looked through the spy-hole into the corridor, which was empty, and walked up and down the cell once or twice until his head became quite clear. Then he stopped in front of Ivanov, who was sitting on the end of the bunk, patiently blowing smoke-rings.

"What are you doing here?" he asked.

"I want to talk to you," Ivanov said. "Lie down again and drink some more brandy."

Rubashov blinked at him ironically through his pince-nez. "Until now," he said, "I was tempted to believe you were acting in good faith. Now I see that you are a swine. Get out of here."

Ivanov did not move. "Be good enough to give the reasons for this assertion," he said.

Rubashov leaned his back against the wall of No. 406 and looked down at Ivanov. Ivanov was smoking with equanimity.

"Point one," said Rubashov. "You knew of my friendship with Bogrov. Therefore you take care that Bogrov—or what was left of him—is taken past my cell on his last journey, as a reminder. To make sure that I do not miss this scene, Bogrov's execution is discreetly announced beforehand, on the assumption that this news will be tapped through to me by my neighbours, which, in fact, happens. A further finesse of the producer's is to inform Bogrov of my presence here, just before he is dragged off—on the further assumption that this final shock will draw from him some audible manifestation; which also happens. The whole thing is calculated to put me into a state of depression. In this darkest hour, Comrade Ivanov appears as a saviour, with a bottle of brandy under his arm. Follows a touching scene of reconciliation, we fall into each other's arms, exchange moving war memories and incidentally sign the statement with my confession. Whereupon the prisoner sinks into a gentle slumber; Comrade Ivanov leaves on the tip of his toes with the statement in his pocket, and is promoted a few days later. . . . Now have the goodness to get out of here."

Ivanov did not move. He blew smoke into the air, smiled and showed his gold teeth. "Do you really think I have such a primitive mind?" he asked. "Or, to be more exact: do you really believe I am such a bad psychologist?"

Rubashov shrugged. "Your tricks disgust me," he said. "I cannot throw you out. If you have a trace of decency left in you, you will now leave me alone. You can't imagine how you all disgust me."

Ivanov lifted the glass from the floor, filled it and drank it. "I propose the following agreement," he said. "You let me speak for five minutes without interrupting me, and listen with a clear head to what I am saying. If after that you still insist on my going—I will go."

"I'm listening," said Rubashov. He stood leaning against the wall opposite Ivanov and glanced at his watch.

"In the first place," said Ivanov, "in order to remove any possible doubts or illusions you may have: Bogrov has in fact been shot. Secondly, he has been in prison for several months, and at the end was tortured for several days. If you mention this during the public trial, or even so much as tap it through to your neighbours, I am done for. About the reasons for treating Bogrov like that, we will speak later. Thirdly, it was intentional that he was taken past your cell, and intentional that he was told of your presence here. Fourthly, this filthy trick, as you call it, was not arranged by me, but by my colleague Gletkin, against my express instructions."

He paused, Rubashov stood leaning against the wall and said nothing.

"I should never have made such a mistake," Ivanov went on; "not out of any regard for your feelings, but because it is contrary to my tactics and to my knowledge of your psychology. You have recently shown a tendency to humanitarian scruples and other sentimentalities of that sort. Besides, the story of Arlova still lies on your stomach. The scene with Bogrov must only intensify your depression and moralistic leanings—that could be foreseen; only a bungler in psychology like Gletkin could have made such a mistake. Gletkin has been dinning into my ears for the last ten days that we should use 'hard methods' on you. For one thing, he doesn't like you because you showed him the holes in your socks; for another, he is used to dealing with peasants. . . . So much for the elucidation of the affair with Bogrov. The brandy, of course, I ordered because you were not in full possession of your wits when I came in. It is not in my interest to make you drunk. It is not in my interest to lay you open to mental shocks. All that only drives you further into your moral exaltation. I need you sober and logical. My only interest is that you should calmly think your case to a conclusion. For, when you have thought the whole thing to a conclusion—then, and only then, will you capitulate. . . ."

Rubashov shrugged his shoulders; but before he could say anything, Ivanov cut in:

"I know that you are convinced that you won't capitulate. Answer me only one thing: *if* you became convinced of the logical necessity and the objective rightness of capitulating—would you then do it?"

Rubashov did not answer at once. He felt dully that the conversation had taken a turn which he should not have allowed. The five minutes had passed, and he had not thrown out Ivanov. That alone, it seemed to him, was a betrayal of Bogrov—and of Arlova; and of Richard and Little Loewy.*

"Go away," he said to Ivanov. "It's no use." He noticed only now that he had for some time been walking up and down his cell in front of Ivanov.

Ivanov was sitting on the bunk. "By your tone of voice, I notice," he said, "that you recognize your mistake concerning my part in the Bogrov affair. Why, then, do you want me to go? Why don't you answer the question I asked? . . ." He bent forward a little and looked at Rubashov mockingly in the face; then he said slowly, emphasizing each word: "*Because you are afraid of me.* Because my way of thinking and of arguing is your own, and you are afraid

* Editors' note: See p. 199.

of the echo in your own head. In a moment you will be calling out: Get thee behind me, Satan. . . ."

Rubashov did not answer. He was walking to and fro by the window, in front of Ivanov. He felt helpless and incapable of clear argument. His consciousness of guilt, which Ivanov called "moral exaltation," could not be expressed in logical formulae—it lay in the realm of the "grammatical fiction." At the same time, every sentence spoken by Ivanov did in fact evoke an echo in him. He felt he ought never to have let himself be drawn into this discussion. He felt as if he were on a smooth, slanting plane, down which one slid irresistibly.

"*Apage Satanas!*" repeated Ivanov and poured himself out another glass of brandy. "In old days, temptation was of carnal nature. Now it takes the form of pure reason. The values change. I would like to write a Passion play in which God and the Devil dispute for the soul of Saint Rubashov. After a life of sin, he has turned to God— to a God with the double chin of industrial liberalism and the charity of the Salvation Army soups. Satan, on the contrary, is thin, ascetic and a fanatical devotee of logic. He reads Machiavelli, Ignatius of Loyola, Marx and Hegel; he is cold and unmerciful to mankind, out of a kind of mathematical mercifulness. He is damned always to do that which is most repugnant to him: to become a slaughterer, in order to abolish slaughtering, to sacrifice lambs so that no more lambs may be slaughtered, to whip people with knouts so that they may learn not to let themselves be whipped, to strip himself of every scruple in the name of a higher scrupulousness, and to challenge the hatred of mankind because of his love for it—an abstract and geometric love. *Apage Satanas!* Comrade Rubashov prefers to become a martyr. The columnists of the liberal Press, who hated him during his lifetime, will sanctify him after his death. He has discovered a conscience, and a conscience renders one as unfit for the revolution as a double chin. Conscience eats through the brain like a cancer, until the whole of the grey matter is devoured. Satan is beaten and withdraws—but don't imagine that he grinds his teeth and spits fire in his fury. He shrugs his shoulders; he is thin and ascetic; he has seen many weaken and creep out of his ranks with pompous pretexts. . . ."

Ivanov paused and poured himself another glass of brandy. Rubashov walked up and down in front of the window. After a while he said:

"Why did you execute Bogrov?"

"Why? Because of the submarine question," said Ivanov. "It concerned the problem of tonnage—an old quarrel, the beginnings of
which must be familiar to you.

"Bogrov advocated the construction of submarines of large tonnage and a long range of action. The Party is in favour of small
submarines with a short range. You can build three times as many
small submarines for your money as big ones. Both parties had valid
technical arguments. The experts made a big display of technical
sketches and algebraic formulae; but the actual problem lay in
quite a different sphere. Big submarines mean: a policy of aggression, to further world revolution. Small submarines mean: coastal
defense—that is, self-defense and postponement of world revolution.
The latter is the point of view of No. 1, and the Party.

"Bogrov had a strong following in the Admiralty and amongst the
officers of the old guard. It would not have been enough to put him
out of the way; he also had to be discredited. A trial was projected
to unmask the partisans of big tonnage as *saboteurs* and traitors.
We had already brought several little engineers to the point of being
willing to confess publicly to whatever we liked. But Bogrov
wouldn't play the game. He declaimed up to the very end of big
tonnage and world revolution. He was two decades behind the times.
He would not understand that the times are against us, that Europe
is passing through a period of reaction, that we are in the hollow of
a wave and must wait until we are lifted by the next. In a public
trial he would only have created confusion amongst the people.
There was no other way possible than to liquidate him adminis-
tratively. Would not you have done the same thing in our position?"

Rubashov did not answer. He stopped walking, and again remained leaning against the wall of No. 406, next to the bucket. A
cloud of sickening stench rose from it. He took off his pince-nez
and looked at Ivanov out of red-rimmed, hunted eyes.

"You did not hear him whimpering," he said.

Ivanov lit a new cigarette on the stump of the old one; he too
found the stench of the bucket rather overpowering.

"No," he said, "I did not hear it. But I have heard and seen similar things. What of it?"

Rubashov was silent. It was no use to try and explain it. The
whimpering and the muffled drumming again penetrated his ears,
like an echo. One could not express that. Nor the curve of Arlova's

breasts, with its warm, steep points. One could express nothing. "Die in silence," had been written on the message given him by the barber.

"What of it?" repeated Ivanov. He stretched out his leg and waited. As no answer came, he went on speaking:

"If I had a spark of pity for you," he said, "I would now leave you alone. But I have not a spark of pity. I drink; for a time, as you know, I drugged myself; but the vice of pity I have up till now managed to avoid. The smallest dose of it, and you are lost. Weeping over humanity and bewailing oneself—you know our race's pathological leaning to it. Our greatest poets destroyed themselves by this poison. Up to forty, fifty, they were revolutionaries—then they became consumed by pity and the world pronounced them holy. You appear to have the same ambition, and to believe it to be an individual process, personal to you, something unprecedented. . . ." He spoke rather louder and puffed out a cloud of smoke. "Beware of these ecstasies," he said: "Every bottle of spirits contains a measurable amount of ecstasy. Unfortunately, only few people, particularly amongst our fellow countrymen, ever realize that the ecstasies of humility and suffering are as cheap as those induced chemically. The time when I woke from the anaesthetic, and found that my body stopped at the left knee, I also experienced a kind of absolute ecstasy of unhappiness. Do you remember the lectures you gave me at the time?" He poured out another glass and emptied it.

"My point is this," he said; "one may not regard the world as a sort of metaphysical brothel for emotions. That is the first commandment for us. Sympathy, conscience, disgust, despair, repentance, and atonement are for us repellent debauchery. To sit down and let oneself be hypnotized by one's own navel, to turn up one's eyes and humbly offer the back of one's neck to Gletkin's revolver— that is an easy solution. The greatest temptation for the like of us is: to renounce violence, to repent, to make peace with oneself. Most great revolutionaries fell before this temptation, from Spartacus to Danton and Dostoevsky; they are the classical form of betrayal of the cause. The temptations of God were always more dangerous for mankind than those of Satan. As long as chaos dominates the world, God is an anachronism; and every compromise with one's own conscience is perfidy. When the accursed inner voice speaks to you, hold your hands over your ears. . . ."

He felt for the bottle behind him and poured out another glass.

Rubashov noticed that the bottle was already half empty. You also could do with a little solace, he thought.

"The greatest criminals in history," Ivanov went on, "are not of the type Nero and Fouché, but of the type Gandhi and Tolstoy. Gandhi's inner voice has done more to prevent the liberation of India than the British guns. To sell oneself for thirty pieces of silver is an honest transaction; but to sell oneself to one's own conscience is to abandon mankind. History is *a priori* amoral; it has no conscience. To want to conduct history according to the maxims of the Sunday school means to leave everything as it is. You know that as well as I do. You know the stakes in this game, and here you come talking about Bogrov's whimpering. . . ."

He emptied his glass and added:

"Or with conscience pricks because of your fat Arlova."

Rubashov knew from before that Ivanov could hold a lot; one did not notice any change in his behaviour, beyond a slightly more emphatic way of speaking than usual. You do need consolation, thought Rubashov again, perhaps more than I do. He sat down on the narrow stool opposite Ivanov and listened. All this was not new to him; he had defended the same point of view for years, with the same or similar words. The difference was that at that time he had known those inner processes of which Ivanov spoke so contemptuously, merely as an abstraction; but since then he had experienced the "grammatical fiction" as a physical reality in his own body. But had these irrational processes become more admissible merely because he had a personal acquaintance with them now? Was it any the less necessary to fight the "mystical intoxication" merely because one had oneself become intoxicated by it? When a year ago he had sent Arlova to her death, he had not had enough imagination to picture the details of an execution. Would he now behave differently merely because he now knew some of its aspects? Either it was right—or it was wrong to sacrifice Richard, Arlova and Little Loewy. But what had Richard's stutter, the shape of Arlova's breasts or Bogrov's whimpering to do with the objective rightness or wrongness of the measure itself?

Rubashov began again to walk up and down in his cell. He felt that everything he had experienced since his imprisonment had been only a prelude; that his cogitations had led him to a dead end—on to the threshold of what Ivanov called the "metaphysical brothel"—and that he must begin again from the beginning. But how much time was there left? He stopped, took the glass out of Ivanov's hand and drained it. Ivanov watched him.

"That's better," he said with a fleeting smile. "Monologues in the form of a dialogue are a useful institution. I hope I reproduced the voice of the tempter effectively. A pity that the opposite party is not represented. But that is part of its tricks, that it never lets itself be drawn into a rational discussion. It always attacks a man in defence-less moments, when he is alone and in some effective *mise en scène:* from burning thorn-bushes or cloud-covered mountain tops—and with a special preference for a sleeping victim. The methods of the great moralist are pretty unfair and theatrical. . . ."

Rubashov was no longer listening. Walking up and down, he was wondering whether to-day, if Arlova were still alive, he would sacrifice her again. This problem fascinated him; it seemed to con-tain the answer to all other questions. . . . He stopped in front of Ivanov and asked him:

"Do you remember 'Raskolnikov'?"

Ivanov smiled at him with irony. "It was to be expected that you would sooner or later come to that. *Crime and Punishment.* . . . You are really becoming childish or senile. . . ."

"Wait a bit. Wait a bit," said Rubashov, walking up and down agitatedly. "All this is just talk, but now we are getting nearer the point. As far as I remember, the problem is, whether the student Raskolnikov has the right to kill the old woman? He is young and talented; he has as it were un unredeemed pledge on life in his pocket; she is old and utterly useless to the world. But the equation does not stand. In the first place, circumstances oblige him to mur-der a second person; that is the unforeseeable and illogical conse-quence of an apparently simple and logical action. Secondly, the equation collapses in any case, because Raskolnikov discovers that twice two are not four when the mathematical units are human beings. . . ."

"Really," said Ivanov. "If you want to hear my opinion, every copy of the book should be burnt. Consider a moment what this humanitarian fog-philosophy would lead to, if we were to take it literally; if we were to stick to the precept that the individual is sacrosanct, and that we must not treat human lives according to the rules of arithmetic. That would mean that a battalion commander may not sacrifice a patrolling party to save the regiment. That we may not sacrifice fools like Bogrov, and must risk our coastal towns being shot to pieces in a couple of years. . . ."

Rubashov shook his head.

"Your examples are all drawn from war—that is, from abnormal circumstances."

"Since the invention of the steam engine," replied Ivanov, "the world has been permanently in an abnormal state; the wars and revolutions are just the visible expressions of this state. Your Raskolnikov is, however, a fool and a criminal; not because he behaves logically in killing the old woman, but because he is doing it in his personal interest. The principle that the end justifies the means is and remains the only rule of political ethics; anything else is just vague chatter and melts away between one's fingers. . . . If Raskolnikov had bumped off the old woman at the command of the Party—for example, to increase strike funds or to install an illegal Press—then the equation would stand, and the novel with its misleading problem would never have been written, and so much the better for humanity."

Rubashov did not answer. He was still fascinated by the problem as to whether to-day, after the experiences of the last few months and days, he would again send Arlova to her death. He did not know. Logically, Ivanov was right in everything he said; the invisible opponent was silent, and only indicated its existence by a dull feeling of uneasiness. And in that, too, Ivanov was right, that this behaviour of the "invisible opponent," in never exposing itself to argument and only attacking people at defenceless moments, showed it in a very dubious light. . . .

"I don't approve of mixing ideologies," Ivanov continued. "There are only two conceptions of human ethics, and they are at opposite poles. One of them is Christian and humane, declares the individual to be sacrosanct, and asserts that the rules of arithmetic are not to be applied to human units. The other starts from the basic principle that a collective aim justifies all means, and not only allows, but demands, that the individual should in every way be subordinated and sacrificed to the community—which may dispose of it as an experimentation rabbit or a sacrificial lamb. The first conception could be called anti-vivisection morality, the second, vivisection morality. Humbugs and dilettantes have always tried to mix the two conceptions; in practice, it is impossible. Whoever is burdened with power and responsibility finds out on the first occasion that he has to choose; and he is fatally driven to the second alternative. Do you know, since the establishment of Christianity as a state religion, a single example of a state which really followed a Christian policy? You can't point out one. In times of need—and politics are chronically in a time of need—the rulers were always able to evoke 'exceptional circumstances,' which demanded exceptional measures of defence. Since the existence of nations and classes, they live in a permanent state of mutual self-defence, which forces them to defer to another time the putting into practice of humanism. . . ."

Rubashov looked through the window. The melted snow had again frozen and sparkled, an irregular surface of yellow-white crystals. The sentinel on the wall marched up and down with shouldered rifle. The sky was clear but moonless; above the machine-gun turret shimmered the Milky Way.

Rubashov shrugged his shoulders. "Admit," he said, "that human-ism and politics, respect for the individual and social progress, are incompatible. Admit that Gandhi is a catastrophe for India; that chasteness in the choice of means leads to political impotence. In negatives we agree. But look where the other alternative has led us. . . ."

"Well," asked Ivanov, "where?"

Rubashov rubbed his pince-nez on his sleeve, and looked at him shortsightedly. "What a mess," he said, "what a mess we have made of our golden age."

Ivanov smiled. "Maybe," he said happily. "Look at the Gracchi and Saint-Just and the Commune of Paris. Up to now, all revolutions have been made by moralizing dilettantes. They were always in good faith and perished because of their dilettantism. We for the first time are consequent. . . ."

"Yes," said Rubashov. "So consequent, that in the interests of a just distribution of land we deliberately let die of starvation about five million farmers and their families in one year. So consequent were we in the liberation of human beings from the shackles of industrial exploitation that we sent about ten million people to do forced labour in the Arctic regions and the jungles of the East, under conditions similar to those of antique galley slaves. So con-sequent that, to settle a difference of opinion, we know only one argument: death, whether it is a matter of submarines, manure, or the Party line to be followed in Indo-China. Our engineers work with the constant knowledge that an error in calculation may take them to prison or the scaffold; the higher officials in our adminis-tration ruin and destroy their subordinates, because they know that they will be held responsible for the slightest slip and be destroyed themselves; our poets settle discussions on questions of style by denunciations to the Secret Police, because the expressionists consider the naturalistic style counter-revolutionary, and *vice versa*. Acting consequentially in the interests of the coming generations, we have laid such terrible privations on the present one that its average length of life is shortened by a quarter. In order to defend the existence of the country, we have to take exceptional measures and make transition-stage laws, which are in every point contrary to the aims of the Revolution. The people's standard of life is lower than it was before the Revolution; the labour conditions are harder, the discipline is more inhuman, the piecework drudgery worse than in colonial countries with native coolies; we have lowered the age limit for capital punishment down to twelve years; our sexual laws are more narrow-minded than those of England, our leader-worship more Byzantine than that of the reactionary dictatorships. Our Press and our schools cultivate Chauvinism, militarism, dogmatism, conformism and ignorance. The arbitrary power of the Government is unlimited, and unexampled in history; freedom of the Press, of opinion and of movement are as thoroughly exterminated as though the proclamation of the Rights of Man had never been. We have built up the most gigantic police apparatus, with informers made a national institution, and with the most refined scientific system of physical and mental torture. We whip the groaning masses of the country towards a theoretical future happiness, which only we can see. For the energies of this generation are exhausted; they were spent in the Revolution; for this generation is bled white and there is nothing left of it but a moaning, numbed, apathetic lump of sacrificial flesh. . . . Those are the consequences of our consequentialness. You called it vivisection morality. To me it sometimes seems as though the experimenters had torn the skin off the victim and left it standing with bared tissues, muscles and nerves. . . ."

"Well, and what of it?" said Ivanov happily. "Don't you find it wonderful? Has anything more wonderful ever happened in history? We are tearing the old skin off mankind and giving it a new one. That is not an occupation for people with weak nerves; but there was once a time when it filled you with enthusiasm. What has so changed you that you are now as pernickety as an old maid?"

Rubashov wanted to answer: "Since then I have heard Bogrov call out my name." But he knew that this answer did not make sense. So he answered instead:

"To continue with the same metaphor: I see the flayed body of this generation: but I see no trace of the new skin. We all thought one could treat history like one experiments in physics. The difference is that in physics one can repeat the experiment a thousand times, but in history only once. Danton and Saint-Just can be sent to the scaffold only once; and if it should turn out that big submarines would after all have been the right thing, Comrade Bogrov will not come to life again."

"And what follows?" asked Ivanov. "Should we sit with idle hands because the consequences of an act are never quite to be foreseen, and hence all action is evil? We vouch for every act with our heads —more cannot be expected of us. In the opposite camp they are not so scrupulous. Any old idiot of a general can experiment with thousands of living bodies, and if he makes a mistake, he will at most be retired. The forces of reaction and counter-revolution have no scruples or ethical problems. Imagine a Sulla, a Galliffet, a Koltschak reading Raskolnikov. Such peculiar birds as you are found only in the trees of revolution. For the others it is easier. . . ."

He looked at his watch. The cell window had turned a dirty grey; the newspaper which was stuck over the broken pane swelled and rustled in the morning breeze. On the rampart opposite, the sentry was still doing his hundred steps up and down.

"For a man with your past," Ivanov went on, "this sudden revulsion against experimenting is rather naïve. Every year several million people are killed quite pointlessly by epidemics and other natural catastrophes. And we should shrink from sacrificing a few hundred thousand for the most promising experiment in history? Not to mention the legions of those who die of undernourishment and tuberculosis in coal and quicksilver mines, rice-fields and cotton plantations. No one takes any notice of them; nobody asks why or what for; but if here we shoot a few thousand objectively harmful people, the humanitarians all over the world foam at the mouth. Yes, we liquidated the parasitic part of the peasantry and let it die of starvation. It was a surgical operation which had to be done once and for all; but in the good old days before the Revolution just as many died in any dry year—only senselessly and pointlessly. The victims of the Yellow River floods in China amount sometimes to hundreds of thousands. Nature is generous in her senseless experiments on mankind. Why should mankind not have the right to experiment on itself?"

He paused; Rubashov did not answer. He went on:

"Have you ever read brochures of an anti-vivisectionist society? They are shattering and heartbreaking; when one reads how some

poor cur which has had its liver cut out, whines and licks his tormentor's hands, one is just as nauseated as you were tonight. But
if these people had their say, we would have no serums against
cholera, typhoid or diphtheria. . . ."

He emptied the rest of the bottle, yawned, stretched and stood
up. He limped over to Rubashov at the window, and looked out.

"It's getting light," he said. "Don't be a fool, Rubashov. Everything I brought up to-night is elementary knowledge, which you
know as well as I. You were in a state of nervous depression, but
now it is over." He stood next to Rubashov at the window, with his
arm round Rubashov's shoulders; his voice was nearly tender. "Now
go and sleep it off, old warhorse; to-morrow the time is up, and we
will both need a clear head to concoct your deposition. Don't shrug
your shoulders—you are yourself at least half convinced that you
will sign. If you deny it, it's just moral cowardice. Moral cowardice
has driven many to martyrdom."

Rubashov looked out into the grey light. The sentry was just
doing a right-about turn. Above the machine-gun turret the sky
was pale grey, with a shade of red. "I'll think it over again," said
Rubashov after a while.

When the door had closed behind his visitor, Rubashov knew
that he had already half-surrendered. He threw himself on the bunk,
exhausted and yet strangely relieved. He felt hollowed-out and
sucked dry, and at the same time as if a weight had been lifted from
him. Bogrov's pathetic appeal had in his memory lost some of its
acoustic sharpness. Who could call it betrayal if, instead of the dead,
one held faith with the living?

THE PROBLEM OF CHOICE

Jean-Paul Sartre

From *Dirty Hands*

ACT V

. . .

JESSICA: Hugo, now is the time.

HUGO: What's that?

JESSICA: You promised me you would try to convince him.

HOEDERER: To convince me?

HUGO: Be quiet. (He tries to disengage himself. She gets in front of him.)

JESSICA: He doesn't agree with you.

HOEDERER (amused):   I noticed that.

JESSICA: He would like to explain.

HOEDERER: Tomorrow! Tomorrow!

JESSICA: Tomorrow will be too late.

HOEDERER: Why?

JESSICA (remaining in front of HUGO):   He—he says he doesn't want to be your secretary if you don't hear him out. Neither of you is sleepy and you have the whole night before you and—and you both had a narrow escape; that should make you feel closer.

HUGO: Drop it, I tell you.

JESSICA: Hugo, you promised me! (To HOEDERER) He says you are a class traitor.

HOEDERER: A class traitor! No less?

JESSICA: Objectively. He said objectively.

HOEDERER (changing his tone and expression):   All right. Well then, my boy, tell me what's on your mind, since we can't prevent it. I suppose I have to settle this matter before going to bed. Why am I a class traitor?

HUGO: Because you have no right to involve the party in your schemes.

HOEDERER: Why not?

HUGO: It's a revolutionary organization and you are going to make it a government party.

HOEDERER: Revolutionary parties are organized to take power.

HUGO: To take it. Yes. To seize power, arms in hand. Not to get it through some swindle.

HOEDERER: Is it the lack of bloodshed you regret? Too bad, but you ought to know that we can't get power through an armed struggle. In case of a civil war the Pentagon * has the arms and the military leaders. It would serve as a perfect framework for counter-revolutionary troops.

HUGO: Who's talking about civil war? Hoederer, I don't understand you; all we need is a little patience. You yourself said that the Red Army will chase out the Regent and we'll have power alone.

HOEDERER: And what will we do to keep it? (A pause.) When the Red Army has crossed our frontiers, I can promise you some nasty moments.

HUGO: The Red Army—

HOEDERER: Yes, yes, I know. I too await its coming. And impatiently. But let me tell you this: all armies at war, whether they come as liberators or not, are alike. They live off the occupied country. Our peasants will detest the Russians, that's sure. How do you suppose they will feel about us, since the Russians will have forced us on them? They'll call us the party of foreigners and maybe worse. The Pentagon will go underground again; it won't have to change its slogans.

HUGO: The Pentagon, I—

HOEDERER: And besides, there's something else: the country is ruined; it may even serve as a battlefield. Any government that succeeds the Regent's will have to take terrible measures, which will make it hated. The morning after the Red Army's departure we would be swept out by an insurrection.

HUGO: An insurrection can be put down. We shall hold the country in an iron grip.

* Editors' note: The "bourgeois liberal, nationalist" party in Illyria.

HOEDERER: An iron grip? Who will support us? Even after the
revolution the proletariat will be the weakest class for a long time
to come. An iron grip! With a bourgeois party that will sabotage
industry and a peasant population that will burn the crops to starve
us out?

HUGO: What of that? The Bolshevik Party survived worse in 1917.

HOEDERER: It wasn't imposed by a foreign power. Listen to me,
son, and try to understand. We can take power with Karsky's liberals
and the Regent's conservatives. No fuss, nobody hurt, a united front.
No one can accuse us of having been put in by a foreign power. I
demanded half the votes on the resistance committee, but I wouldn't
be foolish enough to ask for half the ministries. A minority, that's
what we must be. A minority, leaving to the other parties the responsibility for unpopular measures and thus able to win support by
opposing these measures inside the government. They're cornered:
in two years you'll see the bankruptcy of the liberals, and the whole
country will ask us to take a try.

HUGO: But at that moment the party will be done for.

HOEDERER: Done for? Why?

HUGO: The party has one program: the realization of a socialist
economy, and one method of achieving it: the class struggle. You
are going to use it to pursue a policy of class collaboration in the
framework of a capitalist economy. For years you will have to cheat,
trick, and maneuver; we'll go from compromise to compromise. Before your comrades, you will have to defend the reactionary measures taken by the government in which you participate. No one will
understand: the hardened ones will leave us, the others will lose
whatever political faith they have just acquired. We shall be contaminated, weakened, disoriented; we shall become reformists and
nationalists; in the end the bourgeois parties won't even have to go
to the trouble of liquidating us. Hoederer! This party is yours, you
cannot have forgotten the hardships you endured to forge it, the
sacrifices that were required, the discipline you had to impose. I
beg you: don't sacrifice it with your own hands.

HOEDERER: What babbling! If you don't want to take chances
you shouldn't be in politics.

HUGO: I don't want to run these particular risks.

HOEDERER: Excellent. Then how would you stay in power?

HUGO: Why take it?

HOEDERER: Are you mad? A socialist army is going to occupy the country; would you let it go without profiting by its aid? Such a chance never comes twice. I tell you we are not strong enough to swing the revolution alone.

HUGO: You should not take power at such a price.

HOEDERER: What do you think the party is, a racing stable? Why polish a knife every day if you don't intend to cut something with it? A party is always only a tool. It has only one goal: power.

HUGO: It has only one goal: to make our ideas, all our ideas, and only these victorious.

HOEDERER: That's true. Now you—you have ideas. You'll get over them.

HUGO: You think I'm the only one who has these ideas? Wasn't it for these ideas that our comrades were killed by the Regent's police? Don't you see that we'll betray them if we use the party to whitewash their assassins?

HOEDERER: I don't give a damn for the dead. They died for the party, and the party can decide as it sees fit about them. I pursue a policy of the living for the living.

HUGO: And do you think that the living will agree to your schemes?

HOEDERER: We'll get them to swallow them little by little.

HUGO: By lying to them?

HOEDERER: By lying to them sometimes.

HUGO: You—you seem so real, so solid! How can you stand it to lie to your comrades?

HOEDERER: Why not? We're at war, and it's not customary to keep each individual soldier posted hour by hour on operations.

HUGO: Hoederer, I—I know better than you what lies are like. In my father's home everybody lied to himself, everybody lied to me. I couldn't breathe until I joined the party. Then for the first time I saw men who didn't lie to other men. Everyone could have confidence in everyone else, the humblest militant had the feeling that the orders of the leaders revealed to him his own secret will, and if things got tough, each one knew why he was ready to die. You're not going to—

HOEDERER: What are you talking about?

HUGO: Our party.

HOEDERER: Our party? But we have always told lies, just like any other party. And you, Hugo, are you sure that you've never lied, never lied to yourself, that you are not even lying to me this very moment?

HUGO: I never lie to my comrades. I— Why should you fight for the liberation of men, if you think no more of them than to stuff their heads with falsehoods?

HOEDERER: I'll lie when I must, and I have contempt for no one. I wasn't the one who invented lying. It grew out of a society divided into classes, and each one of us has inherited it from birth. We shall not abolish lying by refusing to tell lies, but by using every means at hand to abolish classes.

HUGO: All means are not good.

HOEDERER: All means are good when they're effective.

HUGO: Then what right have you to condemn the policy of the Regent? He declared war on the U.S.S.R. because this was the most effective way of safeguarding national independence.

HOEDERER: Do you imagine I condemn him? He did what any fellow of his class would have done in his place. We're not fighting against men nor against a policy, but against the class that produces this policy and these men.

HUGO: And the best means you've found to fight that class is to ask it to share power with you?

HOEDERER: Right! Today it's the best means. (A pause.) How you cling to your purity, young man! How afraid you are to soil your hands! All right, stay pure! What good will it do? Why did you join us? Purity is an idea for a yogi or a monk. You intellectuals and bourgeois anarchists use it as a pretext for doing nothing. To do nothing, to remain motionless, arms at your sides, wearing kid gloves. Well, I have dirty hands. Right up to the elbows. I've plunged them in filth and blood. But what do you hope? Do you think you can govern innocently?

HUGO: You'll see some day that I'm not afraid of blood.

HOEDERER: Really! Red gloves, that's elegant. It's the rest that scares you. That's what stinks to your little aristocratic nose.

HUGO: So we're back to that! I'm an aristocrat, a guy who has never gone hungry. Unfortunately for you, I'm not alone in my opinion.

HOEDERER: Not alone? Then you knew something of these negotiations before you came here?

HUGO: N—no. There was some vague talk in the party, and most of the fellows didn't agree. And I swear to you that they weren't aristocrats.

HOEDERER: My boy, you misunderstand something; I know these people of the party who disagree with my policy, and I can tell you that they belong to my tribe and not to yours—as you'll soon discover. If they oppose these negotiations, it's simply because they believe them to be inopportune; under other circumstances they would be the first to launch them. But you are making this a matter of principle.

HUGO: Who spoke of principles?

HOEDERER: Aren't you trying to make this into a matter of principle? Good. Then here is something that ought to convince you: if we deal with the Regent, he'll stop the war; the Illyrian troops will wait very patiently for the Russians to come and disarm them. If we break off these parleys, they'll know the game is off and they'll assail us like mad dogs. Hundreds of thousands of men will lose their hides. What do you say to that? (A pause.) Now what do you say? Can you scratch out a hundred thousand men with the stroke of a pen?

HUGO (with difficulty):   You can't make a revolution with flowers. If there's no other way—

HOEDERER: Then?

HUGO: Why, then, so much the worse!

HOEDERER: There you are! You can see for yourself! You don't love men, Hugo. You love only principles.

HUGO: Men? Why should I love them? Do they love me?

HOEDERER: Then why did you come to us? If you don't love men, you can't fight for them.

HUGO: I joined the party because its cause is just, and I shall leave it when that cause ceases to be just. As for men, it's not what they are that interests me, but what they can become.

HOEDERER: And I, I love them for what they are. With all their filth and all their vices. I love their voices and their warm grasping hands, and their skin, the nudest skin of all, and their uneasy glances, and the desperate struggle each has to pursue against anguish and against death. For me, one man more or less in the world is something that counts. It's something precious. You, I know you now, you are a destroyer. You detest men because you detest yourself. Your purity resembles death. The revolution you dream of is not ours. You don't want to change the world, you want to blow it up.

HUGO (excited):   Hoederer!

HOEDERER: It's not your fault; you're all alike. An intellectual is never a real revolutionary; just good enough to make an assassin.

HUGO: An assassin. Yes!

JESSICA: Hugo! (She slips between them.)

The sound of a key in the lock. Enter SLICK and GEORGE.

GEORGE: So here you are. We've been looking all over for you.

HUGO: Who gave you my key?

SLICK: We have keys to all the doors. Remember—we're body-guards.

GEORGE (to HOEDERER):   You gave us a scare. It was Slick who woke: no Hoederer. You ought to warn us when you want to go out for a breath of air.

HOEDERER: You were sleeping.

SLICK (flustered):   What of it? Since when do you let us sleep when you want to wake us?

HOEDERER (laughing):   That's right: What's got into me? (A pause.) I'll go along with you. Till tomorrow, son. At nine o'clock. We can talk some more then. (HUGO does not answer.) Good-by, Jessica.

JESSICA: Till tomorrow, Hoederer. (They go out. A long silence.)

JESSICA: Well?

HUGO: Well, you were here. You heard.

JESSICA: What are you thinking?

HUGO: What do you want me to think? I told you he was shrewd.

JESSICA: Hugo! He was right.

HUGO: My poor Jessica, what could you know about it?

JESSICA: And you, what do you know about it? You didn't look so big in front of him.

HUGO: Oh, for heaven's sake! With me, he had it lucky. I should like to see how he would make out with Louis. He wouldn't have come out so well.

JESSICA: Perhaps he would have put him in his pocket.

HUGO (laughing):   What? Louis? You don't know him. Louis can't be wrong.

JESSICA: Why?

HUGO: Because. Because he's Louis.

JESSICA: Hugo! You don't mean what you're saying. I watched you while you were arguing with Hoederer: he convinced you.

HUGO: He didn't convince me. No one can convince me that one should lie to one's comrades. But if he had convinced me, that would be one more reason to kill him, because that would prove

that he's capable of convincing others. Tomorrow morning I'll finish
the job.

·   ·   ·

ACT VII *

In Olga's Room

OLGA and HUGO talking in the dark. First their voices are heard, and
then gradually the room is lighted.

OLGA: Was it true? Did you really kill him over Jessica?

HUGO: I—I killed him because I opened the door. That's all I
know. If I hadn't opened that door— He was there, he held Jessica
in his arms, he had lipstick on his chin. It was all so trivial. But I
had been living for so long in tragedy. It was to save the tragedy
that I fired.

OLGA: But weren't you jealous?

HUGO: Jealous? Perhaps. But not about Jessica.

OLGA: Look at me and answer me frankly, for what I am going
to ask now is very important. Are you proud of your deed? Do you
claim it as your own? Would you do it again if necessary?

HUGO: Did I even do it? It wasn't I who killed—it was chance.
If I had opened the door two minutes sooner or two minutes later,
I wouldn't have surprised them in each other's arms, and I wouldn't
have fired. (A pause.) I was coming to tell him that I would let him
help me.

OLGA: Yes.

HUGO: Chance fired three shots, just as in cheap detective stories.
Chance lets you do a lot of "iffing": "*If* I had stayed a bit longer by
the chestnut trees, *if* I had walked to the end of the garden, *if* I
had gone back into the summerhouse. . . ." But me? *Me?* Where
does that put me in the thing? It was an assassination without an
assassin. (A pause.) I often asked myself in prison: what would
Olga say if she were here? What would she want me to think?

OLGA (dryly):   Well?

HUGO: Oh, I know perfectly well what you would have said to
me. You would have said: "Be modest, Hugo. Nobody cares about

* Editors' note: In Act VI Hugo, at first unable to bring himself to kill
Hoederer, does so upon finding him in an embrace with Jessica.

your motives or reasons. We asked you to kill this man and you killed him. What counts is the result." But I—well, I'm not modest, Olga. I can't separate the murder from the motive for it.

OLGA: I like that better.

HUGO: What do you mean, you like that better? Is that really you talking, Olga? The Olga who always told me that—

OLGA: I'll explain. What time is it?

HUGO (looking at his wrist watch):   Twenty minutes to twelve.

OLGA: Good. We have time. What were you saying? That you do not understand your deed.

HUGO: Rather, that I understand it too well. It's a door that any key can open. I could tell myself, if I had a mind to, that I shot him out of political passion and that the rage that came over me when I opened the door was merely the little jolt I needed to make my task easier.

OLGA (observing him with uneasiness):   Do you believe that, Hugo? Do you really believe that you fired for the right reasons?

HUGO: Olga, I believe everything. And at the same time I wonder whether I really killed him at all.

OLGA: What do you mean—at all?

HUGO: What if it were all a comedy?

OLGA: You really pulled the trigger.

HUGO: Yes. I really drew my finger back. Actors do that too, on the stage. Look here: I cock my forefinger, I aim at you. (He aims at her with his right hand, his forefinger coiled back.) It's the same gesture. Perhaps I wasn't real. Perhaps only the bullet was. Why do you smile?

OLGA: Because you make many things easy for me.

HUGO: I thought I was too young. I wanted to hang a crime round my neck, like a stone. And I feared it would be too heavy for me to carry. How wrong I was! It's light, horribly light. It has no weight at all. Look at me: I've grown older, I spent two years in the cooler, I've been separated from Jessica, and I shall lead this life of senseless puzzlement until your pals take it upon themselves to rid me of it. And all this comes from my crime, isn't that right? And yet it has no weight. I don't feel that it's there. It's not around my neck, nor on my shoulders, nor in my heart. It has become my destiny, do you understand? It controls my life from outside, but I can't see it or touch it, it's not mine, it's a fatal disease that kills painlessly. Where is my crime? Does it exist? And yet I fired. The door was open. I loved Hoederer, Olga. I loved him more than I ever loved anyone in the world. I loved to watch him and to hear him talk, I loved his hands and his face, and when I was with him all my fears were calmed. It's not my crime that tortures me but the fact that he's dead. (A pause.) So there you are. Nothing happened. Nothing. I spent ten days in the country and two years in jail; I haven't changed; I'm still the same old chatterbox. Assassins should wear something by which they can be recognized. A poppy in their lapels. (A pause.) Well, then? What's the conclusion?

OLGA: You're coming back to the party.

HUGO: Good.

OLGA: At midnight Louis and Charles will return to kill you. But I won't let them in. I'll tell them you are salvageable.

HUGO (laughs):   Salvageable! What an odd word! That's a word you use for scrap, isn't it?

OLGA: Do you agree?

HUGO: Why not?

OLGA: Tomorrow you'll get new instructions.

HUGO: Good.

OLGA: Thank heaven! (She sinks into a chair.)

HUGO: What's wrong with you?

OLGA: I'm so glad. (A pause.) You talked for three hours and I was frightened all that time.

HUGO: What were you afraid of?

OLGA: Of what I might have had to tell them. But everything is all right now. You'll come back with us now and do a man's work.

HUGO: Will you help me, as before?

OLGA: Yes, Hugo, I'll help you.

HUGO: I do like you, Olga. You are just as you always were. So pure, so clear. It was you who taught me purity.

OLGA: Have I aged?

HUGO: No. (He takes her hand.)

OLGA: I thought of you every day.

HUGO: Tell me, Olga—

OLGA: Yes?

HUGO: About those packages. Did you send them?

OLGA: What packages?

HUGO: The chocolates.

OLGA: No. It wasn't I. But I knew they were going to send them.

HUGO: And you let them?

OLGA: Yes.

HUGO: But what did you think about it?

OLGA (showing her hair):   Look.

HUGO: What's this? White hairs?

OLGA: They came in one night. You must never leave me again. And if there are rough times we'll manage them together.

HUGO (smiling):   You remember: Raskolnikov.

OLGA (leaping to her feet):   Raskolnikov?

HUGO: It's the name you chose for me in the underground. Oh, Olga, you don't remember!

OLGA: Yes. I remember.

HUGO: I'll use it again.

OLGA: No.

HUGO: Why? I liked it. You said it fitted me like a glove.

OLGA: You're too well known under that name.

HUGO: Known? By whom?

OLGA (suddenly limp):   What time is it?

HUGO: Five minutes to.

OLGA: Listen carefully, Hugo. And don't interrupt. I have something to tell you. It isn't much. You mustn't attach any importance to it. You—you'll be surprised at first, but you'll come to understand after a while.

HUGO: Well?

OLGA: I'm happy about what you told me, about your—about your deed. If you had taken pride in it or spoken of it with satisfaction, it would have been more difficult for you.

HUGO: Difficult? Difficult to do what?

OLGA: To forget it.

HUGO: To forget it? But, Olga—

OLGA: Hugo! You must forget it. I'm not asking much of you; you said yourself that you didn't know what you were doing or why you did it. You're not even sure that you killed Hoederer. Very good, you're on the right track. You've got to go just a bit farther, that's all. Forget it; it was a nightmare. Never mention it again; not even to me. The man who killed Hoederer is dead. He was known as Raskolnikov, and he died of eating some poisoned brandy-chocolates. (She strokes his hair.) I'll choose another name for you.

HUGO: What's going on here, Olga? What have you done?

OLGA: The party has changed its policy. (HUGO regards her fixedly.) Don't look at me like that. Try to understand. When we sent you to Hoederer's our communications with the Soviet Union were severed. We had to decide our line by ourselves. Don't look at me that way, Hugo. Don't look at me like that.

HUGO: Then what?

OLGA: Then the contact was renewed. Last winter the U.S.S.R. informed us that for purely military reasons it favored a policy of conciliation with the Regent.

HUGO: And you—did you obey?

OLGA: Yes. We set up a secret committee of six members with the government people and the Pentagon.

HUGO: Six members? And you have three votes?

OLGA: Yes. How did you know?

HUGO: It came into my head, somehow. Go on.

OLGA: Since then our troops have been practically out of the war. We've probably saved a hundred thousand lives. Except that the Germans immediately invaded the country.

HUGO: Just perfect. I suppose the Russians also gave you to understand that they didn't want to give sole power to the Proletarian Party; that they would have trouble with the Allies and that, what's more, you would soon be swept out by an insurrection?

OLGA: But—

HUGO: I seem to have heard all that once before. What about Hoederer?

OLGA: His attempt was premature and he was not the right man to direct such a policy.

HUGO: So he had to be killed; that's clear. But I suppose you have rehabilitated his reputation?

OLGA: We had to.

HUGO: He'll have a statue to him at the end of the war, and streets named after him in all our cities, and his name in the history books. That makes me happy for him. And who was his assassin? What was he? Some character in the pay of Germany?

OLGA: Hugo—

HUGO: Answer me.

OLGA: The comrades know that you were one of us. They never believed it was a crime of passion. Then it was explained to them—as best it could be.

HUGO: You've lied to your comrades.

OLGA: Lied, no. But we—we are at war, Hugo. You can't tell the whole truth to troops. (HUGO bursts into laughter.) What is the matter? Hugo! Hugo!

(HUGO sinks into a chair, laughing to the point of tears.)

HUGO: That's just what he said! Just what he said! Oh, this is a farce.

OLGA: Hugo!

HUGO: Wait, Olga, let me have my laugh. It's been ten years since I've been able to laugh like this. Here's an embarrassing crime: nobody wants to claim it. I don't know why I committed it and you don't know what to do with it. (He looks at her.) You're all alike.

OLGA: Hugo, I beg you—

HUGO: Alike. Hoederer, Louis, and you yourself, all belong to the same tribe. The right tribe. You're the tough ones, the conquerors, the leaders. I am the only one who got in by the wrong door.

OLGA: Hugo, you loved Hoederer.

HUGO: I believe I never before loved him as much as I do at this moment.

OLGA: Then you must help us complete his work. (She recoils under his glance.) Hugo!

HUGO (softly):   Don't be afraid, Olga. I'll not harm you. But you must be quiet. For one minute, just for one minute more, while I put my thoughts in order. Good. So I am salvageable. Excellent. But all alone, naked, without bag or baggage. On condition that I change my skin—if I could develop amnesia, that would be better still. The crime itself cannot be salvaged, isn't that so? It was an error of no significance. To be left in the ash-can. As for me, I'll change my name tomorrow, call myself Julien Sorel or Rastignac or Muishkin, and I'll work hand in hand with the guys of the Pentagon.

OLGA: I'm going—

HUGO: Quiet, Olga. I beg you, don't say a word. (He reflects a moment.) The answer is no.

OLGA: What?

HUGO: My answer is no. I won't work with you.

OLGA: Then you can't have understood, Hugo. They're coming with their revolvers—

HUGO: I understand perfectly well. They're even a little late.

OLGA: You're not going to let them kill you like a dog. You can't be willing to die for nothing! We will trust you, Hugo. You'll see, you'll be our comrade for good, you have proved yourself. . . . (A car. The sound of a motor.)

HUGO: Here they are.

OLGA: Hugo, it would be criminal. The party—

HUGO: No big words, Olga. There are too many big words in this story already and they've done much harm. (The car passes on.)

It's not their car. I have time to explain it to you. Listen: I don't know why I killed Hoederer, but I know why it was right to kill him: because his policy was wrong, because he lied to the rank and file and jeopardized the life of the party. If I had had the courage to shoot when I was alone with him in his office, he would be dead for these reasons and I could think of myself without shame. But I am ashamed because I killed him—afterwards. And now you want me to dishonor myself even more and to agree that I killed him for nothing. Olga, what I thought about Hoederer's line I continue to think. When I was in prison I believed that you agreed with me, and that's what kept me going. I know now that I'm alone in my opinion, but I won't change. (The sound of a motor.)

OLGA: This time they're here. Listen, I can't—take this revolver, go out through my bedroom and make a try.

HUGO (not taking the gun): You have made Hoederer a great man. But I loved him more than you could ever love him. If I renounced my deed he would become a nameless corpse, a throw-off of the party. (The car stops.) Killed by accident. Killed over a woman.

OLGA: Get out of here.

HUGO: A man like Hoederer doesn't die by accident. He dies for his ideas, for his political program; he's responsible for his death. If I openly claim my crime and declare myself Raskolnikov and am willing to pay the necessary price, then he will have the death he deserves. (A rap on the door.)

OLGA: Hugo, I—

HUGO (going to the door): I have not yet killed Hoederer, Olga. Not yet. But I am going to kill him now, along with myself. (More knocking.)

OLGA (shouting): Go on! Get out!

(Hugo kicks open the door.)

HUGO (shouting): Unsalvageable!

CURTAIN

AN APOLOGIA

Bertolt Brecht

"To Posterity"

Indeed I live in the dark ages!
A guileless word is an absurdity. A smooth forehead betokens
A hard heart. He who laughs
Has not yet heard
The terrible tidings.

Ah, what an age it is
When to speak of trees is almost a crime
For it is a kind of silence about injustice!
And he who walks calmly across the street,
Is he not out of reach of his friends
In trouble?

It is true: I earn my living
But, believe me, it is only an accident.
Nothing that I do entitles me to eat my fill.
By chance I was spared. (If my luck leaves me
I am lost.)

They tell me: eat and drink. Be glad you have it!
But how can I eat and drink
When my food is snatched from the hungry
And my glass of water belongs to the thirsty?
And yet I eat and drink.

I would gladly be wise.
The old books tell us what wisdom is:
Avoid the strife of the world, live out your little time
Fearing no one,

From *Selected Poems of Bertolt Brecht,* translated by H. R. Hays, copyright, 1947, by Bertolt Brecht and H. R. Hays. Reprinted by permission of Harcourt, Brace & World, Inc.

Using no violence,
Returning good for evil—
Not fulfillment of desire but forgetfulness
Passes for wisdom.
I can do none of this:
Indeed I live in the dark ages!

2

I came to the cities in a time of disorder
When hunger ruled.
I came among men in a time of uprising
And I revolted with them.
So the time passed away
Which on earth was given me.

I ate my food between massacres.
The shadow of murder lay upon my sleep.
And when I loved, I loved with indifference.
I looked upon my nature with impatience.
So the time passed away
Which on earth was given me.

In my time streets lead to the quicksand.
Speech betrayed me to the slaughterer.
There was little I could do. But without me
The rulers would have been more secure. This was my hope.
So the time passed away
Which on earth was given me.
Men's strength was little. The goal
Lay far in the distance,
Easy to see if for me
Scarcely attainable.
So the time passed away
Which on earth was given me.

3

You, who shall emerge from the flood
In which we are sinking,
Think—
When you speak of our weaknesses,

Also of the dark time
That brought them forth.
For we went, changing our country more often than our shoes,
In the class war, despairing
When there was only injustice and no resistance.

For we knew only too well:
Even the hatred of squalor
Makes the brow grow stern.
Even anger against injustice
Makes the voice grow harsh. Alas, we
Who wished to lay the foundations of kindness
Could not ourselves be kind.

But you, when at last it comes to pass
That man can help his fellow man,
Do not judge us
Too harshly.

A TERRIBLE BEAUTY

William Butler Yeats

"Easter 1916"

I have met them at close of day
Coming with vivid faces
From counter or desk among grey
Eighteenth-century houses.
I have passed with a nod of the head
Or polite meaningless words,
Or have lingered awhile and said
Polite meaningless words,
And thought before I had done

Of a mocking tale or a gibe
To please a companion
Around the fire at the club,
Being certain that they and I
But lived where motley is worn:
All changed, changed utterly:
A terrible beauty is born.

That woman's days were spent
In ignorant good will,
Her nights in argument
Until her voice grew shrill.
What voice more sweet than hers
When, young and beautiful,
She rode to harriers?
This man had kept a school
And rode our winged horse;
This other his helper and friend
Was coming into his force;
He might have won fame in the end,
So sensitive his nature seemed,
So daring and sweet his thought.
This other man I have dreamed
A drunken, vainglorious lout.
He had done most bitter wrong
To some who are near my heart,
Yet I number him in the song;
He, too, has resigned his part
In the casual comedy;
He, too, has been changed in his turn,
Transformed utterly:
A terrible beauty is born.

Hearts with one purpose alone
Through summer and winter seem
Enchanted to a stone
To trouble the living stream.
The horse that comes from the road,
The rider, the birds that range
From cloud to tumbling cloud,
Minute by minute they change;

A shadow of cloud on the stream
Changes minute by minute;
A horse-hoof slides on the brim,
And a horse plashes within it;
The long legged moor hens dive,
And hens to moor-cocks call;
Minute by minute they live:
The stone's in the midst of all.

Too long a sacrifice
Can make a stone of the heart.
O when may it suffice?
That is Heaven's part, our part
To murmur name upon name,
As a mother names her child
When sleep at last has come
On limbs that had run wild.
What is it but nightfall?
No, no, not night but death;
Was it needless death after all?
For England may keep faith
For all that is done and said.
We know their dream; enough
To know they dreamed and are dead;
And what if excess of love
Bewildered them till they died?
I write it out in a verse—
MacDonagh and MacBride
And Connolly and Pearse
Now and in time to be,
Wherever green is worn,
Are changed, changed utterly:
A terrible beauty is born.

THE USE OF FORCE

William Carlos Williams

"The Use of Force"

They were new patients to me, all I had was the name, Olson. Please come down as soon as you can, my daughter is very sick.

When I arrived I was met by the mother, a big startled looking woman, very clean and apologetic who merely said, Is this the doctor? and let me in. In the back, she added. You must excuse us, doctor, we have her in the kitchen where it is warm. It is very damp here sometimes.

The child was fully dressed and sitting on her father's lap near the kitchen table. He tried to get up, but I motioned for him not to bother, took off my overcoat and started to look things over. I could see that they were all very nervous, eyeing me up and down distrustfully. As often, in such cases, they weren't telling me more than they had to, it was up to me to tell them; that's why they were spending three dollars on me.

The child was fairly eating me up with her cold, steady eyes, and no expression to her face whatever. She did not move and seemed, inwardly, quiet; an unusually attractive little thing, and as strong as a heifer in appearance. But her face was flushed, she was breathing rapidly, and I realized that she had a high fever. She had magnificent blonde hair, in profusion. One of those picture children often reproduced in advertising leaflets and the photogravure sections of the Sunday papers.

She's had a fever for three days, began the father and we don't know what it comes from. My wife has given her things, you know, like people do, but it don't do no good. And there's been a lot of sickness around. So we tho't you'd better look her over and tell us what is the matter.

As doctors often do I took a trial shot at it as a point of departure. Has she had a sore throat?

Both parents answered me together, No . . . No, she says her throat don't hurt her.

Does your throat hurt you? added the mother to the child. But the little girl's expression didn't change nor did she move her eyes from my face.

Have you looked?

I tried to, said the mother, but I couldn't see.

As it happens we had been having a number of cases of diphtheria in the school to which this child went during that month and we were all, quite apparently, thinking of that, though no one had as yet spoken of the thing.

Well, I said, suppose we take a look at the throat first. I smiled in my best professional manner and asking for the child's first name I said, come on, Mathilda, open your mouth and let's take a look at your throat.

Nothing doing.

Aw, come on, I coaxed, just open your mouth wide and let me take a look. Look, I said opening both hands wide, I haven't anything in my hands. Just open up and let me see.

Such a nice man, put in the mother. Look how kind he is to you. Come on, do what he tells you to. He won't hurt you.

At that I ground my teeth in disgust. If only they wouldn't use the word "hurt" I might be able to get somewhere. But I did not allow myself to be hurried or disturbed but speaking quietly and slowly I approached the child again.

As I moved my chair a little nearer suddenly with one catlike movement both her hands clawed instinctivly for my eyes and she almost reached them too. In fact she knocked my glasses flying and they fell, though unbroken, several feet away from me on the kitchen floor.

Both the mother and father almost turned themselves inside out in embarrassment and apology. You bad girl, said the mother, taking her and shaking her by one arm. Look what you've done. The nice man . . .

For heaven's sake, I broke in. Don't call me a nice man to her. I'm here to look at her throat on the chance that she might have diphtheria and possibly die of it. But that's nothing to her. Look here, I said to the child, we're going to look at your throat. You're old enough to understand what I'm saying. Will you open it now by yourself or shall we have to open it for you?

Not a move. Even her expression hadn't changed. Her breaths

however were coming faster and faster. Then the battle began. I had to do it. I had to have a throat culture for her own protection. But first I told the parents that it was entirely up to them. I explained the danger but said that I would not insist on a throat examination so long as they would take the responsibility.

If you don't do what the doctor says you'll have to go to the hospital, the mother admonished her severely.

Oh yeah? I had to smile to myself. After all, I had already fallen in love with the savage brat, the parents were contemptible to me. In the ensuing struggle they grew more and more abject, crushed, exhausted while she surely rose to magnificent heights of insane fury of effort bred of her terror of me.

The father tried his best, and he was a big man but the fact that she was his daughter, his shame at her behavior and his dread of hurting her made him release her just at the critical moment several times when I had almost achieved success, till I wanted to kill him. But his dread also that she might have diphtheria made him tell me to go on, go on though he himself was almost fainting, while the mother moved back and forth behind us raising and lowering her hands in an agony of apprehension.

Put her in front of you on your lap, I ordered, and hold both her wrists.

But as soon as he did the child let out a scream. Don't, you're hurting me. Let go of my hands. Let them go I tell you. Then she shrieked terrifyingly, hysterically. Stop it! Stop it! You're killing me!

Do you think she can stand it, doctor! said the mother.

You get out, said the husband to his wife. Do you want her to die of diphtheria?

Come on now, hold her, I said.

Then I grasped the child's head with my left hand and tried to get the wooden tongue depressor between her teeth. She fought, with clenched teeth, desperately! But now I also had grown furious —at the child. I tried to hold myself down but I couldn't. I know how to expose a throat for inspection. And I did my best. When finally I got the wooden spatula behind the last teeth and just the point of it into the mouth cavity, she opened up for an instant but before I could see anything she came down again and gripping the wooden blade between her molars she reduced it to splinters before I could get it out again.

Aren't you ashamed, the mother yelled at her. Aren't you ashamed to act like that in front of the doctor?

Get me a smooth-handled spoon of some sort, I told the mother. We're going through with this. The child's mouth was already bleeding. Her tongue was cut and she was screaming in wild hysterical shrieks. Perhaps I should have desisted and come back in an hour or more. No doubt it would have been better. But I have seen at least two children lying dead in bed of neglect in such cases, and feeling that I must get a diagnosis now or never I went at it again. But the worst of it was that I too had got beyond reason. I could have torn the child apart in my own fury and enjoyed it. It was a pleasure to attack her. My face was burning with it.

The damned little brat must be protected against her own idiocy, one says to one's self at such times. Others must be protected against her. It is social necessity. And all these things are true. But a blind fury, a feeling of adult shame, bred of a longing for muscular release are the operatives. One goes on to the end.

In a final unreasoning assault I overpowered the child's neck and jaws. I forced the heavy silver spoon back of her teeth and down her throat till she gagged. And there it was—both tonsils covered with membrane. She had fought valiantly to keep me from knowing her secret. She had been hiding that sore throat for three days at least and lying to her parents in order to escape just such an outcome as this.

Now truly she *was* furious. She had been on the defensive before but now she attacked. Tried to get off her father's lap and fly at me while tears of defeat blinded her eyes.

MORALITY IN POLITICS

Robert Penn Warren

From *All the King's Men*

I saw the Boss in shirt sleeves, cocked back in an easy chair with his sock-feet propped on a straight chair in front of him, and his tie askew, and his eyes bugging out and a forefinger out in the air in front of him as though it were the stock of a bull whip. Then I saw what the snapper of the bull whip would have been flicking the flies off of if that forefinger of the Boss had been the stock of a bull whip: it was Mr. Byram B. White, State Auditor, and his long bony paraffin-colored face was oozing a few painful drops of moisture and his eyes reached out and grabbed me like the last hope.

I took in the fact that I was intruding.

"Excuse me," I said, and started to back out of the door.

"Shut the door and sit down," the Boss said, and his voice moved right on without any punctuation to something it had been saying before my entrance, and the forefinger snapped, "—and you can just damned well remember you aren't supposed to get rich. A fellow like you, fifty years old and gut-shot and teeth gone and never had a dime, if God-Almighty had ever intended you to be rich he'd done it long back. Look at yourself, damn it! You to figure you're supposed to be rich, it is plain blasphemy. Look at yourself. Ain't it a fact?" And the forefinger leveled at Mr. Byram B. White.

But Mr. White did not answer. He just stood there in his unhappiness and looked at the finger.

"God damn it, has the cat got your tongue?" the Boss demanded. "Can't you answer a civil question?"

"Yes," Mr. White managed with gray lips that scarcely moved.

"Speak up, don't mumble, say, 'It's a fact, it's a blasphemous fact,'" the Boss insisted, still pointing the finger.

Mr. White's lips went grayer, and the voice was less than loud and clear, but he said it. Every word.

"All right, that's better," the Boss said. "Now you know what you're supposed to do. You're supposed to stay pore and take orders. I don't care about your chastity, which from the looks of you you don't have any trouble keeping plenty of, but I mean it's poverty and obedience and don't you forget it. Especially the last. There'll be a little something coming to you now and then in the way of sweetening, but Duffy'll tend to that. Don't you go setting up on your own any more. There just aren't going to be any one-man bonanzas. You got that? Speak up!"

"Yes," Mr. White said.

"Louder! And say, 'I got that.'"

He said it. Louder.

"All right," the Boss said, "I'm going to stop this impeachment business for you. But don't go and get the notion it's because I love you. It's just because those fellows can't get the idea they can just up and knock off somebody. Are my motives clear?"

"Yes," Mr. White said.

"All right, then sit down over there at that desk." And the Boss pointed at the little desk with the pen tray and telephone. "Get a sheet of plain paper out of the drawer and take your pen in hand." He waited until Mr. White had glided spectrally across the room and settled himself at the desk, making himself remarkably small, like the genie getting ready to go back into the bottle, drawing himself into a hunch as though he wanted to assume the prenatal position and be little and warm and safe in the dark. But the Boss was saying, "Now write what I say." Then he began to dictate: "Dear Governor Stark,—because of ill health—which renders it difficult for me to attend conscientiously—" The Boss interrupted himself, saying, "Be sure you put that *conscientiously* in now, you wouldn't want to leave that out," and then continued in the business voice—"to the duties of my position as Auditor—I wish to offer my resignation—to take effect as soon after the above date—as you can relieve me." He eyed the hunched figure, and added, "Respectfully yours."

There was silence, and the pen scratched across the paper, then stopped. But Mr. White's tall, bald, narrow head remained bent over close to the paper, as though he were nearsighted, or praying, or had lost whatever it is in the back of a neck that keeps a head up straight.

The Boss studied the back of the bent head. Then he demanded, "Did you sign it?"

"No," the voice said.

"Well, God damn it, sign!" Then when the pen had again stopped scratching across the paper, "Don't put any date on it. I can fill that in when I want."

Mr. White's head did not lift. From where I sat I could see that his hand still held the pen staff, the point still touching the paper at the end of the last letter of his name.

"Bring it here," the Boss said.

Mr. White rose and turned, and I looked at his still bent-over face to see what I could see. His eyes didn't have any appeal in them now as he swung them past me. They didn't have anything in them. They were as numb and expressionless as a brace of gray oysters on the half shell.

He held out the sheet to the Boss, who read it, folded it, tossed it over to the foot of the bed near which he sat. "Yeah," he said, "I'll fill in the date when I need to. If I need to. It all depends on you. But you know, Byram—why I didn't get one of those undated resignations from you from the start I don't know. I got a stack of 'em. But I just misjudged you. I just took one look at you, and said, 'Shucks, there ain't any harm in the old bugger.' I figured you were so beat down you'd know the good Lord never meant for you to be rich. I figured you never would try to pull any shines. Shucks, I figured you didn't have any more initiative than a wet washrag dropped on the bathroom floor in a rooming house for old maids. I was wrong, Byram, I am free to confess. Fifty years old and all that time just waiting your one big chance. Waiting for your ship to come in. Saving up one little twitch and try like a one-nut for his wedding night. Waiting for the big chance, and this was it, and everything was going to be different. But—" and he whipped the forefinger at Mr. White again— "you were wrong, Byram. This was not your chance. And there never will be one. Not for the likes of you. Now get out!"

Mr. White got out. One second he was there, and the next second he wasn't there, and there had been scarcely a sound for his passing. There was just the empty space which had been occupied by the empty space which went by the name of Mr. Byram B. White.

"Well," I said to the Boss, "you gave yourself a good time."

"Damn it," he said, "it's just something in their eyes makes you do it. This fellow now, he'd lick spit, and you can see that, and it makes you do it."

"Yeah," I said, "it looks like he's a long worm with no turning, all right."

"I gave him every chance," the Boss said glumly. "Every chance. He didn't have to say what I told him to say. He didn't have to listen to me. He could have just walked out the door and kept on walking. He could have put a date on that resignation and handed it to me. He could have done a dozen things. But did he? Hell, no. Not Byram, and he just stands there and his eyes blink right quick like a dog's do when he leans up against your leg before you hit him, and, by God, you have the feeling if you don't do it you won't be doing God's will. You do it because you are helping Byram fulfill his nature."

"Not that it's any of my business," I said, "but what's all the shouting about?"

"Didn't you read the paper?"

"No, I was on vacation."

"And Sadie didn't tell you?"

"Just got here," I said.

"Well, Byram rigged him up a nice little scheme to get rich. Got himself a tie-in with a realty outfit and fixed things up with Hamill in the Tax Lands Bureau. Pretty, only they wanted it all to themselves and somebody got sore at not being cut in, and squawked to the MacMurfee boys in the Legislature. And if I get my hands on who it was—"

"Was what?"

"Squawked to the MacMurfee outfit. Ought to take it up with Duffy. Everybody knows he's supposed to handle complaints. And now we got this impeachment business."

"Of who?"

"Byram."

"What's happened to Hamill?"

"He's moved to Cuba. You know, better climate. And, from reports, he moved fast. Duffy went around this morning, and Hamill caught a train. But we got to handle this impeachment."

"I don't think they could put it through."

"They ain't even going to try. You let a thing like that get started and no telling what'll happen. The time to stomp 'em is now. I've got boys out picking up soreheads and wobblies and getting 'em to town. Sadie's been on the phone all day taking the news. Some of the birds are hiding out, for the word must have got round by this time, but the boys are running 'em down. Brought in three this afternoon, and we gave 'em what it took. But we had something ready on them all. You ought to've seen Jeff Hopkins's face when he found out I knew about his pappy selling likker out of that little one-horse drugstore he's got over in Talmadge and then forging prescriptions for the record. Or Martten's when he found out I knew how the bank over in Okaloosa holds a mortgage on his place falling due in about five weeks. Well—" and he wriggled his toes comfortably inside of the socks—"I quieted their nerves. It's the old tonic, but it still soothes."

"What am I supposed to do?"

"Get over to Harmonville tomorrow and see if you can beat some sense into Sim Harmon's head."

"That all?"

Before he could answer Sadie popped her head in the door, and said the boys had brought in Witherspoon, who was a representative from the north tip of the state.

"Put him in the other room," the Boss said, "and let him stew." Then, as Sadie popped out again, he turned to me and answered my question. "All, except get me together all you have on Al Coyle before you leave town. The boys are trying to run him down and I want to be heeled when they book him."

"O.K.," I said, and stood up.

He looked at me as though he were about to say something. For a second I had the notion that he was working himself up to it, and I stood in front of my chair, waiting. But Sadie stuck her head in. "Mr. Miller would like to see you," she said to the Boss, and didn't give the impression of glad tidings.

"Send him in," the Boss ordered, and I could tell that, no matter what he had on his mind to say to me a second before, he had something else on it now. He had Hugh Miller, Harvard Law School, Lafayette Escadrille, Croix de Guerre, clean hands, pure heart, Attorney General, on his mind.

"He won't like it," I said.

"No," he said, "he won't."

And then in the doorway stood the tall, lean, somewhat stooped man, with swarthy face and unkempt dark hair and sad eyes under black brows, and with a Phi Beta Kappa key slung across his untidy blue serge. He stood there for a second, blinking the sad eyes, as though he had come out of darkness into a sudden light, or had stumbled into the wrong room. He looked like the wrong thing to be coming through that door, all right.

The Boss had stood up and padded across in his sock-feet, holding out his hand, saying, "Hello, Hugh."

Hugh Miller shook hands, and stepped into the room, and I started to edge out the door. Then I caught the Boss's eye, and he nodded, quick, toward my chair. So I shook hands with Hugh Miller, too, and sat back down.

"Have a seat," the Boss said to Hugh Miller.

"No, thanks, Willie," Hugh Miller replied in his slow solemn way. "But you sit down, Willie."

The Boss dropped back into his chair, cocked his feet up again, and demanded, "What's on your mind?"

"I reckon you know," Hugh Miller said.

"I reckon I do," the Boss said.

"You are saving White's hide, aren't you?"

"I don't give a damn about White's hide," the Boss said. "I'm saving something else."

"He's guilty."

"As hell," the Boss agreed cheerfully. "If the category of guilt and innocence can be said to have any relevance to something like Byram B. White."

"He's guilty," Hugh Miller said.

"My God, you talk like Byram was human! He's a thing! You don't prosecute an adding machine if a spring goes bust and makes a mistake. You fix it. Well, I fixed Byram. I fixed him so his unborn great-grandchildren will wet their pants on this anniversary and not know why. Boy, it will be the shock in the genes. Hell, Byram is just something you use, and he'll sure be useful from now on."

"That sounds fine, Willie, but it just boils down to the fact you're saving White's hide."

"White's hide be damned," the Boss said, "I'm saving something else. You let that gang of MacMurfee's boys in the Legislature get the notion they can pull something like this and there's no telling where they'd stop. Do you think they like anything that's been done? The extraction tax? Raising the royalty rate on state land? The income tax? The highway program? The Public Health Bill?"

"No, they don't," Hugh Miller admitted. "Or rather, the people behind MacMurfee don't like it."

"Do you like it?"

"Yes," Hugh Miller said, "I like *it*. But I can't say I like some of the stuff around it."

"Hugh," the Boss said, and grinned, "the trouble with you is you are a lawyer. You are a damned fine lawyer."

"You're a lawyer," Hugh Miller said.

"No," the Boss corrected, "I'm not a lawyer. I know some law. In fact, I know a lot of law. And I made me some money out of law. But I'm not a lawyer. That's why I can see what the law is like. It's like a single-bed blanket on a double bed and three folks in the bed and a cold night. There ain't ever enough blanket to cover the case, no matter how much pulling and hauling, and somebody is always going to nigh catch pneumonia. Hell, the law is like the pants you bought last year for a growing boy, but it is always this year and the seams are popped and the shankbone's to the breeze. The law is always too short and too tight for growing humankind. The best you can do is do something and then make up some law to fit and by the time the law gets on the books you would have done something different. Do you think half the things I've done were clear, distinct, and simple in the constitution of this state?"

"The Supreme Court has ruled—" Hugh Miller began.

"Yeah, and they ruled because I put 'em there to rule it, and they saw what had to be done. Half the things *weren't* in the constitution but they are now, by God. And how did they get there? Simply because somebody did 'em."

The blood began to climb up in Hugh Miller's face, and he shook his head just a little, just barely, the way a slow animal does when a fly skims by. Then he said, "There's nothing in the constitution says that Byram B. White can commit a felony with impunity."

"Hugh," the Boss began, soft, "don't you see that Byram doesn't mean a thing? Not in this situation. What they're after is to break the administration. They don't care about Byram, except so far as it's human nature to hate to think somebody else is getting something when you aren't. What they care about is undoing what this administration has done. And now is the time to stomp 'em. And when you start out to do something—" he sat up straight in the chair now, with his hands on the overstuffed sides, and thrust his head forward at Hugh Miller—"you got to use what you've got. You got to use fellows like Byram, and Tiny Duffy, and that scum down in the Legislature. You can't make bricks without straw, and most of the time all the straw you got is secondhand straw from the cowpen. And if you think you can make it any different, you're crazy as a hoot owl."

Hugh Miller straightened his shoulders a little. He did not look at the Boss but at the wall beyond the Boss. "I am offering my resignation as Attorney General," he said. "You will have it in writing, by messenger, in the morning."

"You took a long time to do it," the Boss said softly. "A long time, Hugh. What made you take such a long time?"

Hugh Miller didn't answer, but he did move his gaze from the wall to the Boss's face.

"I'll tell you, Hugh," the Boss said. "You sat in your law office fifteen years and watched the sons-of-bitches warm chairs in this state and not do a thing, and the rich get richer and the pore get porer. Then I came along and slipped a Louisville Slugger in your hand and whispered low, 'You want to step in there and lay round you a little?' And you did. You had a wonderful time. You made the fur fly and you put nine tin-horn grafters in the pen. But you never touched what was behind 'em. The law isn't made for that. All you can do about that is take the damned government away from the behind guys and keep it away from 'em. Whatever way you can. You know that down in your heart. You want to keep your Harvard hands clean, but way down in your heart you know I'm telling the truth, and you're asking the benefit of somebody getting his little panties potty-black. You know you're welching if you pull out. That," he said, softer than ever, and leaned toward Hugh Miller, peering up at him, "is why it took you so long to do it. To pull out."

Hugh Miller looked down at him a half minute, down into the beefy upturned face and the steady protruding eyes. There was a shadowed, puzzled expression on Hugh Miller's face, as though he were trying to read something in a bad light, or in a foreign language he didn't know very well. Then he said, "My mind is made up."

"I know your mind's made up," the Boss said. "I know I couldn't change your mind, Hugh." He stood up in front of his chair, hitched his trousers up, the way a fellow has to who is putting it on some around the middle, and sock-footed over to Hugh Miller. "Too bad," he said. "You and me make quite a team. Your brains and my brawn."

Hugh Miller gave something which resembled an incipient smile.

"No hard feelings?" the Boss said, and stuck out his hand.

Hugh Miller took it.

"If you don't give up likker, you might drop in and have a drink with me some time," the Boss said. "I won't talk politics."

"All right," Hugh Miller said, and turned toward the door.

He had just about made the door, when the Boss said, "Hugh." Hugh Miller stopped and looked back.

"You're leaving me all alone," the Boss said, in semicomic woe, "with the sons-of-bitches. Mine and the other fellow's."

Hugh Miller smiled in a stiff, embarrassed way, shook his head, said, "Hell—Willie—" let his voice trail off without ever saying what he had started to say, and then Harvard Law School, Lafayette Escadrille, Croix de Guerre, clean hands and pure heart, was with us no longer.

The Boss sank down on the foot of the bed, heaved his left ankle up over his right knee; and while he meditatively scratched the left foot, the way a farmer does when he takes off his shoes at night, he stared at the closed door.

"With the sons-of-bitches," he said, and let the foot slip off the knee and plop to the floor, while he still stared at the door.

Chapter **V**

Revolution

Whether the law should be obeyed, whether the majority or a minority is "right," and whether the end justifies the means are questions that must be given extremely ambiguous answers in concrete situations. We may go further. In the crucible of action it will often not be at all possible to relate such abstract questions to the rush of events, which have an appearance of necessity about them, which occur with such immense force as to transcend the categories of political thought. Such an occurrence is revolution, one of the most constant of all political phenomena: the collapse of the legitimacy of an old order, its rightness no longer believed in by a substantial number of its citizens; the appearance of men who hope to transform completely the institutions under which they have lived.

Social scientists have disputed continually with each other concerning the type of event that is indicated by the name revolution: What are its chief characteristics? How do we know when we are in the presence of a "real" revolution and when we are not? If, however, we take the literary imagination for our guide, we see that some of these conceptual difficulties may be overcome. For those writers who have created (or recreated) a moment of revolutionary politics, be it the politics of class warfare or the politics of national independence, almost always have turned out to be discovering the same thing in their imaginative descriptions. We may call their discovery the revolutionary spirit, as it appears in both successful and failed revolutions and in mere rebellions. We can identify this spirit by noting some of its major components.

There is a deeply felt, emotional and intellectual recognition on the part of great numbers of people that the conditions under which they live are simply no longer to be borne. The English historian and essayist Thomas Carlyle, in his sensitive and imaginative reconstruction of the greatest modern revolution, captured the inmost meaning of that event in words that can easily be applied to other places and other times:

> Forward, ye maddened sons of France; be it toward this destiny or toward that! Around you is but starvation, falsehood, corruption and the clam of death. Where ye are is no abiding.

This complete disaffection with the existing society, in addition, is accompanied, as one might expect, by an insistent vision of a future society that will be radically different in every way—that will truly be a better world. Such visions—which usually look back to a "golden age" as much as they look forward to a "new" society—are to be found in the writings of modern revolutionaries from the English Puritans to Marx and Engels. In the preface to his poem Milton, the eighteenth century poet William Blake expressed in four brief stanzas that combination of despair, insistence, and hope that marks the revolutionary spirit.

Just as masses of people recognize the desperation of their situation, so they also (as Marx and Engels prophesied in The Communist Manifesto) find in desperate necessity the will and the ability to act in solidarity. As individuals they have accomplished nothing; as a united mass they have the strength to overturn everything. ("Great," said Carlyle, "is the combined voice of men.") Carlyle's description of the events leading up to the storming of the Bastille and Malraux's account of the Chinese movement for national independence in the 1920's, describe from the outside the stages by which revolutionary leaders and hitherto disorganized masses come together to form a revolutionary movement. In Émile Zola's Germinal, in contrast, we are under the skin, so to speak, of a revolutionary crowd, in this case of striking mineworkers; we see from the inside out how the once apathetic mass is propelled forward by its leaders in new-found solidarity.

At the same time, however, we must remember that to continue on to fruition, a revolution must be more than a temporary upheaval, more than a mere riot. In the group of selections on ends and means in Chapter IV, "Easter 1916," W. B. Yeats's memorial to the martyred leaders of the Dublin Rising for Irish independence, gives an intimation of the lasting enthusiasm and morale that can be bred by the human solidarity of the revolutionary spirit:

> MacDonagh and MacBride
> And Connolly and Pearse
> Now and in time to be,
> Wherever green is worn,
> Are changed, changed utterly:
> A terrible beauty is born.

Not only do revolutionaries act together but they also, and it seems inevitably, act with violence: That is a crucial aspect of their solidarity. Those who do not think of their own lives as requiring revolutionary violence for improvement will, of course, have difficulty in understanding the motives that drive revolutionaries. Why cannot all men, they will ask, abide by the civilized rules of gradual nonviolent change from which we ourselves have benefited? The question certainly is a relevant one: Anyone must want to think twice before justifying or condoning the kinds of actions that threaten to tear apart the fabric of all social order. To that question, however, there are also some relevant answers.

In the first place, violence of all kinds is more widespread throughout the world than those who live in peaceful communities like to admit. The poet T. S. Eliot once wrote:

> It is hard for those who live near a Bank
> To doubt the security of their money;
> It is hard for those who live near a Police Station
> To believe in the triumph of violence.*

It is equally hard for those who live, or think they live, in a stable polity to believe in either the necessity or the inevitability of

* From "Choruses from 'The Rock,'" *Collected Poems 1909–1962*. Reprinted by permission of Harcourt, Brace & World, Inc., and Faber and Faber Ltd.

social upheaval. Yet almost everywhere but in the most stable liberal democracies (and in some cases, as illustrated by American race relations, not even in those), the established order itself rests on coercion, intimidation, and often simple brute force. The violence of revolutionaries such as Zola's miners or the Irish nationalists is but a more straightforward version, as they see it, of the repression to which they themselves are subjected.

Moreover, especially in developing colonial societies, it is not at all clear that the goods of life—freedom, well-being and so forth—can in fact be achieved for most people except at an immense cost. No doubt impersonal, underlying historical tendencies proceeding without deliberate mass violence may gradually overturn an old order and replace it with a new one; we refer to such an occurrence, for example, when we speak of the Industrial Revolution. But such massive social change has in fact usually been accompanied by widespread violence in some guise or other; and in the modern world with its terribly quickened pace of change, it seems less likely than ever before that the conditions which permitted gradual economic development in Britain, the United States, and even nineteenth century Japan can possibly be duplicated. Furthermore, even supposedly nonviolent developmental processes have their own significant unintended side-effects, such as those depicted in Joyce Cary's account of the "modernization" process in Africa, from his novel Mister Johnson. Destruction is the order of the day even in this kind of "revolution," despite the absence of brutal mass action. To say which of the two types of change is "better" requires a value judgment so complex and so perplexing that no one can make it with any real sense of certainty.

But in any event, all such ambivalent remarks are really beside the point: They indicate misunderstanding of the kind of calculation that goes on, and that can go on, in revolutionary situations. One can hope for gradualism, and has every right to do so; but one simply cannot ask for it and expect always to be heeded. For to those who have been possessed by the revolutionary spirit, who want the future now because the present is literally unbearable, it is not enough to wait for history; they must have change for themselves, not for some hypothetical descendants of theirs.

(*It is the emphasis both on underlying impersonal trends and on men's rising up and making their own history—a dual emphasis logically contradictory yet psychologically satisfying—that is the major part of Marxism's appeal to the oppressed.*) And because others, who benefit from the old order, will certainly fight to maintain it and will often themselves use violence even in response to nonviolent pressures, the question "Who shall rule?" becomes one that at such times can only be settled by force. In Seven Red Sundays the Spanish writer Ramon Sender, writing of the Spanish Civil War, suggests the pathological state toward which the revolutionary spirit can sometimes tend once the need for and logic of violence have been recognized.

Finally, the study of history seems to suggest that the frequency of revolution is almost equalled by the frequency with which revolutions are said to have been "betrayed"—the expectations they aroused come to nothing or worse; "necessary" violence leading in the end to indiscriminate terror; "Jerusalem," the society of equals, receding into the future. The betrayal of visionary hopes is the subject of the brief poem "Parnell," by Yeats, and the short story "Gedali," by the post-Revolutionary Russian writer Isaac Babel. But one must be cautious about drawing final conclusions on the basis of such literature. To participate with all these writers, Yeats and Babel included, in the revolutionary experience—to feel the sense of despair and visionary hope they convey—is necessarily to feel sharply that other sense of futility and loss. But it is also to understand the moral and emotional imperatives out of which revolutions grow. Thus we are left once again with the feeling that to the most profound questions about what is to be done no single answer is wholly satisfactory.

JERUSALEM

William Blake

From the Preface to *Milton*

And did those feet in ancient time
Walk upon England's mountains green?
And was the holy Lamb of God
On England's pleasant pastures seen?

And did the Countenance Divine
Shine forth upon our clouded hills?
And was Jerusalem builded here
Among these dark Satanic Mills?

Bring me my Bow of burning gold!
Bring me my Arrows of desire!
Bring me my Spear! O clouds unfold!
Bring me my Chariot of fire!

I will not cease from Mental Fight,
Nor shall my Sword sleep in my hand,
Till we have built Jerusalem
In England's green and pleasant Land.

THE STORMING OF THE BASTILLE

Thomas Carlyle

From *The French Revolution*

On Monday the huge city has awoke, not to its weekday industry:
to what a different one! The working man has become a fighting

Book V, Chs. 5 and 6. All footnotes deleted.

man; has one want only; that of arms. The industry of all crafts, has paused; except it be the smith's fiercely hammering pikes; and, in a faint degree, the kitchener's cooking off-hand victuals; for *bouche va toujours*. Women too are sewing cockades; not now of *green,* which being D'Artois color, the Hôtel-de-Ville has had to interfere in it; but of *red* and *blue,* our old Paris colors; these, once based on a ground of constitutional *white,* are the famed tricolor, which (if prophecy err not) "will go round the world."

All shops, unless it be the baker's and vintner's, are shut: Paris is in the streets; rushing, foaming like some Venice wine-glass into which you had dropped poison. The tocsin, by order, is pealing madly from all steeples. Arms, ye elector municipals; thou Flesselles with thy Echevins, give us arms! Flesselles gives what he can; fallacious, perhaps insidious promises of arms from Charleville; order to seek arms here, order to seek them there. The new municipals give what they can; some three hundred and sixty indifferent firelocks, the equipment of the city-watch; "a man in wooden shoes, and without coat, directly clutches one of them, and mounts guard." Also as hinted, an order to all smiths to make pikes with their whole soul.

Heads of districts are in fervent consultation; subordinate patriotism roams distracted, ravenous for arms. Hitherto at the Hôtel-de-Ville was only such modicum of indifferent firelocks as we have seen. At the so-called arsenal, there lies nothing but rust, rubbish and saltpetre, overlooked too by the guns of the Bastille. His majesty's repository, what they call *Garde-Meuble,* is forced and ransacked; tapestries enough, and gauderies; but of serviceable fighting-gear small stock! Two silver-mounted cannons there are; an ancient gift from his majesty of Siam to Louis Fourteenth; gilt sword of the Good Henri; antique chivalry arms and armor. These, and such as these, a necessitous patriotism snatches greedily, for want of better. The Siamese cannons go trundling, on an errand they were not meant for. Among the indifferent firelocks are seen tourney-lances; the princely helm and hauberk glittering amid ill-hatted heads, as in a time when all times and their possessions are suddenly sent jumbling!

At the *Maison de Saint-Lazare,* Lazar-House once, now a correction-house with priests, there was no trace of arms; but, on the other hand, corn, plainly to a culpable extent. Out with it, to market; in this scarcity of grains! Heavens, will "fifty-two carts," in long row, hardly carry it to the *Halle aux Bleds?* Well, truly, ye reverend fathers, was your pantry filled; fat are your larders; over-generous your wine-bins, ye plotting exasperators of the poor; traitorous fore-stallers of bread!

Vain is protesting, entreaty on bare knees: the House of Saint-Lazarus has that in it which comes not out by protesting. Behold, how, from every window, it *vomits;* mere torrents of furniture, of bellowing and hurlyburly; the cellars also leaking wine. Till, as was natural, smoke rose, kindled some say, by the desperate Saint-Lazaristes themselves, desperate of other riddance; and the estab-lishment vanished from this world in flame. Remark nevertheless that "a thief" (set on or not by aristocrats), being detected there, is "instantly hanged."

Look also at the Châtelet prison. The debtors' prison of La Force is broken from without; and they that sat in bondage to aristocrats go free: hearing of which the felons at the Châtelet do likewise "dig up their pavements," and stand on the offensive; with the best prospects, had not patriotism, passing that way, "fired a volley," into the felon world; and crushed it down again under hatches. Patriotism consorts not with thieving and felony; surely also punish-ment, this day, hitches (if she still hitch) after crime, with frightful shoes-of-swiftness! "Some score or two" of wretched persons, found prostrate with drink in the cellars of that Saint-Lazare, "are indig-nantly haled to prison; the jailer has no room; whereupon, other place of security not suggesting itself, is it written, *on les pendit,* they hanged them." Brief is the word; not without significance, be it true or untrue!

In such circumstances, the aristocrat, the unpatriotic rich man is packing up for departure. But he shall not get departed. A wooden-shod force has seized all barriers, burned or not; all that enters, all that seeks to issue, is stopped there, and dragged to the Hôtel-de-Ville: coaches, tumbrils, plate, furniture, "many meal-sacks," in time even "flocks and herds" encumber the Place de Grève."

And so it roars, and rages, and brays; drums beating, steeples pealing; criers rushing with hand-bells: "Oyez, oyez. All men to their districts to be enrolled!" The districts have met in gardens, open squares; are getting marshaled into volunteer troops. No red-hot ball has yet fallen from Besenval's camp; on the contrary, deserters with their arms are continually dropping in: nay now, joy of joys, at two in the afternoon, the Gardes Françaises, being or-dered to Saint-Denis, and flatly declining, have come over in a body!

It is a fact worth many. Three thousand six hundred of the best
fighting men, with complete accouterment; with cannoneers even,
and cannon! Their officers are left standing alone; could not so much
as succeed in "spiking the guns." The very Swiss, it may now be
hoped, Château-Vieux and the others, will have doubts about fighting.

Our Parisian militia, which some think it were better to name
national guard, is prospering as heart could wish. It promised to be
forty-eight thousand; but will in few hours double and quadruple
that number; invincible, if we had only arms!

But see, the promised Charleville boxes, marked *Artillerie!* Here,
then, are arms enough? Conceive the blank face of patriotism, when
it found them filled with rags, foul linen, candle-ends, and bits of
wood! Provost of the merchants, how is this? Neither at the Char-
teaux Convent, whither we were sent with signed order, is there or
ever was there any weapon of war. Nay here, in this Seine boat,
safe under tarpaulings (had not the nose of patriotism been of the
finest), are "five thousand-weight of gunpowder"; not coming *in*, but
surreptitiously going out! What meanest thou, Flesselles? 'Tis a
ticklish game, that of "amusing" us. Cat plays with captive mouse;
but mouse with enraged cat, with enraged national tiger? Meanwhile, the faster, oh, ye black-aproned smiths, smite with strong
arm and willing heart. This man and that, all stroke from head to
heel, shall thunder alternating, and ply the great forge-hammer, till
stithy reel and ring again; while ever and anon, overhead, booms
the alarm-cannon, for the city has now got gunpowder. Pikes are
fabricated; fifty thousand of them, in six-and-thirty hours; judge
whether the black-aproned have been idle. Dig trenches, unpave the
streets, ye others, assiduous, man and maid; cram the earth in
barrel-barricades, at each of them a volunteer sentry: pile the whin-
stones in window-sills and upper rooms. Have scalding pitch, at
least boiling water ready, ye weak and old women, to pour it and
dash it on Royal-Allemand, with your old skinny arms: your shrill
curses along with it will not be wanting! Patrols of the newborn
national guard, bearing torches, scour the streets, all that night;
which otherwise are vacant, yet illuminated in every window by
order. Strange-looking; like some naphtha-lighted city of the dead,
with here and there a flight of perturbed ghosts.

Oh, poor mortals, how ye make this earth bitter for each other;
this fearful and wonderful life fearful and horrible; and Satan has

his place in all hearts! Such agonies and ragings and wailings ye have and have had, in all times: to be buried all, in so deep silence; and the salt sea is not swollen with your tears.

Great meanwhile is the moment, when tidings of freedom reach us; when the long-enthralled soul, from amid its chains and squalid stagnancy, arises, were it still only in blindness and bewilderment, and swears by Him that made it, that it will be *free!* Free? Understand that well, it is the deep commandment, dimmer or clearer, of our whole being, to be *free.* Freedom is the one purport, wisely aimed at, or unwisely, of all man's struggles, toilings and sufferings, in this earth. Yes, supreme is such a moment (if thou have known it); first vision as of a flame-girt Sinai, in this our waste pilgrimage, which thenceforth wants not its pillar of cloud by day, and pillar of fire by night! Something it is even, nay, something considerable, when the chains have grown *corrosive,* poisonous, to be free "from oppression by our fellow-man." Forward, ye maddened sons of France; be it toward this destiny or toward that! Around you is but starvation, falsehood, corruption and the clam of death. Where ye are is no abiding.

Imagination, may, imperfectly, figure how commandant Besenval, in the Champ-de-Mars, has worn out these sorrowful hours. Insurrection raging all round; his men melting away! From Versailles, to the most pressing messages, comes no answer; or once only some vague word of answer which is worse than none. A council of officers can decide merely that there is no decision: colonels inform him "weeping," that they do not think their men will fight. Cruel uncertainty is here: war-god Broglie sits yonder, inaccessible in his Olympus; does not descend terror-clad, does not produce his whiff of grapeshot; sends no orders.

Truly, in the château of Versailles all seems mystery: in the town of Versailles, were we there, all is rumor, alarm and indignation. An august national assembly sits, to appearance, menaced with death; endeavoring to defy death. It has resolved "that Necker carries with him the regrets of the nation." It has sent solemn deputation over to the château, with entreaty to have these troops withdrawn. In vain: his majesty, with a singular composure, invites us to be busy rather with our own duty, making the constitution! Foreign Pandours, and suchlike, go pricking and prancing with a swash-buckler air; with an eye too probably to the *Salle des Menus,* were it not for the "grim-looking countenances" that crowd all avenues there. Be firm, ye national senators; the cynosure of a firm, grim-looking people!

The august national senators determine that there shall, at least, be permanent session till this thing end. Wherein, however, consider that worthy Lafranc de Pompignan, our new president, whom we have named Bailly's successor, is an old man, wearied with many things. He is the brother of that Pompignan who meditated lamentably on the book of *Lamentations*;

> Savez-vous pourquoi Jérémie
> Se lamentait toute sa vie?
> C'est qu'il prévoyait
> Que Pompignan le traduirait!

Poor Bishop Pompignan withdraws; having got Lafayette for helper or substitute: this latter, as nocturnal vice-president, with a thin house in disconsolate humor, sits sleepless, with lights unsnuffed; waiting what the hours will bring.

So at Versailles. But at Paris, agitated Besenval, before retiring for the night, has stepped over to old M. de Sombreuil, of the *Hôtel des Invalides* hard by. M. de Sombreuil has, what is a great secret, some eight-and-twenty thousand stand of muskets deposited in his cellars there; but no trust in the temper of his invalides. This day, for example, he sent twenty of the fellows down to unscrew those muskets; lest sedition might snatch at them: but scarcely, in six hours, had the twenty unscrewed twenty gun-locks, or dogsheads (*chiens*) of locks, each invalide his dogshead! If ordered to fire, they would, he imagines, turn their cannon against himself.

Unfortunate old military gentleman, it is your hour, not of glory! Old Marquis de Launay too, of the Bastille, has pulled up his draw-bridges long since, "and retired into his interior"; with sentries walking on his battlements, under the midnight sky, aloft over the glare of illuminated Paris; whom a national patrol, passing that way, takes the liberty of firing at: "seven shots toward twelve at night," which do not take effect. This was the 13th day of July, 1789; a worse day many said than the last 13th was when only hail fell out of heaven, not madness rose out of Tophet ruining worse than crops!

In these same days as chronology will teach us, hot old Marquis Mirabeau lies stricken down, at Argenteuil, *not* within sound of these alarm-guns; for *he* properly is not there and only the body of

him now lies deaf and cold forever. It was on Saturday night that
he drawing his last life-breaths gave up the ghost there; leaving a
world which would never go to his mind now broken out seemingly
into deliration and the *culbute générale*. What is it to him departing
elsewhither on his long journey? The old Château Mirabeau stands
silent far off on its scarped rock in that "gorge of two windy valleys";
the pale-fading specter now of a château: this huge world-riot and
France and the world itself fades also like a shadow on the great
still mirror-sea; and all shall be as God wills.

Young Mirabeau sad of heart, for he loved this crabbed brave old
father; sad of heart and occupied with sad cares, is withdrawn from
public history. The great crisis transacts itself without him.

.   .   .

But, to the living and the struggling, a new fourteenth morning
dawns. Under all roofs of this distracted city is the nodus of a
drama, not untragical, crowding toward solution. The bustlings and
preparings, the tremors and menaces; the tears that fell from old
eyes! This day, my sons, ye shall quit you like men. By the memory
of your father's wrongs, by the hope of your children's rights!
Tyranny impends in red wrath: help for you is none, if not in your
own right hands. This day ye must do or die.

From earliest light, a sleepless permanent committee has heard
the old cry, now waxing almost frantic, mutinous: Arms! Arms!
Provost Flesselles, or, what traitors there are among you may think
of those Charleville boxes. A hundred and fifty thousand of us; and
but the third man furnished with so much as a pike! Arms are the
one thing needful; with arms we are an unconquerable man-edify-
ing national guard; without arms, a rabble to be whiffed with
grapeshot.

Happily the word has arisen, for no secret can be kept, that there
lie muskets at the *Hôtel des Invalides*. Thither will we: king's procureur M. Ethys de Corny, and whatsoever of authority a permanent committee can lend, shall go with us. Besenval's camp is there;
perhaps he will not fire on us; if he kills us, we shall but die.

Alas, poor Besenval, with his troops melting away in that manner,
has not the smallest humor to fire! At five o'clock this morning, as he
lay dreaming, oblivious in the *Ecole Militaire*, a "figure" stood
suddenly at his bedside; "with face rather handsome; eyes inflamed,
speech rapid and curt, air 'audacious'"; such a figure drew Priam's
curtains: The message and monition of the figure was, that resistance would be hopeless; that if blood flowed, woe to him who shed

it. Thus spoke the figure: and vanished. "Withal there was a kind of eloquence that struck one." Besenval admits that he should have arrested him, but did not. Who this figure with inflamed eyes, with speech rapid and curt, might be? Besenval knows, but mentions not. Camille Desmoulins? Pythagorean Marquis Valadi, inflamed with "violent motions all night at the Palais Royal?" Fame names him "Young M. Meillar," then shuts her lips about him forever.

In any case, behold, about nine in the morning, our national volunteers rolling in long wide flood south-westward to the *Hôtel des Invalides;* in search of the one thing needful. King's procureur M. Ethys de Corny and officials are there; the Curé of Saint-Etienne du Mont marches unpacific at the head of his militant parish; the clerks of the Basoche in red coats we see marching, now volunteers of the Basoche; the volunteers of the Palais Royal: national volunteers, numerable by tens of thousands; of one heart and mind. The king's muskets are the nation's; think, old M. de Sombreuil, how, in this extremity, thou wilt refuse them! Old M. de Sombreuil would fain hold parley, send couriers; but it skills not: the walls are scaled, no invalide firing a shot; the gates must be flung open. Patriotism rushes in, tumultuous, from grunsel up to ridge-tile, through all rooms and passages; rummaging distractedly for arms. What cellar, or what cranny can escape it? The arms are found; all safe there; lying packed in straw, apparently with a view to being burned! More ravenous than famishing lions over dead prey, the multitude, with clangor and vociferation, pounces on them; struggling, dashing, clutching: to the jamming-up, to the pressure, fracture and probable extinction of the weaker patriot. And so, with such protracted crash of deafening, most discordant orchestra-music, the scene is changed; and eight-and-twenty thousand sufficient fire-locks are on the shoulders of as many national guards, lifted thereby out of darkness into fiery light.

Let Besenval look at the glitter of these muskets, as they flash by! Gardes Françaises, it is said, have cannon leveled on him; ready to open, if need were, from the other side of the river. Motionless sits he; "astonished," one may flatter oneself, "at the proud bearing (*fière contenance*) of the Parisians." And, now, to the Bastille, ye intrepid Parisians! There grapeshot still threatens; thither all men's thoughts and steps are now tending.

Old De Launay, as we hinted, withdrew "into his interior" soon after midnight of Sunday. He remains there ever since, hampered, as all military gentlemen now are, in the saddest conflict of uncertainties. The Hôtel-de-Ville "invites" him to admit national soldiers, which is a soft name for surrendering. On the other hand, his majesty's orders were precise. His garrison is but eighty-two old invalides, reinforced by thirty-two young Swiss; his walls indeed are nine feet thick, he has cannon and powder; but alas, only one day's provision of victuals. The city too is French, the poor garrison mostly French. Rigorous old De Launay, think what thou wilt do!

All morning, since nine, there has been a cry everywhere: To the Bastille! Repeated "deputations of citizens" have been here, passionate for arms; whom De Launay has got dismissed by soft speeches through portholes. Toward noon, elector Thuriot de la Rosière gains admittance; finds De Launay indisposed for surrender; nay disposed for blowing up the place rather. Thuriot mounts with him to the battlements: heaps of paving-stones, old iron and missiles lie piled; cannon all duly leveled; in every embrasure a cannon, only drawn back a little! But outward, behold, oh, Thuriot, how the multitude flows on, welling through every street: tocsin furiously pealing, all drums beating the *générale*: the suburb Saint-Antoine rolling hitherward wholly, as one man! Such vision (spectral yet real) thou, oh Thuriot, as from thy mount of vision, beholdest in this moment; prophetic of what other phantasmagories, and loud-gibbering spectral realities, which thou yet beholdest not but shalt: "*Que voulez-vous?*" said De Launay, turning pale at the sight, with an air of reproach, almost of menace. "Monsieur," said Thuriot, rising into the moral-sublime, "what mean *you?* Consider if I could not precipitate *both* of us from this height," say only a hundred feet, exclusive of the walled ditch! Whereupon De Launay fell silent. Thuriot shows himself from some pinnacle, to comfort the multitude becoming suspicious, fremescent; then descends; departs with protest; with warning addressed also to the invalides, on whom, however, it produces but a mixed indistinct impression. The old heads are none of the clearest; besides, it is said, De Launay has been profuse of beverages (*prodigue des boissons*). They think, they will not fire, if not fired on, if they can help it; but must, on the whole, be ruled considerably by circumstances.

Woe to thee, De Launay, in such an hour, if thou canst not, taking some one firm decision, *rule* circumstances! Soft speeches will not serve; hard grapeshot is questionable; but hovering between the two is *un*questionable. Ever wilder swells the tide of men; their infinite hum waxing ever louder, into imprecations, perhaps into cackle of stray musketry, which latter, on walls nine feet thick, cannot do execution. The outer drawbridge has been lowered for Thuriot; new *deputation of citizens* (it is the third, and noisiest of all) penetrates that way into the outer court; soft speeches producing no clearance of these, De Launay gives fire; pulls up his drawbridge. A slight sputter; which has *kindled* the too combustible chaos; made it a roaring fire-chaos! Bursts forth insurrection, at sight of its own blood (for there were deaths by that sputter of fire), into endless rolling explosion of musketry, distraction, execration; and overhead, from the fortress, let one great gun, with its grapeshot, go booming, to show what we *could* do. The Bastille is besieged!

On, then, all Frenchmen, that have hearts in your bodies! Roar with all your throats, of cartilage and metal, ye sons of liberty; stir spasmodically whatsoever of utmost faculty is in you, soul, body, or spirit; for it is the hour! Smite, thou Louis Tournay, cartwright of the Marais, old-soldier of the Regiment Dauphiné; smite at that outer drawbridge chain, though the fiery hail whistles round thee: Never, over nave or felloe, did thy axe strike such a stroke. Down with it, man; down with it to Orcus: let the whole accursed edifice sink thither, and tyranny be swallowed up forever! Mounted, some say, on the roof of the guard-room, some "on bayonets stuck into joints of the wall," Louis Tournay smites, brave Aubin Bonnemère (also an old soldier) seconding him: the chain yields, breaks; the huge drawbridge slams down, thundering (*avec fracas*). Glorious; and yet, alas, it is still but the outworks. The eight grim towers, with their invalide musketry, their paving-stones and cannon-mouths, still soar aloft intact; ditch yawning impassable, stone-faced; the inner drawbridge with its *back* toward us; the Bastille is still to take!

To describe this siege of the Bastille (thought to be one of the most important in history) perhaps transcends the talent of mortals. Could one but, after infinite reading, get to understand so much as the plan of the building! But there is open esplanade, at the end of the Rue Saint-Antoine; there are such forecourts, *Cour Avancé, Cour de l'Orme,* arched gateway (where Louis Tournay now fights); then new drawbridges, dormant-bridges, rampart-bastions, and the grim eight towers; a labyrinthic mass, high-frowning there, of all ages from twenty years to four hundred and twenty; beleagued, in this its last hour, as we said, by mere chaos come again! Ordnance of all calibres; throats of all capacities; men of all plans, every man his own engineer: seldom since the war of Pygmies and Cranes was there seen so anomalous a thing. Half-pay Elie is home for a suit of regimentals; no one would heed him in colored clothes: half-pay Hulin is haranguing Gardes Françaises in the Place de Grève. Frantic patriots pick up the grapeshots; bear them, still hot (or seemingly so), to the Hôtel-de-Ville: Paris, you perceive, is to be burned! Flesselles is "pale to the very lips," for the roar of the multitude grows deep. Paris wholly has got to the acme of its frenzy; whirled all ways by panic madness. At every street-barricade, there whirls simmering a minor whirlpool, strengthening the barricade, since God knows what is coming; and all minor whirlpools play distractedly into that grand fire-maelstrom which is lashing round the Bastille.

And so it lashes and it roars. Cholat the wine-merchant has become an impromptu cannoneer. See Georget, of the marine service, fresh from Brest, ply the king of Siam's cannon. Singular (if we were not used to the like); Georget lay, last night taking his ease at his inn; the king of Siam's cannon also lay, knowing nothing of *him*, for a hundred years. Yet now, at the right instant, they have got together, and discourse eloquent music. For, hearing what was toward, Georget sprang from the Brest diligence, and ran. Gardes Françaises also will be here with real artillery: were not the walls so thick! Upward from the esplanade, horizontally from all neighboring roofs and windows, flashes one irregular deluge of musketry, without effect. The invalides lie flat, firing comparatively at their ease from behind stone; hardly through portholes show the tip of a nose. We fall, shot; and make no impression!

Let conflagration rage; of whatsoever is combustible! Guardrooms are burnt, invalides mess-rooms. A distracted "Perukemaker with two fiery torches" is burning "the saltpetres of the arsenal"; had not a woman run screaming; had not a patriot, with some tincture of natural philosophy, instantly struck the wind out of him (butt of musket on pit of stomach), overturned barrels, and stayed the devouring element. A young beautiful lady, seized escaping in these outer courts, and thought falsely to be De Launay's daughter, shall be burned in De Launay's sight; she lies swooned on a paillasse: but again a patriot, it is brave Aubin Bonnemère the old soldier, dashes in, and rescues her. Straw is burned; three cart loads of it, hauled thither, go up in white smoke: almost to the choking of patriotism itself; so that Elie had, with singed brows, to drag back one cart; and Réole the "gigantic haberdasher" another. Smoke as of Tophet; confusion as of Babel; noise as of the crack of doom!

Blood flows; the aliment of new madness. The wounded are carried into houses of the Rue Cerisaie; the dying leave their last mandate not to yield till the accursed stronghold fall. And yet, alas, how fall? The walls are so thick! Deputations, three in number, arrive from the Hôtel-de-Ville; Abbé Fauchet (who was of one) can say, with what almost superhuman courage of benevolence. These wave their town-flag in the arched gateway; and stand, rolling their drum; but to no purpose. In such crack of doom, De Launay cannot hear them, dare not believe them; they return, with justified rage, the whew of lead still singing in their ears. What to do? The firemen are here, squirting with their fire-pumps on the invalides cannon to wet the touch holes; they unfortunately cannot squirt so high; but produce only clouds of spray. Individuals of classical knowledge propose catapults. Santerre, the sonorous brewer of the Suburb Saint-Antoine, advises rather that the place be fired, by a "mixture of phosphorus and oil-of-turpentine spouted up through forcing-pumps"; O Spinola-Santerre, hast thou the mixture *ready?* Every man his own engineer! And still the fire-deluge abates not; even women are firing, and Turks; at least one woman (with her sweetheart), and one Turk. Gardes Françaises have come: real cannon, real cannoneers. Usher Maillard is busy; half-pay Elie, half-pay Hulin rage in the midst of thousands.

How the great Bastille clock ticks (inaudible) in its inner court there, at its ease, hour after hour; as if nothing special, for it or the world, were passing! It tolled one when the firing began; and is now pointing toward five, and still the firing slakes not. Far down, in their vaults, the seven prisoners hear muffled din as of earthquakes; their turnkeys answer vaguely.

Woe to thee, De Launay, with thy poor hundred invalides! Broglie is distant, and his ears heavy: Besenval hears, but can send no help. One poor troop of Hussars has crept, reconnoitering, cautiously along the Quais, as far as the Pont Neuf. "We are come to join you," said the captain; for the crowd seems shoreless. A large-headed dwarfish individual, of smoke-bleared aspect, shambles forward, opening his blue lips, for there is sense in him; and croaks: "Alight then, and give up your arms!" The Hussar-captain is too happy to be escorted to the barriers, and dismissed on parole. Who the squat individual was? Men answer, It is M. Marat, author of the excellent pacific "Avis au Peuple!" Great truly O, thou remarkable Dogleech, is this thy day of emergence and new-birth; and yet this same day come four years! But let the curtains of the future hang.

What shall De Launay do? One thing only De Launay could have done; what he said he would do. Fancy him sitting, from the first, with lighted taper, within arm's length of the powder-magazine; motionless, like old Roman senator, or bronze lamp-holder; coldly apprising Thuriot, and all men, by a slight motion of his eye, what his resolution was: Harmless he sat there, while unharmed; but the king's fortress, meanwhile, could, might, would or should in nowise be surrendered, save to the king's messenger: one old man's life is worthless, so it be lost with honor; but think, ye bawling *canaille,* how will it be when a whole Bastille springs skyward: In such statuesque, taper-holding attitude, one fancies De Launay might have left Thuriot, the red clerks of the Basoche, curé of Saint-Stephen and all the tagrag-and-bobtail of the world, to work their will.

And yet, withal, he could not do it. Hast thou considered how each man's heart is so tremulously responsive to the hearts of all men; hast thou noted how omnipotent is the very sound of many men? How their shriek of indignation palsies the strong soul; their howl of contumely withers with unfelt pangs? The Ritter Gluck confessed that the ground-tone of the noblest passage, in one of his noblest operas, was the voice of the populace he had heard at Vienna, crying to their kaiser: Bread! Bread! Great is the combined voice of men; the utterance of their *instincts,* which are truer than their *thoughts:* it is the greatest a man encounters, among the sounds and shadows which make up this world of time. He who can resist that, has his footing somewhere *beyond* time. De Launay could not do it. Distracted, he hovers between two; hopes in the middle of despair; surrenders not his fortress; declares that he will blow it up, seizes torches to blow it up, and does not blow it. Unhappy old De Launay, it is the death-agony of thy Bastille and thee! Jail, jailering and jailer, all three, such as they may have been, must finish.

For four hours now has the world-Bedlam roared: call it the world-chimaera, blowing fire! The poor invalides have sunk under their battlements, or rise only with reversed muskets: they have made a white flag of napkins; go beating the *chamade,* or seeming to beat, for one can bear nothing. The very Swiss at the portcullis look weary of firing; disheartened in the fire-deluge: a porthole at the drawbridge is opened, as by one that would speak. See Huissier Maillard, the shifty man! On his plank, swinging over the abyss of that stone ditch; plank resting on parapet, balanced by weight of patriots, he hovers perilous: such a dove toward such an ark! Deftly, thou shifty usher; one man already fell; and lies smashed, far down there, against the masonry! Usher Maillard falls not: deftly, unerring he walks, with outspread palm. The Swiss holds a paper through his porthole; the shifty usher snatches it, and returns. Terms of surrender: pardon, immunity to all! Are they accepted: *"Foi d'officier,* On the word of an officer,"* answers half-pay Hulin, or half-pay Elie, for men do not agree on it, "they are!" Sinks the drawbridge, Usher Maillard bolting it when down; rushes in the living deluge: the Bastille is fallen: *Victoire! La Bastille est prise!*

A WAR OF NATIONAL LIBERATION

André Malraux

"Outward Bound"

June 25th

A general strike has been declared at Canton. This wireless message, underlined in red, was put up yesterday.

As far as eye can reach, the Indian Ocean, glassy, motionless, without a ripple. A sky of shapeless clouds seems to distill a hothouse atmosphere, wrapping us round in a blanket of warm, thick, damp air. And the passengers pace up and down the deck, counting their steps and keeping fairly close to the white notice-board on which the messages received during the night will soon appear. Through these daily radiograms the first act of the drama unfolds itself, growing steadily more and more actual, more and more threatening, until it obsesses everyone on board. Hitherto the hostility of the Canton Government had gone no further than words, now the wireless shows that it is proceeding to deeds. What impresses us all most profoundly is not so much strikes, rioting and street fights, but this unexpected determination, as tenacious as that of Great Britain itself, the determination to have done with mere words and to strike at the British Empire, by attacking what is dearest to it—its prestige and its wealth.

The boycotting of all British goods, even when offered for sale by Chinese, throughout all the provinces depending on Canton, the method of controlling first one market, then another, the destruction of machinery by the factory hands of Hong Kong; finally this general strike—its effect on trade throughout the whole of this British possession, while, according to newspaper correspondents, the military schools are seething with unusual activity: all this seems to bring the passengers face to face with an entirely new kind of warfare, with a war waged by the anarchical powers of Southern China in conjunction with mysterious collaborators, against the very symbol of British domination in the Far East, that fortified rock of Hong Kong whence the empire of the sword surveys its subjects.

Hong Kong. There, on the map, is the Island—a clearly marked black spot, closing the Pearl River like a bolt. Along the river banks stretches the gray mass which is Canton, with dots indicating straggling suburbs, hardly more than a few hours away from the British cannon. Every day the passengers look—at first eagerly, now with an intense anxiety—at that little black spot as if they expected it to reveal something, as if they were trying to guess how that fortress on which their lives depend—how that richest rock in the world—would be defended.

If, sooner or later, it were to suffer some serious reverse, if it were to be reduced to the rank of a small port, if it were to be assailed in any way, then China, in her struggle against the white race, might be able to organize herself, in a manner hitherto impossible, and there might be an end of European domination. The dealers in cotton and horses among my fellow passengers are keenly aware of this, and the wondering look on their anxious faces—"how will it affect my business?"—is itself a reflection of the gigantic struggle being waged by the empire of disorder, hastily organizing itself, against a nation which stands above all others for strength, determination, and tenacity.

There is a stir on deck—passengers hurry, push and press: the wireless has appeared.

"England, Belgium, the United States," nothing of importance there—but what next? Russia? Ah! No, nothing worth noting. "China." At last!

"The President of the Republic."

What then?

"Canton."

The radiogram is long; and the passengers on the edge of the crowd push so hard that we are wedged against the partition.

> THE CADETS OF THE WHAMPOA MILITARY SCHOOL, COMMANDED BY RUSSIAN OFFICERS, AND FORMING THE REAR GUARD OF A HUGE PROCESSION OF STUDENTS AND WORKMEN, HAVE OPENED FIRE ON SHAMEEN.* THE EUROPEAN SAILORS, WHO WERE PROTECTING THE BRIDGES, REPLIED WITH THEIR MACHINE GUNS. THE CADETS, URGED ON BY THEIR RUSSIAN OFFICERS, MADE SEVERAL ATTEMPTS TO STORM THE BRIDGES, BUT WERE REPULSED WITH HEAVY LOSS.
>
> THE EUROPEAN WOMEN AND CHILDREN OF SHAMEEN ARE, IF POSSIBLE, TO BE REMOVED TO HONG KONG ON AMERICAN BOATS. THE DEPARTURE OF THE ENGLISH TROOPS IS IMMINENT.

A sudden silence falls.

The suspense is over. Not a single word is spoken. The passengers disperse in consternation. On the right, however, two Frenchmen meet one another: "Really, sir, whenever are the Powers going to make up their minds to take some strong measure, which . . . ?" And, as they move towards the bar, the noise of the engines drowns the end of the sentence.

Tomorrow, Singapore. We shall not reach Hong Kong for another ten days.

Five o'clock

An additional wireless message has most unusually appeared.

> SHAMEEN. THE ELECTRIC LIGHT HAS FAILED. THE WHOLE CONCESSION IS IN DARKNESS. THE BRIDGES HAVE BEEN HASTILY FORTIFIED AND PROTECTED BY BARBED WIRE. THEY ARE LIT BY SEARCHLIGHTS FROM THE GUNBOATS.

SINGAPORE: 7 A.M.
June 26th

Interminable delay—the stamping of passports. A long line of motorcars for hire, some thirty of them, waiting behind the docks. Malay children flourish newspapers—*The Straits Times, The Malay Gazette.* They are instantly surrounded, the papers seized and torn open; sheets falling to the ground are picked up in a trice, while those who have not had the luck to get papers look over the shoulders of their more fortunate companions all to no avail; for the latest news in these evening papers is but a repetition of the radiograms we have seen on board.

* The European Concession at Canton. *Tr.*

Jumping into the first car I can find, I fly through the deserted oriental suburb, where the macadamized road winds round a pagoda, the sides of which have been converted into hoardings for advertisements. Crossing the bridge, I come on the blue and green Chinese town, and on the *arroyo* with its sampans, packed closely together like cattle. On the right is the English town—banks, steamship companies' offices, vast sheds of reinforced concrete, housing some hundred offices, at the foot of hills surrounded by lawns and dotted with villas.

These bastions of British trade, brooded over by the arsenal guns, would indicate that here at least for the present Great Britain's strength remains unshaken.

Here is the junk port and the Raffles Hotel, with its stiff, bare garden, its palms from the Botanical Gardens, its Sikh porter and its Chinese "boys." Its lemonade with a shaddock flavor is the best in Asia. Here perhaps one may be able to hear news.

The bar is crowded. Alone and lounging lazily at the middle table, in a suit of cream-colored linen, is a big man whose mouth I seem to recognize: his lips are full, slightly curved and protruding —sucking, babbling lips. Yes, it is Rensky, a Russian, who was once a collector and who now travels at the expense of a Boston museum, in search of masterpieces of Asiatic art.

He sits near the great square of green baize onto which the radiograms are fixed with drawing pins. (A "boy" puts them up as soon as they are received and, as on Test Match days, gives copies to anyone who has tipped him.)

I go up to Rensky. After the customary Russian effusions, he says, pointing to five little ebony elephants he has arranged pipewise on the table:

"As you see, my friend (I have met him about five times), I am buying little elephants. When we begin our excavations I shall put them in the tombs. Then the tombs will be closed; and half a century later, when they are reopened and these little things are discovered at the bottom, all encrusted and corroded, the archaeologists will wonder. I love the idea of puzzling posterity. On one of the Angkor-Wat towers I have engraved an obscene inscription, which I have carefully defiled. Finot will decipher it. These austere people must be scandalized a little. . . ."

I barely listen to him; for, from the opposite side of the table, I am reading over his shoulder:

HONG KONG. THE SITUATION IS EXTREMELY GRAVE. IN VIEW OF
THE POSSIBLE DESPATCH OF A BRITISH EXPEDITIONARY FORCE FROM
HONG KONG TO CANTON, THE CHINESE HERE, TO THE NUMBER OF
MORE THAN FIFTY THOUSAND, HAVE BEGUN TO STRIKE.

"You are slandering the gods, Rensky."

"One must amuse oneself. And there are so few amusements for
a man like me, my dear fellow. A medium here told me that the
spirits of the dead are so bored during the night, when darkness
prevents their watching those who are alive, that their only pleasure
is to make, by moonlight, patterns out of the down of pillows, like
hairdressers make out of hair. And it's quite true, my dear chap,
quite true. Just open your pillow gently one morning and you will
find in it all manner of designs in feathers—question marks, crosses,
aigrettes, birds. . . . I have arranged some myself, just to puzzle
the spirits, which is much more thrilling than trying to puzzle
scholars. Still, I can't spend my life in doing this. So you see I get as
bored as the spirits. Only my night is longer than theirs. It seems
unending."

"You are depressed, Rensky."

"No. But I miss love and irony. It is high time I returned to
Europe, whither they have both of them fled."

The "boy" brings in a new sheet.

HONG KONG. THE STRIKE IS SPREADING TO THE STEAMSHIP COM-
PANIES, BOTH COASTAL AND UP-COUNTRY. ALL THE BUTTERFIELD AND
SWIRE BOATS AND THOSE OF THE HONG KONG, CANTON AND MACAO
STEAMBOAT COMPANY HAVE BEEN DESERTED BY THEIR CHINESE
CREWS.

"You do not like China?"

"I have no quarrel with her new gods—mirrors, electricity, phonographs. For that god with a trumpet, the phonograph, *is* a creature,
you know. A light green pavilion insinuating itself curiously behind
the altar of the ancestors, suggests strange thoughts. The idea that
phonographs are spirits tormenting the dead might be worth preaching. . . . It would certainly be accepted in the North. . . . Look at
that plan of Singapore hanging on the column to your right. Note
the blue of the sea growing less and less marked from bottom to top.
Time is like that in China. In the North, time does not exist. The
map is a clean slate. It's a fine thing, my dear fellow, the indifference
with which that hoary empire up here, just like a drowning man,
has its eyes fixed on its necklace of cannon—its new fetishes—and at

the same time on its bloodstained antiquity stretching far back into history. It is playing the game. That is enough. Have you ever noticed how it has put the world into its domino? Figure and flowers—and, above, both worth considering—happiness and wind. . . ."

Here comes the "boy" again.

HONG KONG. BRITAIN REPLIES TO THE CHINESE GENERAL STRIKE BY PROHIBITING THE EXPORT OF RICE. NO CHINESE RICE IN HONG KONG WAREHOUSES IS ALLOWED TO LEAVE THE PORT. THE EXASPERATION OF THE CHINESE KNOWS NO BOUNDS.

Now Rensky has seen what I am looking at.

"Yes, the real game, the Game with a Capital G, must be followed in the South—in the South where the blue is deep because time has passed rather too quickly. But you must notice the preliminaries— that droll Americanization of China with all its comforts and sensuality. . . . At Canton, where once were ancient pagodas, there are now California hotels, shops with thirteen stories, and those terrible skyscrapers, which have a cinema on the ground floor, a theater on the first, all manner of amusements on the second— automatic machines, bowls, acrobats, gladiators, dancers; on the third, a smoke-room; on the fourth, a tearoom; on the fifth, a select brothel; on the sixth, offices. Higher still, flats occupied by ladies of doubtful reputation, and higher yet, more offices. On the roof, a garden and a Russo-European restaurant. Four. . . ."

"What a marvelous description. You know it all by heart."

"That is what I do with my heart in Asia! But I was about to say 'four lifts,' when you interrupted me, showing that you are sadly wanting in curiosity."

"I await the sequel to your 'lifts' with ill-concealed impatience."

"The sequel to 'my lifts' is the Revolution. You know that the Canton Government depends for its existence mainly on the contributions of the poor. But many of the rich merchants also contribute, sending their donations in hard cash to the Kuomintang. That fat Chinese, sitting alone at a table near the bar, to whom the 'boy' is now taking the radiograms, is Koo-Chen, the President of the party here."

I recognize him; for I have his photograph in my pocket.

"He is worth several million dollars. He stakes his fortune on the Revolution, and, during the last few days, on war."

"The game may become dangerous."

"Do you think so? In a certain delightful street at Hong Kong, there are houses with closed shutters, surrounded by large gardens. . . ."

Another radiogram!

HARBIN, THE BOLSHEVIK DIRECTORS OF THE CHINESE EASTERN RAIL- WAY HAVE ORDERED THEIR EMPLOYEES TO TAKE THEIR SHARE OF THE CONTRIBUTIONS IN AID OF THE HONG KONG STRIKERS. THIS PRECEDENT WILL BE FOLLOWED SPEEDILY THROUGHOUT THE WHOLE OF EASTERN SIBERIA.

HONG KONG. ALL BANKS ARE CLOSED.

"They are not boardinghouses—far from it; they are private dwell- ings, to which the Chinese leaders used to send their numerous wives, when peace was threatened in China. Nothing thicker than a partition wall separated the favorite wives or concubines of certain revolutionary leaders. Sometimes they called on one another, and when fortune favored the generals, the dictators, driven out one by one, met in these bystreets. Sun Yat-sen came here, and doubtless recalled memories of his college days."

"Those days are past."

"Who can tell?"

"Sometimes, Rensky, one can tell. One can tell, for example, that this action of the Canton Government in venturing to attack Britain is not within the realm . . ."

"Of pure fantasy?"

"Charming as that realm may be, and one through which you yourself have just been wandering."

He was silent. Then he rejoined sadly:

"China is a country in which everything is possible. To attack Britain! Since the Revolution of 1911, the Kuomintang has per- meated China. Now it is reorganizing itself at Canton, from defeat to defeat or from victory to victory, much as budding Protestanism reorganized itself at Geneva. With a strange blend of stupidity and greatness, they have been endeavoring to establish their Republic for the last fourteen years. . . . The real change set in on the death of Sun, with the hold over the party and the government acquired by the committees controlled by Bolshevists. Bolshevists! And yet a man like Garine is far from being a true Bolshevist."

"In what way?"

"Well, my friend, if by Bolshevist you mean revolutionary, then Garine is a Bolshevist. But, if you mean, as I do, a particular type of revolutionary, who, among many other characteristics, is distinguished by a belief in Marxism, then Garine is no Bolshevist—at least in my opinion; but I am talking about things of which I really know very little. And, moreover, does anyone know Garine, does anyone know Borodin? Borodin's real name is Braun I-don't-know-what. He is a Lettish Jew. And Garine is no more Russian than he. His father was Swiss. He was almost entirely educated in France. That is all I know. (Strange that our information about the real opinions and character of the men who are set on rousing China against us, should be so meager. . . .) By the way, if such people interest you, there is a personage here, who is beginning to be talked about, and who seems to me very strange, very strange: he is a young Chinese, called Hong, one of the leaders of the terrorists. Have you heard of him?"

"Not yet."

"That is a pity. I don't quite recollect all that has been told me about him, but it is very interesting. Ah! what fun it will be to see the very persons whom the Bolshevists are now educating turning against them. . . ."

The "boy" serves us with cocoa, milk ice and at the same time with the latest radiograms from Hong Kong.

> AT SHAMEEN THE POSTAL SERVICE IS SUSPENDED. THE TELEPHONE WIRES HAVE BEEN CUT.

Five o'clock

We shall be starting in a few minutes. Here are the newspaper boys at last. They rush across the gangway. Their newspapers, still damp, are bought up immediately. We read:

"Canton. The British steamboats in the harbor have been commandeered. The women and children still in the town have been evacuated to Hong Kong. Shameen is now nothing but a camp."

That will be good for British trade!

"The despatch of British and Indian troops to Canton is imminent."

What a mistake! Now for Hong Kong.

"Hong Kong. Trade is at a standstill. In private houses, hotels and hospitals, Chinese servants refuse to work."

"UNDER STRICT RESERVATION—The strike of employees on the big steamboats will be declared this afternoon."

One of the barmen is hurrying up and down deck, ringing a bell, which is the signal that we are starting. The Indian money-changers are leaving the boat, rattling the coins in their moneybags. At the end of the gangway, Japanese hawkers are calling out their wares—rattan armchairs, soap, ties, perfumes. Malay fruit sellers are landing awkwardly, encumbered with huge hampers bristling with plumes of banana leaves and filled with yellow mangosteens, kakis like tomatoes, and great green oranges.

There is a lull. A deep, deafening, rhythmic sound vibrates through the boat. It comes from the engines. Rensky hastily takes his leave. He has hardly left me when the gangway is pulled up.

Night falls. We can barely see that we are coasting along the shore of an inland sea, that we are passing the islands of the strait, crowned with Chinese shrubs. Soon we can discern nothing but lighthouses.

I am writing on the bar terrace. . . . The whole of that Americanized China, which Rensky was describing just now, with its islands dimly outlined and silent seems fading into the past. Another China is emerging, wavering and maladroit, animated by an unformed, self-tormenting soul. At Singapore, while monuments, names, landscapes, everything, dwindle into unimportance, there rises a new spirit, the spirit of the main body of the town, a spirit as clearly defined as the spirit of the past, a spirit which says: "Grow rich and grow strong." It would be hard to imagine a grander battle: British energy on the one hand, Chinese on the other, both fighting for money, and beneath, amorphous and yet active, the mass of revolution, flowing underground like a river. But, in this great business city, re-echoing with the constant screech of ships' sirens, all this is barely distinguishable. The old Dutch gabled houses, the British Victorian homes, the squarely built dwellings seem planted like stakes in this warm red earth; but on the other side of this European and of this Russo-Malay scene of painted houses, I see a very different town: the native town inhabited by poor sordid creatures, a town of modest Chinese offices, the offices of the revolutionary committee of the island, of the committee of the Sultanate of Johore, of the committee of the Malay States, of the branches of the committees of Kuala-Lumpur, Malacca, Bangkok, Batavia, Sourabaya, Sumatra, Borneo . . . the syndicated union of rickshaw pushers, of restaurant "boys," of servants (not a single European without a servant), of dock laborers, all adherents of the town Kuomintang. All this is inert at present, almost asleep. No revolt as yet. But every day, dollars, bills and checks leave Singapore for Canton, while the half-naked fat old secretaries of revolu-

tionary organizations sleep sanctimoniously in the equatorial heat,
undisturbed by the whirring of the ventilating fans, their hands
folded over their stomachs, under the very eyes of the police officers
who have them under observation.

Five o'clock

HONG KONG. THE GOVERNOR'S DEPARTURE IS POSTPONED. LETTERS
AND NEWSPAPERS ARE TO BE CENSORED.

SHANGHAI. AGITATION IS SPREADING THROUGH ALL THE SOUTHERN
PROVINCES. FOREIGN CONSULS HAVE BEEN STONED.

HONG KONG. ADMIRAL FROCHOT, COMMANDER OF THE FRENCH
NAVAL FORCES IN THE FAR EAST, STARTED FOR CANTON AT NOON
YESTERDAY.

FURTHER ACTS OF VIOLENCE BY TERRORISTS. THE BRITISH VOLUN-
TEERS HAVE BEEN MOBILIZED.

The fête, which was to have taken place on board, has been can-
celed. Everyone is weighed down by anxiety, which is as pervasive
as the heat. No waiters are to be seen. They keep out of the way in
order to avoid the grumblings of the passengers at the slightest
thing that goes wrong. It is only the women and men who do not
avoid one another. Everyone points out irritably the poverty of the
telegraph clerks' announcements, although we are all perfectly aware
of it. Men, old and young, make the round of the boat, walking
briskly, as if bent on tiring themselves out. Then, during the greatest
heat of the day, they sleep in their deck chairs, waking with a start
at the slightest sound, cross and peevish.

Ten o'clock

HONG KONG. MORE THAN TWENTY PACKET BOATS ARE LYING TO IN
THE PORT. THE PROCLAMATION OF A STATE OF SIEGE IS BEING DIS-
CUSSED.

In six days. . . .

SAÏGON
June 29th

A deserted, desolate provincial town, with long, straight avenues
and boulevards, where grass grows under widespreading tropical
trees. After a long drive we reach the Chinese quarter, where there
are beautiful gilded signs inscribed with black letters, little banks
and all kinds of agencies. Before us, down the middle of a broad,

grass-grown avenue, runs a little railway, Numbers 37, 35, 33. Here we stop in front of a house like all the others in the quarter: a mere compartment. Apparently a business house. All round the door are plates bearing the names of obscure Canton companies. Inside, behind dusty, dilapidated counters doze two Chinese clerks: one corpselike, dressed in white, the other obese, of a terra-cotta complexion, naked to the waist. On the wall are chromographs of Shanghai, of girls with fringes plastered on their foreheads, monsters, landscapes. In front of me is a tangle of three bicycles. This is the headquarters of the President of the Cochin-China Kuomintang. I ask in Cantonese:

"Is the chief in?"

"He has not returned yet, sir. But go up and make yourself at home."

I reach the first floor by a kind of ladder. No one there. I sit down and look round lazily: a European chest, a Louis Philippe marble-topped table, a Chinese sofa in black wood, and two magnificent American armchairs, equipped with all kinds of devices. Stuck into the mirror above me is a large portrait of Sun Yat-sen, and a smaller photograph of the master of the house.

A sputtering sound and the strong smell of Chinese fat frying come in through the alcove.

The sound of steps on the ladder.

The chief comes in. With him are two other Chinese and the Frenchman, Gérard, whom I have come to meet. I am given green tea and told to assure the Central Committee of the loyalty of the whole of French Indo-China to those democratic institutions, which, etc. . . .

Finally Gérard and I go out. He is a special delegate from the Kuomintang to Indo-China, who has been here only a few days. A little man with mustache and beard growing gray, he suggests the Czar Nicholas II; he has his worried, hesitating look and his benevolent air; he is a cross between a shortsighted professor and a provincial doctor. He walks by my side with a dragging step, and far in front of him is a cigarette, fixed to the extremity of a long cigarette holder.

His car is waiting for us at the corner of the street. We get in and drive slowly out into the country. The movement of the air seems to transport us into another climate and to enable us to relax our strained and fatigued muscles.

"What news?"

He hesitates, not knowing whether to address me as "Sir" or "Comrade."

"Not much. Hardly anything beyond what you have read in the newspapers. The strike proclamation seems to have been obeyed implicitly by the various committees of workmen. . . . And the English are apparently at a loss for any countermeasures. The organization of volunteers is a farce; all very well, perhaps, in case of a riot, but useless against a strike. The prohibition of the export of rice guarantees the food supply of Hong Kong for some time, but to starve out the town was never our object. What use would it be? For the rich Chinese who support counterrevolutionary organizations this prohibition is a staggering blow. . . ."

"But since yesterday?"

"Nothing."

"Do you think the Cochin-China Government has suppressed the radiograms?"

"No. The wireless employees are nearly all members of 'the Young-Annam.' We should have been informed. The reason is, doubtless, that Hong Kong has ceased to transmit."

A pause.

"And what about the Chinese stations?"

"The Chinese stations are all under the influence of our Propaganda department. That explains everything. The rumor that the Chamber of Commerce has asked its President to declare war on England, that the Cantonese have imprisoned English soldiers in Shameen, that very significant manifestations are in course of preparation—all this is nonsense. What is really serious and certain is that the English in Hong Kong see wealth escaping from them. The boycott was good. The strike is better. What will be the sequel to the strike? A pity we don't know anything! I ought to hear something soon. For the last two days not a single boat has sailed for Hong Kong. They are all there in the River. . . ."

"And here?"

"We are not doing badly. You can take six thousand dollars at least away with you. I expect six hundred more, but am not certain. And remember that those six thousand dollars I am going to give you come, almost all of them, from poor people: coolies, dock laborers, artisans."

"And they have good reason to hope. The Hong Kong and Shameen affairs. . . ."

"Certainly—this latent war against Great Britain and her lack of energy intoxicate them. But all this is very un-Chinese."

"Are you sure of that?"

He is silent. Wedged into a corner of the car, with his eyes half closed, he may be reflecting or he may be merely giving himself up to the delicious sensation of the current of fresh air, which is as restful as a bath. In the blue evening haze, the rice fields whizz by, vast mirrors painted here and there or finely stenciled with clumps of bushes and pagodas, all dominated by the soaring poles of the wireless. Compressing his lips and pulling at his mustache, he replies:

"Have you heard of the Monad conspiracy that the English have just discovered at Hong Kong?"

"I know nothing; I have just arrived."

"Good. Well, the Monad is a secret society. You must know that at present the only connection between Hong Kong and Canton is by means of a little steamboat, the *Honan*. When the boat is in port at Hong Kong, it is guarded by a British officer and a few sailors. The representatives of the Society are shrewd enough to realize the importance of preventing the boat from leaving Canton when its cargo consists of arms, which the British are sending to the antirevolutionaries."

"Have we no one on this boat?"

"No; it was impossible. The boat takes up its cargo of arms at some lonely spot on the Pearl River—just in the same way as hashish is smuggled at Suez.

"But to return to our plot. Six of the conspirators—at the risk of their lives, as they well know—kill the British officer and the sailors in the night, take command of the boat, work on board for four hours, and are made prisoners at dawn, by a patrol of British volunteers, at the very moment when they were setting sail, carrying off—guess what?—one of those blocks of wood, painted with two eyes, which a Chinese boat carries at its prow."

"I don't quite understand."

"The eyes serve as a guide to the boat. A blind boat would be wrecked inevitably."

"Oh! I see."

"You are astonished, and so am I. But, this is the kind of society —more or less—that we have to deal with. Groups of fanatics—brave —there is no doubt about that—of a few plutocrats out for notoriety or for security—and crowds of students and coolies."

"Is not such a society, like any other, at the mercy of a few energetic leaders?"

"Certainly. But that does not simplify matters."

"Energy is always energy."

"Not in the least. It is all a question of how it is employed.
Would you, now, as a way of sinking vessels, go and capture a plank
with eyes painted on it, at the risk of being shot in the attempt?"

"Were they shot?"

"No, the British did not go so far as that. But this is the type of
energetic person with whom we can do nothing. Some of them, consumed with enthusiasm, are ready for any sacrifice. With them all
is well. But woe to those chattering, idiotic students, who quote
Marx as if he were Confucius! I don't know who the leaders of the
Monad were. The Society was not in communication with us. But it
counted among its adherents a large number of students who had
returned from American Universities. . . . You must always remember that the most serious of these Societies, the one in which
you place the greatest confidence, is capable at any moment of
giving up everything in order to go off in search of an eye painted
on a piece of wood."

And, seeing me smile, he exclaims:

"Ah! you think I exaggerate. But you will see, you will see. Why,
Borodin and Garine could give you a hundred examples of such
things."

"Do you know Garine well?"

"Why yes! We have worked together. What do you want to hear
about him? You know how he behaved as Director of Propaganda?"

"I have heard very little about it."

"He. . . . It is difficult to explain. You know how innocent China
used to be of any ideas tending to action. Now they have taken
possession of her much as the idea of equality took possession of the
French in '89. The same thing may have been occurring throughout
the whole of yellow Asia. In Japan, when German lecturers began
to preach Nietzsche, fanatical students cast themselves down from
the rocks. Now at Canton, things were not so simple, but no less
terrible. Of no kind of individualism had they the remotest idea.
Today coolies are beginning to discover that they exist, simply that
they exist. . . . Among the masses there is a certain type of ideol-
ogy, as there is a certain type of art, which is not a popularization,
but something quite different. . . . Borodin's propaganda said to
peasants and workingmen: 'You are fine fellows because you are

peasants and workingmen, and because in you reside the two greatest
forces of the State.' Such an announcement had no effect whatever.
They could not see how suffering blows and dying of hunger could
constitute the greatest forces of the State. They were convinced
that as peasants and as workingmen they were merely despicable.
They were afraid that the Revolution would end and that they
would be plunged back into that humiliation, out of which they had
hoped to rise. Nationalist propaganda, as carried on by Garine, told
them something quite different; it moved them, in a way quite un-
foreseen and extraordinarily violent, by teaching them to believe in
their own dignity—their own importance, if you prefer the term. To
realize the effect of this you should watch a dozen of these laborers
with their sly little cat's faces, their rags and their wickerwork hats,
drilling like volunteers, surrounded by an admiring crowd. The
strength of the French Revolution and of the Russian Revolution,
lay in the fact that they gave everyone his land. This revolution is
giving everyone his life. Against such a revolution every Western
State is powerless. . . . Hatred! people want to make hatred the
key to everything! And yet how simple it all is! The revolutionary
ardor of our volunteers arises from many things, but primarily from
their craving for a life . . . a life in which they can do nothing but
. . . spit upon the others! This Borodin has not yet understood. . . ."

THE REVOLUTIONARY CROWD

Émile Zola

From *Germinal*

And the troop went off over the flat plain, white with frost
beneath the pale winter sun, and overflowed the path as they passed
through the beetroot fields.

From the Fourche-aux-Boeufs, Étienne had assumed command.
He cried his orders while the crowd moved on, and organized the
march. Jeanlin galloped at the head, performing barbarous music

From the book *Germinal* by Émile Zola. Translated by Havelock Ellis. Everyman's Library Edition. Reprinted by permission of E. P. Dutton & Co., Inc., and
J. M. Dent & Sons Ltd.: Publishers. From Part V, Chs. 4 and 5.

on his horn. Then the women came in the first ranks, some of them armed with sticks: Maheude, with wild eyes seemed to be seeking afar for the promised city of justice, Mother Brulé, the Levaque woman, Mouquette, striding along beneath their rags, like soldiers setting out for the seat of war. If they had any encounters, we should see if the police dared to strike women. And the men followed in a confused flock, a stream that grew larger and larger, bristling with iron bars and dominated by Levaque's single axe, with its blade glistening in the sun. Étienne, in the middle, kept Chaval in sight, forcing him to walk before him; while Maheu, behind, gloomily kept an eye on Catherine, the only woman among these men, obstinately trotting near her lover for fear that he would be hurt. Bare heads were dishevelled in the air; only the clank of sabots could be heard, like the movement of released cattle, carried away by Jeanlin's wild trumpeting.

But suddenly a new cry arose:

"Bread! bread! bread!"

It was midday; the hunger of six weeks on strike was awaking in these empty stomachs, whipped up by this race across the fields. The few crusts of the morning and Mouquette's chestnuts had long been forgotten; their stomachs were crying out, and this suffering was added to their fury against the traitors.

"To the pits! No more work! Bread!"

Étienne, who had refused to eat his share at the settlement, felt an unbearable tearing sensation in his chest. He made no complaint, but mechanically took his tin from time to time and swallowed a gulp of gin, shaking so much that he thought he needed it to carry him to the end. His cheeks were heated and his eyes inflamed. He kept his head, however, and still wished to avoid needless destruction.

As they arrived at the Joiselle road a Vandame pikeman, who had joined the band for revenge on his master, impelled the men towards the right, shouting:

"To Gaston-Marie! Must stop the pump! Let the water ruin Jean-Bart!"

The mob was already turning, in spite of the protests of Étienne, who begged them to let the pumping continue. What was the good of destroying the galleries? It offended his workman's heart, in spite of his resentment. Maheu also thought it unjust to take revenge on a machine. But the pikeman still shouted his cry of vengeance, and Étienne had to cry still louder:

"To Mirou! There are traitors down there! To Mirou! to Mirou!"

With a gesture, he had turned the crowd towards the left road; while Jeanlin, going ahead, was blowing louder than ever. An eddy was produced in the crowd; this time Gaston-Marie was saved.

And the four kilometres which separated them from Mirou were traversed in half an hour, almost at running pace, across the interminable plain. The canal on this side cut it with a long icy ribbon. The leafless trees on the banks, changed by the frost into giant candelabra, alone broke this pale uniformity, prolonged and lost in the sky at the horizon as in a sea. An undulation of the ground hid Montsou and Marchiennes; there was nothing but bare immensity.

They reached the pit, and found a captain standing on a footbridge at the screening-shed to receive them. They all well knew Father Quandieu, the doyen of the Montsou captains, an old man whose skin and hair were quite white, and who was in his seventies, a miracle of fine health in the mines.

"What have you come after here, you pack of meddlers?" he shouted.

The band stopped. It was no longer a master, it was a mate; and a certain respect held them back before this old workman.

"There are men down below," said Étienne. "Make them come up."

"Yes, there are men there," said Father Quandieu, "some six dozen; the others were afraid of you evil beggars! But I warn you that not one comes up, or you will have to deal with me!"

Exclamations arose, the men pushed, the women advanced. Quickly coming down from the footbridge, the captain now barred the door.

Then Maheu tried to interfere.

"It is our right, old man. How can we make the strike general if we don't force all the mates to be on our side?"

The old man was silent a moment. Evidently his ignorance on the subject of coalition equalled the pikeman's. At last he replied: "It may be your right, I don't say. But I only know my orders. I am alone here; the men are down till three, and they shall stay there till three."

The last words were lost in hooting. Fists were threateningly advanced, the women deafened him, and their hot breath blew in his face. But he still held out, his head erect, and his beard and hair white as snow; his courage had so swollen his voice that he could be heard distinctly over the tumult.

"By God! you shall not pass! As true as the sun shines, I would rather die than let you touch the cables. Don't push any more, or I'm damned if I don't fling myself down the shaft before you!"

The crowd drew back shuddering and impressed. He went on:

"Where is the beast who does not understand that? I am only a workman like you others. I have been told to guard here, and I'm guarding."

That was as far as Father Quandieu's intelligence went, stiffened by his obstinacy of military duty, his narrow skull, and eyes dimmed by the black melancholy of half a century spent underground. The men looked at him moved, feeling within them an echo of what he said, this military obedience, the sense of fraternity and resignation in danger. He saw that they were hesitating still, and repeated:

"I'm damned if I don't fling myself down the shaft before you!"

A great recoil carried away the mob. They all turned, and in the rush took the right-hand road, which stretched far away through the fields. Again cries arose:

"To Madeleine! To Crèvecœur! no more work! Bread! bread!"

But in the centre, as they went on, there was hustling. It was Chaval, they said, who was trying to take advantage of an opportunity to escape. Étienne had seized him by the arm, threatening to do for him if he was planning some treachery. And the other struggled and protested furiously:

"What's all this for? Isn't a man free? I've been freezing the last hour. I want to clean myself. Let me go!"

He was, in fact, suffering from the coal glued to his skin by sweat, and his woollen garment was no protection.

"On you go, or we'll clean you," replied Étienne. "Don't expect to get your life at a bargain."

They were still running, and he turned towards Catherine, who was keeping up well. It annoyed him to feel her so near him, so miserable, shivering beneath her man's old jacket and her muddy trousers. She must be nearly dead of fatigue, she was running all the same.

"You can go off, you can," he said at last.

Catherine seemed not to hear. Her eyes, on meeting Étienne's, only flamed with reproach for a moment. She did not stop. Why did he want her to leave her man? Chaval was not at all kind, it was true; he would even beat her sometimes. But he was her man, the one who had had her first; and it enraged her that they should throw themselves on him—more than a thousand of them. She would have defended him without any tenderness at all, out of pride.

"Off you go!" repeated Maheu, violently.

Her father's order slackened her course for a moment. She trembled, and her eyelids swelled with tears. Then, in spite of her fear, she came back to the same place again, still running. Then they let her be.

The mob crossed the Joiselle road, went a short distance up the Cron road and then mounted towards Cougny. On this side, factory chimneys striped the flat horizon; wooden sheds, brick workshops with large dusty windows, appeared along the street. They passed one after another the low buildings of two settlements—that of the Cent-Quatre-Vingts, then that of the Soixante-Seize; and from each of them, at the sound of the horn and the clamour arising from every mouth, whole families came out—men, women, and children—running to join their mates in the rear. When they came up to Madeleine there were at least fifteen hundred. The road descended in a gentle slope; the rumbling flood of strikers had to turn round the pit-bank before they could spread over the mine square.

It was now not more than two o'clock. But the captains had been warned and were hastening the ascent as the band arrived. The men were all up, only some twenty remained and were now disembarking from the cage. They fled and were pursued with stones. Two were struck, another left the sleeve of his jacket behind. This man-hunt saved the material, and neither the cables nor the boilers were touched. The flood was already moving away, rolling on towards the next pit.

This one, Crèvecœur, was only five hundred metres away from Madeleine. There, also, the mob arrived in the midst of the ascent. A putter-girl was taken and whipped by the women with her breeches split open and her buttocks exposed before the laughing men. The trammer-boys had their ears boxed, the pikemen got away, their sides blue from blows and their noses bleeding. And in this growing ferocity, in this old need of revenge which was turning every head with madness, the choked cries went on, death to traitors, hatred against ill-paid work, the roaring of bellies after bread. They began to cut the cables, but the file would not bite, and the task was too long now that the fever was on them for moving onward, for ever onward. At the boilers a tap was broken; while the water, thrown by bucketsful into the stoves, made the metal gratings burst.

Outside they were talking of marching on Saint-Thomas. This was the best disciplined pit. The strike had not touched it, nearly seven hundred men must have gone down there. This exasperated them; they would wait for these men with sticks, ranged for battle, just to see who would get the best of it. But the rumour ran along that there were gendarmes at Saint-Thomas, the gendarmes of the morning whom they had made fun of. How was this known? nobody could say. No matter! they were seized by fear and decided on Feutry-Cantel. Their giddiness carried them on, all were on the road, clanking their sabots, rushing forward. To Feutry-Cantel! to Feutry-Cantel! The cowards there were certainly four hundred in number and there would be fun! Situated three kilometres away, this pit lay in a fold of the ground near the Scarpe. They were already climbing the slope of the Platrières, beyond the road to Beaugnies, when a voice, no one knew from whom, threw out the idea that the soldiers were, perhaps, down there at Feutry-Cantel. Then from one to the other of the column it was repeated that the soldiers were down there. They slackened their march, panic gradually spread in the country, idle without work, which they had been scouring for hours. Why had they not come across any soldiers? This impunity troubled them, at the thought of the repression which they felt to be coming.

Without any one knowing where it came from, a new word of command turned them towards another pit.

"To the Victoire! to the Victoire!"

Were there, then, neither soldiers nor police at the Victoire? Nobody knew. All seemed reassured. And turning round they descended from the Beaumont side and cut across the fields to reach the Joiselle road. The railway line barred their passage, and they crossed it, pulling down the palings. Now they were approaching Montsou, the gradual undulation of the landscape grew less, the sea of beetroot fields enlarged, reaching far away to the black houses at Marchiennes.

This time it was a march of five good kilometres. So strong an impulse pushed them on that they had no feeling of their terrible fatigue, or of their bruised and wounded feet. The rear continued to lengthen, increased by mates enlisted on the roads and in the settlements. When they had passed the canal at the Magache bridge, and appeared before the Victoire, there were two thousand of them. But three o'clock had struck, the ascent was completed, not a man remained below. Their disappointment was spent in vain threats; they could only heave broken bricks at the workmen who had arrived to take their duty at the earth-cutting. There was a rush, and the deserted pit belonged to them. And in their rage at not finding a traitor's face to strike, they attacked things. A rankling abscess was bursting within them, a poisoned boil of slow growth. Years and years of hunger tortured them with a thirst for massacre and destruction.

Behind a shed Étienne saw some porters filling a wagon with coal.

"Will you just clear out of the bloody place!" he shouted. "Not a bit of coal goes out!"

At his orders some hundred strikers ran up, and the porters only had time to escape. Men unharnessed the horses, which were frightened and set off, struck in the haunches; while others, overturning the wagon, broke the shafts.

Levaque, with violent blows of his axe, had thrown himself on the platforms to break down the footbridges. They resisted, and it occurred to him to tear up the rails, destroying the line from one end of the square to the other. Soon the whole band set to this task. Maheu made the metal chairs leap up, armed with his iron bar which he used as a lever. During this time Mother Brulé led away the women and invaded the lamp cabin, where their sticks covered the soil with a carnage of lamps. Maheude, carried out of herself, was laying about her as vigorously as the Levaque woman. All were soaked in oil, and Mouquette dried her hands on her skirt, laughing to find herself so dirty. Jeanlin for a joke, had emptied a lamp down her neck. But all this revenge produced nothing to eat. Stomachs were crying out louder than ever. And the great lamentation dominated still:

"Bread! bread! bread!"

A former captain at the Victoire kept a stall near by. No doubt he had fled in fear, for his shed was abandoned. When the women came back, and the men had finished destroying the railway, they besieged the stall, the shutters of which yielded at once. They found no bread there; there were only two pieces of raw flesh and a sack of potatoes. But in the pillage they discovered some fifty bottles of gin, which disappeared like a drop of water drunk up by the sand.

Étienne, having emptied his tin, was able to refill it. Little by little a terrible drunkenness, the drunkenness of the starved, was inflaming his eyes and baring his teeth like a wolf's between his

pallid lips. Suddenly he perceived that Chaval had gone off in the
midst of the tumult. He swore, and men ran to seize the fugitive,
who was hiding with Catherine behind the timber supply.

"Ah! you dirty swine; you are afraid of getting into trouble!"
shouted Étienne. "It was you in the forest who called for a strike of
the engine-men, to stop the pumps, and now you want to play us
a filthy trick! Very well! By God! we will go back to Gaston-Marie.
I will have you smash the pump; yes, by God! you shall smash it!"

He was drunk; he was urging his men against this pump which
he had saved a few hours earlier.

"To Gaston-Marie! to Gaston-Marie!"

They all cheered, and rushed on, while Chaval, seized by the
shoulders, was drawn and pushed violently along, while he con-
stantly asked to be allowed to wash.

"Will you take yourself off, then?" cried Maheu to Catherine who
had also begun to run again.

This time she did not even draw back, but turned her burning
eyes on her father, and went on running.

Once more the mob ploughed through the flat-plain. They were
retracing their steps over the long straight paths, by the fields endlessly spread out. It was four o'clock; the sun which approached the
horizon, lengthened the shadows of this horde with their furious
gestures over the frozen soil.

They avoided Montsou, and farther on rejoined the Joiselle road;
to spare the journey round Fourche-aux-Bœufs, they passed beneath the walls of Piolaine. The Grégoires had just gone out, having
to visit a lawyer before going to dine with the Hennebeaus, where
they would find Cécile. The estate seemed asleep, with its avenue
of deserted limes, its kitchen garden and its orchard bared by the
winter. Nothing was stirring in the house, and the closed windows
were dulled by the warm steam within. Out of the profound silence
an impression of good-natured comfort arose, the patriarchal sensation of good beds and a good table, the wise happiness of the proprietor's existence.

Without stopping, the band cast gloomy looks through the grating
and at the length of protecting walls, bristling with broken bottles.
The cry arose again:

"Bread! bread! bread!"

The dogs alone replied, by barking ferociously, a pair of Great
Danes, with rough coats, who stood with open jaws. And behind
the closed blind there were only the servants. Mélanie the cook and

Honorine the housemaid, attracted by this cry, pale and perspiring with fear at seeing these savages go by. They fell on their knees, and thought themselves killed on hearing a single stone breaking a pane of a neighbouring window. It was a joke of Jeanlin's; he had manufactured a sling with a piece of cord, and had just sent a little passing greeting to the Grégoires. Already he was again blowing his horn, the band was lost in the distance, and the cry grew fainter:

"Bread! bread! bread!"

They arrived at Gaston-Marie in still greater numbers, more than two thousand five hundred madmen, breaking everything, sweeping away everything, with the force of a torrent which gains strength as it moves. The police had passed here an hour earlier, and had gone off towards Saint-Thomas, led astray by some peasants; in their haste they had not even taken the precaution of leaving a few men behind to guard the pit. In less than a quarter of an hour the fires were overturned, the boilers emptied, the buildings torn down and devastated. But it was the pump which they specially threatened. It was not enough to stop it in the last expiring breath of its steam; they threw themselves on it as on a living person whose life they required.

"The first blow is yours!" repeated Étienne, putting a hammer into Chaval's hand. "Come! you have sworn with the others!"

Chaval drew back trembling, and in the hustling the hammer fell; while other men, without waiting, battered the pump with blows from iron bars, blows from bricks, blows from anything they could lay their hands on. Some even broke sticks over it. The nuts leapt off, the pieces of steel and copper were dislocated like torn limbs. The blow of a shovel, delivered with full force, fractured the metal body; the water escaped and emptied itself, and there was a supreme gurgle like an agonizing death-rattle.

That was the end, and the mob found themselves outside again, madly pushing on behind Étienne, who would not let Chaval go.

"Kill him! the traitor! To the shaft! to the shaft!"

The livid wretch, clinging with imbecile obstinacy to his fixed idea, continued to stammer his need of cleaning himself.

"Wait, if that bothers you," said the Levaque woman. "Here! here's a bucket?"

There was a pond there, an infiltration of the water from the pump. It was white with a thick layer of ice; and they struck it and broke the ice, forcing him to dip his head in this cold water.

"Duck then," repeated Mother Brulé. "By God! if you don't duck we'll shove you in. And now you shall have a drink of it; yes, yes, like a beast, with your jaws in the trough!"

He had to drink on all fours. They all laughed, with cruel laughter. One woman pulled his ears, another woman threw in his face a handful of dung found fresh on the road. His old woollen jacket in tatters no longer held together. He was haggard, stumbling, and with struggling movements of his hips he tried to flee.

Maheu had pushed him, and Maheude was among those who grew furious, both of them satisfying their old spite; even Mouquette, who generally remained such good friends with her old lovers, was wild with this one, treating him as a good-for-nothing, and talking of taking his breeches down to see if he was still a man.

Étienne made her hold her tongue.

"That's enough. There's no need for all to set to it. If you like, you, we will just settle it together."

His fists closed and his eyes were lit up with homicidal fury; his intoxication was turning into the desire to kill.

"Are you ready? One of us must stay here. Give him a knife; I've got mine."

Catherine, exhausted and terrified, gazed at him. She remembered his confidences, his desire to devour a man when he had drunk, poisoned after the third glass, to such an extent had his drunkards of parents put this beastliness into his body. Suddenly she leapt forward, struck him with both her woman's hands, and choking with indignation shouted into his face:

"Coward! coward! coward! Isn't it enough, then, all these abominations? You want to kill him now that he can't stand upright any longer!"

She turned towards her father and her mother; she turned towards the others.

"You are cowards! cowards! Kill me, then, with him! I will tear your eyes out, I will, if you touch him again. Oh! the cowards!"

And she planted herself before her man to defend him, forgetting the blows, forgetting the life of misery, lifted up by the idea that she belonged to him since he had taken her, and that it was a shame for her when they so crushed him.

Étienne had grown pale beneath this girl's blows. At first he had been about to knock her down; then, after having wiped his face with the movement of a man who is recovering from intoxication, he said to Chaval, in the midst of deep silence:

"She is right; that's enough. Off you go."

Immediately Chaval was away, and Catherine galloped behind him. The crowd gazed at them as they disappeared round a corner of the road; but Maheude muttered:

"You were wrong; ought to have kept him. He is sure to be after some treachery."

But the mob began to march on again. Five o'clock was about to strike. The sun, as red as a furnace on the edge of the horizon, seemed to set fire to the whole plain. A pedlar who was passing informed them that the military were descending from the Crèvecœur side. Then they turned. An order ran:

"To Montsou! To the manager!—Bread! bread! bread!"

.   .   .

The twilight was already darkening the room; it was five o'clock when a disturbance made M. Hennebeau jump, as he sat dazed and inert with his elbows in his papers. He thought that it was the two wretches coming back. But the tumult increased, and a terrible cry broke out just as he was going to the window:

"Bread! bread! bread!"

It was the strikers, now invading Montsou, while the police, expecting an attack on the Voreux, were galloping off in the opposite direction to occupy that pit.

Just then, two kilometres away from the first houses, a little beyond the crossways where the main road cut the Vandame road, Madame Hennebeau and the young ladies had witnessed the passing of the mob. The day had been spent pleasantly at Marchiennes; there had been a delightful lunch with the manager of the Forges, then an interesting visit to the workshops and to the neighbouring glass works to occupy the afternoon; and as they were now going home in the limpid decline of the beautiful winter day, Cécile had had the whim to drink a glass of milk, as she noticed a little farm near the edge of the road. They all then got down from the carriage, and Négrel gallantly leapt off his horse; while the peasant-woman, alarmed by all these fine people, rushed about, and spoke of laying a cloth before serving the milk. But Lucie and Jeanne wanted to see the cow milked, and they went into the cattle-shed with their cups, making a little rural party, and laughing greatly at the litter in which one sank.

Madame Hennebeau, with her complacent maternal air, was drinking with the edge of her lips, when a strange roaring noise from without disturbed her.

"What is that, then?"

The cattle-shed, built at the edge of the road, had a large door for carts, for it was also used as a barn for hay. The young girls, who had put out their heads, were astonished to see on the left a black flood, a shouting band which was moving along the Vandame road.

"The deuce!" muttered Négrel, who had also gone out. "Are our brawlers getting angry at last?"

"It is perhaps the colliers again," said the peasant-woman. "This is twice they've passed. Seems things are not going well; they're masters of the country."

She uttered every word prudently, watching the effect on their faces; and when she noticed the fright of all of them, and their deep anxiety at this encounter, she hastened to conclude:

"Oh, the rascals! the rascals!"

Négrel, seeing that it was too late to get into their carriage and reach Montsou, ordered the coachman to bring the vehicle into the farmyard, where it would remain hidden behind a shed. He himself fastened his horse, which a lad had been holding, beneath the shed. When he came back he found his aunt and the young girls distracted, and ready to follow the peasant-woman, who proposed that they should take refuge in her house. But he was of the opinion that they would be safer where they were, for certainly no one would come and look for them in the hay. The door, however, shut very badly, and had such large chinks in it, that the road could be seen between the worm-eaten planks.

"Come, courage!" he said. "We will sell our lives dearly."

This joke increased their fear. The noise grew louder, but nothing could yet be seen; along the vacant road the wind of a tempest seemed to be blowing, like those sudden gusts which precede great storms.

"No, no! I don't want to look," said Cécile, going to hide herself in the hay.

Madame Hennebeau, who was very pale and felt angry with these people who had spoilt her pleasure, stood in the background with a sidelong look of repugnance; while Lucie and Jeanne, though trembling, had placed their eyes at a crack, anxious to lose nothing of the spectacle.

A sound of thunder came near, the earth was shaken, and Jeanlin galloped up first, blowing into his horn.

"Take out your scent-bottles, the sweat of the people is passing by!" murmured Négrel, who, in spite of his republican convictions, liked to make fun of the populace when he was with ladies.

But this witticism was carried away in the hurricane of gestures and cries. The women had appeared, nearly a thousand of them, with outspread hair dishevelled by running, the naked skin appearing through their rags, the nakedness of females weary with giving birth to starvelings. A few held their little ones in their arms, raising them and shaking them like banners of mourning and vengeance. Others, who were younger with the swollen breasts of amazons, brandished sticks; while frightful old women were yelling so loudly that the cords of their fleshless necks seemed to be breaking. And then the men came up, two thousand madmen—trammers, pikemen, menders—a compact mass which rolled along like a single block in confused serried rank so that it was impossible to distinguish their faded trousers or ragged woollen jackets, all effaced in the same earthy uniformity. Their eyes were burning, and one only distinguished the holes of black mouths singing the *Marseillaise;* the stanzas were lost in a confused roar, accompanied by the clang of sabots over the hard earth. Above their heads, amid the bristling iron bars, an axe passed by, carried erect; and this single axe, which seemed to be the standard of the band, showed in the clear air the sharp profile of a guillotine-blade.

"What atrocious faces!" stammered Madame Hennebeau.

Négrel said between his teeth:

"Devil take me if I can recognize one of them! Where do the bandits spring from?"

And in fact anger, hunger, these two months of suffering and this enraged helter-skelter through the pits had lengthened the placid faces of the Montsou colliers into the muzzles of wild beasts. At this moment the sun was setting; its last rays of sombre purple cast a gleam of blood over the plain. The road seemed to be full of blood; men and women continued to rush by, bloody as butchers in the midst of slaughter.

"Oh! superb!" whispered Lucie and Jeanne, stirred in their artistic tastes by the beautiful horror of it.

They were frightened, however, and drew back close to Madame Hennebeau, who was leaning on a trough. She was frozen at the thought that a glance between the planks of that disjointed door might suffice to murder them. Négrel also, who was usually very brave, felt himself grow pale, seized by a terror that was superior to his will, the terror which comes from the unknown. Cécile, in the hay, no longer stirred; and the others, in spite of the wish to turn away their eyes, could not do so: they were compelled to gaze.

It was the red vision of the revolution, which would one day inevitably carry them all away, on some bloody evening at the end of the century. Yes, some evening the people, unbridled at last, would thus gallop along the roads, making the blood of the middle class flow, parading severed heads and sprinkling gold from disembowelled coffers. The women would yell, the men would have those wolf-like jaws open to bite. Yes, the same rags, the same thunder of great sabots, the same terrible troop, with dirty skins and tainted breath, sweeping away the old world beneath an overflowing flood of barbarians. Fires would flame; they would not leave standing one stone of the towns; they would return to the savage life of the woods, after the great rut, the great feast-day, when the poor in one night would emaciate the wives and empty the cellars of the rich. There would be nothing left, not a sou of the great fortunes, not a title-deed of properties acquired; until the day dawned when a new earth would perhaps spring up once more. Yes, it was these things which were passing along the road; it was the force of nature herself, and they were receiving the terrible wind of it in their faces.

A great cry arose, dominating the *Marseillaise:*

"Bread! bread! bread!"

Lucie and Jeanne pressed themselves against Madame Hennebeau, who was almost fainting; while Négrel placed himself before them as though to protect them by his body. Was the old social order cracking this very evening? And what they saw immediately after completed their stupefaction. The band had nearly passed by, there were only a few stragglers left, when Mouquette came up. She was delaying, watching the bourgeois at their garden gates or the windows of their houses; and whenever she saw them, as she was not able to spit in their faces, she showed them what for her was the climax of contempt. Doubtless she perceived someone now, for suddenly she raised her skirts, bent her back, and showed her enormous buttocks, naked beneath the last rays of the sun. There was nothing obscene in those fierce buttocks, and nobody laughed.

Everything disappeared: the flood rolled on to Montsou along the turns of the road, between the low houses streaked with bright colours. The carriage was drawn out of the yard, but the coachman would not take it upon him to convey back madame and the young ladies without delay; the strikers occupied the street. And the worst was, there was no other road.

"We must go back, however, for dinner will be ready," said Madame Hennebeau, exasperated by annoyance and fear. "These dirty workpeople have again chosen a day when I have visitors. How can you do good to such creatures?"

Lucie and Jeanne were occupied in pulling Cécile out of the hay. She was struggling, believing that those savages were still passing by, and repeating that she did not want to see them. At last they all took their places in the carriage again. It then occurred to Négrel, who had remounted, that they might go through the Réquillart lanes.

"Go gently," he said to the coachman, "for the road is atrocious. If any groups prevent you from returning to the road over there, you can stop behind the old pit, and we will return on foot through the little garden door, while you can put up the carriage and horses anywhere, in some inn outhouse."

They set out. The band, far away, was streaming into Montsou. As they had twice seen police and military, the inhabitants were agitated and seized by panic. Abominable stories were circulating; it was said that written placards had been set up threatening to rip open the bellies of the bourgeois. Nobody had read them, but all the same they were able to quote the exact words. At the lawyer's especially the terror was at its height, for he had just received by post an anonymous letter warning him that a barrel of powder was buried in his cellar, and that it would be blown up if he did not declare himself on the side of the people. Just then the Grégoires, prolonging their visit on the arrival of this letter, were discussing it, and decided that it must be the work of a joker, when the invasion of the mob completed the terror of the house. They, however, smiled, drawing back a corner of the curtain to look out, and refused to admit that there was any danger, certain, they said, that all would finish up well. Five o'clock struck, and they had time to wait until the street was free for them to cross the road to dine with the Hennebeaus, where Cécile, who had surely returned, must be waiting for them. But no one in Montsou seemed to share their confidence. People were wildly running about; doors and windows were banged to. They saw Maigrat, on the other side of the road, barricading his shop with a large supply of iron bars, and looking so pale and trembling that his feeble little wife was obliged to fasten the screws. The band had come to a halt before the manager's villa, and the cry echoed:

"Bread! bread! bread!"

M. Hennebeau was standing at the window when Hippolyte came in to close the shutters, for fear the windows should be broken by stones. He closed all on the ground floor, and then went up to the first floor; the creak of the window-fasteners was heard and the clack of the shutters one by one. Unfortunately, it was not possible to shut the kitchen window in the area in the same way, a window made disquietingly ruddy by the gleams from the saucepans and the spit.

Mechanically, M. Hennebeau, who wished to look out, went up to Paul's room on the second floor: it was on the left, the best situated, for it commanded the road as far as the Company's Yards. And he stood behind the blinds overlooking the crowd. But this room had again overcome him, the toilet table sponged and in order, the cold bed with neat and well-drawn sheets. All his rage of the afternoon, that furious battle in the depths of his silent solitude, had now turned to an immense fatigue. His whole being was now like this room, grown cold, swept of the filth of the morning, returned to its habitual correctness. What was the good of a scandal? had anything really changed in his house? His wife had simply taken another lover; that she had chosen him in the family scarcely aggravated the fact; perhaps even it was an advantage, for she thus preserved appearances. He pitied himself when he thought of his mad jealousy. How ridiculous to have struck that bed with his fists! Since he had tolerated another man, he could certainly tolerate this one. It was only a matter of a little more contempt. A terrible bitterness was poisoning his mouth, the uselessness of everything, the eternal pain of existence, shame for himself who always adored and desired this woman in the dirt in which he had abandoned her.

Beneath the window the yells broke out with increased violence:
"Bread! bread! bread!"

"Idiots!" said M. Hennebeau between his clenched teeth.

He heard them abusing him for his large salary, calling him a bloated idler, a bloody beast who stuffed himself to indigestion with good things, while the worker was dying of hunger. The women had noticed the kitchen, and there was a tempest of imprecations against the pheasant roasting there, against the sauces that with fat odours irritated their empty stomachs. Ah! the stinking bourgeois, they should be stuffed with champagne and truffles till their guts burst.

"Bread! bread! bread!"

"Idiots!" repeated M. Hennebeau; "am I happy?"

Anger arose in him against these people who could not understand. He would willingly have made them a present of his large

salary to possess their hard skin and their facility of coupling without regret. Why could he not seat them at his table and stuff them
with his pheasant, while he went to fornicate behind the hedges,
to tumble the girls over, making fun of those who had tumbled
them over before him! He would have given everything, his education, his comfort, his luxury, his power as manager, if he could be
for one day the vilest of the wretches who obeyed him, free of his
flesh, enough of a blackguard to beat his wife and to take his pleasure
with his neighbours' wives. And he longed also to be dying of hunger, to have an empty belly, a stomach twisted by cramps that
would make his head turn with giddiness: perhaps that would have
killed the eternal pain. Ah! to live like a brute, to possess nothing,
to scour the fields with the ugliest and dirtiest putter, and to be able
to be happy!

"Bread! bread! bread!"

Then he grew angry and shouted furiously in the tumult:

"Bread! is that enough, idiots!"

He could eat, and all the same he was groaning with torment.
His desolate household, his whole wounded life, choked him at the
throat like a death agony. Things were not all for the best because
one had bread. Who was the fool who placed earthly happiness in
the partition of wealth? These revolutionary dreamers might de-
molish society and rebuild another society; they would not add one
joy to humanity, they would not take away one pain, by cutting
bread-and-butter for everybody. They would even enlarge the unhappiness of the earth; they would one day make the very dogs
howl with despair when they had taken them out of the tranquil
satisfaction of instinct, to raise them to the unappeasable suffering
of passion. No, the one good thing was not to exist, and if one existed, to be a tree, a stone, less still, a grain of sand, which cannot
bleed beneath the heels of the passer-by.

And in this exasperation of his torment, tears swelled in M. Hennebeau's eyes, and broke in burning drops on his cheeks. The twilight was drowning the road when stones began to riddle the front
of the villa. With no anger now against these starving people, only
enraged by the burning wound at his heart he continued to stammer
in the midst of his tears:

"Idiots! idiots!"

But the cry of the belly dominated, and a roar blew like a tempest, sweeping everything before it:

"Bread! bread! bread!"

THE TWO FACES OF PROGRESS

Joyce Cary

From *Mister Johnson*

The road, at this place, is merely a long narrow strip of hard mud, littered with half-burnt chips, which passes out of sight in both directions into the high, primeval bush, familiar to them all. On every side the enormous columns of the trees stand dusty and motionless as stone, under the dark roof of foliage. The narrow crack in that roof, which lets in a strip of light sky above the brown strip of road, is like a single knife cut, already closing. Branches reach across overhead; at a little distance the edges seem to join.

The little group of hoe men, their naked bodies glistening with sweat, who stand under these enormous vaults in the hot gloom, are at home. They smile at the road, because they have made it and sung of it, but they have no idea of its beginning or end. They are still like men brought up on a forgotten island far from ship routes, to whom the rest of the world is as much a mystery, a blank inhabited by monsters, as to their ancestors of the old Stone Age. They do not even imagine it. Suddenly, in the immense silence of the morning, familiar as the forest twilight, which seems like the very substance of it, they hear a strange noise, between drumming and gunfire. It increases quickly. Two of the pagans dart among the trees and disappear into the silence. The rest stiffen. They do not seem to move, but each muscle is tense; their eyes open widely and stare with fixed and blank apprehension.

A lorry comes pounding out of the shadows, and at once they know what it must be. Two or three voices together cry, "Motor!"

All grin with astonishment and delight. They lift their hoes and rush forward, shouting greetings. The lorry driver, a tall Yoruba in blue dungarees, with a stub of cigarette stuck to his lips, pays no attention to them. He clanks and rattles past and disappears from sight. He doesn't even know he is the first man to drive over the Fada road. The gang burst into excited talk. One of them dances,

Pp. 180–187 from *Mister Johnson* by Joyce Cary (Harper & Brothers, 1951). Reprinted by permission of Harper & Row, Publishers, and Curtis Brown Ltd.

another gives a whoop. Rudbeck is seen cantering toward them on his brown pony. He pulls up and asks, "Did you see a motor?"

"Yes, master, a motor—a big motor." They surround him laughing, shouting, waving their arms. "It was a motor—from the north—he went through, poot, poot."

Rudbeck says, "I suppose that means that the last bridge is finished. Have you seen Tasuki?"

"No, we haven't seen Tasuki, but it was a motor—a big motor."

Rudbeck, with a puzzled, disconcerted expression rides away to find Tasuki. He has not realized perhaps that the road would open itself.

But next day the villagers, except a few ditchers, are going home. Tasuki has discharged the last bridge gang. The chip fires are still smoldering in the clearing, but there is no sound of drum or ax. In the bush camp, Johnson, Tasuki and Audu are counting tools and paying off the headmen. Rudbeck is answering arrears of mail and listening to cases. He is surprised to find how much his court work has increased in the last three months, not only with cases due to the new road, such as disputed bargains, complaints of extortion, adulteration, fraud, highway robbery; but purely local ones, such as theft, assault, quarrels between villages, disputes between chiefs and their people, disputed claims to all kinds of rights; and even wife-beating, kidnapping and divorce. There is a crime wave in Fada and every time the Waziri reports to Rudbeck, he mentions it and says with the appearance of innocence, "It is a most strange thing, but all the thieves and blackguards in the country have come to Fada, especially from the north. The Fada people, too, have never been so insolent. They are getting spoiled."

"You can't say it's the motors—there's only been one."

"Oh, no, Zaki, it's nothing to do with your road. For that we are all grateful—we thank God for it. No, but for the last six months a lot of new people have been coming to Fada. I don't know why; small traders and rascals of that kind, from the north. They always make trouble. They stir up the people against us even in the villages. I fear there will be big trouble—we need more police already."

Rudbeck authorizes four more police on the Emir's roll and warns the Waziri against the prejudice that roads and motors bring trouble to a state.

"When the motors begin to use this road, you will see the advantage of it. Fada market will be twice as big and all your people will get good cash prices for their produce. Motor roads are very good things, Waziri. The Governor himself has given the order for them. Native officials and even Emirs who try to prevent them by spreading false reports that they do harm will displease the Governor very much. In that case, of course, it is possible that their pay will not go up; it may even come down."

Waziri bows to the ground and cries out, "Master, lord, but the Emir admires motor roads above everything—and so do I. We pray for them and for you. We pray that you make still more road and bring many more motors to Fada."

"All right, Waziri. I salute the Emir. Good-by."

"God be with you, lord, provider of roads, benefactor of Fada."

Waziri goes home in a fright and the next day, not only he, but the Treasurer, the Master of the Horse and the Chief Justice all come ten miles down the road, to the first bush camp, in order to congratulate Rudbeck on the road and to assure him that it is a blessing to them all.

RUDBECK is most gracious and promises them a golden age for Fada. But when they have gone he is left with a sensation of confusion and disappointment. He feels that something is wrong, but he can't make out what it is. He suspects that he has been misled and even that he has misled others; but how, when or where he cannot discover. He shouts, in sudden anger, at a headman who is dragging a bundle of ax-helves across the camp, "Don't kick up all that dust—isn't there enough as it is?"

He is disgusted with the camp. The place where he has enjoyed some of the happiest hours of his life, of which he has loved even the fire glow half a mile away, has become a squalid rubbish heap. Everywhere there are heaps of filth, broken tools, cracked calabashes, rotten mats, tottering huts, half-burnt embers, rusty tins. All the trees about are splintered, singed by fires; their branches are broken and their leaves shriveled. Over all there is a stink, never noticed before, of rottenness and badly sealed latrines.

The Fada road is finished, the great idea is realized, and suddenly Rudbeck feels as if life holds nothing more for him. There is, of course, plenty of work waiting for him; the new assessment, a new census, a questionnaire about the infantile death rate, another town-planning circular, as well as arrears of office and court work. But he thinks of them merely as routine jobs, figures to be gathered, columns to be filled.

"More eyewash about sanitation," he says to Celia, throwing a blue circular on the breakfast table.

"Poor darling." Celia already has a maternal kindness for her husband; and the maternal absent-mindedness.

"As if you can plan towns without cash—and there won't be any cash to spare in Fada until we have some real trade."

"Yes, darling, more motor roads."

Rudbeck looks still more gloomy. "We can't do any more. I've tapped all the local trade with this north-south route. Now we can only wait for the other divisions to do something—and the central government."

"Couldn't you do just one more little road?"

Rudbeck glances at her and says, "Keep the children amused."

Celia does not answer. She is counting her knitting stitches. Probably she has not heard Rudbeck. He continues to stare at her for a moment and then gives a snort of laughter. She looks at him affectionately and says, "Three more lorries went through this morning and one of them was loaded."

"You're interested in roads, what?"

"Oh, dear, is that another hole in your shirt?"

"No, it's only a bit of dirt." He disappears into the store hut and can be heard snorting again there. It is his only protest against the maternal distraction.

It is time to go back to Fada. After breakfast Celia begins to pack. She is neither depressed nor pleased. Her air is still that of the accomplished and cheerful traveler who carries her home with her, and sets up her household, complete with family and knitting bag, even in trains and tram shelters. She packs with careful art and when each uniform trunk has been dusted, papered and carefully filled with exactly folded clothes, her glance of appreciation, before she closes the lid, merges at once into the look of pleased expectancy with which she opens the next one and says to Jamesu, "We ought to get the rest of the bush kit in here if we don't waste any corners."

Rudbeck hates packing even more than he dislikes putting figures into forms. He wanders about the camp, pipe in mouth and wonders vaguely why he feels so wretched, bored and disgusted. It is exactly as if he has just returned after three months' debauch to ordinary life and finds it more stupid and pointless than before.

Even the road gives him no pleasure. He looks sulkily and doubtfully at the great raw cut extending through the forest as far as the eye can reach, until on the horizon it becomes a mere nick in the dark sky-line, like the back sight of a rifle. A grand job. Far bigger and grander than he had ever thought possible. But what was it doing to Fada? Where were all the good results? Could it be that dirty old savages like the Emir and Waziri were right in their detestation of motor roads; that roads upset things, brought confusion, revolution. And wasn't there confusion enough? Wasn't everybody complaining that the world was getting into such confusion that civilization itself would disappear.

Ideas like these, or rather feelings which cannot take form as ideas for lack of clear definition, are as common to Redbeck as everyone else who reads the newspapers and can't distinguish between their sense and their nonsense. Over a thousand lunch tables and camp fires he has discussed them with his friends, and tossed about these words, "confusion," "chaos," "breakdown of civilization," without offering or reaching any kind of conclusion. He knows only that certain conclusions are not popular with his seniors. He has said to Bulteel, "But, sir, if native civilization does break down, there'll be a proper mess one day."

Bulteel takes off his hat, lifts it in the air in a line with the sun, and then at once puts it on again. They are taking their evening walk along the river road at Dorua.

"Ah! That's a big question." Bulteel hates talking shop out of office hours.

"We're obviously breaking up the old native tribal organization or it's breaking by itself. The people are bored with it."

"Yes, yes, and I'm not surprised," Bulteel says.

Rudbeck is greatly surprised. "Don't you believe in the native civilization?"

"Well, how would you like it yourself?" Bulteel smiles at him sideways with a kind of twinkle.

"Then you think it will go to pieces?"

"Yes, I think so, if it hasn't gone already."

"But what's going to happen then? Are we going to give them any new civilization, or simply let them slide downhill?"

"No idea," Bulteel says cheerfully. He takes off his hat again and replaces it at once because he finds it a nuisance to hold at arm's length above his bald head.

"I suppose one mustn't talk about a plan," Rudbeck says.

"Oh, no, no, no. They'll take you for a Bolshy."

"Well, sir, an idea. I suppose some people do have an idea of what life ought to be like—the Catholics did and the missionaries do, or ought to—and I suppose old Arnold did."

"Oh, Arnold, the Rugby man—yesss."

"I don't mean their ideas would do now, but only that a general idea might be possible—something to work to."

"Well, what idea?"

"That's the question."

"Yes, that's the question."

There is a short pause and then Rudbeck, seeing that Bulteel is not going to make any suggestions, says, "But it's a question you mustn't put up to the Secretariat."

"Oh, no, no—no. Not at all." Bulteel pauses. He dislikes this kind of conversation, which, as he says, gets you nowhere. But after a moment his affection for Rudbeck overcomes his disinclination to spoil the evening's walk and he says gravely, "But don't think it's the Secretariat's fault—people think they've been held up by the Secretariat when it's really Service conditions."

Rudbeck perfectly understands this phrase. He accepts it as a reasonable explanation of the fact that obstacles stand in the way of every constructive plan. He understands that people in themselves, full of good will and good sense, can form, in an organization, simply an obstructive mass blocking all creative energy; not from any conspiracy or jealousy, but simply from the nature of rules and routine, of official life. He accepts this cheerfully and says to Bulteel, "Ours not to reason why."

"Exactly; the higher the fewer or words to that effect. It doesn't do you any good or anyone else," and, stopping at the station garden, he says in the same good-natured, laughing tone, too cheerful to be called cynical, "What do you think of my zinnias? I hope you don't despise zinnias. They have one great merit as flowers—they always come up."

Rudbeck has at once dropped the problem from his mind. He has not thought about it again for perhaps a year. He is too busy.

But now his road work finished, he notices it again, and for a moment, it seems so large and urgent that he wonders how he ever forgot it.

The road itself seems to speak to him. "I'm smashing up the old Fada—I shall change everything and everybody in it. I am abolishing the old ways, the old ideas, the old law; I am bringing wealth and opportunity for good as well as vice, new powers to men and therefore new conflicts. I am the revolution. I am giving you plenty

of trouble already, you governors, and I am going to give you plenty
more. I destroy and I make new. What are you going to do about it?
I am your idea. You made me, so I suppose you know."

Rudbeck, staring at the road, feels rather than understands this
question and he feels again a sense of confusion and frustration. It
seems to him, not to his reason, but his feelings, that he has been
used and driven like a blind instrument. This gives him a very disagreeable sensation. He stands for several minutes smoking and
gazing, with a kind of disgusted surprise, and then gives a snort so
loud that a passing headman bobs a curtsy and says in a mildly
apologetic tone, "*Zaki.*"

The headmen, with their usual nonchalant and world-worn air,
are collecting their stores for return to Fada. They are not depressed.
They have forgotten already their enthusiasm for the great Fada
road. It is already a part of Fada to them, like the ground and the
air. Johnson, too, shouting to Tasuki across the dusty waste, is in
excellent spirits.

"Tasuki, hi-monkey-beard."

"*Naam,* clerk."

"What about the pot you borrowed from Waziri?"

"He took it back."

"I mean the other one—the one that didn't leak."

"It got broken when number three gang had that fight."

"What, another shilling pot broken?"

"Allah, clerk, it wasn't my fault."

Rudbeck turns away toward the office hut. It has been surrounded
three deep, for at least two hours, by applicants and petitioners. He
gives a sigh, taps his pipe with his thumb, and slowly makes his way
toward a boring duty; rolling in his walk, swinging his arms, stooping his broad thick shoulders as if his burden of confusion and blind
treadmill effort has turned into a physical weight on his back.

THE EXTREME OF VIOLENCE

Ramon Sender

From *Seven Red Sundays*

The corporal says to me:

"Auntie Isabela. None of us here has had a loss like yours."

It is true, but when I see them all eager to avenge my Germinal, I feel as if my son hadn't died. The worst will be when all this is over, and I have to go back to everyday life. The corporal says that that won't happen.

"Why not?"

"Because we are going to finish up everything."

I have seen too much in my life to be so sure. Many people will have to be killed, and for that uniforms are necessary. In a jacket and cap you can't kill more than a single guard.

I tell them about the bombs. I went out ready to blow up the town, and then I had to give them up to my son's comrades. The corporal burst out laughing. He laughed in my face, and as I didn't want to answer back, I went to the kitchen. Lucrecia doesn't want me to help her and would send me to bed as if I were a useless old wreck. But I insist on helping her. It would be the limit. Me to go to sleep when for forty years I've been the last in the house to go to bed and the first to get up! Bed is for old people; I am not old yet, and I must be the last to go to bed.

"Then you won't go to bed at all, Auntie Isabela."

"Why not?"

"There will be people here all night."

"All right; what about it? Surely sleep isn't the only thing in this life?"

When they see that I'll have my way, they let me help to clear up. There are voices in the room next door. I sit down and begin to nod. Every now and then I hear steps and wake up. More men come in. Some old ones who would be much better in bed. One in particular who drags his feet, has running eyes and a shaky hand. All go to the corporal's bedroom. I begin to pray so as to keep from falling asleep. I take out my rosary and get on with it. "For my son, that he may be in glory." When I remember that the agents are in my house, I can't go on praying. "Blessed Sacrament!" If only we could catch them in the woods! God says "Forgive your enemies," but He said nothing about agents and guards. My son died in the street with his head full of goodness. I can't pray to God to forgive him. I am sure there is no need for anyone to forgive him. And he hadn't anything against God either, to accuse Him or to forgive Him. The two of them had nothing against each other. I pray that he shall have peace and glory in the other world as he had in this world. Although he fought and they killed him, he always had peace, because he never thought one thing today and another to-morrow, and never said one thing and did another. And as for heaven, I think it is a place where everyone has enough to eat, all speak well of each other and see the best of each other and respect each other. It was that way my Germinal had peace and glory here, and I am going to pray that he gets them in the other world too.

But I don't finish. I sleep. I suddenly kick the floor and the corporal asks me:

"What's the matter, old lady?"

"Christ! I was sleeping."

"Don't get angry about that, mother. Go to bed."

And as I am not getting on well, I let myself doze off. A good thing to sleep—I dream a lot at night. Last night I dreamt that all the gentry and their women had left the streets and that we were the masters. There were no guards nor police and we were cooking on a stove in the Puerta del Sol and the Cibeles. Now and then a door opened, and some little lady pushed out her hand: "For the love of God, a pinch of salt!" We went and spat in it. A balcony window opened a bit and a marquis pushed out his snout:

"A match, for the love of God!"

And then my Germinal, who was alive although he was torn in pieces, got up and broke all the windows with a stone. Then we began to dance, and the widow Cleta lifted up her petticoats in the middle of a ring of people and waved her arms, saying that she was a soldier's widow.

That was the day before yesterday. Now—all right, we'll see! I am in bed and ask myself if I am asleep. Because sometimes I go to sleep sitting in a chair, and then when I go to bed I can't get to sleep again. It is all because of this old body which is like a broken clock. I hear new voices outside there. Lucrecia goes to the kitchen and makes a noise with cooking dishes. The voices are raised. Someone calls for silence and then I hear Samar speaking. Christ! This is not a time to stay in bed. I dress myself, and go to see what is happening. The door is open, and some men come in and creep along the wall like caterpillars without making any noise. They go to the corporal's bedroom, and when I look in there is no one. In a few minutes a lame old man comes out crossing himself. Samar asks him:

"What are you doing that for?"

The old man looks at him and says in a solemn voice:

"Oh, my boy!"

Then he points to the bedroom:

"It is like the Holy Mother for the poor. When you see, you'll cross yourself too!"

I go back to the bedroom. No one is there. I rub my eyes and go to the door of the house. Out there four or five ragged men are sleeping on the ground. A little way off two comrades are on guard. This is the poorest part of the suburb. There are only thieves and starving men. Lucrecia's house is like an archbishop's palace alongside such wretchedness. Madrid is in darkness. It seems as if they had cut with scissors all the wires that carry light to the houses. Well done! In this suburb among all these people, abandoned by God, light isn't much use. What can it do? Only show up lice and dirt! But there is Madrid over there. And my son?

"And you, what do you think about Germinal?"

"Me?" replies a shapeless dark figure, breathing there alongside me, "what would you have me think? He is now at peace."

"But there isn't another like him, is there?"

"Well, there is a soul in every body."

We were silent for a minute and then I asked him:

"Why do you come here?"

He looked at me strangely:

"If you don't know, I am not going to tell you."

Damn their mysteries! The corporal, coming in, said with a mixture of alarm and pleasure:

"Everyone in the suburb knows about it, and the police haven't found out. But now we are going to shift it to a safe place."

At last, when two more passed into the bedroom, I followed them. At the side of the bed there is a trap door in the floor. They raise it and a steep staircase is seen. If it isn't for a woman they'll have to tell me. Down below there are about three dozen people. As the ceiling is very low, they have to bend their heads and some have to double up. Others, to be more comfortable, are kneeling. It is almost dark, except for two candles at the end of the room. All are still and silent, and as no one can hold his head up, it seems as if they are praying. Someone alongside me says:

"The day is drawing near."

"What day?" I ask.

"The day of true justice."

The man used to come to our house sometimes. Besides, I recognize almost all the faces in the room. I ask what it is, and they say a word I don't understand. Not to look like a fool, I don't ask anything more, but elbow and push my way to the front. People are talking in low tones. When I get to the front row, I see Graco snuffing a candle. In the front is a machine, tall and lean like a greyhound, with three legs. It doesn't surprise me, knowing what Lucrecia is, that it is clean and polished. I ask again what it is, and they say the same word as before, but now I remember it:

"A machine-gun."

I believe it can fire five hundred shots a minute. Never before had I seen one. The men gaze at it in silence, each of them thinking his own thoughts. I think that on the day of the burial this machine could have done in all the guards of Spain, and that with two of them my poor Germinal would be avenged. Alongside me a very lean man is breathing heavily, with his hat in his hand, like all the rest of them. The machine-gun is silent and strong, and at its side there is a heap of metal cases, and two boxes which must be for repairing it. They all look as if they are praying, and not to be different and because I don't know what to do on my knees unless I am praying, I make a prayer of my own:

"Dear God, praise and thanks because Thou hast allowed a machine like this to come to our aid; praise and thanks because Thou hast given us the wits to make it." I recite a paternoster, praying that those who use it do not come to any harm, and that their bullets find the hearts of those who killed my son.

Behind me I hear the anarchists moving up and down. Graco says that they are going to pack it up and everyone must go on as before, guarding the secret carefully in the name of Mother Anarchy. Two voices in the circle protest:

"Communists can keep a secret just as well."

Graco replies to them:

"Of course, I know that. But we mustn't have misunderstandings;

you must not provoke people, for this isn't a moment for disputes."

I turn to look at them. If these men can do what they want, the machine will buzz, putting shots through the windows of the *bourgeois*. Tonight there won't be a *bourgeois* left in the world. Someone asks:

"Whose is the machine?"

Four or five reply:

"It belongs to the revolution."

Graco comes up to me:

"Look at it, grandmother! How clean and swelling with youth. It is one of the first that have come to our side. But there are others, whores, bitches, handled by the Civil Guard. Comrades," he went on, addressing them all, "here you have it! A machine-gun Hotchkiss, American model! It is the best weapon——"

An old man interrupts:

"Forgive me, comrade Graco. There is another weapon, still more effective—culture."

They all laugh. The machine is packed up. Graco says:

"Culture is a trick of the *bourgeois*, because there is nothing like *bourgeois* culture to enslave us."

"We don't want culture! To hell with culture! The machine-gun will help us to sink culture."

The communists cry out:

"Culture began with Marx."

The old man with the white whiskers said:

"And Greece? and Rome? Does not Demosthenes stand for something? And Plato?"

The youngest of them shout him down:

"Bloody nonsense! *bourgeois* dirt!"

As the old man is getting ready to make a speech, Graco puts out the candles, and goes off. I hold on to his jacket and go out first, lest they come to blows. From the staircase Graco calls out:

"Outside all of you, comrades!"

They come out lighting matches. The old man wishes to argue with the young ones, and they chaff him. Now I go to sleep peacefully.

I lie down and pray. I address the machine instead of St. Joseph. I don't know, but perhaps if we had turned to this Virgin before, they wouldn't have killed Germinal, and I wouldn't have colds or be the rough-tongued person they call me. Because there wouldn't have been these dogs of police in the world.

But we have them. Without muzzles, and with their tickets and
badges. They will turn up their coat collars and clear out. It is for
that, that all these young men, white or yellow, are in front of the
machine, silent and purposeful. I say "yellow" because there was a
socialist. But everyone prays to this Virgin. Talking stops there.
Pray! Pray! The men creep in like caterpillars, crouching down,
but they come to the Virgin Hotchkiss, they raise their heads, speak
their piece, and go back to struggle with hunger, but all the same,
contented as one comes back from Mass. I can't tell what I'd give
for Germinal to have had that machine. Now that something has
come on Germinal's side, so strong, so sharp and cunning, so clean
and so brave, it is easy to see that we can make a good job firing in
the streets.

But I don't know what I am saying, because I am falling asleep.
I see a sea of unshaven faces. Graco is standing up at one side and
the old man with white whiskers at the other. Graco calls out:

"All machines enslave us except our Virgin Hotchkiss."

The crowd replies like an angry sea:

"The Virgin Hotchkiss is our Holy Mother."

The old man with the whiskers calls out:

"Our Mother will tell us that anarchy is the best."

No one takes any notice. Graco speaks again:

"With our own hands we have wrought the machine-gun."

"The Virgin Hotchkiss, "they all reply, "is our daughter."

Graco stands up, holding out his revolver:

"Let us put our trust and our hope in the machine of the revolution."

"The Virgin Hotchkiss is our soul. Hurrah! Hurrah!"

Then Graco begins to pray as if he were reciting a litany:

"Ministers, Director-Generals, Archbishops, Duchess-bitches."

"You shall die at our hands!"

"Elegant highbrows! servile journalists! pimps of luxury!"

"You shall die at our hands!"

"Members of Parliament, Governors, Priests!"

"You shall till the land, harnessed to our plough!"

"Nuns!"

"For the first time you shall smile, pumping milk from your dry
breasts!"

"Saints of the Church!"

"Splintered into chips they shall warm the soup of our cohorts."

"The Holy Vessels!"

"We shall use them to celebrate our great day of blasphemy."

"Certificates of Government stock, patents of nobility, wills and armorial bearings!"

"They shall blaze in the streets, and our children shall singe their shoes leaping over them!"

"The Holy Virgin!"

"She shall bring forth in sorrow!"

"Jesus, the Son of God!"

"We shall send him to a school for defectives!"

"God, One in Three and Three in One, the Almighty!"

'There is no God! We have done with God!"

"We shall use the holy napkins of His ritual as swaddling clothes for our new-born babes!"

"There is nothing but the revolution!"

"The revolution!"

"Nothing else?"

"Nothing else! And as its symbol we accept only one kind of machine: the Virgin Hotchkiss!"

THE REVOLUTION BETRAYED

Isaac Babel

"Gedali"

On Sabbath eves I am oppressed by the dense melancholy of memories. In bygone days on these occasions my grandfather would stroke the volumes of Ibn Ezra with his yellow beard. His old woman in her lace cap would trace fortunes with her knotty fingers over the Sabbath candles, and sob softly to herself. On those evenings my child's heart was rocked like a little ship upon enchanted waves. O the rotted Talmuds of my childhood! O the dense melancholy of memories!

I roam through Zhitomir in search of a shy star. By the ancient synagogue, by its yellow and indifferent walls, old Jews with prophets' beards and passionate rags on their sunken chests sell chalk and wicks and bluing.

Here before me is the market, and the death of the market. Gone is the fat soul of plenty. Dumb padlocks hang upon the booths, and the granite paving is as clean as a skull. My shy star blinks, and fades from sight.

Success came to me later on; success came just before sunset. Gedali's little shop was hidden away in a row of others, all hermetically closed. Where was your kindly shade that evening, Dickens? In that little old curiosity shop you would have seen gilt slippers, ship's cables, an ancient compass, a stuffed eagle, a Winchester with the date 1810 engraved upon it, a broken saucepan.

Old Gedali, the little proprietor in smoked glasses and a green frock coat down to the ground, meandered around his treasures in the roseate void of evening. He rubbed his small white hands, plucked at his little gray beard, and listened, head bent, to the mysterious voices wafting down to him.

The shop was like the box of an important and knowledge-loving little boy who will grow up to be a professor of botany. There were buttons in it, and a dead butterfly, and its small owner went by the name of Gedali. All had abandoned the market; but Gedali had remained. He wound in and out of a labyrinth of globes, skulls, and dead flowers, waving a bright feather duster of cock's plumes and blowing dust from the dead flowers.

And so we sat upon small beer-barrels, Gedali twisting and untwisting his narrow beard. Like a little black tower, his hat swayed above us. Warm air flowed past. The sky changed color. Blood, delicate-hued, poured down from an overturned bottle up there, and a vague odor of corruption enfolded me.

"The Revolution—we will say 'yes' to it, but are we to say 'no' to the Sabbath?" began Gedali, winding about me the straps of his smoke-hidden eyes. "Yes, I cry to the Revolution. Yes, I cry to it, but it hides its face from Gedali and sends out in front nought but shooting . . ."

"The sunlight doesn't enter eyes that are closed," I answered the old man. "But we will cut open those closed eyes . . ."

"A Pole closed my eyes," whispered the old man, in a voice that was barely audible. "The Poles are bad-tempered dogs. They take the Jew and pluck out his beard, the curs! And now they are being beaten, the bad-tempered dogs. That is splendid, that is the Revolution. And then those who have beaten the Poles say to me: 'Hand your phonograph over to the State, Gedali . . .' 'I am fond of music, Pani,' I say to the Revolution. 'You don't know what you are fond of, Gedali. I'll shoot you and then you'll know. I cannot do without shooting, because I am the Revolution.' "

"She cannot do without shooting, Gedali," I told the old man, "because she is the Revolution."

"But the Poles, kind sir, shot because they were the Counter-Revolution. You shoot because you are the Revolution. But surely the Revolution means joy. And joy does not like orphans in the house. Good men do good deeds. The Revolution is the good deed of good men. But good men do not kill. So it is bad people that are making the Revolution. But the Poles are bad people too. Then how is Gedali to tell which is Revolution and which is Counter-Revolution? I used to study the Talmud, I love Rashi's Commentaries and the books of Maimonides. And there are yet other understanding folk in Zhitomir. And here we are, all of us learned people, falling on our faces and crying out in a loud voice: 'Woe unto us, where is the joy-giving Revolution?' "

The old man fell silent. And we saw the first star pierce through the Milky Way.

"The Sabbath has begun," Gedali stated solemnly; "Jews should be going to the synagogue. Pan comrade," he said, rising, his top hat like a little black tower swaying on his head, "bring a few good people to Zhitomir. Oh, there's a scarcity of good people in our town. Oh, what a scarcity! Bring them along and we will hand over all our phonographs to them. We are not ignoramuses. The International—we know what the International is. And I want an International of good people. I would like every soul to be listed and given first-category rations. There, soul, please eat and enjoy life's pleasures. Pan comrade, you don't know what the International is eaten with . . ."

"It is eaten with gunpowder," I answered the old man, "and spiced with best-quality blood."

And then, from out of the blue gloom, the young Sabbath came to take her seat of honor.

"Gedali," I said, "today is Friday, and it's already evening. Where are Jewish biscuits to be got, and a Jewish glass of tea, and a little of that pensioned-off God in a glass of tea?"

"Not to be had," Gedali replied, hanging the padlock on his little booth. "Not to be had. Next door is a tavern, and they were good people who served in it; but nobody eats there now, people weep there."

He buttoned his green frock coat on three bone buttons, flicked himself with the cock's feathers, sprinkled a little water on his soft palms, and departed, a tiny, lonely visionary in a black top hat, carrying a big prayerbook under his arm.

The Sabbath is coming. Gedali, the founder of an impossible International, has gone to the synagogue to pray.

William Butler Yeats

"Parnell"

Parnell came down the road, he said to a cheering man:
"Ireland shall get her freedom and you still break stone."

Reprinted from *Collected Poems of W. B. Yeats* with permission of M. B. Yeats, The Macmillan Company of Canada, and The Macmillan Company of New York. Copyright 1940 by Georgie Yeats.

Chapter **VI**

Political Institutions

Like other forms of human activity, politics requires certain enclosed spaces within which its participants can live and work and establish the routines of their calling. Institutions can be described as systems of spatial arrangements and work patterns developed (at least, initially) for some particular purpose. Political institutions are arrangements and patterns developed for the purpose of exercising power over other men—that is, over all those who live and work outside. Though in theory political institutions need not be exclusive, occupied and run by small minorities, in practice they have almost always been so. Hence the crucial distinction, which so many writers have explored, between the participants and the others, the governors and the governed, officials and their beneficiaries or victims. Some men live inside the world of government; they are kings, courtiers, judges, bureaucrats, assemblymen; they move about within the enclosed spaces and act out the established routines. Most men live outside, watched over and protected, or so it is said, by the wielders of power. Occasionally, however, the quiet lives of these ordinary men and women are dramatically impinged upon; they are dragged into political space, forced to submit to official procedures: drafted, arrested, required to appear in court, confronted by officious bureaucrats. Charles Dickens' Court of Chancery is perhaps the classic description of an entangling institution, a Venus flytrap for citizens. Franz Kafka's K. (in both The Trial

and The Castle) is the classic case of the entrapped man, captured by officials, haunted by the myth (but perhaps it is not a
myth . . .) of their ultimate helpfulness, broken by their endless routines.

Neither the officials nor the citizens are free: hence the twin
romances of the escaped official, who breaks loose from institutional patterns—as in the film Roman Holiday—and of the poor
boy who leaves misery behind by marrying a princess. Hence also
the special and, some might say, the jaundiced view which the
greatest writers have generally taken of political institutions. Perhaps these institutions serve important human purposes, perhaps
they provide crucial restraints and necessary channels. Writers
from Jonathan Swift to Kafka, however, have explored them as
sources and centers of man's unfreedom. Royal courts and courts
of law, bureaucratic offices and legislative assemblies have been
described as so many puppet stages on which men are driven (by
the roles they play and all the organizational strings and wires)
to act in peculiarly artificial and unnatural ways. The most outrageous performances become acceptable once they are established within some institutional process. Thus the antics of
Swift's Lilliputian courtiers symbolize all those absurd routines
by which officials have ever been required to prove their merit in
some other way than by doing their jobs. And the tiny courtiers
themselves represent all those men compelled to debase themselves for the sake of their office, by "leaping and creeping" as
the rules require.

Nor is this a matter of occasional irrationality. Swift's satire is
more basic than that. This is the way royal courts are, he means
to suggest, or any institution marked by the presence of a single
all-powerful individual who must be pleased. Similarly, the deceit
and self-deceit of kings and courtiers in Hans Christian Ander-
son's famous tale "The Emperor's New Clothes" is inherent in
the court as an institution and may even be taken, for all its light-
ness, to typify the dilemma of the official who can never trust his
subordinates to tell the truth. Lying is not so much a sign of their
human frailty as a function of their office.

Rationality itself is no guarantee against confusion, waste,
injury and deception. Dickens' Chancery and Kafka's Castle are

both "rational-legal" institutions—even though they don't conform strictly to Max Weber's ideal type. In Chancery ancient precedents still prevail; the organizational chart of the Castle is less clear than a student of public administration might wish. Still, both institutions are relatively free of personal authority; both are dominated by rules and by officials who act more or less strictly in accordance with the rules. And yet in both cases the whole system of rules has somehow outgrown or outlived the human purposes for which it was originally intended. It has proliferated in some extravagant and independent fashion and grown impenetrable. The men inside are prisoners; and however reasonable their day-to-day activity, however efficient and meticulous their official routines, their behavior, viewed from the outside, can only be called absurd.

Even in free institutions, whose routines are open to question and amendment and whose officials are never wholly absorbed by their roles, entrapment persists and patterns all too often prevail over men. Less has been written about parliaments and democratic assemblies, however, than about royal courts and authoritarian bureaucracies. Doubtless both the human risks and losses are radically diminished, along with the oppressive power of the institution, when the possibilities of dissent and escape are made freely available. Free institutions are, in this sense at least, less exciting, less dangerous, less in need of exposure or surrealistic analysis. Still, what Marxists call "parliamentary cretinism"—the reduction of political men to wordmongers, the routine enactment of meaningless legislation—is certainly real enough. Debate, however free, can often be both wasteful and injurious when it serves only to conceal the impossibility of action or the private agreement on all sides as to what action will finally be taken. Emptied of content, reduced to its routines, even free government can become an absurd performance—as in Dickens' satirical description of a nineteenth century English cabinet crisis: "England has been in a dreadful state for some weeks. Lord Coodle would go out, Sir Thomas Doodle wouldn't come in, and there being nobody in Great Britain (to speak of) except Coodle and Doodle, there had been no government." Anthony Trollope writes in this spirit in his description of the high comedy of parliamentary "conservatism" and "liberalism." He sets the supposed moral and political commitments of men no different from Coodle and Doodle against the institutional patterns and the requirements of an everyday politics and describes the predictable results.

Lastly, we have included a description of one institutional process that (sometimes) does more or less what it is supposed to do. George Eliot's account of an encounter in the democratic marketplace is satirical in style: The marketplace, she knows, is no center of rational argument; its patterns also require a special kind of performance—exaggerated, loud, aggressive. The gentle, mindless, patronizing Mr. Brooke, who is not up to it, is ruthlessly cut down. But his defeat is no loss to the nation, even if the victory of his opponent is no great gain. The best institutional arrangements are no guarantee of the best results, but they may at least provide some recourse against stupidity and waste.

THE ROYAL COURT

Jonathan Swift

From *Gulliver's Travels*

My gentleness and good behaviour had gained so far on the
Emperor and his court, and indeed upon the army and people in
general, that I began to conceive hopes of getting my liberty in a
short time. I took all possible methods to cultivate this favourable
disposition. The natives came by degrees to be less apprehensive of
any danger from me. I would sometimes lie down, and let five or
six of them dance on my hand. And at last the boys and girls would
venture to come and play at hide and seek in my hair. I had now
made a good progress in understanding and speaking their language. The Emperor had a mind one day to entertain me with several of the country shows, wherein they exceed all nations I have
known, both for dexterity and magnificence. I was diverted with
none so much as that of the rope-dances, performed upon a slender
white thread, extended about two foot, and twelve inches from the
ground. Upon which I shall desire liberty, with the reader's patience,
to enlarge a little.

This diversion is only practised by those persons who are candidates for great employments and high favour at court. They are
trained in this art from their youth, and are not always of noble
birth, or liberal education. When a great office is vacant either by
death or disgrace (which often happens) five or six of those candidates petition the Emperor to entertain his Majesty and the court
with a dance on the rope, and whoever jumps the highest without
falling, succeeds in the office. Very often the chief ministers themselves are commanded to show their skill, and to convince the Emperor that they have not lost their faculty. Flimnap, the Treasurer,
is allowed to cut a caper on the straight rope, at least an inch higher
than any other lord in the whole empire. I have seen him do the
summerset several times together upon a trencher fixed on the rope,
which is no thicker than a common packthread in England. My
friend Reldresal, principal Secretary for Private Affairs, is, in my

From Ch. 3.

opinion, if I am not partial, the second after the Treasurer; the rest of the great officers are much upon a par.

These diversions are often attended with fatal accidents, whereof great numbers are on record. I myself have seen two or three candidates break a limb. But the danger is much greater when the ministers themselves are commanded to show their dexterity; for by contending to excel themselves and their fellows, they strain so far, that there is hardly one of them who hath not received a fall, and some of them two or three. I was assured that a year or two before my arrival, Flimnap would have infallibly broke his neck, if one of the King's cushions, that accidentally lay on the ground, had not weakened the force of his fall.

There is likewise another diversion, which is only shown before the Emperor and Empress, and first minister, upon particular occasions. The Emperor lays on the table three fine silken threads of six inches long. One is blue, the other red, and the third green. These threads are proposed as prizes for those persons whom the Emperor hath a mind to distinguish by a peculiar mark of his favour. The ceremony is performed in his Majesty's great chamber of state, where the candidates are to undergo a trial of dexterity very different from the former, and such as I have not observed the least resemblance of in any other country of the old or the new world. The Emperor holds a stick in his hands, both ends parallel to the horizon, while the candidates, advancing one by one, sometimes leap over the stick, sometimes creep under it backwards and forwards several times, according as the stick is advanced or depressed. Sometimes the Emperor holds one end of the stick, and his first minister the other; sometimes the minister has it entirely to himself. Whoever performs his part with most agility, and holds out the longest in leaping and creeping, is rewarded with the blue-coloured silk; the red is given to the next, and the green to the third, which they all wear girt twice round about the middle; and you see few great persons about this court who are not adorned with one of these girdles.

THE ROYAL COURT (*Continued*)

Hans Christian Andersen

"The Emperor's New Clothes"

Many years ago there lived an Emperor, who was so excessively fond of grand new clothes that he spent all his money upon them, that he might be very fine. He did not care about his soldiers, nor about the theatre, and only liked to drive out and show his new clothes. He had a coat for every hour of the day; and just as they say of a king, "He is in council," so they always said of him, "The Emperor is in the wardrobe."

In the great city in which he lived it was always very merry; every day came many strangers; one day two rogues came; they gave themselves out as weavers, and declared they could weave the finest stuff any one could imagine. Not only were their colors and patterns, they said, uncommonly beautiful, but the clothes made of the stuff possessed the wonderful quality that they became invisible to any one who was unfit for the office he held, or was incorrigibly stupid.

"Those would be capital clothes!" thought the Emperor. "If I wore those, I should be able to find out what men in my empire are not fit for the places they have; I could tell the clever from the dunces. Yes, the stuff must be woven for me directly!"

And he gave the two rogues a great deal of cash in hand, that they might begin their work at once.

As for them, they put up two looms, and pretended to be working; but they had nothing at all on their looms. They at once demanded the finest silk and the costliest gold; this they put into their own pockets, and worked at the empty looms till late into the night.

"I should like to know how far they have got on with the stuff," thought the Emperor. But he felt quite uncomfortable when he thought that those who were not fit for their offices could not see it. He believed, indeed, that he had nothing to fear for himself, but yet he preferred first to send some one else to see how matters stood. All the people in the city knew what peculiar power the stuff possessed, and all were anxious to see how bad or how stupid their neighbors were.

"I will send my honest old Minister to the weavers," thought the Emperor. "He can judge best how the stuff looks, for he has sense, and no one understands his office better than he."

Now the good old Minister went out into the hall where the two rogues sat working at the empty looms.

"Mercy on us!" thought the old Minister, and he opened his eyes wide. "I cannot see anything at all!" But he did not say this.

Both the rogues begged him to be so good as to come nearer, and asked if he did not approve of the colors and the pattern. Then they pointed to the empty loom, and the poor old Minister went on opening his eyes; but he could see nothing, for there was nothing to see.

"Mercy!" thought he, "can I indeed be so stupid? I never thought that, and not a soul must know it. Am I not fit for my office? No, it will never do for me to tell that I could not see the stuff."

"Don't you say anything to it?" asked one, as he went on weaving.

"O, it is charming—quite enchanting!" answered the old Minister, as he peered through his spectacles. "What a fine pattern, and what colors! Yes, I shall tell the Emperor that I am very much pleased with it."

"Well, we are glad of that," said both the weavers; and then they named the colors, and explained the strange pattern. The old Minister listened attentively, that he might be able to repeat it when the Emperor came. And he did so.

Now the rogues asked for more money, and silk and gold, which they declared they wanted for weaving. They put all into their own pockets, and not a thread was put upon the loom; they continued to work at the empty frames as before.

The Emperor soon sent again, dispatching another honest officer of the court, to see how the weaving was going on, and if the stuff would soon be ready. He fared just like the first: he looked and looked, but, as there was nothing to be seen but the empty looms, he could see nothing.

"Is not that a pretty piece of stuff?" asked the two rogues; and they displayed and explained the handsome pattern which was not there at all.

"I am not stupid!" thought the man: "it must be my good office, for which I am not fit. It is funny enough, but I must not let it be noticed." And so he praised the stuff which he did not see, and expressed his pleasure at the beautiful colors and charming pattern. "Yes, it is enchanting," he told the Emperor.

All the people in the town were talking of the gorgeous stuff. The Emperor wished to see it himself while it was still upon the loom. With a whole crowd of chosen men, among whom were also the two honest statesmen who had already been there, he went to the two cunning rogues, who were now weaving with might and main without fibre or thread.

"Is not that splendid?" said the two statesmen, who had already been there once. "Does not your Majesty remark the pattern and the colors?" And they pointed to the empty loom, for they thought that the others could see the stuff.

"What's this?" thought the Emperor. "I can see nothing at all! That is terrible. Am I stupid? Am I not fit to be Emperor? That would be the most dreadful thing that could happen to me. O, it is *very* pretty!" he said aloud. "It has our highest approbation." And he nodded in a contented way, and gazed at the empty loom, for he would not say that he saw nothing. The whole suite whom he had with him looked and looked, and saw nothing, any more than the rest; but, like the Emperor, they said, "That *is* pretty!" and counseled him to wear the splendid new clothes for the first time at the great procession that was presently to take place. "It is splendid, excellent!" went from mouth to mouth. On all sides there seemed to be general rejoicing, and the Emperor gave the rogues the title of Imperial Court Weavers.

The whole night before the morning on which the procession was to take place, the rogues were up, and kept more than sixteen candles burning. The people could see that they were hard at work, completing the Emperor's new clothes. They pretended to take the stuff down from the loom; they made cuts in the air with great scissors; they sewed with needles without thread; and at last they said, "Now the clothes are ready!"

The Emperor came himself with his noblest cavaliers; and the two rogues lifted up one arm as if they were holding something, and said, "See, here are the trousers! here is the coat! here is the cloak!" and so on. "It is as light as a spider's web: one would think one had nothing on; but that is just the beauty of it."

"Yes," said all the cavaliers; but they could not see anything, for nothing was there.

"Will your Imperial Majesty please to condescend to take off your clothes?" said the rogues; "then we will put on you the new clothes here in front of the great mirror."

The Emperor took off his clothes, and the rogues pretended to put on him each new garment as it was ready; and the Emperor turned round and round before the mirror.

"O, how well they look! how capitally they fit!" said all. "What a pattern! what colors! That *is* a splendid dress!"

"They are standing outside with the canopy which is to be borne above your Majesty in the procession!" announced the head Master of the Ceremonies.

"Well, I am ready," replied the Emperor. "Does it not suit me well?" And then he turned again to the mirror, for he wanted it to appear as if he contemplated his adornment with great interest.

The two chamberlains, who were to carry the train, stooped down with their hands toward the floor, just as if they were picking up the mantle; then they pretended to be holding something in the air. They did not dare to let it be noticed that they saw nothing.

So the Emperor went in procession under the rich canopy, and everyone in the streets, said, "How incomparable are the Emperor's new clothes! What a train he has to his mantle! how it fits him!" No one would let it be perceived that he could see nothing, for that would have shown that he was not fit for his office, or was very stupid. No clothes of the Emperor's had ever had such a success as these.

"But he has nothing on!" a little child cried out at last.

"Just hear what that innocent says!" said the father; and one whispered to another what the child had said.

"But he has nothing on!" said the whole people at length. That touched the Emperor, for it seemed to him that they were right; but he thought within himself, "I must go through with the procession." And so he held himself a little higher, and the chamberlains held on tighter than ever, and carried the train which did not exist at all.

THE LEGAL MORASS

Charles Dickens

"In Chancery"

London, Michaelmas term lately over, and the Lord Chancellor sitting in Lincoln's Inn Hall. Implacable November weather. As much mud in the streets as if the waters had but newly retired from the face of the earth, and it would not be wonderful to meet a Megalosaurus, forty feet long or so, waddling like an elephantine lizard up Holborn Hill. Smoke lowering down from chimney-pots, making a soft black drizzle, with flakes of soot in it as big as full-grown snowflakes—gone into mourning, one might imagine, for the death of the sun. Dogs, undistinguishable in mire. Horses, scarcely better; splashed to their very blinkers. Foot passengers, jostling one another's umbrellas in a general infection of ill temper, and losing their foot-hold at street-corners, where tens of thousands of other foot passengers have been slipping and sliding since the day broke (if this day ever broke), adding new deposits to the crust upon crust of mud, sticking at those points tenaciously to the pavement, and accumulating at compound interest.

Fog everywhere. Fog up the river, where it flows among green aits and meadows; fog down the river, where it rolls defiled among the tiers of shipping and the waterside pollutions of a great (and dirty) city. Fog on the Essex marshes, fog on the Kentish heights. Fog creeping into the cabooses of collier-brigs; fog lying out on the yards and hovering in the rigging of great ships; fog drooping on the gunwales of barges and small boats. Fog in the eyes and throats of ancient Greenwich pensioners, wheezing by the firesides of their wards; fog in the stem and bowl of the afternoon pipe of the wrathful skipper, down in his close cabin; fog cruelly pinching the toes and fingers of his shivering little 'prentice boy on deck. Chance people on the bridges peeping over the parapets into a nether sky of fog, with fog all round them, as if they were up in a balloon and hanging in the misty clouds.

Gas looming through the fog in divers places in the streets, much

From *Bleak House*, Ch. 1.

as the sun may, from the spongey fields, be seen to loom by husbandman and ploughboy. Most of the shops lighted two hours before their time—as the gas seems to know, for it has a haggard and
unwilling look.

The raw afternoon is rawest, and the dense fog is densest, and
the muddy streets are muddiest near that leaden-headed old ob-
struction, appropriate ornament for the threshold or a leaden-headed
old corporation, Temple Bar. And hard by Temple Bar, in Lincoln's
Inn Hall, at the very heart of the fog, sits the Lord High Chancellor
in his High Court of Chancery.

Never can there come fog too thick, never can there come mud
and mire too deep, to assort with the groping and floundering condition which this High Court of Chancery, most pestilent of hoary
sinners, holds this day in the sight of heaven and earth.

On such an afternoon, if ever, the Lord High Chancellor ought
to be sitting here—as here he is—with a foggy glory round his head,
softly fenced in with crimson cloth and curtains, addressed by a
large advocate with great whiskers, a little voice, and an interminable brief, and outwardly directing his contemplation to the lantern
in the roof, where he can see nothing but fog. On such an afternoon
some score of members of the High Court of Chancery bar ought to
be—as here they are—mistily engaged in one of the ten thousand
stages of an endless cause, tripping one another up on slippery
precedents, groping knee-deep in technicalities, running their goat-
hair and horsehair warded heads against walls of words and making
a pretence of equity with serious faces as players might. On such an
afternoon the various solicitors on the cause, some two or three of
whom have inherited it from their fathers, who made a fortune by
it, ought to be—as are they not?—ranged in a line, in a long matted
well (but one might look in vain for truth at the bottom of it) between the registrar's red table and the silk gowns, with bills, cross-
bills, answers, rejoinders, injunctions, affidavits, issues, references to
masters, masters' reports, mountains of costly nonsense piled before
them. Well may the court be dim, with wasting candles here and
there; well may the fog hang heavy in it, as if it would never get
out; well may the stained-glass windows lose their colour and admit
no light of day into the place; well may the uninitiated from the
streets, who peep in through the glass panes in the door, be deterred
from entrance by its owlish aspect and by the drawl, languidly
echoing to the roof from the padded dais where the Lord High
Chancellor looks into the lantern that has no light in it and where

the attendant wigs are all stuck in a fog-bank! This is the Court of Chancery, which has its decaying houses and its blighted lands in every shire, which has its worn-out lunatic in every madhouse and its dead in every churchyard, which has its ruined suitor with his slipshod heels and threadbare dress borrowing and begging through the round of every man's acquaintance, which gives to monied might the means abundantly of wearing out the right, which so exhausts finances, patience, courage, hope, so overthrows the brain and breaks the heart, that there is not an honourable man among its practitioners who would not give—who does not often give—the warning, "Suffer any wrong that can be done you rather than come here!"

Who happen to be in the Lord Chancellor's court this murky afternoon besides the Lord Chancellor, the counsel in the cause, two or three counsel who are never in any cause, and the well of solicitors before mentioned? There is the registrar below the judge, in wig and gown; and there are two or three maces, or petty-bags, or privy purses, or whatever they may be, in legal court suits. These are all yawning, for no crumb of amusement ever falls from Jarndyce and Jarndyce (the cause in hand), which was squeezed dry years upon years ago. The short-hand writers, the reporters of the court, and the reporters of the newspapers invariably decamp with the rest of the regulars when Jarndyce and Jarndyce comes on. Their places are a blank. Standing on a seat at the side of the hall, the better to peer into the curtained sanctuary, is a little mad old woman in a squeezed bonnet who is always in court, from its sitting to its rising, and always expecting some incomprehensible judgment to be given in her favour. Some say she really is, or was, a party to a suit, but no one knows for certain because no one cares. She carries some small litter in a reticule which she calls her documents, principally consisting of paper matches and dry lavender. A sallow prisoner has come up, in custody, for the half-dozenth time to make a personal application "to purge himself of his contempt," which, being a solitary surviving executor who has fallen into a state of conglomeration about accounts of which it is not pretended that he had ever any knowledge, he is not at all likely ever to do. In the meantime his prospects in life are ended. Another ruined suitor, who periodically appears from Shropshire and breaks out into efforts to address the Chancellor at the close of the day's business and who can by no means be made to understand that the Chancellor is legally ignorant of his existence after making it desolate for a quarter of a century, plants himself in a good place and keeps an eye on the judge, ready to call out "My Lord!" in a voice of sonorous complaint on the instant of his rising. A few lawyers' clerks and others who know this suitor by sight linger on the chance of his furnishing some fun and enlivening the dismal weather a little.

Jarndyce and Jarndyce drones on. This scarecrow of a suit has, in course of time, become so complicated that no man alive knows what it means. The parties to it understand it least, but it has been observed that no two Chancery lawyers can talk about it for five minutes without coming to a total disagreement as to all the premises. Innumerable children have been born into the cause; innumerable young people have married into it; innumerable old people have died out of it. Scores of persons have deliriously found themselves made parties in Jarndyce and Jarndyce without knowing how or why; whole families have inherited legendary hatreds with the suit. The little plaintiff or defendant who was promised a new rocking-horse when Jarndyce and Jarndyce should be settled has grown up, possessed himself of a real horse, and trotted away into the other world. Fair wards of court have faded into mothers and grandmothers; a long procession of Chancellors has come in and gone out; the legion of bills in the suit have been transformed into mere bills of mortality; there are not three Jarndyces left upon the earth perhaps since old Tom Jarndyce in despair blew his brains out at a coffee-house in Chancery Lane; but Jarndyce and Jarndyce still drags its dreary length before the court, perennially hopeless.

Jarndyce and Jarndyce has passed into a joke. That is the only good that has ever come of it. It has been death to many, but it is a joke in the profession. Every master in Chancery has had a reference out of it. Every Chancellor was "in it," for somebody or other, when he was counsel at the bar. Good things have been said about it by blue-nosed, bulbous-shoed old benchers in select port-wine committee after dinner in hall. Articled clerks have been in the habit of fleshing their legal wit upon it. The last Lord Chancellor handled it neatly, when, correcting Mr. Blowers, the eminent silk gown who said that such a thing might happen when the sky rained potatoes, he observed, "or when we get through Jarndyce and Jarndyce, Mr. Blowers"—a pleasantry that particularly tickled the maces, bags, and purses.

How many people out of the suit Jarndyce and Jarndyce has stretched forth its unwholesome hand to spoil and corrupt would be a very wide question. From the master upon whose impaling files reams of dusty warrants in Jarndyce and Jarndyce have grimly writhed into many shapes, down to the copying-clerk in the Six Clerks' Office who has copied his tens of thousands of Chancery folio-pages under that eternal heading, no man's nature has been made better by it. In trickery, evasion, procrastination, spoliation, botheration, under false pretences of all sorts, there are influences that can never come to good. The very solicitors' boys who have kept the wretched suitors at bay, by protesting time out of mind that Mr. Chizzle, Mizzle, or otherwise was particularly engaged and had appointments until dinner, may have got an extra moral twist and shuffle into themselves out of Jarndyce and Jarndyce. The receiver in the cause has acquired a goodly sum of money by it but has acquired too a distrust of his own mother and a contempt for his own kind. Chizzle, Mizzle, and otherwise have lapsed into a habit of vaguely promising themselves that they will look into that outstanding little matter and see what can be done for Drizzle— who was not well used—when Jarndyce and Jarndyce shall be got out of the office. Shirking and sharking in all their many varieties have been sown broadcast by the ill-fated cause; and even those who have contemplated its history from the outermost circle of such evil have been insensibly tempted into a loose way of letting bad things alone to take their own bad course, and a loose belief that if the world go wrong it was in some off-hand manner never meant to go right.

Thus, in the midst of the mud and at the heart of the fog, sits the Lord High Chancellor in his High Court of Chancery.

"Mr. Tangle," says the Lord High Chancellor, latterly something restless under the eloquence of that learned gentleman.

"Mlud," says Mr. Tangle. Mr. Tangle knows more of Jarndyce and Jarndyce than anybody. He is famous for it—supposed never to have read anything else since he left school.

"Have you nearly concluded your argument?"

"Mlud, no—variety of points—feel it my duty tsubmit—ludship," is the reply that slides out of Mr. Tangle.

"Several members of the bar are still to be heard, I believe?" says the Chancellor with a slight smile.

Eighteen of Mr. Tangle's learned friends, each armed with a little summary of eighteen hundred sheets, bob up like eighteen hammers in a pianoforte, make eighteen bows, and drop into their eighteen places of obscurity.

We will proceed with the hearing on Wednesday fortnight," says the Chancellor. For the question at issue is only a question of costs, a mere bud on the forest tree of the parent suit, and really will come to a settlement one of these days.

The Chancellor rises; the bar rises; the prisoner is brought forward in a hurry; the man from Shropshire cries, "My lord!" Maces, bags, and purses indignantly proclaim silence and frown at the man from Shropshire.

"In reference," proceeds the Chancellor, still on Jarndyce and Jarndyce, "to the young girl——"

"Begludship's pardon—boy," says Mr. Tangle prematurely.

"In reference," proceeds the Chancellor with extra distinctness, "to the young girl and boy, the two young people"—Mr. Tangle crushed—"whom I directed to be in attendance to-day and who are now in my private room, I will see them and satisfy myself as to the expediency of making the order for their residing with their uncle."

Mr. Tangle on his legs again. "Begludship's pardon—dead."

"With their"—Chancellor looking through his double eyeglass at the papers on his desk—"grandfather."

"Begludship's pardon—victim of rash action—brains."

Suddenly a very little counsel with a terrific bass voice arises, fully inflated, in the back settlements of the fog, and says, "Will your lordship allow me? I appear for him. He is a cousin, several times removed. I am not at the moment prepared to inform the court in what exact remove he is a cousin, but he *is* a cousin."

Leaving this address (delivered like a sepulchral message) ringing in the rafters of the roof, the very little counsel drops, and the fog knows him no more. Everybody looks for him. Nobody can see him.

"I will speak with both the young people," says the Chancellor anew, "and satisfy myself on the subject of their residing with their cousin. I will mention the matter tomorrow morning when I take my seat."

The Chancellor is about to bow to the bar when the prisoner is presented. Nothing can possibly come of the prisoner's conglomeration but his being sent back to prison, which is soon done. The man from Shropshire ventures another remonstrative "My lord!" but the Chancellor, being aware of him, has dexterously vanished. Everybody else quickly vanishes too. A battery of blue bags is loaded with heavy charges of papers and carried off by clerks; the little mad old woman marches off with her documents; the empty court is locked

up. If all the injustice it has committed and all the misery it has
caused could only be locked up with it, and the whole burnt away
in a great funeral pyre—why so much the better for other parties
than the parties in Jarndyce and Jarndyce!

BUREAUCRACY

Franz Kafka

From *The Castle*

K. soon found his opinion of the authorities of the place confirmed when he went to see the Mayor. The Mayor, a kindly, stout,
clean-shaven man, was laid up; he was suffering from a severe attack of gout, and received K. in bed. "So here is our Land-Surveyor," he said, and tried to sit up, failed in the attempt, and flung
himself back again on the cushions, pointing apologetically to his
leg. In the faint light of the room, where the tiny windows were
still further darkened by curtains, a noiseless, almost shadowy
woman pushed forward a chair for K. and placed it beside the bed.
"Take a seat, Land-Surveyor, take a seat," said the Mayor, "and let
me know your wishes." K. read out Klamm's letter and adjoined a
few remarks to it. Again he had this sense of extraordinary ease in
intercourse with the authorities. They seemed literally to bear every
burden, one could lay everything on their shoulders and remain
free and untouched oneself. As if he too felt this in his way, the
Mayor made a movement of discomfort on the bed. At length he
said: "I know about the whole business, as, indeed, you have remarked. The reason why I've done nothing is, first, that I've been
unwell, and secondly that you've been so long in coming: I thought
finally that you had given up the business. But now that you've
been so kind as to look me up, really I must tell you the plain un-
varnished truth of the matter. You've been taken on as Land-Surveyor, as you say, but, unfortunately, we have no need of a land-
surveyor. There wouldn't be the least use for one here. The frontiers

of our little state are marked out and all officially recorded. So what should we do with a land-surveyor?" Though he had not given the matter a moment's thought before, K. was convinced now at the bottom of his heart that he had expected some such response as this. Exactly for that reason he was able to reply immediately: "This is a great surprise for me. It throws all my calculations out. I can only hope that there's some misunderstanding." "No, unfortunately," said the Mayor, "it's as I've said." "But how is that possible?" cried K. "Surely I haven't made this endless journey just to be sent back again!" "That's another question," replied the Mayor, "which isn't for me to decide, but how this misunderstanding became possible, I can certainly explain that. In such a large governmental office as the Count's, it may occasionally happen that one department ordains this, another that; neither knows of the other, and though the supreme control is absolutely efficient, it comes by its nature too late, and so every now and then a trifling miscalculation arises. Of course that applies only to the pettiest little affairs, as for example your case. In great matters I've never known of any error yet, but even little affairs are often painful enough. Now as for your case, I'll be open with you about its history, and make no official mystery of it—I'm not enough of the official for that, I'm a farmer and always will remain one. A long time ago—I had only been Mayor for a few months—there came an order, I can't remember from what department, in which, in the usual categorical way of the gentlemen up there, it was made known that a Land-Surveyor was to be called in, and the municipality were instructed to hold themselves ready for the plans and measurements necessary for his work. This order obviously couldn't have concerned you, for it was many years ago, and I shouldn't have remembered it if I wasn't ill just now and with ample time in bed to think of the most absurd things. Mizzi," he said, suddenly interrupting his narrative, to the woman who was still flitting about the room in incomprehensible activity, "please have a look in the cabinet, perhaps you'll find the order. You see, it belongs to my first months here," he explained to K.; "at that time I still filed everything away." The woman opened the cabinet at once. K. and the Mayor looked on. The cabinet was crammed full of papers. When it was opened two large packages of papers rolled out, tied in round bundles, as one usually binds firewood; the woman sprang back in alarm. "It must be down below, at the bottom," said the Mayor, directing operations from the bed. Gathering the papers in both arms, the woman obediently threw them all out of the cabinet so as to reach those at the bottom. The papers now covered half the floor. "A great deal of work is got through here," said the Mayor nodding his head, "and that's only a small fraction of it. I've put away the most important pile in the shed, but the great mass of it has simply gone astray. Who could keep it all together? But there are piles and piles more in the shed. Will you be able to find the order?" he said turning again to his wife, "you must look for a document with the word 'Land-Surveyor' underlined in blue pencil." "It's too dark," said the woman, "I'll get a candle," and she stamped through the papers to the door. "My wife is a great help to me," said the Mayor, "in these difficult official affairs, and yet we can never quite keep up with them. True, I have another assistant for the writing that has to be done, the teacher; but all the same it's impossible to get things shipshape, there's always a lot of business that has to be left lying; it has been put away in that chest there," and he pointed to another cabinet. "And just now, when I'm laid up, it has got the upper hand," he said, and lay back with a weary, yet proud air. "Couldn't I," asked K., seeing that the woman had now returned with the candle and was kneeling before the chest looking for the paper, "couldn't I help your wife to look for it?" The Mayor smilingly shook his head: "As I said before, I don't want to make any parade of official secrecy before you; but to let you look through these papers yourself—no, I can't go so far as that." Now stillness fell in the room, only the rustling of the papers was to be heard; it looked, indeed, for a few minutes, as if the Mayor were dozing. A faint rapping on the door made K. turn round. It was of course the assistants. All the same, they showed already some of the effects of their training, they did not rush at once into the room, but whispered at first through the door, which was slightly ajar: "It's cold out here." "Who's that?" asked the Mayor, starting up. "It's only my assistants," replied K. "I don't know where to ask them to wait for me; it's too cold outside, and here they would be in the way." "They won't disturb me," said the Mayor indulgently. "Ask them to come in. Besides, I know them. Old acquaintances." "But they're in *my* way," K. replied bluntly, letting his gaze wander from the assistants to the Mayor and back again, and finding on the faces of all three the same smile. "But seeing you're here," he went on experimentally, "stay and help the Mayor's lady there to look for a document with the word 'Land-Surveyor' underlined in blue pencil." The Mayor raised no objection. What had not been permitted to K. was allowed to the assistants; they threw themselves at once on the papers, but they did not so much seek for anything as rummage about in the heap, and while one was spelling out a document, the other would immediately snatch it out of his hand. The woman meanwhile knelt before the empty chest, she seemed to have completely given up looking; in any case the candle was standing quite far away from her.

"The assistants," said the Mayor with a self-complacent smile, which seemed to indicate that he had the lead, though nobody was in a position even to assume this, "they're in your way, then? Yet they're your own assistants." "No," replied K. coolly, "they only ran into me here." "Ran into you," said the Mayor; "you mean, of course, were assigned to you." "All right, then, were assigned to me," said K., "but they might as well have fallen from the sky, for all the thought that was spent in choosing them." "Nothing here is done without taking thought," said the Mayor, actually forgetting the pain in his foot and sitting up. "Nothing!" said K., "and what about me being summoned here, then?" "Even your being summoned was carefully considered," said the Mayor; "it was only certain auxiliary circumstances that entered and confused the matter, I'll prove it to you from the official papers." "The papers will not be found," said K. "Not be found?" said the Mayor. "Mizzi, please hurry up a bit. Still, I can tell you the story even without the papers. We replied with thanks to the order that I've mentioned already, saying that we didn't need a land-surveyor. But this reply doesn't appear to have reached the original department—I'll call it A—but by mistake went to another department, B. So Department A remained without an answer, but unfortunately our full reply didn't reach B either; whether it was that the order itself was not enclosed by us, or whether it got lost on the way—it was certainly not lost in my department, that I can vouch for—in any case all that arrived at Department B was the covering letter, in which was merely noted that the enclosed order, unfortunately an impractical one, was concerned with the engagement of a land-surveyor. Meanwhile Department A was waiting for our answer; they had, of course, made a memorandum of the case, but as, excusably enough, often happens and is bound to happen even under the most efficient handling, our correspondent trusted to the fact that we would answer him, after which he would either summon the Land-Surveyor or else, if need be, write us further about the matter. As a result he never thought of referring to his memorandum, and the whole thing fell into oblivion. But in Department B the covering letter came into the hands of a correspondent famed for his conscientiousness, Sordini by name, an Italian; it is incomprehensible even to me, though I am one of the initiated, why a man of his capacities is left in an almost subordinate position. This Sordini naturally sent us back the unaccompanied covering letter for completion. Now months, if not years, had passed by this time since that first communication from Department A, which is understandable enough, for when—as is the rule—a document goes the proper route, it reaches the department at the outside in a day and is settled that day, but when it once in a while loses its way, then in an organization so efficient as ours its proper destination must be sought for literally with desperation; otherwise it mightn't be found; and then—well, then the search may last really for a long time. Accordingly, when we got Sordini's note we had only a vague memory of the affair; there were only two of us to do the work at that time, Mizzi and myself, the teacher hadn't yet been assigned to us; we only kept copies in the most important instances, so we could only reply in the most vague terms that we knew nothing of this engagement of a land-surveyor and that as far as we knew there was no need for one.

"But"—here the Mayor interrupted himself as if, carried on by his tale, he had gone too far, or as if at least it was possible that he had gone too far, "doesn't the story bore you?"

"No," said K., "it amuses me."

Thereupon the Mayor said: "I'm not telling it to amuse you."

"It only amuses me," said K., "because it gives me an insight into the ludicrous bungling that in certain circumstances may decide the life of a human being."

"You haven't been given any insight into that yet," replied the Mayor gravely, "and I can go on with my story. Naturally Sordini was not satisfied with our reply. I admire the man, though he is a plague to me. He literally distrusts everyone; even if, for instance, he has come to know somebody, through countless circumstances, as the most reliable man in the world, he distrusts him as soon as fresh circumstances arise, as if he didn't want to know him, or rather as if he wanted to know that he was a scoundrel. I consider that right and proper, an official must behave like that; unfortunately, with my nature I can't follow out this principle; you see yourself how frank I am with you, a stranger, about those things, I can't act in any other way. But Sordini, on the contrary, was seized by suspicion when he read our reply. Now a huge correspondence began to grow. Sordini inquired how I had suddenly recalled that a land-surveyor shouldn't

be summoned. I replied, drawing on Mizzi's splendid memory, that
the first suggestion had come from the bureau itself (but that it had
come from a different department we had of course forgotten long
before this). Sordini countered: why had I only mentioned this official order now? I replied: because I had just remembered it. Sordini: that was very extraordinary. Myself: it was not in the least
extraordinary in such a long-drawn-out business. Sordini: yes, it
was extraordinary, for the order that I remembered didn't exist.
Myself: of course it didn't exist, for the whole document had been
lost. Sordini: but there must be a memorandum extant relating to
this first communication, and there wasn't one extant. That made me
halt, for that an error should happen in Sordini's department I dared
neither maintain nor believe. Perhaps, my dear Land-Surveyor,
you'll make the reproach against Sordini in your mind that in consideration of my assertion he should have been moved at least to
make inquiries in the other departments about the affair. But that is
just what would have been wrong; I don't want any blame to attach
to this man, no, not even in your thoughts. It's a working principle
of the head bureau that the very possibility of error must be ruled
out of account. This ground principle is justified by the consummate
organization of the whole authority, and it is necessary if the maxi-
mum speed in transacting business is to be attained. So it wasn't
within Sordini's power to make inquiries in other departments; besides, they simply wouldn't have answered, because they would
have guessed at once that it was a case of hunting out a possible
error."

"Allow me, Mr. Mayor, to interrupt you with a question," said K.
"Did you not mention once before a Control Authority? From your
description the whole economy is one that would rouse one's appre-
hensions if one could imagine the Control failing."

"You're very strict," said the Mayor, "but multiply your strictness
a thousand times and it would still be nothing compared with the
strictness that the Authority imposes on itself. Only a total stranger
could ask a question like yours. Is there a Control Authority? There
are only Control authorities. Frankly, it isn't their function to hunt
out errors in the vulgar sense, for errors don't happen, and even
when once in a while an error does happen, as in your case, who
can say finally that it's an error?"

"This is news indeed!" cried K.

"It's very old news to me," said the Mayor. "Not unlike yourself,
I'm convinced that an error has occurred, and as a result Sordini is

quite ill with despair, and the first Control officials, whom we have
to thank for discovering the source of error, recognize that there is
an error. But who can guarantee that the second Control officials
will decide in the same way, and the third and all the others?"

"That may be," said K. "I would much rather not mix in these
speculations yet; besides, this is the first mention I've heard of those
Control officials and naturally I can't understand them yet. But I
fancy that two things must be distinguished here: first, what is
transacted in the offices and can be construed again officially this
way or that, and, secondly, my own actual person, me myself, situated outside of the offices and threatened by their encroachments,
which are so meaningless that I can't even yet believe in the seriousness of the danger. The first evidently is covered by what you,
Mr. Mayor, tell me in such extraordinary and disconcerting detail;
all the same, I should like to hear a word now about myself."

"I'm coming to that too," said the Mayor, "but you couldn't understand it without my giving a few more preliminary details. My
mentioning the Control officials just now was premature. So I must
turn back to the discrepancies with Sordini. As I said, my defense
gradually weakened. But whenever Sordini has in his hands even
the slightest hold against anyone, he has as good as won, for then
his vigilance, energy, and alertness are actually increased and it's a
terrible moment for the victim, and a glorious one for the victim's
enemies. It's only because in other circumstances I have experienced
this last feeling that I'm able to speak of him as I do. All the same,
I have never managed yet to come within sight of him. He can't get
down here, he's so overwhelmed with work; from the descriptions
I've heard of his room, every wall is covered with pillars of documents tied together, piled on top of one another; those are only the
documents that Sordini is working on at the time, and as bundles
of papers are continually being taken away and brought in, and all
in great haste, those columns are always falling on the floor, and
it's just those perpetual crashes, following fast on one another, that
have come to distinguish Sordini's workroom. Yes, Sordini is a
worker, and he gives the same scrupulous care to the smallest case
as to the greatest."

"Mr. Mayor," said K., "you always call my case one of the smallest, and yet it has given hosts of officials a great deal of trouble,
and if, perhaps, it was unimportant at the start, yet through the diligence of officials of Sordini's type it has grown into a great affair.
Very much against my will, unfortunately, for my ambition doesn't

run to seeing columns of documents, all about me, rising and crashing together, but to working quietly at my drawing-board as a humble land-surveyor."

"No," said the Superintendent, "it's not at all a great affair, in that respect you've no ground for complaint—it's one of the least important among the least important. The importance of a case is not determined by the amount of work it involves; you're far from understanding the authorities if you believe that. But even if it's a question of the amount of work, your case would remain one of the slightest; ordinary cases—those without any so-called errors, I mean—provide far more work and far more profitable work as well. Besides, you know absolutely nothing yet of the actual work that was caused by your case. I'll tell you about that now. . . ."

PARLIAMENTARY CRETINISM

Anthony Trollope

From *Phineas Redux*

Before the 11th of November, the day on which Parliament was to meet, the whole country was in a hubbub. Consternation and triumph were perhaps equally predominant, and equally strong. There were those who declared that now at length was Great Britain to be ruined in actual present truth; and those who asserted that, of a sudden, after a fashion so wholly unexpected as to be divine,—as great fires, great famines, and great wars are called divine,—a mighty hand had been stretched out to take away the remaining incubus of superstition, priestcraft, and bigotry under which England had hitherto been labouring. The proposed disestablishment of the State Church of England was, of course, the subject of this diversity of opinion.

And there was not only diversity, but with it great confusion. The political feelings of the country are, as a rule, so well marked that it is easy, as to almost every question, to separate the sheep from the goats. With but few exceptions one can tell where to look

for the supporters and where for the opponents of one measure or
of another. Meetings are called in this or in that public hall to assist
or to combat the Minister of the day, and men know what they are
about. But now it was not so. It was understood that Mr. Daubeny,
the accredited leader of the Conservatives, was about to bring in
the bill, but no one as yet knew who would support the bill. His
own party, to a man,—without a single exception,—were certainly
opposed to the measure in their minds. It must be so. It could not
but be certain that they should hate it. Each individual sitting on
the Conservative side in either House did most certainly within his
own bosom cry Ichabod when the fatal news reached his ears. But
such private opinions and inward wailings need not, and probably
would not, guide the body. Ichabod had been cried before, though
probably never with such intensity of feeling. Disestablishment
might be worse than Free Trade or Household Suffrage, but was not
more absolutely opposed to Conservative convictions than had been
those great measures. And yet the party, as a party, had swallowed
them both. To the first and lesser evil, a compact little body of
staunch Commoners had stood forth in opposition,—but nothing had
come of it to those true Britons beyond a feeling of living in the
cold shade of exclusion. When the greater evil arrived, that of
Household Suffrage,—a measure which twenty years since would
hardly have been advocated by the advanced Liberals of the day,—
the Conservatives had learned to acknowledge the folly of clinging
to their own convictions, and had swallowed the dose without serious disruption of their ranks. Every man,—with but an exception or
two,—took the measure up, some with faces so singularly distorted
as to create true pity, some with an assumption of indifference, some
with affected glee. But in the double process the party had become
used to this mode of carrying on the public service. As poor old
England must go to the dogs, as the doom had been pronounced
against the country that it should be ruled by the folly of the many
foolish, and not by the wisdom of the few wise, why should the few
wise remain out in the cold,—seeing, as they did, that by so doing
no good would be done to the country? Dissensions among their
foes did, when properly used, give them power,—but such power
they could only use by carrying measures which they themselves
believed to be ruinous. But the ruin would be as certain should they
abstain. Each individual might have gloried in standing aloof,—in
hiding his face beneath his toga, and in remembering that Rome did
once exist in her splendour. But a party cannot afford to hide its

face in its toga. A party has to be practical. A party can only live by having its share of Garters, lord-lieutenants, bishops, and attorney-generals. Though the country were ruined, the party should be supported. Hitherto the party had been supported, and had latterly enjoyed almost its share of stars and Garters,—thanks to the individual skill and strategy of that great English political Von Moltke Mr. Daubeny.

And now what would the party say about the disestablishment of the Church? Even a party must draw the line somewhere. It was bad to sacrifice things mundane; but this thing was the very Holy of Holies! Was nothing to be conserved by a Conservative party? What if Mr. Daubeny were to explain some day to the electors of East Barsetshire that an hereditary peerage was an absurdity? What if in some rural nook of his Boeotia he should suggest in ambiguous language to the farmers that a Republic was the only form of Government capable of a logical defence? Duke had already said to Duke, and Earl to Earl, and Baronet to Baronet that there must be a line somewhere. Bishops as a rule say but little to each other, and now were afraid to say anything. The Church, which had been, which was, so truly beloved;—surely that must be beyond the line! And yet there crept through the very marrow of the party an agonising belief that Mr. Daubeny would carry the bulk of his party with him into the lobby of the House of Commons.

But if such was the dismay of the Conservatives, how shall any writer depict the consternation of the Liberals? If there be a feeling odious to the mind of a sober, hardworking man, it is the feeling that the bread he has earned is to be taken out of his mouth. The pay, the patronage, the powers, and the pleasure of Government were all due to the Liberals. "God bless my soul," said Mr. Ratler, who always saw things in a practical light, "we have a larger fighting majority than any party has had since Lord Liverpool's time. They have no right to attempt it. They are bound to go out." "There's nothing of honesty left in politics," said Mr. Bonteen, declaring that he was sick of the life. Barrington Erle thought that the whole Liberal party should oppose the measure. Though they were Liberals they were not democrats; nor yet infidels. But when Barrington Erle said this, the great leaders of the Liberal party had not as yet decided on their ground of action.

There was much difficulty in reaching any decision. It had been asserted so often that the disestablishment of the Church was only a question of time, that the intelligence of the country had gradually so learned to regard it. Who had said so, men did not know and did not inquire;—but the words were spoken everywhere. Parsons with sad hearts,—men who in their own parishes were enthusiastic, pure, pious, and useful,—whispered them in the dead of the night to the wives of their bosoms. Bishops, who had become less pure by contact with the world at clubs, shrugged their shoulders and wagged their heads, and remembered comfortably the sanctity of vested interests. Statesmen listened to them with politeness, and did not deny that they were true. In the free intercourse of closest friendships the matter was discussed between ex-Secretaries of State. The Press teemed with the assertion that it was only a question of time. Some fervent, credulous friends predicted another century of life;—some hard-hearted logical opponents thought that twenty years would put an end to the anomaly:—a few stout enemies had sworn on the hustings with an anathema that the present Session should see the deposition from her high place of this eldest daughter of the woman of Babylon. But none had expected the blow so soon as this; and none certainly had expected it from this hand.

But what should the Liberal party do? Ratler was for opposing Mr. Daubeny with all their force, without touching the merits of the case. It was no fitting work for Mr. Daubeny, and the suddenness of the proposition coming from such a quarter would justify them now and for ever, even though they themselves should disestablish everything before the Session were over. Barrington Erle, suffering under a real political conviction for once in his life, was desirous of a positive and chivalric defence of the Church. He believed in the twenty years. Mr. Bonteen shut himself up in disgust. Things were amiss; and, as he thought, the evil was due to want of party zeal on the part of his own leader, Mr. Gresham. He did not dare to say this, lest, when the house door should at last be opened, he might not be invited to enter with the others; but such was his conviction. "If we were all a little less in the abstract, and a little more in the concrete, it would be better for us." Laurence Fitzgibbon, when these words had been whispered to him by Mr. Bonteen, had hardly understood them; but it had been explained to him that his friend had meant "men, not measures." When Parliament met, Mr. Gresham, the leader of the Liberal party, had not as yet expressed any desire to his general followers.

The Queen's Speech was read, and the one paragraph which seemed to possess any great public interest was almost a repetition of the words which Mr. Daubeny had spoken to the electors of East Barsetshire. "It will probably be necessary for you to review the connection which still exists between, and which binds together, the Church and the State." Mr. Daubeny's words had of course been more fluent, but the gist of the expression was the same. He had been quite in earnest when addressing his friends in the country. And though there had been but an interval of a few weeks, the Conservative party in the two Houses heard the paragraph read without surprise and without a murmur. Some said that the gentlemen on the Treasury Bench in the House of Commons did not look to be comfortable. Mr. Daubeny sat with his hat over his brow, mute, apparently impassive and unapproachable, during the reading of the Speech and the moving and seconding of the Address. The House was very full, and there was much murmuring on the side of the Opposition;—but from the Government benches hardly a sound was heard, as a young gentleman, from one of the Midland counties, in a deputy-lieutenant's uniform, who had hitherto been known for no particular ideas of his own, but had been believed to be at any rate true to the Church, explained, not in very clear language, that the time had at length come when the interests of religion demanded a wider support and a fuller sympathy than could be afforded under that system of Church endowment and State establishment for which the country had hitherto been so grateful, and for which the country had such boundless occasion for gratitude. Another gentleman, in the uniform of the Guards, seconded the Address, and declared that in nothing was the sagacity of a Legislature so necessary as in discerning the period in which that which had hitherto been good ceased to be serviceable. The status pupillaris was mentioned, and it was understood that he had implied that England was now old enough to go on in matters of religion without a tutor in the shape of a State Church.

Who makes the speeches, absolutely puts together the words, which are uttered when the Address is moved and seconded? It can hardly be that lessons are prepared and sent to the noble lords and honourable gentlemen to be learned by heart like a school-boy's task. And yet, from their construction, style, and general tone,—from the platitudes which they contain as well as from the general safety and good sense of the remarks,—from the absence of any attempt to improve a great occasion by the fire of oratory, one cannot but be convinced that a very absolute control is exercised. The gorgeously apparelled speakers, who seem to have great latitude allowed them in the matter of clothing, have certainly very little in the matter of language. And then it always seems that either of the four might have made the speech of any of the others. It could not have been the case that the Hon. Colonel Mowbray Dick, the Member for West Bustard, had really elaborated out of his own head that theory of the status pupillaris. A better fellow, or a more popular officer, or a sweeter-tempered gentleman than Mowbray Dick does not exist; but he certainly never entertained advanced opinions respecting the religious education of his country. When he is at home with his family, he always goes to church, and there has been an end of it.

And then the fight began. The thunderbolts of opposition were unloosed, and the fires of political rancour blazed high. Mr. Gresham rose to his legs, and declared to all the world that which he had hitherto kept secret from his own party. It was known afterwards that in discussion with his own dearly-beloved political friend, Lord Cantrip, he had expressed his unbounded anger at the duplicity, greed for power, and want of patriotism displayed by his opponent; but he had acknowledged that the blow had come so quick and so unexpectedly that he thought it better to leave the matter to the House without instruction from himself. He now revelled in sarcasm, and before his speech was over raged into wrath. He would move an amendment to the Address for two reasons,—first because this was no moment for bringing before Parliament the question of the Church establishment, when as yet no well-considered opportunity of expressing itself on the subject had been afforded to the country, and secondly because any measure of reform on that matter should certainly not come to them from the right honourable gentleman opposite. As to the first objection, he should withhold his arguments till the bill suggested had been presented to them. It was in handling the second that he displayed his great power of invective. All those men who then sat in the House, and who on that night crowded the galleries, remember his tones as, turning to the dissenters who usually supported him, and pointing over the table to his opponents, he uttered that well-worn quotation, *Quod minime reris,*—then he paused, and began again, *Quod minime reris,— Graiâ pandetur ab urbe.* The power and inflexion of his voice at the word *Graiâ* were certainly very wonderful. He ended by moving an amendment to the Address, and asking for support equally from one side of the House as from the other.

When at length Mr. Daubeny moved his hat from his brow and rose to his legs he began by expressing his thankfulness that he had not been made a victim to the personal violence of the right honourable gentleman. He continued the same strain of badinage throughout,—in which he was thought to have been wrong, as it was a method of defence, or attack, for which his peculiar powers hardly suited him. As to any bill that was to be laid upon the table, he had not as yet produced it. He did not doubt that the dissenting interests of the country would welcome relief from an anomaly, let it come whence it might, even *Graiâ ab urbe,* and he waved his hand back to the clustering Conservatives who sat behind him. That the right honourable gentleman should be angry he could understand, as the return to power of the right honourable gentleman and his party had been anticipated, and he might almost say discounted as a certainty.

Then, when Mr. Daubeny sat down, the House was adjourned.

THE DEMOCRATIC MARKETPLACE

George Eliot

From *Middlemarch*

There were plenty of reasons why he should not go—public reasons why he should not quit his post at this crisis, leaving Mr. Brooke in the lurch when he needed "coaching" for the election, and when there was so much canvassing, direct and indirect, to be carried on. Will could not like to leave his own chessman in the heat of a game; and any candidate on the right side, even his brain and marrow had been as soft as was consistent with a gentlemanly bearing, might help to turn a majority. To coach Mr. Brooke and keep him steadily to the idea that he must pledge himself to vote for the actual Reform Bill, instead of insisting on his independence and power of pulling up in time, was not an easy task. Mr. Farebrother's prophecy of a fourth candidate "in the bag" had not yet been fulfilled, neither the Parliamentary Candidate Society nor any other power on the watch to secure a reforming majority seeing a worthy nodus for interference while there was a second reforming

From Ch. 51.

candidate like Mr. Brooke, who might be returned at his own expense; and the fight lay entirely between Pinkerton the old Tory member, Bagster the new Whig member returned at the last election, and Brooke the future independent member, who was to fetter himself for this occasion only. Mr. Hawley and his party would bend all their forces to the return of Pinkerton, and Mr. Brooke's success must depend either on plumpers which would leave Bagster in the rear, or on the new minting of Tory votes into reforming votes. The latter means, of course, would be preferable.

This prospect of converting votes was a dangerous distraction to Mr. Brooke: his impression that waverers were likely to be allured by wavering statements, and also the liability of his mind to stick afresh at opposing arguments as they turned up in his memory, gave Will Ladislaw much trouble.

"You know there are tactics in these things," said Mr. Brooke; "meeting people half-way—tempering your ideas—saying, 'Well now, there's something in that,' and so on. I agree with you that this is a peculiar occasion—the country with a will of its own—political unions—that sort of thing—but we sometimes cut with rather too sharp a knife, Ladislaw. These ten-pound householders, now: why ten? Draw the line somewhere—yes; but why just at ten? That's a difficult question, now, if you go into it."

"Of course it is," said Will, impatiently. "But if you are to wait till we get a logical Bill, you must put yourself forward as a revolutionist, and then Middlemarch would not elect you, I fancy. As for trimming, this is not a time for trimming."

Mr. Brooke always ended by agreeing with Ladislaw, who still appeared to him a sort of Burke with a leaven of Shelley; but after an interval the wisdom of his own methods reasserted itself, and he was again drawn into using them with much hopefulness. At this stage of affairs he was in excellent spirits, which even supported him under large advances of money; for his powers of convincing and persuading had not yet been tested by anything more difficult than a chairman's speech introducing other orators, or a dialogue with a Middlemarch voter, from which he came away with a sense that he was a tactician by nature, and that it was a pity he had not gone earlier into this kind of thing. He was a little conscious of defeat, however, with Mr. Mawmsey, a chief representative in Middlemarch of that great social power, the retail trader, and naturally one of the most doubtful voters in the borough—willing for his own part to supply an equal quality of teas and sugars to reformer and anti-reformer, as well as to agree impartially with both, and feeling like the burgesses of old that this necessity of electing members was a great burden to a town; for even if there were no danger in holding out hopes to all parties beforehand, there would be the painful necessity at last of disappointing respectable people whose names were on his books. He was accustomed to receive large orders from Mr. Brooke of Tipton; but then, there were many of Pinkerton's committee whose opinions had a great weight of grocery on their side. Mr. Mawmsey thinking that Mr. Brooke, as not too "clever in his intellects," was the more likely to forgive a grocer who gave a hostile vote under pressure, had become confidential in his back parlor.

"As to Reform, sir, put it in a family light," he said, rattling the small silver in his pocket, and smiling affably. "Will it support Mrs. Mawmsey, and enable her to bring up six children when I am no more? I put the question *fictiously,* knowing what must be the answer. Very well, sir. I ask you what, as a husband and a father, I am to do when gentlemen come to me and say, 'Do as you like, Mawmsey; but if you vote against us, I shall get my groceries elsewhere: when I sugar my liquor, I like to feel that I am benefitting the country by maintaining tradesmen of the right colour.' Those very words have been spoken to me, sir, in the very chair where you are now sitting. I don't mean by your honourable self, Mr. Brooke."

"No, no, no—that's narrow, you know. Until my butler complains to me of your goods, Mr. Mawmsey," said Mr. Brooke, soothingly, "until I hear that you send bad sugars, spices,—that sort of thing,—I shall never order him to go elsewhere."

"Sir, I am your humble servant, and greatly obliged," said Mr. Mawmsey, feeling that politics were clearing up a little. "There would be some pleasure in voting for a gentleman who speaks in that honourable manner."

"Well, you know, Mr. Mawmsey, you would find it the right thing to put yourself on our side. This Reform will touch everybody by-and-by,—a thoroughly popular measure,—a sort of A, B, C, you know, that must come first before the rest can follow. I quite agree with you that you've got to look at the thing in a family light: but public spirit, now. We're all one family, you know—it's all one cupboard. Such a thing as a vote, now: why, it may help to make men's fortunes at the Cape,—there's no knowing what may be the effect of a vote," Mr. Brooke ended, with a sense of being a little out at sea, though finding it still enjoyable. But Mr. Mawmsey answered in a tone of decisive check.

"I beg your pardon, sir, but I can't afford that. When I give a vote I must know what I am doing; I must look to what will be the effects on my till and ledger, speaking respectfully. Prices, I'll admit, are what nobody can know the merits of; and the sudden falls after you've bought in currants, which are a goods that will not keep— I've never myself seen into the ins and outs there; which is a rebuke to human pride. But as to one family, there's debtor and creditor, I hope; they're not going to reform that away; else I should vote for things staying as they are. Few men have less need to cry for change than I have, personally speaking,—that is, for self and family. I am not one of those who have nothing to lose; I mean as to respectability both in parish and private business, and noways in respect of your honourable self and custom, which you was good enough to say you would not withdraw from me, vote or no vote, while the article sent in was satisfactory."

After this conversation Mr. Mawmsey went up and boasted to his wife that he had been rather too many for Brooke of Tipton, and that he didn't mind so much now about going to the poll.

Mr. Brooke on this occasion abstained from boasting of his tactics to Ladislaw, who for his part was glad enough to persuade himself that he had no concern with any canvassing except the purely argumentative sort, and that he worked no meaner engine than knowledge. Mr. Brooke, necessarily, had his agents, who understood the nature of the Middlemarch voter and the means of enlisting his ignorance on the side of the Bill,—which were remarkably similar to the means of enlisting it on the side against the Bill. Will stopped his ears. Occasionally Parliament, like the rest of our lives, even to our eating and apparel, could hardly go on if our imaginations were too active about processes. There were plenty of dirty-handed men in the world to do dirty business; and Will protested to himself that his share in bringing Mr. Brooke through would be quite innocent.

But whether he should succeed in that mode of contributing to the majority on the right side was very doubtful to him. He had written out various speeches and memoranda for speeches, but he had begun to perceive that Mr. Brooke's mind, if it had the burden of remembering any train of thought, would let it drop, run away in search of it, and not easily come back again. To collect documents is one mode of serving your country, and to remember the contents of a document is another. No! the only way in which Mr. Brooke could be coerced into thinking of the right arguments at the right time was to be well plied with them till they took up all the room in his brain. But here there was the difficulty of finding room, so many things having been taken in beforehand. Mr. Brooke himself observed that his ideas stood rather in his way when he was speaking.

However, Ladislaw's coaching was forthwith to be put to the test, for before the day of nomination Mr. Brooke was to explain himself to the worthy electors of Middlemarch from the balcony of the White Hart, which looked out advantageously at an angle of the market-place, commanding a large area in front and two converging streets. It was a fine May morning, and everything seemed hopeful: there was some prospect of an understanding between Bagster's committee and Brooke's, to which Mr. Bulstrode, Mr. Standish as a Liberal lawyer, and such manufacturers as Mr. Plymdale and Mr. Vincy, gave a solidity which almost counterbalanced Mr. Hawley and his associates who sat for Pinkerton at the Green Dragon. Mr. Brooke, conscious of having weakened the blasts of the "Trumpet" against him, by his reforms as a landlord in the last half year, and hearing himself cheered a little as he drove into the town, felt his heart tolerably light under his buff-coloured waistcoat. But with regard to critical occasions, it often happens that all moments seem comfortably remote until the last.

"This looks well, eh?" said Mr. Brooke as the crowd gathered. "I shall have a good audience, at any rate. I like this, now—this kind of public made up of one's own neighbours, you know."

The weavers and tanners of Middlemarch, unlike Mr. Mawmsey, had never thought of Mr. Brooke as a neighbour, and were not more attached to him than if he had been sent in a box from London. But they listened without much disturbance to the speakers who introduced the candidate, though one of them—a political personage from Brassing, who came to tell Middlemarch its duty—spoke so fully that it was alarming to think what the candidate could find to say after him. Meanwhile the crowd became denser, and as the political personage neared the end of his speech, Mr. Brooke felt a remarkable change in his sensations while he still handled his eye-glass, trifled with documents before him, and exchanged remarks with his committee, as a man to whom the moment of summons was indifferent.

"I'll take another glass of sherry, Ladislaw," he said, with an easy air, to Will, who was close behind him, and presently handed him the supposed fortifier. It was ill-chosen; for Mr. Brooke was an abstemious man, and to drink a second glass of sherry quickly at no great interval from the first was a surprise to his system which tended to scatter his energies instead of collecting them. Pray pity him: so many English gentlemen make themselves miserable by speechifying on entirely private grounds! whereas Mr. Brooke wished to serve his country by standing for Parliament—which, indeed, may also be done on private grounds, but being once undertaken does absolutely demand some speechifying.

It was not about the beginning of his speech that Mr. Brooke was at all anxious; this, he felt sure, would be all right; he should have it quite pat, cut out as neatly as a set of couplets from Pope. Embarking would be easy, but the vision of open sea that might come after was alarming. "And questions, now," hinted the demon just waking up in his stomach, "somebody may put questions about the schedules—Ladislaw," he continued, aloud, "just hand me the memorandum of the schedules."

When Mr. Brooke presented himself on the balcony, the cheers were quite loud enough to counterbalance the yells, groans, brayings, and other expressions of adverse theory, which were so moderate that Mr. Standish (decidedly an old bird) observed in the ear next to him, "This looks dangerous, by God! Hawley has got some deeper plan than this." Still, the cheers were exhilarating, and no candidate could look more amiable than Mr. Brooke, with the memorandum in his breast-pocket, his left hand on the rail of the balcony, and his right trifling with his eye-glass. The striking points in his appearance were his buff waistcoat, short-clipped blond hair, and neutral physiognomy. He began with some confidence.

"Gentlemen—Electors of Middlemarch!"

This was so much the right thing that a little pause after it seemed natural.

"I'm uncommonly glad to be here—I was never so proud and happy in my life—never so happy, you know."

This was a bold figure of speech, but not exactly the right thing; for, unhappily, the pat opening had slipped away,—even couplets from Pope may be but "fallings from us, vanishings," when fear clutches us, and a glass of sherry is hurrying like smoke among our ideas. Ladislaw, who stood at the window behind the speaker, thought, "It's all up now. The only chance is that, since the best thing won't always do, floundering may answer for once." Mr. Brooke, meanwhile, having lost other clews, fell back on himself and his qualifications,—always an appropriate graceful subject for a candidate.

"I am a close neighbour of yours, my good friends—you've known me on the bench a good while—I've always gone a good deal into public questions—machinery, now, and machine-breaking—you're many of you concerned with machinery, and I've been going into that lately. It won't do, you know, breaking machines: everything must go on—trade, manufactures, commerce, interchange of staples —that kind of thing—since Adam Smith, that must go on. We must look all over the globe:—'Observation with extensive view,' must look everywhere, 'from China to Peru,' as somebody says—Johnson, I think, 'The Rambler,' you know. That is what I have done up to a certain point—not as far as Peru; but I've not always stayed at home—I saw it wouldn't do. I've been in the Levant, where some of your Middlemarch goods go—and then, again, in the Baltic. The Baltic, now."

Plying among his recollections in this way, Mr. Brooke might have got along, easily to himself, and would have come back from the remotest seas without trouble; but a diabolical procedure had been set up by the enemy. At one and the same moment there had risen above the shoulders of the crowd, nearly opposite Mr. Brooke, and within ten yards of him, the effigy of himself: buff-coloured waistcoat, eye-glass, and neutral physiognomy, painted on rag; and there had arisen, apparently in the air, like the note of the cuckoo, a parrot-like, Punch-voiced echo of his words. Everybody looked up at the open windows in the houses at the opposite angles of the converging streets; but they were either blank, or filled by laughing listeners. The most innocent echo has an impish mockery in it when it follows a gravely persistent speaker, and this echo was not at all innocent; if it did not follow with the precision of a natural echo, it had a wicked choice of the words it overtook. By the time it said, "The Baltic, now," the laugh which had been running through the audience became a general shout, and but for the sobering effects of party and that great public cause which the entanglement of things had identified with "Brooke of Tipton," the laugh might have caught his committee. Mr. Bulstrode asked, reprehensively, what the new police was doing; but a voice could not well be collared, and an attack on the effigy of the candidate would have been too equivocal, since Hawley probably meant it to be pelted.

Mr. Brooke himself was not in a position to be quickly conscious of anything except a general slipping away of ideas within himself:

he had even a little singing in the ears, and he was the only person who had not yet taken distinct account of the echo or discerned the image of himself. Few things hold the perceptions more thoroughly captive than anxiety about what we have got to say. Mr. Brooke heard the laughter; but he had expected some Tory efforts at disturbance, and he was at this moment additionally excited by the tickling, stinging sense that his lost exordium was coming back to fetch him from the Baltic.

"That reminds me," he went on, thrusting a hand into his side-pocket, with an easy air, "if I wanted a precedent, you know—but we never want a precedent for the right thing—but there is Chatham, now; I can't say I should have supported Chatham, or Pitt, the younger Pitt—he was not a man of ideas, and we want ideas, you know."

"Blast your ideas! we want the Bill," said a loud rough voice from the crowd below.

Immediately the invisible Punch, who had hitherto followed Mr. Brooke, repeated, "Blast your ideas! we want the Bill." The laugh was louder than ever, and for the first time Mr. Brooke being himself silent, heard distinctly the mocking echo. But it seemed to ridicule his interrupter, and in that light was encouraging; so he replied with amenity,—

"There is something in what you say, my good friend, and what do we meet for but to speak our minds—freedom of opinion, freedom of the press, liberty—that kind of thing? The Bill, now—you shall have the Bill"—here Mr. Brooke paused a moment to fix his eye-glass and take the paper from his breast-pocket, with a sense of being practical and coming to particulars. The invisible Punch followed:—

"You shall have the Bill, Mr. Brooke, per electioneering contest, and a seat outside Parliament as delivered, five thousand pounds seven shillings and fourpence."

Mr. Brooke, amid the roars of laughter, turned red, let his eye-glass fall, and looking about him confusedly, saw the image of himself, which had come nearer. The next moment he saw it dolorously bespattered with eggs. His spirit rose a little, and his voice too.

"Buffoonery, tricks, ridicule the test of truth—all that is very well" —here an unpleasant egg broke on Mr. Brooke's shoulder, as the echo said, "All that is very well"; then came a hail of eggs, chiefly aimed at the image, but occasionally hitting the original, as if by chance. There was a stream of new men pushing among the crowd;

whistles, yells, bellowings, and fifes made all the greater hubbub because there was shouting and struggling to put them down. No voice would have had wing enough to rise above the uproar, and Mr. Brooke, disagreeably anointed, stood his ground no longer. The frustration would have been less exasperating if it had been less gamesome and boyish: a serious assault of which the newspaper reporter "can aver that it endangered the learned gentleman's ribs," or can respectfully bear witness to "the soles of that gentleman's boots having been visible above the railing," has perhaps more consolations attached to it.

Mr. Brooke re-entered the committee room, saying, as carelessly as he could, "This is a little too bad, you know. I should have got the ear of the people by-and-by—but they didn't give me time. I should have gone into the Bill by-and-by, you know," he added, glancing at Ladislaw. "However, things will come all right at the nomination."

But it was not resolved unanimously that things would come right; on the contrary, the committee looked rather grim, and the political personage from Brassing was writing busily, as if he were brewing new devices.

"It was Bowyer who did it," said Mr. Standish, evasively. "I know it as well as if he had been advertised. He's uncommonly good at ventriloquism, and he did it uncommonly well, by God! Hawley has been having him to dinner lately: there's a fund of talent in Bowyer."

"Well, you know, you never mentioned him to me, Standish, else I would have invited him to dine," said poor Mr. Brooke, who had gone through a great deal of inviting for the good of his country.

"There's not a more paltry fellow in Middlemarch than Bowyer," said Ladislaw, indignantly, "but it seems as if the paltry fellows were always to turn the scale."

Will was thoroughly out of temper with himself as well as with his "principal," and he went to shut himself in his rooms with a half-formed resolve to throw up the "Pioneer" and Mr. Brooke together. Why should he stay?

Chapter **VII**

Political Leadership

The distinction between leaders and led is not necessarily the same as that between governors and governed. The world of governors (as the selections in Chapter VI suggest) is a group world. It is generally closed to unusual and outstanding individuals—the entrepreneur and the rebel, for example—who might call into question its established routines. The chief bureaucrat, ideally, is a man who has lived within its enclosed spaces longer and obeyed its rules more meticulously than anyone else. He is not really a leader, but a follower in conventional paths of advancement. Insofar as he changes the institution, he does so through conventional forms of aggrandizement. But he does not invent new rules or conquer new spaces. That is the role of the great leader. Whether he maneuvers inside old institutions or breaks out of them entirely, the leader always sets his own will and vision above the rules, seeks legitimacy and support outside the conventions, takes unprecedented risks, and leaves behind a legacy absolutely different from that of the most efficient official. When new states are founded, dangerous battles won, ancient religions reformed, kings and emperors overthrown, the political hero is at work.

That, at any rate, is the tale so often told in storybooks and histories. There is no figure more common in political literature than the great leader. In the old epics he appears chiefly as a warrior, and if war ought in principle to be distinguished from politics, it is still true that leadership in an army is one of the

central forms of political authority. Thus The Iliad can be read
—it is not the only way of reading it—as a study in army politics,
a prototypical tale of conflict between authority (Agamemnon)
and personal force (Achilles). We have chosen, however, a passage that represents nothing more than the convention of the
great man: Achilles enters the battle and all alone makes all the
difference; the enemy is routed. "So sweeps the hero through the
wasted shores." Another heroic convention that must also be
illustrated emphasizes skill and craftiness rather than courage and
prowess, and self-conscious wickedness rather than innocent
virility. Renaissance writers, especially, were fascinated by the
Machiavellian prince, the perfect politician, who uses all his arts
for purely egoistic ends. He too is a great man, who invents
extraordinary schemes and alters the world he lives in. The distance, moral as well as literary, between Homer's Achilles and
Shakespeare's Richard III is undoubtedly great. But this stress is
constant throughout: The leader is a figure of large proportions
(even the stunted, twisted Richard) and grand effects, whether
for good or evil.

It is just this view of leadership that has been challenged in the
past century—challenged intellectually, one should say, though
in practice reaffirmed. For the past one hundred years have hardly
been free of hero worship. Rarely in history, indeed, have so
many men claimed to be not merely leaders, but Great Leaders.
Rarely in history have these claims been treated with such skepti-
cism by the best writers of the age. The modernist challenge to
the conventions of political heroism has taken two forms, one
historicist and sociological, the other psychological. The first calls
into question the hero's great effects, suggesting the existence of
complex historical processes and social forces of which the leader
himself and all his achievements are alike the products. The second calls into question the hero's large proportions, either reducing him to his psychic states and calling these neurotic and ob-
sessive or denying him his charisma and insisting that the
submission he was once thought to inspire derives instead from
the psychic weakness of his followers. His leadership is the prod-
uct of their neuroses.

Leo Tolstoi's essay on Napoleon and the Russian general

Kutuzov belongs to the philosophy of history; but it is at the same time so much the work of the novelist, the argument hangs so heavily on character and incident, that we have not hesitated to include it here. It is one of the most impressive critiques of heroic achievement that has ever been written (its very success, perhaps, tells against its author) and also one of the best defenses of the social novel. For how better can those "many forces acting simultaneously in different directions" be revealed than by an artist committed to explore the multiple interaction of circumstance, role, and personality from which they result? George Orwell's memoir of British rule in Burma, "Shooting an Elephant," illustrates just one of those interactions and suggests dramatically both its unintended outcome and what might be called the "choicelessness" of its hero. When the white man turns tyrant, Orwell suggests, it is his own freedom that is lost. But isn't this true of any man who claims to command his fellows?

Perhaps not; surely there have been leaders who refused, so to speak, to shoot the elephant; who resisted the pressure of the thousands of human wills at their backs and even changed the goals of their followers. What sort of personal force makes this possible? Herman Melville provides a characteristically modern answer to this question. His Captain Ahab is, perhaps, a free man; at least he does not conform to the expectations of his crew or heed their will. But Melville only means to explore another kind of "unfreedom." For Ahab is a slave to his vision of the White Whale. It is only in the grip of his obsession that he is able to rouse his men to enthusiastic obedience. And even this is nothing more than a pale and momentary reflection of his own servitude. But Ahab is still a large man, dominant, imposing, even if mad. It is a further sophistication of the psychological approach to suggest that most often the great leader has no greatness at all. The Austrian Emperor, as briefly pictured in Heinrich Mann's *Little Superman*, is a parade balloon and nothing more, inflated by the baseness of his subjects. Mann's Diederich, on the other hand, is an almost clinical portrait of the "authoritarian personality" (for a further description, see Chapter IX) who requires and so creates and sustains the Power before which he grovels.

Alongside the hostility modern writers have expressed toward the convention of the great man there has developed the new myth of the revolutionary leader. Indeed, much of the most recent discussion of the significance of leadership in political life may be read as a gloss on the career of Lenin. Tolstoi could certainly explain that career without altering his vision of historical necessity. Nevertheless, this new man, the hero of the masses, has left his mark on modern thought and art. He is usually not (though Lenin perhaps was) a man of overpowering will, but rather a representative figure who somehow evokes the latent willfulness of oppressed and passive individuals. Arthur Koestler's The Gladiators is a study in the failure of revolutionary leadership, but along the way the author sketches a portrait of Spartacus that is both like and unlike the old conventions. In battle Spartacus is not so different from Achilles, but he can talk to slaves in a way Achilles never could. Isaac Babel's brilliant little parable "Line and Color" captures the new leader perfectly. He is not a man wrapped up in visions of his own; nor does he nurse private obsessions. Instead, he puts on his spectacles and actually looks at the people he hopes to "lead"—not simply his followers but also his future comrades. It need hardly be said that the parable is more admonition than description. Most would-be leaders of the people resemble Ahab or the Emperor far more than Babel's Trotsky.

Even when writers on revolutionary leadership suspend their modernist disbelief, they do not simply return to the "great man" convention. They stress the interaction and mutual dependence of leaders and followers and so open the way for a view of leadership toward which modern political theorists also are groping, free of both heroic mythology and social determinism. Babel's parable, it might be said, puts him in the very forefront of contemporary political thought.

THE CONVENTIONAL HERO

Homer

From *The Iliad*

"O Greeks! (he cries, and every rank alarms)
Join battle, man to man, and arms to arms!
'Tis not in me, though favour'd by the sky,
To mow whole troops, and make whole armies fly:
No god can singly such a host engage,
Not Mars himself, nor great Minerva's rage.
But whatsoe'er Achilles can inspire,
Whate'er of active force, or acting fire;
Whate'er this heart can prompt, or hand obey;
All, all Achilles, Greeks! is yours to-day.
Through yon wide host this arm shall scatter fear,
And thin the squadrons with my single spear."

. . .

Then fierce Achilles, shouting to the skies,
On Troy's whole force with boundless fury flies.
First falls Iphytion, at his army's head;
Brave was the chief, and brave the host he led;
From great Otrynteus he derived his blood,
His mother was a Naïs of the flood;
Beneath the shades of Tmolus, crown'd with snow,
From Hydè's walls he ruled the lands below.
Fierce as he springs, the sword his head divides:
The parted visage falls on equal sides:
With loud resounding arms he strikes the plain;
While thus Achilles glories o'er the slain:
"Lie there, Otryntides! the Trojan earth
Receives thee dead, though Gygae boast thy birth;
Those beauteous fields where Hyllus' waves are roll'd,
And plenteous Hermus swells with tides of gold,
Are thine no more."—The insulting hero said,
And left him sleeping in eternal shade.

Book XX, Lines 403–414, 436–484, 574–590; translated by Alexander Pope.

The rolling wheels of Greece the body tore,
And dash'd their axles with no vulgar gore.
　　Demoleon next, Antenor's offspring, laid
Breathless in dust, the price of rashness paid.
The impatient steel with full-descending sway
Forced through his brazen helm its furious way,
Resistless drove the batter'd skull before,
And dash'd and mingled all the brains with gore.
This sees Hippodamas, and, seized with fright,
Deserts his chariot for a swifter flight:
The lance arrests him: an ignoble wound
The panting Trojan rivets to the ground.
He groans away his soul: not louder roars,
At Neptune's shrine on Helice's high shores,
The victim bull; the rocks re-bellow round,
And ocean listens to the grateful sound.
　　Then fell on Polydore his vengeful rage,
The youngest hope of Priam's stooping age:
(Whose feet for swiftness in the race surpass'd:)
Of all his sons, the dearest, and the last.
To the forbidden field he takes his flight,
In the first folly of a youthful knight,
To vaunt his swiftness wheels around the plain,
But vaunts not long, with all his swiftness slain:
Struck where the crossing belts unite behind,
And golden rings the double back-plate join'd,
Forth through the navel burst the thrilling steel;
And on his knees with piercing shrieks he fell;
The rushing entrails pour'd upon the ground
His hands collect; and darkness wraps him round.

.　.　.

So sweeps the hero through the wasted shores;
Around him wide, immense destruction pours,
And earth is deluged with the sanguine showers.
As with autumnal harvests cover'd o'er,
And thick bestrown, lies Ceres' sacred floor;
When round and round, with never-wearied pain,
The trampling steers beat out the unnumbered grain:
So the fierce coursers, as the chariot rolls,
Tread down whole ranks, and crush out heroes' souls.
Dash'd from their hoofs while o'er the dead they fly,

Black, bloody drops the smoking chariot dye:
The spiky wheels through heaps of carnage tore;
And thick the groaning axles dropp'd with gore.
High o'er the scene of death Achilles stood,
All grim with dust, all horrible in blood:
Yet still insatiate, still with rage on flame;
Such is the lust of never-dying fame!

THE MACHIAVELLIAN HERO

William Shakespeare

From *Richard III*

ACT I

Scene 1: [London. A street.]

Enter RICHARD, DUKE OF GLOUCESTER, *solus.*

RICH.: Now is the winter of our discontent
Made glorious summer by this sun of York;
And all the clouds that lowered upon our house
In the deep bosom of the ocean buried.
Now are our brows bound with victorious wreaths,
Our bruised arms hung up for monuments,
Our stern alarums changed to merry meetings,
Our dreadful marches to delightful measures.
Grim-visaged war hath smoothed his wrinkled front,
And now, instead of mounting barbed steeds
To fright the souls of fearful adversaries,
He capers nimbly in a lady's chamber
To the lascivious pleasing of a lute.
But I, that am not shaped for sportive tricks
Nor made to court an amorous looking glass;
I, that am rudely stamped, and want love's majesty
To strut before a wanton ambling nymph;
I, that am curtailed of this fair proportion,

Cheated of feature by dissembling Nature,
Deformed, unfinished, sent before my time
Into this breathing world, scarce half made up,
And that so lamely and unfashionable
That dogs bark at me as I halt by them—
Why, I, in this weak piping time of peace,
Have no delight to pass away the time,
Unless to see my shadow in the sun
And descant on mine own deformity.
And therefore, since I cannot prove a lover
To entertain these fair well-spoken days,
I am determined to prove a villain
And hate the idle pleasures of these days.
Plots have I laid, inductions dangerous,
By drunken prophecies, libels, and dreams,
To set my brother Clarence and the King
In deadly hate the one against the other;
And if King Edward be as true and just
As I am subtle, false, and treacherous,
This day should Clarence closely be mewed up
About a prophecy which says that G
Of Edward's heirs the murderer shall be.
Dive, thoughts, down to my soul: here Clarence comes!

> *Enter* CLARENCE, *guarded, and* BRAKENBURY [LIEUTENANT OF THE
> TOWER].

Brother, good day. What means this armed guard
That waits upon your Grace?
    CLAR.:   His Majesty,
Tend'ring my person's safety, hath appointed
This conduct to convey me to the Tower.
    RICH.:   Upon what cause?
    CLAR.:   Because my name is George.
    RICH.:   Alack, my lord, that fault is none of yours:
He should for that commit your godfathers.
O, belike his Majesty hath some intent
That you should be new-christ'ned in the Tower.
But what's the matter, Clarence, may I know?
    CLAR.:   Yea, Richard, when I know; but I protest
As yet I do not. But, as I can learn,
He hearkens after prophecies and dreams,

And from the cross-row plucks the letter G,
And says a wizard told him that by G
His issue disinherited should be.
And, for my name of George begins with G,
It follows in his thought that I am he.
These, as I learn, and suchlike toys as these,
Have moved his Highness to commit me now.

RICH.: Why, this it is, when men are ruled by women:
'Tis not the King that sends you to the Tower;
My Lady Grey his wife, Clarence, 'tis she
That tempts him to this harsh extremity.
Was it not she, and that good man of worship,
Anthony Woodville, her brother there,
That made him send Lord Hastings to the Tower,
From whence this present day he is delivered?
We are not safe, Clarence, we are not safe.

CLAR.: By heaven, I think there is no man secure
But the Queen's kindred, and night-walking heralds
That trudge betwixt the King and Mistress Shore.
Heard you not what an humble suppliant
Lord Hastings was for his delivery?

RICH.: Humbly complaining to her deity
Got my Lord Chamberlain his liberty.
I'll tell you what, I think it is our way,
If we will keep in favor with the King,
To be her men and wear her livery.
The jealous o'erworn widow and herself,
Since that our brother dubbed them gentlewomen,
Are mighty gossips in our monarchy.

BRAK.: I beseech your Graces both to pardon me:
His Majesty hath straitly given in charge
That no man shall have private conference,
Of what degree soever, with your brother.

RICH.: Even so? And please your worship, Brakenbury,
You may partake of anything we say.
We speak no treason, man. We say the King
Is wise and virtuous, and his noble Queen
Well struck in years, fair, and not jealous.
We say that Shore's wife hath a pretty foot,
A cherry lip, a bonny eye, a passing pleasing tongue;
And that the Queen's kindred are made gentlefolks.

How say you, sir? Can you deny all this?

BRAK.: With this, my lord, myself have naught to do.

RICH.: Naught to do with Mistress Shore? I tell thee, fellow,
He that doth naught with her, excepting one,
Were best to do it secretly alone.

BRAK.: What one, my lord?

RICH.: Her husband, knave. Wouldst thou betray me?

BRAK.: I do beseech your Grace to pardon me, and withal
Forbear your conference with the noble Duke.

CLAR.: We know thy charge, Brakenbury, and will obey.

RICH.: We are the Queen's abjects, and must obey.
Brother, farewell. I will unto the King;
And whatsoe'er you will employ me in,
Were it to call King Edward's widow sister,
I will perform it to enfranchise you.
Meantime, this deep disgrace in brotherhood
Touches me deeper than you can imagine.

CLAR.: I know it pleaseth neither of us well.

RICH.: Well, your imprisonment shall not be long:
I will deliver you, or else lie for you.
Meantime, have patience.

CLAR.:   I must perforce. Farewell.

Exit CLARENCE, [*with* BRAKENBURY *and* GUARD].

RICH.: Go tread the path that thou shalt ne'er return:
Simple, plain Clarence, I do love thee so
That I will shortly send thy soul to heaven,
If heaven will take the present at our hands.
But who comes here? The new-delivered Hastings?

Enter LORD HASTINGS.

HAST.: Good time of day unto my gracious lord.

RICH.: As much unto my good Lord Chamberlain.
Well are you welcome to this open air.
How hath your lordship brooked imprisonment?

HAST.: With patience, noble lord, as prisoners must;
But I shall live, my lord, to give them thanks
That were the cause of my imprisonment.

RICH.: No doubt, no doubt; and so shall Clarence too,
For they that were your enemies are his,
And have prevailed as much on him as you.

HAST.:   More pity that the eagles should be mewed,
Whiles kites and buzzards prey at liberty.
RICH.:   What news abroad?
HAST.:   No news so bad abroad as this at home:
The King is sickly, weak, and melancholy,
And his physicians fear him mightily.
RICH.:   Now, by Saint John, that news is bad indeed!
O, he hath kept an evil diet long
And overmuch consumed his royal person:
'Tis very grievous to be thought upon.
Where is he? In his bed?
HAST.:   He is.
RICH.:   Go you before, and I will follow you.

   Exit HASTINGS.

He cannot live, I hope, and must not die
Till George be packed with post horse up to heaven.
I'll in, to urge his hatred more to Clarence,
With lies well steeled with weighty arguments;
And, if I fail not in my deep intent,
Clarence hath not another day to live:
Which done, God take King Edward to his mercy,
And leave the world for me to bustle in!
For then I'll marry Warwick's youngest daughter.
What though I killed her husband and her father?
The readiest way to make the wench amends
Is to become her husband and her father:
The which will I—not all so much for love
As for another secret close intent,
By marrying her which I must reach unto.
But yet I run before my horse to market:
Clarence still breathes; Edward still lives and reigns;
When they are gone, then must I count my gains.

   Exit.

THE LEADER IN HISTORY

Leo Tolstoi

From *War and Peace*

The combination of causes of phenomena is beyond the grasp of the human intellect. But the impulse to seek causes is innate in the soul of man. And the human intellect, with no inkling of the immense variety and complexity of circumstances conditioning a phenomenon, any one of which may be separately conceived of as the cause of it, snatches at the first and most easily understood approximation, and says here is the cause. In historical events, where the actions of men form the subject of observation, the most primitive conception of a cause was the will of the gods, succeeded later on by the will of those men who stand in the historical foreground—the heroes of history. But one had but to look below the surface of any historical event, to look, that is, into the movement of the whole mass of men taking part in that event, to be convinced that the will of the hero of history, so far from controlling the actions of the multitude, is continually controlled by them. It may be thought that it is a matter of no importance whether historical events are interpreted in one way or in another. But between the man who says that the peoples of the West marched into the East, because Napoleon willed they should do so, and the man who says that that movement came to pass because it was bound to come to pass, there exists the same difference as between the men who maintained that the earth was stationary and the planets revolved about it, and the men who said that they did not know what holds the earth in its place, but they did know that there were laws controlling its motions and the motions of the other planets. Causes of historical events—there are not and cannot be, save the one cause of all causes. But there are laws controlling these events; laws partly unknown, partly accessible to us. The discovery of these laws is only possible when we entirely give up looking for a cause in the will of one man, just as the discovery of the laws of the motions of the planets has only become

Part 13, Sections I–X. Translated by Constance Garnett.

possible since men have given up the conception of the earth being stationary.

After the battle of Borodino, and the taking and burning of Moscow, historians consider the most important episode of the war of 1812 to be the movement of the Russian army from the Ryazan to the Kaluga road and to the Tarutino camp, the so-called oblique march behind Krasnaya Pahra. Historians ascribe the credit of this stroke of genius to various persons, and dispute to whom it is rightfully due. Even foreign, even French historians, admit the genius of the Russian generals when they mention this flank march. But why military writers, and others following their lead, assume this oblique movement to be a project profoundly planned by some one person for the deliverance of Russia and the overthrow of Napoleon it is very difficult to see. It is difficult in the first place to see wherein the profound wisdom and genius of this march lies; for no great intellectual effort is needed to guess that the best position for an army, when not being attacked, is where supplies are most plentiful. And every one, even a stupid boy of thirteen, could have guessed that the most advantageous position for the army in 1812, after the retreat from Moscow, would be on the Kaluga road. And so one cannot understand, in the first place, what conclusions led the historians to see some deep wisdom in this manoeuvre. Secondly, it is even more difficult to understand why the historians ascribe to this manoeuvre the deliverance of Russia and the overthrow of the French; for, had other circumstances preceded, accompanied, or followed it, this flank movement might as well have led to the destruction of the Russian army and the deliverance of the French. If the position of the Russian army did, in fact, begin to improve from the time of that march, it does not at all follow that the improvement was caused by it.

That oblique march might have been not simply of no use; it might have led to the destruction of the Russian army, but for the conjunction of other circumstances. What would have happened if Moscow had not been burnt? If Murat had not lost sight of the Russians? If Napoleon had not remained inactive? If, as Bennigsen and Barclay advised, the Russians had given battle near Krasnaya Pahra? What would have happened if the French had attacked the Russians when they were marching behind Pahra? What would have happened if later on Napoleon, on reaching Tarutino, had attacked the Russians with one-tenth of the energy with which he had attacked them at Smolensk? What would have happened if the

French had marched to Petersburg? . . . On any of these hypotheses, the oblique march might have led to ruin instead of to safety.

The third point, most difficult of all to understand, is that students of history seem intentionally to refuse to see that this march cannot be ascribed to any one man, that no one foresaw it at any time, that, like the retreat to Fili, the manoeuvre was, in reality, never conceived of by any one in its entirety, but arose step by step, incident by incident, moment by moment from a countless multitude of the most diverse circumstances, and is only conceived of in its entirety, when it is an accomplished fact, and has become the past.

At the council at Fili the accepted idea among the Russians—the course taken for granted in fact—was retreat in a direct line back, that is, along the Nizhni road. Evidence of this is that the majority of votes at the council were for adopting this course, and the commander-in-chief's famous conversation after the council with Lansky, the head of the commissariat department, is an even more striking proof of it. Lansky submitted to the commander-in-chief that the chief supplies for the army were stored along the Oka, in the Tula and Kazan provinces, and that if they retreated along the Nizhni road, the army would be cut off from its supplies by the broad river Oka, across which transport in the early winter was impossible. This was the first proof of the necessity of departing from the course that had at first seemed the most natural one, the retreat along the Nizhni road. The army kept more to the south along the Ryazan road, closer to its supplies. Later on the inactivity of the French, who positively lost sight of the Russian army, anxiety for the defence of the Tula arsenal, and above all, the advantage of being near their supplies led the army to turn even more to the south, to the Tula road. After crossing by a forced march behind Pahra to the Tula road, the generals of the Russian army intended to remain at Podolsk, and had no idea of the Tarutino position. But an infinite number of circumstances, among them the reappearance of French troops on the scene, and plans for giving battle, and most of all, the abundance of supplies in Kaluga, led our army to turn even more to the south, and to pass from the Tula to the Kaluga road to Tarutino, a central position between their lines of communication with their supplies. Just as it is impossible to answer the question at what date Moscow was abandoned, it is impossible too to say precisely when and by whom it was decided to move the army to Tarutino. It was only after the army, through the action of innumerable infinitesimally small forces, had been brought to Tarutino, that people began to protest to themselves that that was the course they had desired, and had long foreseen as the right one.

.   .   .

The famous oblique movement consisted simply in this. The Russian troops, which had been retreating directly back from the French, as soon as the French attack ceased, turned off from that direction, and seeing they were not pursued, moved naturally in the direction where they were drawn by the abundance of supplies.

If we imagine, instead of generals of genius at the head of the Russian army, an army acting alone, without leadership of any kind, such an army could have done nothing else but move back again towards Moscow, describing a semicircle through the country that was best provided with necessaries, and where supplies were most plentiful.

So natural was this oblique movement from the Nizhni to the Ryazan, Tula, and Kaluga road, that that direction was the one taken by the flying bands of marauders from the Russian army, and the one which the authorities in Petersburg insisted upon Kutuzov's taking. At Tarutino Kutuzov received what was almost a reprimand from the Tsar for moving the army to the Ryazan road, and he was directed to take up the very position facing Kaluga, in which he was encamped at the time when the Tsar's letter reached him.

After recoiling in the direction of the shock received during the whole campaign, and at the battle of Borodino, the ball of the Russian army, as the force of that blow spent itself, and no new blow came, took the direction that was natural for it.

Kutuzov's merit lay in no sort of military genius, as it is called, in no strategic manoeuvre, but in the fact that he alone grasped the significance of what had taken place. He alone grasped even then the significance of the inactivity of the French army; he alone persisted in maintaining that the battle of Borodino was a victory; he alone—the man who from his position as commander-in-chief might have been expected to be the first to be eager for battle—he alone did everything in his power to hold the Russian army back from useless fighting.

The wild beast wounded at Borodino lay where the fleeing hunter had left him; but whether alive and strong, or only feigning, the hunter knew not. All at once a moan was heard from the creature.

The moan of that wounded creature, the French army, that betrayed its hopeless plight, was the despatch of Lauriston to the camp of Kutuzov with overtures for peace.

Napoleon, with his conviction that not what was right was right, but whatever came into his head was right, wrote to Kutuzov the first words that occurred to his mind, words that had no meaning at all.

"M. LE PRINCE KOUTOUZOFF," he wrote,

> I am sending you one of my aides-de-camp to converse with you on various interesting subjects. I desire that your highness will put faith in what he says, especially when he expresses the sentiments of esteem and particular consideration that I have long entertained for your person. This letter having no other object, I pray God to have you in His holy and powerful keeping.
>
> (Signed) NAPOLEON.

"*Moscow, October* 30, 1812."

"I should be cursed by posterity if I were regarded as the first instigator of any sort of settlement. *Tel est l'esprit actuel de ma nation*," answered Kutuzov, and went on doing everything in his power to hold the army back from advance.

A month spent by the French army in pillaging Moscow, and by the Russian army quietly encamped at Tarutino, brought about a change in the relative strength of the two armies, a change both in spirit and in numbers, which was all to the advantage of the Russians. Although the position of the French army and its numbers were unknown to the Russians, as soon as their relative strength had changed, a great number of signs began to show that an attack would be inevitable. Among the causes that contributed to bring about this result were Lauriston's mission, and the abundance of provisions at Tarutino, and the reports that were continually coming in from all sides of the inactivity and lack of discipline in the French army, and the filling up of our regiments by recruits, and the fine weather, and the long rest enjoyed by the Russian soldiers, and the impatience to do the work for which they have been brought together, that always arises in troops after repose, and curiosity to know what was going on in the French army, of which they had so long seen nothing, and the daring with which the Russian outposts dashed in among the French encamped at Tarutino, and the news of the easy victories gained by bands of peasants and free-lances over the French, and the envy aroused by them, and the desire of revenge, that every man cherished at heart so long as the French were in Moscow; and—stronger than all—the vague sense growing up in every soldier's heart that the relative strength of the armies had changed, and the preponderance was now on our side. The relative strength of the armies had really changed, and advance had become inevitable. And at once, as surely as the chimes in a clock begin to beat and play when the hand has made the full round of the dial, was this change reflected in the increased activity, and bustle and stir of wheels within wheels in the higher spheres.

. . .

The Russian army was commanded by Kutuzov and his staff and by the Tsar from Petersburg. Before the news of the abandonment of Moscow had reached Petersburg a detailed plan of the whole campaign had been drawn up and sent to Kutuzov for his guidance. In spite of the fact that this plan had been made on the supposition that Moscow was still in our hands, it was approved by the staff, and accepted as the plan to be carried out. Kutuzov simply wrote that directions from a distance were always difficult to carry out. And to solve any difficulties that might arise, fresh instructions were sent, together with newer persons, whose duty it was to be to keep a watch on his movements, and to report upon them.

Apart from these new authorities, the whole staff of generals in the Russian army was now transferred. The places of Bagration, who had been killed, and Barclay, who had taken offence and retired, had to be filled. The question was deliberated with the greatest seriousness: whether A should be put in B's place, and B in the place of D, or whether, on the other hand, D in A's place, and so on, as though the matter affected anything whatever except the satisfaction of A and B and D.

In consequence of Kutuzov's hostility to the head officer of his staff, Bennigsen, and the presence of confidential advisers of the Tsar, and these various new appointments, the struggle of parties at headquarters was even more complicated than usual. A was trying to undermine B's position, D to undermine C's position, and so on, in all the possible combinations and permutations. In all these conflicting currents the object of intrigue was for the most part the management of the war, which all these men supposed they were controlling, though it did, in fact, follow its inevitable course quite apart from their action, a course that never corresponded with their schemes, but was the outcome of the forces interacting in the masses. All these schemes, thwarting and stultifying one another, were simply accepted in the higher spheres as the correct reflection of what was bound to come to pass.

"Prince Mihail Ilarionovitch!" the Tsar wrote on the 2nd of October, a letter received by Kutuzov after the battle of Tarutino.

> From the 2nd of September Moscow has been in the hands of the enemy. Your last reports were dated the 20th; and in the course of all this time since, no attempt has been made to act against the enemy, and to relieve the ancient capital, and you have even, from your last reports, retreated further. Serpuhov is by now occupied by a detachment of the enemy, and Tula, with its famous arsenal, of such importance to the army, is in danger. From the reports received from General Wintzengerode, I see that a corps of the enemy, ten thousand strong, is marching along the Petersburg road. Another, numbering some thousands, is already close upon Dmitrov. A third is advancing along the Vladimir road. A fourth force of considerable strength is stationed between Ruza and Mozhaisk. Napoleon himself was in Moscow on the 25th. In face of these facts, with the enemy's forces split up into these detached bodies, and Napoleon himself with his guards in Moscow, is it possible that the enemy's forces confronting you are too strong to permit of your acting on the offensive? One may, with far more probability, assume that you are being pursued by detachments, or at most a corps by far inferior to the army under your command. It would seem that taking advantage of these circumstances, you might with advantage have attacked forces inferior in strength to your army, and have destroyed them, or at least have forced them to retreat, and have kept in our hands a considerable part of the province now occupied by the enemy, and thereby have averted all danger from Tula and the other towns of the interior. You will be responsible, if the enemy is able to send a considerable body of men to Petersburg, to menace that capital, in which it has been impossible to keep any great number of troops; for with the army under your command, acting with energy and decision, you have ample means at your disposal for averting such a calamity. Recollect that you have still to answer to your humiliated country for the loss of Moscow. You have had experience of my readiness to reward you. That readiness is no less now, but Russia and I have the right to expect from you all the energy, decision, and success, which your intellect, your military talents, and the valour of the troops under your command should guarantee us.

But while this letter, proving that the change in the relative strength of the armies was by now reflected in opinion at Petersburg, was on its road, Kutuzov had been unable to hold the army back, and a battle had already been fought.

On the 2nd of October, a Cossack Shapovalov, out scouting, shot one hare and wounded a second. Shapovalov was led on in pursuit of the game far into the forest, and came across the left flank of Murats' army, which was encamped and quite off guard. The Cossack told his comrades with laughter the tale of how he had all but fallen into the hands of the French. The ensign, who heard the story, repeated it to his superior officer. The Cossack was sent for and questioned. The officers of the Cossacks wanted to take advantage of this to carry off some horses from the French, but one of them, who was intimate with some of the higher authorities in the army, mentioned the incident to a general on the staff. On the staff the position of late had been strained to the utmost. A few days previously, Yermolov had gone to Bennigsen and besought him to use his influence with the commander-in-chief to bring about an attack.

"If I did not know you, I should suppose you did not desire that result. I have only to advise one course for his highness to be sure to adopt the opposite one," answered Bennigsen.

The news brought by the Cossack, confirmed by scouts, proved conclusively that the time was ripe. The strained string broke, and the wheels of the clock whirred, and the chimes began to strike. In spite of all his supposed power, his intellect, his experience, and his knowledge of men, Kutuzov, taking into consideration the note from Bennigsen, who was sending a personal report on the subject to the Tsar, the desire expressed by all the generals alike, the desire assumed by them to be the Tsar's wish, and the news brought by the Cossack, could hold back the inevitable movement no longer, and gave orders for what he regarded as useless and mischievous— gave his assent, in fact, to the accomplished fact.

. . .

The note submitted by Bennigsen, and the report sent in by the Cossacks of the enemy's left flank being unguarded, were simply the last straws that showed the inevitability of giving the signal for advance, and it was arranged to advance to attack on the 5th of October.

On the morning of the 4th, Kutuzov signed the disposition of the forces. Toll read it to Yermolov, proposing that he should superintend the further instructions for carrying it out.

"Very good, very good, I haven't time just now," said Yermolov, and he hurried out of the cottage. The arrangement of the troops as drawn up by Toll was an excellent one. The disposition had been written out, as at Austerlitz, though not in German:

"The First Column marches here and there, the Second Column occupies this place," and so on.

On paper all these columns were in their proper place at a fixed time and annihilated the enemy. Everything had been, as in all such cases, carefully thought of, and as in all such cases not a single column did reach its right place at the right time. When a sufficient number of copies of the disposition were ready, an officer was summoned and sent off to give them to Yermolov, that he might see that instructions were given in accordance with them. A young officer of the horseguards, in waiting on Kutuzov, set off for Yermolov's quarters, delighted at the importance of the commission with which he was intrusted.

"Not at home," Yermolov's servant told him. The officer of the horseguards set off to the quarters of the general, with whom Yermolov was often to be found.

"Not here, nor the general either," he was told.

The officer mounted his horse again and rode off to another general's.

"No, not at home."

"If only I don't get into trouble for the delay! How annoying!" thought the officer.

He rode all over the camp. One man told him he had seen Yermolov riding away in company with some other generals; another said he was sure to be at home again by now. The officer was hunting him till six o'clock in the evening without stopping for dinner. Yermolov was nowhere to be found, and no one knew where he was. The officer took a hasty meal at a comrade's, and trotted back to the advance guard to see Miloradovitch. Miloradovitch, too, was not at home, but there he was told that he was at a ball at General Kikin's and that, most likely, Yermolov was there too.

"But where is that?"

"At Etchkino, that way," said an officer of the Cossacks, pointing out to him a country house in the far distance.

"Out there! beyond our lines!"

"Two regiments of our fellows have been sent out to the outposts, and there is a spree going on there now, fine doings! Two bands, three choruses of singers."

The officer rode out beyond our lines to Etchkino. While yet a long way off, he heard the gay sounds of a soldier's dance tune sung in chorus.

"In the meadows . . . in the meadows," he heard with a whistle and string music, drowned from time to time in a roar of voices. The officer's spirits, too, rose at these sounds, but at the same time he was in terror lest he should be held responsible for having so long delayed giving the important message intrusted to him. It was by now nearly nine o'clock. He dismounted and walked up to the entrance of a big manor-house that had been left uninjured between the French and the Russian lines. Footmen were bustling about with wines and edibles in the vestibule and the buffet. Choruses were standing under the windows. The officer was led up to a door, and he saw all at once all the most important generals in the army, among them the big, impressive figure of Yermolov. All the generals were standing in a semicircle, laughing loudly, their uniforms unbuttoned, and their faces flushed and animated. In the middle of the room a handsome, short general with a red face, was smartly and jauntily executing the steps of the *trepak*.

"Ha, ha, ha! Bravo, Nikolay Ivanovitch! ha, ha! . . ."

The officer felt doubly guilty in breaking in at such a moment with important business, and he would have waited; but one of the generals caught sight of him, and hearing what he had come for, told Yermolov. The latter, with a frowning face, came out to the officer, and hearing his story, took the papers from him without a word.

"Do you suppose it was by chance that he was not at home?" said a comrade of the officer's who was on the staff, speaking of Yermolov that evening. "That's all stuff and nonsense; it was all done on purpose. To play a trick on Konovnitsyn. You see, there'll be a pretty kettle of fish to-morrow!"

. . .

The decrepit old man, Kutuzov, had bade them wake him early next day, and in the early morning he said his prayers, dressed, and with a disagreeable consciousness that he had to command in a battle of which he did not approve, he got into his carriage and drove from Letashevka, five versts behind Tarutino, to the place where the attacking columns were to be gathered together. Kutuzov drove along, dropping asleep and waking up again, and listening to hear whether that were the sound of shots on the right, whether the action had not begun. But everything was still quiet. A damp and cloudy autumn day was dawning. As he approached Tarutino, Kutuzov noticed cavalry soldiers leading their horses to a watercourse across the road along which he was riding. Kutuzov looked at them, stopped his carriage, and asked what regiment did they belong to. They belonged to a column which was to have been far away in front in ambush.

"A mistake, perhaps," thought the old commander-in-chief. But as he drove on further, Kutuzov saw infantry regiments with their arms stacked, and the soldiers in their drawers busy cooking porridge and fetching wood. He sent for their officer. The officer submitted that no command to advance had been given.

"No command . . ." Kutuzov began, but he checked himself at once, and ordered the senior officer to be summoned to him. Getting out of the carriage, with drooping head he walked to and fro in silence, breathing heavily. When the general staff officer, Eichen, for whom he had sent, arrived, Kutuzov turned purple with rage, not because that officer was to blame for the mistake, but because he was an object of sufficient importance for him to vent his wrath on. And staggering and gasping, the old man fell into that state of fury in which he would sometimes roll on the ground in frenzy, and flew at Eichen, shaking his fists, and shouting abuse in the language of the gutter. Another officer, Captain Brozin, who was in no way to blame, happening to appear, suffered the same fate.

"What will the blackguards do next? Shoot them! The scoundrels!" he shouted hoarsely, shaking his fist and staggering. He was in a state of actual physical suffering. He, his highness the commander-in-chief, who was assured by every one that no one in Russia had ever had such power as he, he put into this position—made a laughing-stock to the whole army. "Worrying myself, praying over to-day, not sleeping all night, and thinking about everything—all for nothing!" he thought about himself. "When I was a mere boy of an officer no one would have dared to make a laughing-stock of me like this . . . And now!" He was in a state of physical suffering, as though from corporal punishment, and could not help expressing it in wrathful and agonised outcries. But soon his strength was exhausted, and looking about him, feeling that he had said a great deal that was unjust, he got into his carriage and drove back in silence.

His wrath once spent did not return again, and Kutuzov, blinking feebly, listened to explanations and self-justifications (Yermolov himself did not put in an appearance till next day), and to the earnest representation of Bennigsen, Konovnitsyn, and Toll that the battle that had not come off should take place on the following day. And again Kutuzov had to acquiesce.

Next day the troops were massed in their appointed places by the evening, and were moving forward in the night. It was an autumn night with a sky overcast by purplish-black clouds, but free from rain. The earth was damp, but not muddy, and the troops advanced noiselessly, except for a hardly audible jingling now and then from the artillery. They were forbidden to talk aloud, to smoke or to strike a light; the horses were kept from neighing. The secrecy of the enterprise increased its attractiveness. The men marched on gaily. Several columns halted, stacked their guns in piles, and lay down on the chilly ground, supposing they had reached their destination. Other columns (the majority) marched all night long, and arrived somewhere, unmistakably not where they were meant to be.

Count Orlov-Denisov with his Cossacks (the detachment of least importance of the lot) was the only one that reached the right place at the right time. This detachment halted at the extreme edge of a forest, on a path from the village of Stromilovo to Dmitrovskoe.

Before dawn Count Orlov, who had fallen asleep, was waked up. A deserter from the French camp was brought to him. It was a Polish under-officer of Poniatovsky's corps. This under-officer explained in Polish that he had deserted because he had been insulted in the service; because he ought long ago to have been an officer, and was braver than any of them, and so he had thrown them up and wanted to punish them. He said that Murat was camping for the night a verst from them, and that if they would give him a convoy of a hundred men he would take him alive. Count Orlov-Denisov took council with his comrades. The proposition was too alluring to be refused. Every one clamoured to go, everyone advised making the attempt. After many disputes and confabulations, it was settled that Major-General Grekov, with two regiments of Cossacks, should go with the Polish deserter.

"Now, remember," said Count Orlov-Denisov to the Polish deserter, as he dismissed him, "if you have been lying, I will have you shot like a dog, but if it's true, a hundred crowns."

The deserter made no reply to these words, and with a resolute air mounted his horse and rode off with Grekov's men, who were hurriedly gathered together. They disappeared into the wood. Count Orlov, shivering from the freshness of the dawning morning, and excited by the enterprise he had undertaken on his own responsibility, came out of the wood, accompanying Grekov, and began scrutinising the enemy's camp, faintly visible now in the deceptive light of the approaching dawn and the smouldering camp-fires. On the open copse on Count Orlov-Denisov's right our columns ought to have been visible. Count Orlov-Denisov looked in that direction; but although they could have been seen even if a long distance away, these columns were not in sight. Count Orlov-Denisov fancied, and his adjutant, who was extremely long-sighted, confirmed the idea, and they were beginning to move in the French camp.

"Oh, of course it's too late," said Count Orlov, staring at the camp. As so often happens when the man in whom we are putting faith is no longer before our eyes, it all seemed at once perfectly clear and obvious to him that the deserter had been playing them false, that he had been telling them lies, and was only spoiling the whole attack by removing these two regiments, which he was leading away—God only knew where! As if it were possible to capture the general out of such a mass of troops.

"No doubt he was lying, the scoundrel," said the Count.

"We can turn them back," said one of the suite, who was feeling just the same mistrust in the undertaking as he gazed at the camp.

"Ah! Yes . . . what do you think, or shall we leave them? Or not?"

"Do you command them to return?"

"To return, yes, to return!" Count Orlov said, with sudden decision, looking at his watch; "it will be too late; it's quite light."

And an adjutant galloped into the wood after Grekov. When Grekov came back, Count Orlov-Denisov, excited by giving up this enterprise, and by vainly waiting for the infantry columns, which still did not appear, and by the enemy's being so near (every man in his detachment was feeling the same), resolved to attack.

In a whisper he gave the command: "Mount!"

The men got into their places, crossed themselves . . . "In God's name, off!"

"Hurrah!" rang out in the wood, and the Cossacks, with spears lowered, flew gaily, one hundred after another, across the stream into the camp, as though they were being shot out of a sack.

One desperate, frightened scream from the first Frenchman who caught sight of the Cossacks, and every creature in the camp, undressed and half-asleep, was running away, abandoning cannons, muskets, and horses.

If the Cossacks had pursued the French without regard to what they left all around and behind them, they could have captured Murat and all there was there. Their commanding officers tried to make them do so. But there was no making the Cossacks budge when they had got booty and prisoners. No one heeded the word of command. They had taken fifteen hundred prisoners, thirty-eight cannons, flags, and, what was of most consequence in the eyes of the Cossacks, horses, saddles, coverings, and various other objects. All of this they wanted to see after, to secure the prisoners and the cannons, to divide the booty, to shout at and even fight with one another over the spoils; and all this absorbed the Cossacks' attention. The Frenchmen, finding themselves not pursued further, began to rally; they formed into companies and began firing. Orlov-Denisov still expected the other columns to arrive, and did not advance further.

Meanwhile, in accordance with the disposition—"*die erste Colonne marschirt*," and so on—the infantry regiments of the belated columns, under the command of Bennigsen and the direction of Toll, had started off in due course, and had, in the usual way, arrived somewhere, but not where they were intended to arrive. In the usual way too, the soldiers who had set off gaily, began to halt; there were murmurs of dissatisfaction and a sense of muddle, and they were marched back to some point. Adjutants and generals galloped to and fro, shouting angrily, quarrelling, declaring they had come utterly wrong and were too late, upbraiding some one, and so on; and finally, all washed their hands of the business in despair, and marched on simply in order to get somewhere. "We must arrive somewhere sooner or later!" And so they did, in fact, arrive somewhere, but not where they were wanted. And some did even reach their destination, but reached it so late that their doing so was of no use at all, and only resulted in their being fired at for nothing. Toll, who in this battle played the part of Weierother in the battle of Austerlitz, galloped with unflagging energy from one part of the field to another, and found everything at sixes and sevens everywhere. So, for instance, he found Bagovut's corps in the wood, when it was broad daylight, though the corps ought to have been there long before, and to have gone to support Orlov-Denisov. Disappointed and excited at the failure, and supposing some one must be to blame for it, Toll galloped up to the general in command of the corps, and began sternly reprimanding him, declaring that he deserved to be shot. Bagovut, a sturdy old general of placid disposition, had been worried too by all the delays, the muddles, and the contradictory orders, and, to the amazement of everybody, he flew into a violent rage, quite out of keeping with his character, and said some very nasty things to Toll.

"I am not going to be taught my duty by anybody, but I can face death with my men as well as any one," he said, and he marched forward with one division. The valiant Bagovut, not considering in his excitement whether his advance into action now with a single division was likely to be of use or not, marched his men straight forward into the enemy's fire. Danger, shells, and bullets were just what he wanted in his fury. One of the first bullets killed him, the other bullets killed many of his men. And his division remained for sometime under fire for no object whatever.

. . .

Meanwhile another column was to have fallen upon the French in the centre, but of this column Kutuzov was in command. He knew very well that nothing but muddle would come of this battle, begun against his will, and, as far as it was in his power, he held his forces back. He did not move.

Kutuzov rode mutely about on his grey horse, making languid replies to the suggestions for an attack.

"You can all talk about attacking, but you don't see that we don't know how to execute complicated manoeuvres," he said to Milorado-vitch, who was begging to be allowed to advance.

"We couldn't take Murat alive in the morning, nor be in our places in time; now there's nothing to be done!" he said to another.

When it was reported to Kutuzov that there were now two bat-talions of Poles in the rear of the French, where according to the earlier reports of the Cossacks there had been none, he took a side-long glance behind him at Yermolov, to whom he had not spoken since the previous day.

"Here they are begging to advance, proposing projects of all sorts, and as soon as you get to work, there's nothing ready, and the enemy, forewarned, takes his measures."

Yermolov half closed his eyelids, and faintly smiled, as he heard those words. He knew that the storm had blown over him, and that Kutuzov would not go beyond that hint.

"That's his little joke at my expense," said Yermolov softly, poking Raevsky, near him, with his knee.

Soon after that, Yermolov moved forward to Kutuzov and respect-fully submitted:

"The time has not passed, your highness; the enemy has not gone away. If you were to command an advance? Or else the guards won't have a sight of smoke."

Kutuzov said nothing, but when news was brought him that

Murat's troops were in retreat, he gave orders for an advance; but every hundred paces he halted for three-quarters of an hour.

The whole battle was confined to what had been done by the Cossacks of Orlov-Denisov; the rest of the troops simply lost a few hundreds of men for nothing.

In consequence of this battle, Kutuzov received a diamond decoration; Bennigsen, too, was rewarded with diamonds and a hundred thousand roubles; and the other generals, too, received agreeable recognition according to their rank, and more changes were made on the staff.

"That's how things are always done among us, everything topsy-turvy!" the Russian officers and generals said after the battle of Tarutino; just as they say it nowadays, with an assumption that some stupid person had muddled everything, while *we* would have managed quite differently. But the men who speak like this either do not understand what they are talking of, or intentionally deceive themselves. Every battle—Tarutino, Borodino, Austerlitz—fails to come off as those who planned it expected it to do. That is inevitable.

An innumerable collection of freely acting forces (and nowhere is a man freer than on the field of battle, where it is a question of life and death) influence the direction taken by a battle, and that can never be known beforehand and never corresponds with the direction of any one force.

If many forces are acting simultaneously in different directions on any body, the direction of its motion will not correspond with any one of the forces, but will always follow a middle course, the summary of them, what is expressed in mechanics by the diagonal of the parallelogram of forces.

If in the accounts given us by historians, especially by French ones, we find that wars and battles appear to follow a definite plan laid down beforehand, the only deduction we can make from that is that these accounts are not true.

The battle of Tarutino obviously failed to attain the aim which Toll had in view: to lead the army into action in accordance with his disposition of the troops, or the aim which Count Orlov-Denisov may have had; to take Murat prisoner; or the aim of destroying at one blow the whole corps; which Bennigsen and others may have entertained; or the aim of the officer who desired to distinguish himself under fire; or the Cossack, who wanted to obtain more booty than he did attain, and so on. But if we regard the object of the battle as what was actually accomplished by it, and what was the universal desire of all Russians (the expulsion of the French from Russia and the destruction of their army), it will be perfectly evident that the battle of Tarutino, precisely in consequence of its incongruities, was exactly what was wanted at that period of the campaign. It is difficult or impossible to imagine any issue of that battle more in accordance with that object than its actual result. With the very smallest effort, in spite of the greatest muddle, and with the most trifling loss, the most important results in the whole campaign were obtained—the transition was made from retreat to attack, the weakness of the French was revealed, and the shock was given which was all that was needed to put Napoleon's army to flight.

·   ·   ·

Napoleon enters Moscow after the brilliant victory *de la Moskowa:* there can be no doubt of the victory, since the French are left in possession of the field of battle. The Russians retreat and leave Moscow—well stocked with provisions, arms, implements, and countless riches—in the hands of Napoleon. The Russian army, of one-half the strength of the French, during the course of a whole month makes no effort to attack. Napoleon's position is most brilliant. One would have supposed that no great genius was needed with an army of double the strength to fall upon the Russian forces and destroy them, to negotiate an advantageous peace; or, in case of negotiations being refused, to make a menacing march upon Petersburg, or even, in case of failure in this, to return to Smolensk or to Vilna, or to remain in Moscow, to retain, in short, the brilliant position in which the French army now found themselves. To do all this it was only necessary to take the simplest and easiest measures: to keep the soldiers from pillage, to prepare winter clothes (of which there was a supply in Moscow amply sufficient for the whole army), and regularly to collect the provisions, of which the supply in Moscow was, on the showing of the French historians, sufficient to feed the whole army for six months. Napoleon, the greatest of all military geniuses, with absolute power, as historians assert, over the army, did nothing of all this.

Far from doing anything of the sort, he used his power to select out of all the various courses open to him the stupidest and most pernicious of all. Of all the different things Napoleon might have done —spending the winter in Moscow, going to Petersburg, going to Nizhni-Novgorod, going back a little more to the north or to the south, by the road Kutuzov afterwards took—no course one can imagine could have been more ruinous for his army (as the sequel proved) than the one Napoleon actually did adopt; that is, the course of staying in Moscow till October, letting the troops plunder the town, then in hesitation leaving a garrison behind, marching out of Moscow, going to meet Kutuzov and not giving battle, turning to the right and going as far as Maley Yaroslavets, again refusing to risk a battle, and finally retreating, not by the road Kutuzov had taken, but by Mozhaisk and the Smolensk route through devastated country. Let the most skilful tacticians, supposing that Napoleon's object was the destruction of his army, try and devise a series of actions which could, apart from any measures that might be taken by the Russian forces, have ensured with such certainty the complete destruction of the whole French army as the course taken by Napoleon.

This the genius Napoleon did. But to say that Napoleon ruined his army because he wanted to do so, or because he was very stupid, would be just as unjust as to say that Napoleon got his troops to Moscow because he wanted to, and because he was very clever and a great genius.

In both cases his personal activity, having no more force than the personal activity of every soldier, was merely coincidental with the laws by which the event was determined.

Quite falsely (and simply because the sequel did not justify Napoleon's actions) do historians represent Napoleon's faculties as flagging at Moscow. Just as before, and afterwards in the year 1813, he used all his powers and faculties to do the best for himself and his army, Napoleon's activity at this time was no less marvellous than in Egypt, in Italy, in Austria, and in Prussia. We do not know with any certainty how real was the genius of Napoleon in Egypt, where forty centuries looked down upon his greatness, because all his great exploits there are recounted to us by none but Frenchmen. We cannot judge with certainty of his genius in Austria and Prussia, as the accounts of his doings there must be drawn from French and German sources. And the unaccountable surrender of corps of soldiers without a battle, and of fortresses without a siege, must dispose Germans to postulate Napoleon's genius as the unique explanation of the war as it was waged in Germany. But we have, thank God, no need to plead his genius to cloak our shame. We have paid for the right to look facts simply and squarely in the face, and that right we will not give up.

His activity in Moscow was as marvellous and as full of genius as anywhere else. Command upon command and plan upon plan was continually being issued by him from the time he entered Moscow to the time he left it. The absence of the citizens and of a deputation, and even the burning of Moscow, did not daunt him. He did not lose sight of the welfare of his army, nor of the doings of the enemy, nor of the welfare of the people of Russia, nor the conduct of affairs at Paris, nor of diplomatic negotiations as to the terms of peace.

.   .   .

On the military side, immediately on entering Moscow, Napoleon gives General Sebastiani strict orders to keep a watch on the movements of the Russian army, sends detachments along the various roads, and charges Murat to find Kutuzov. Then he gives careful instructions for the fortification of the Kremlin; then he makes a plan of the coming campaign over the whole map of Russia; that was a work of genius, indeed. On the diplomatic side, Napoleon summons to his presence Captain Yakovlev, who had been robbed and reduced to rags and did not know how to get out of Moscow, expounds to him minutely his whole policy and his magnanimity; and after writing a letter to the Emperor Alexander, in which he considers it his duty to inform his friend and brother that Rastoptchin had performed his duties very badly in Moscow, he despatches Yakovlev with it to Petersburg.

Expounding his views and his magnanimity with equal minuteness to Tutolmin, he despatches that old man too to Petersburg to open negotiations.

On the judicial side, orders were issued, immediately after the fires broke out, for the guilty persons to be found and executed. And the miscreant Rastoptchin was punished by the order to set fire to his houses.

On the administrative side, Moscow was presented with a constitution. A municipal council was instituted, and the following proclamation was issued:—

Citizens of Moscow

Your misfortunes have been cruel, but his majesty the Emperor and King wishes to put an end to them. Terrible examples have shown you how he punishes crime and breach of discipline. Stern measures have been taken to put an end to disorder and to restore public security. A paternal council, chosen from among yourselves, will compose your municipality or town council. It will care for you, for your needs and your interests. The members of it will be distinguished by a red ribbon, which they will wear across the shoulder, and the mayor will wear a white sash over it. But except when discharging their duties, they will wear only a red ribbon round the left arm.

The city police are established on their former footing, and they are already restoring order. The government has appointed two general commissioners, or superintendents of police, and twenty commissioners, or police inspectors, stationed in the different quarters of the town. You will recognise them by the white ribbon they will wear round the left arm. Several churches of various denominations have been opened, and divine service is performed in them without hindrance. Your fellow-citizens are returning every day to their dwellings, and orders have been given that they should find in them the aid and protection due to misfortune. These are the measures which the government has adopted to restore order and alleviate your position; but to attain that end, it is necessary that you should unite your efforts with them; should forget, if possible, the misfortunes you have suffered; should look hopefully at a fate that is not so cruel; should believe that a shameful death inevitably awaits those guilty of violence against your persons or your deserted property, and consequently leaves no doubt that they will be preserved, since such is the will of the greatest and most just of monarchs. Soldiers and citizens of whatever nation you may be! Restore public confidence, the source of the prosperity of a state; live like brothers, give mutual aid and protection to one another; unite in confounding the projects of the evil-minded; obey the civil and military authorities, and your tears will soon cease to flow.

On the commissariat side, Napoleon issued orders for all the troops to enter Moscow in turn, *à la maraude,* to gather supplies for themselves; so that in that way the army was provided with supplies for the future.

On the religious side, Napoleon ordered the priests to be brought back, and services to be performed again in the churches.

With a view to encouraging commerce and providing supplies for the troops, the following notice was placarded everywhere:—

PROCLAMATION

You, peaceable inhabitants of Moscow, artisans, and working men, who have been driven out of the city by the disturbance, and you, scattered tillers of the soil, who are still kept in the fields by groundless terror, hear! Tranquillity is returning to this capital, and order is being restored in it. Your fellow-countrymen are coming boldly out of their hiding-places, seeing that they are treated with respect. Every act of violence against them or their property is promptly punished. His Majesty the Emperor and King protects them, and he reckons none among you his enemies but such as disobey his commands. He wishes to put an end to your trouble, and to bring you back to your homes and your families. Co-operate with his beneficent designs and come to us without apprehension. Citizens! Return with confidence to your habitations; you will soon find the means of satisfying your needs! Artisans and industrious handicraftsmen! Return to your employment; houses, shops, and guards to protect them are awaiting you, and you will receive the payment due to you for your toil! And you, too, peasants, come out of the forests where you have been hiding in terror, return without fear to your huts in secure reliance on finding protection. Markets have been established in the city, where peasants can bring their spare stores and country produce. The government has taken the following measures to secure freedom of sale for them: (1) From this day forward, peasants, husbandmen, and inhabitants of the environs of Moscow can, without any danger, bring their goods of any kind to two appointed markets—namely, the Mohovaya and the Ohotny Ryad. (2) Goods shall be bought from them at such a price as seller and buyer shall agree upon together; but if the seller cannot get what he asks for as a fair price, he will be at liberty to take his goods back to his village, and no one can hinder his doing so on any pretext whatever. (3) Every Sunday and Wednesday are fixed for weekly market days: to that end a sufficient number of troops will be stationed on Tuesdays and Saturdays along all the high roads at such a distance from the town as to protect the carts coming in. (4) Similar measures will be taken that the peasants with their carts and horses may meet with no hindrance on their homeward way. (5) Steps will be immediately taken to re-establish the ordinary shops.

Inhabitants of the city and of the country, and you workmen and handicraftsmen of whatever nationality you may be! You are called upon to carry out the paternal designs of his majesty the Emperor and King, and to co-operate with him for the public welfare. Lay your respect and confidence at his feet, and do not delay to unite with us!

With a view to keeping up the spirits of the troops and the people, reviews were continually being held, and rewards were distributed.

The Emperor rode about the streets and entertained the inhabitants; and in spite of his preoccupation with affairs of state, visited in person the theatre set up by his orders.

As regards philanthropy, too—the fairest jewel in the conqueror's crown—Napoleon did everything that lay within him. On the benevolent institutions he ordered the inscription to be put up, *"Maison de ma mère,"* thereby combining a touching filial sentiment with a monarch's grandeur of virtue. He visited the Foundling Home; and as he gave the orphans he had saved his white hands to kiss, he conversed graciously with Tutolmin. Then, as Thiers eloquently recounts, he ordered his soldiers' pay to be distributed among them in the false Russian notes he had counterfeited:—

> Reinforcing the use of these methods by an act worthy of him and of the French army, he had assistance distributed to those who had suffered loss from the fire. But as provisions were too precious to be given to strangers, mostly enemies, Napoleon preferred to furnish them with money for them to provide themselves from without, and ordered paper roubles to be distributed among them.

With a view to maintaining discipline in the army, orders were continually being issued for severely punishing nonfulfilment of military duty and for putting an end to pillaging.

. . .

But, strange to say, all these arrangements, these efforts and plans, which were no whit inferior to those that had been made on similar occasions before, never touched the root of the matter; like the hands on the face of a clock, when detached from the mechanism, they turned aimlessly and arbitrarily, without catching the wheels.

The plan of campaign, that work of genius, of which Thiers says, that his genius never imagined anything more profound, more skilful, and more admirable, and entering into a polemical discussion with M. Fenn, proves that the composition of this work of genius is to be referred, not to the 4th, but to the 15th of October—that plan never was and never could be put into execution, because it had nothing in common with the actual facts of the position. The fortification of the Kremlin, for which it was necessary to pull down la Mosquée (as Napoleon called the church of Vassily the Blessed) turned out to be perfectly useless. The mining of the Kremlin was only of use for carrying out the desire the Emperor expressed on leaving Moscow, to blow up the Kremlin, like a child that beats the floor against which it has hurt itself. The pursuit of the Russian army, on which Napoleon laid so much stress, led to an unheard-of result. The French generals lost sight of the sixty thousand men of the Russian army, and it was only, in the words of Thiers, thanks to the skill, and apparently also the genius, of Murat that they succeeded at last in finding, like a lost pin, this army of sixty thousand men.

On the diplomatic side, all Napoleon's expositions of his magnanimity and justice, both to Tutolmin and to Yakovlev (the latter was principally interested in finding himself a great-coat and a conveyance for travelling) turned out to be fruitless. Alexander would not receive these envoys, and made no reply to the message they brought.

On the side of law, of order, after the execution of the supposed incendiaries, the other half of Moscow was burnt down.

The establishment of a municipal council did not check pillage, and was no benefit to any one but the few persons, who were members of it, and were able on the pretext of preserving order to plunder Moscow on their own account, or to save their own property from being plundered.

On the religious side, the difficulty had so easily been settled by Napoleon's visit to a mosque in Egypt, but here similar measures led to no results whatever. Two or three priests, picked up in Moscow, did attempt to carry out Napoleon's desire; but one of them was slapped in the face by a French soldier during the service, and in regard to the other, the following report was made by a French official: "The priest, whom I had discovered and invited to resume saying the Mass, cleaned and closed the church. In the night they came again to break in the doors, break the padlocks, tear the books, and commit other disorders."

As for the encouragement of commerce, the proclamation to "industrious artisans and peasants," met with no response at all. Industrious artisans there were none in Moscow, and the peasants set upon the messengers who ventured too far from the town with the proclamation and killed them.

The attempts to entertain the people and the troops with theatres were equally unsuccessful. The theatres set up in the Kremlin and Poznyakov's house were closed again immediately, because the actors and actresses were stripped of their belongings by the soldiers.

Even philanthropy did not bring the desired results. Moscow was full of paper money, genuine and counterfeit, and the notes had no value. The French, accumulating booty, cared for nothing but gold. The counterfeit notes, which Napoleon so generously bestowed on the unfortunate, were of no value, and even silver fell below its standard value in relation to gold.

But the most striking example of the ineffectiveness of all efforts made by the authorities was Napoleon's vain endeavour to check plunder, and to maintain discipline.

Here are reports sent in by the military authorities:—

Pillage continues in the city, in spite of the orders to stop it. Order is not yet restored, and there is not a single merchant carrying on trade in a lawful fashion. But the canteen-keepers permit themselves to sell the fruits of pillage.

Part of my district continues to be a prey to the pillaging of the soldiers of the 3rd corps who, not satisfied with tearing from the poor wretches, who have taken refuge in the underground cellars, the little they have left, have even the ferocity to wound them with sword-cuts, as I have seen in several instances.

Nothing new, but that the soldiers give themselves up to robbery and plunder. October 9th.

Robbery and pillage continue. There is a band of robbers in our district, which would need strong guards to arrest it. October 11th.

The Emperor is exceedingly displeased that, in spite of the strict orders to stop pillage, bands of marauders from the guards are continually returning to the Kremlin. In the Old Guards, the disorder and pillaging have been more violent than ever last night and to-day. The Emperor sees, with regret, that the picked soldiers, appointed to guard his person, who should set an example to the rest, are losing discipline to such a degree as to break into the cellars and stores prepared for the army. Others are so degraded that they refuse to obey sentinels and officers on guard, abuse them, and strike them.

The chief marshal of the palace complains bitterly that, in spite of repeated prohibitions, the soldiers continue to commit nuisances in all the courtyards, and even before the Emperor's own windows.

The army, like a herd of cattle run wild, and trampling underfoot the fodder that might have saved them from starvation, was falling to pieces, and getting nearer to its ruin with every day it remained in Moscow.

But it did not move.

It only started running when it was seized by panic fear at the capture of a transport on the Smolensk road and the battle of Tarutino. The news of the battle of Tarutino reached Napoleon unexpectedly in the middle of a review, and aroused in him—so Thiers tells us—a desire to punish the Russians, and he gave the order for departure that all the army was clamouring for.

In their flight from Moscow, the soldiers carried with them all the plunder they had collected. Napoleon, too, carried off his own private *trésor*. Seeing the great train of waggons, loaded with the booty of the army, Napoleon was alarmed (as Thiers tells us). But with his military experience, he did not order all unecessary waggons of goods to be burnt, as he had done with a marshal's baggage on the way to Moscow. He gazed at those carts and carriages, filled with soldiers, and said that it was very well, that those conveyances would come in useful for provisions, the sick, and the wounded.

The plight of the army was like the plight of a wounded beast, that feels its death at hand, and knows not what it is doing. Studying the intricate manoeuvres and schemes of Napoleon and his army from the time of entering Moscow up to the time of the destruction of that army is much like watching the death struggles and convulsions of a beast mortally wounded. Very often the wounded creature, hearing a stir, rushes to meet the hunter's shot, runs forward and back again, and itself hastens its end. Napoleon under the pressure of his army did likewise. Panic-stricken at the rumour of the battle of Tarutino, like a wild beast, the army made a rush towards the shot, reached the hunter, and ran back again; and at last, like every wild creature took the old familiar track, that was the worst and most disastrous way for it.

Napoleon is represented to us as the leader in all this movement, just as the figurehead in the prow of a ship to the savage seems the force that guides the ship on its course. Napoleon in his activity all this time was like a child, sitting in a carriage, pulling the straps within it, and fancying he is moving it along.

THE UNFREE LEADER

George Orwell

"Shooting an Elephant"

In Moulmein, in Lower Burma, I was hated by large numbers of people—the only time in my life that I have been important enough for this to happen to me. I was sub-divisional police officer of the town, and in an aimless, petty kind of way anti-European feeling was very bitter. No one had the guts to raise a riot, but if a European woman went through the bazaars alone somebody would probably spit betel juice over her dress. As a police officer I was an obvious target and was baited whenever it seemed safe to do so. When a nimble Burman tripped me up on the football field and the referee

From *Shooting an Elephant and Other Essays* by George Orwell, copyright, 1945, 1946, 1949, 1950, by Sonia Brownell Orwell. Reprinted by permission of Harcourt, Brace & World, Inc., Sonia Brownell, and Secker & Warburg Ltd.

(another Burman) looked the other way, the crowd yelled with hideous laughter. This happened more than once. In the end the sneering yellow faces of young men that met me everywhere, the insults hooted after me when I was at a safe distance, got badly on my nerves. The young Buddhist priests were the worst of all. There were several thousands of them in the town and none of them seemed to have anything to do except stand on street corners and jeer at Europeans.

All this was perplexing and upsetting. For at that time I had already made up my mind that imperialism was an evil thing and the sooner I chucked up my job and got out of it the better. Theoretically—and secretly, of course—I was all for the Burmese and all against their oppressors, the British. As for the job I was doing, I hated it more bitterly than I can perhaps make clear. In a job like that you see the dirty work of Empire at close quarters. The wretched prisoners huddling in the stinking cages of the lock-ups, the grey, cowed faces of the long-term convicts, the scarred buttocks of the men who had been flogged with bamboos—all these oppressed me with an intolerable sense of guilt. But I could get nothing into perspective. I was young and ill-educated and I had had to think out my problems in the utter silence that is imposed on every Englishman in the East. I did not even know that the British Empire is dying, still less did I know that it is a great deal better than the younger empires that are going to supplant it. All I knew was that I was stuck between my hatred of the empire I served and my rage against the evil-spirited little beasts who tried to make my job impossible. With one part of my mind I thought of the British Raj as an unbreakable tyranny, as something clamped down, in *saecula saeculorum,* upon the will of prostrate peoples; with another part I thought that the greatest joy in the world would be to drive a bayonet into a Buddhist priest's guts. Feelings like these are the normal by-products of imperialism; ask any Anglo-Indian official, if you can catch him off duty.

One day something happened which in a roundabout way was enlightening. It was a tiny incident in itself, but it gave me a better glimpse than I had had before of the real nature of imperialism—the real motives for which despotic governments act. Early one morning the sub-inspector at a police station the other end of the town rang me up on the 'phone and said that an elephant was ravaging the bazaar. Would I please come and do something about it? I did not know what I could do, but I wanted to see what was happening and

I got on to a pony and started out. I took my rifle, an old .44 Winchester and much too small to kill an elephant, but I thought the noise might be useful *in terrorem*. Various Burmans stopped me on the way and told me about the elephant's doings. It was not, of course, a wild elephant, but a tame one which had gone "must." It had been chained up, as tame elephants always are when their attack of "must" is due, but on the previous night it had broken its chain and escaped. Its mahout, the only person who could manage it when it was in that state, had set out in pursuit, but had taken the wrong direction and was now twelve hours' journey away, and in the morning the elephant had suddenly reappeared in the town. The Burmese population had no weapons and were quite helpless against it. It had already destroyed somebody's bamboo hut, killed a cow and raided some fruit-stalls and devoured the stock; also it had met the municipal rubbish van and, when the driver jumped out and took to his heels, had turned the van over and inflicted violences upon it.

The Burmese sub-inspector and some Indian constables were waiting for me in the quarter where the elephant had been seen. It was a very poor quarter, a labyrinth of squalid bamboo huts, thatched with palm-leaf, winding all over a steep hillside. I remember that it was a cloudy, stuffy morning at the beginning of the rains. We began questioning the people as to where the elephant had gone and, as usual, failed to get any definite information. That is invariably the case in the East; a story always sounds clear enough at a distance, but the nearer you get to the scene of events the vaguer it becomes. Some of the people said that the elephant had gone in one direction, some said that he had gone in another, some professed not even to have heard of any elephant. I had almost made up my mind that the whole story was a pack of lies, when we heard yells a little distance away. There was a loud, scandalized cry of "Go away, child! Go away this instant!" and an old woman with a switch in her hand came round the corner of a hut, violently shooing away a crowd of naked children. Some more women followed, clicking their tongues and exclaiming; evidently there was something that the children ought not to have seen. I rounded the hut and saw a man's dead body sprawling in the mud. He was an Indian, a black Dravidian coolie, almost naked, and he could not have been dead many minutes. The people said that the elephant had come suddenly upon him around the corner of the hut, caught him with its trunk, put its foot on his back and ground him into the earth. This was the rainy season and the ground was soft, and his face had scored a trench a foot deep and a couple of yards long. He was lying on his belly with arms crucified and head sharply twisted to one side. His face was coated with mud, the eyes wide open, the teeth bared and grinning with an expression of unendurable agony. (Never tell me, by the way, that the dead look peaceful. Most of the corpses I have seen looked devilish.) The friction of the great beast's foot had stripped the skin from his back as neatly as one skins a rabbit. As soon as I saw the dead man I sent an orderly to a friend's house nearby to borrow an elephant rifle. I had already sent back the pony, not wanting it to go mad with fright and throw me if it smelt the elephant.

The orderly came back in a few minutes with a rifle and five cartridges, and meanwhile some Burmans had arrived and told us that the elephant was in the paddy fields below, only a few hundred yards away. As I started forward practically the whole population of the quarter flocked out of the houses and followed me. They had seen the rifle and were all shouting excitedly that I was going to shoot the elephant. They had not shown much interest in the elephant when he was merely ravaging their homes, but it was different now that he was going to be shot. It was a bit of fun to them, as it would be to an English crowd; besides they wanted the meat. It made me vaguely uneasy. I had no intention of shooting the elephant—I had merely sent for the rifle to defend myself if necessary— and it is always unnerving to have a crowd following you. I marched down the hill, looking and feeling a fool, with the rifle over my shoulder and an ever-growing army of people jostling at my heels. At the bottom, when you got away from the huts, there was a metalled road and beyond that a miry waste of paddy fields a thousand yards across, not yet ploughed but soggy from the first rains and dotted with coarse grass. The elephant was standing eight yards from the road, his left side towards us. He took not the slightest notice of the crowd's approach. He was tearing up bunches of grass, beating them against his knees to clean them and stuffing them into his mouth.

I had halted on the road. As soon as I saw the elephant I knew with perfect certainty that I ought not to shoot him. It is a serious matter to shoot a working elephant—it is comparable to destroying a huge and costly piece of machinery—and obviously one ought not to do it if it can possibly be avoided. And at that distance, peacefully eating, the elephant looked no more dangerous than a cow. I thought then and I think now that his attack of "must" was already passing off; in which case he would merely wander harmlessly about until the mahout came back and caught him. Moreover, I did not in the least want to shoot him. I decided that I would watch him for a little while to make sure that he did not turn savage again, and then go home.

But at that moment I glanced round at the crowd that had followed me. It was an immense crowd, two thousand at the least and growing every minute. It blocked the road for a long distance on either side. I looked at the sea of yellow faces above the garish clothes—faces all happy and excited over this bit of fun, all certain that the elephant was going to be shot. They were watching me as they would watch a conjurer about to perform a trick. They did not like me, but with the magical rifle in my hands I was momentarily worth watching. And suddenly I realized that I should have to shoot the elephant after all. The people expected it of me and I had got to do it; I could feel their two thousand wills pressing me forward, irresistibly. And it was at this moment, as I stood there with the rifle in my hands, that I first grasped the hollowness, the futility of the white man's dominion in the East. Here was I, the white man with his gun, standing in front of the unarmed native crowd—seemingly the leading actor of the piece; but in reality I was only an absurd puppet pushed to and fro by the will of those yellow faces behind. I perceived in this moment that when the white man turns tyrant it is his own freedom that he destroys. He becomes a sort of hollow, posing dummy, the conventionalized figure of a sahib. For it is the condition of his rule that he shall spend his life in trying to impress the "natives," and so in every crisis he has got to do what the "natives" expect of him. He wears a mask, and his face grows to fit it. I had got to shoot the elephant. I had committed myself to doing it when I sent for the rifle. A sahib has got to act like a sahib; he has got to appear resolute, to know his own mind and do definite things. To come all that way, rifle in hand, with two thousand people marching at my heels, and then to trail feebly away, having done nothing—no, that was impossible. The crowd would laugh at me. And my whole life, every white man's life in the East, was one long struggle not to be laughed at.

But I did not want to shoot the elephant. I watched him beating his bunch of grass against his knees, with that preoccupied grandmotherly air that elephants have. It seemed to me that it would be murder to shoot him. At that age I was not squeamish about killing animals, but I had never shot an elephant and never wanted to. (Somehow it always seems worse to kill a *large* animal.) Besides, there was the beast's owner to be considered. Alive, the elephant was worth at least a hundred pounds; dead, he would only be worth the value of his tusks, five pounds, possibly. But I had got to act quickly. I turned to some experienced-looking Burmans who had been there when we arrived, and asked them how the elephant had been behaving. They all said the same thing: he took no notice of you if you left him alone, but he might charge if you went too close to him.

It was perfectly clear to me what I ought to do. I ought to walk up to within, say, twenty-five yards of the elephant and test his behavior. If he charged, I could shoot; if he took no notice of me, it would be safe to leave him until the mahout came back. But also I knew that I was going to do no such thing. I was a poor shot with a rifle and the ground was soft mud into which one would sink at every step. If the elephant charged and I missed him, I should have about as much chance as a toad under a steam-roller. But even then I was not thinking particularly of my own skin, only of the watchful yellow faces behind. For at that moment, with the crowd watching me, I was not afraid in the ordinary sense, as I would have been if I had been alone. A white man mustn't be frightened in front of "natives"; and so, in general, he isn't frightened. The sole thought in my mind was that if anything went wrong those two thousand Burmans would see me pursued, caught, trampled on and reduced to a grinning corpse like that Indian up the hill. And if that happened it was quite probable that some of them would laugh. That would never do. There was only one alternative. I shoved the cartridges into the magazine and lay down on the road to get a better aim.

The crowd grew very still, and a deep, low, happy sigh, as of people who see the theater curtain go up at last, breathed from innumerable throats. They were going to have their bit of fun after all. The rifle was a beautiful German thing with cross-hair sights. I did not then know that in shooting an elephant one would shoot to cut an imaginary bar running from ear-hole to ear-hole. I ought, therefore, as the elephant was sideways on, to have aimed straight at his ear-hole; actually I aimed several inches in front of this, thinking the brain would be further forward.

When I pulled the trigger I did not hear the bang or feel the kick—one never does when a shot goes home—but I heard the devilish roar of glee that went up from the crowd. In that instant, in too short a time, one would have thought, even for the bullet to get there, a mysterious, terrible change had come over the elephant. He neither stirred nor fell, but every line of his body had altered. He looked suddenly stricken, shrunken, immensely old, as though the frightful impact of the bullet had paralyzed him without knocking him down. At last, after what seemed a long time—it might have been five seconds, I dare say—he sagged flabbily to his knees. His mouth slobbered. An enormous senility seemed to have settled upon him. One could have imagined him thousands of years old. I fired again into the same spot. At the second shot he did not collapse but climbed with desperate slowness to his feet and stood weakly upright, with legs sagging and head drooping. I fired a third time. That was the shot that did for him. You could see the agony of it jolt his whole body and knock the last remnant of strength from his legs. But in falling he seemed for a moment to rise, for as his hind legs collapsed beneath him he seemed to tower upward like a huge rock toppling, his trunk reaching skywards like a tree. He trumpeted, for the first and only time. And then down he came, his belly towards me, with a crash that seemed to shake the ground even where I lay.

I got up. The Burmans were already racing past me across the mud. It was obvious that the elephant would never rise again, but he was not dead. He was breathing very rhythmically with long rattling gasps, his great mound of a side painfully rising and falling. His mouth was wide open—I could see far down into caverns of pale pink throat. I waited a long time for him to die, but his breathing did not weaken. Finally I fired my two remaining shots into the spot where I thought his heart must be. The thick blood welled out of him like red velvet, but still he did not die. His body did not even jerk when the shots hit him, the tortured breathing continued without a pause. He was dying, very slowly and in great agony, but in some world remote from me where not even a bullet could damage him further. I felt that I had got to put an end to that dreadful noise. It seemed dreadful to see the great beast lying there, powerless to move and yet powerless to die, and not even to be able to finish him. I sent back for my small rifle and poured shot after shot into his heart and down his throat. They seemed to make no impression. The tortured gasps continued as steadily as the ticking of a clock.

In the end I could not stand it any longer and went away. I heard later that it took him half an hour to die. Burmans were bringing

dahs and baskets even before I left, and I was told they had stripped
his body almost to the bones by the afternoon.

Afterwards, of course, there were endless discussions about the
shooting of the elephant. The owner was furious, but he was only
an Indian and could do nothing. Besides, legally I had done the right
thing, for a mad elephant has to be killed, like a mad dog, if its
owner fails to control it. Among the Europeans opinion was divided.
The older men said I was right, the younger men said it was a damn
shame to shoot an elephant for killing a coolie, because an elephant
was worth more than any damn Coringhee coolie. And afterwards I
was very glad that the coolie had been killed; it put me legally in the
right and it gave me a sufficient pretext for shooting the elephant. I
often wondered whether any of the others grasped that I had done
it solely to avoid looking a fool.

THE POWER OF OBSESSION

Herman Melville

From *Moby Dick*

It was not a great while after the affair of the pipe, that one morning shortly after breakfast, Ahab, as was his wont, ascended the
cabin-gangway to the deck. There most sea-captains usually walk
at that hour, as country gentlemen, after the same meal, take a few
turns in the garden.

Soon his steady, ivory stride was heard, as to and fro he paced his
old rounds, upon planks so familiar to his tread, that they were all
over dented, like geological stones, with the peculiar mark of his
walk. Did you fixedly gaze, too, upon that ribbed and dented brow;
there also, you would see still stranger foot-prints—the foot-prints
of his one unsleeping, ever-pacing thought.

But on the occasion in question, those dents looked deeper, even
as his nervous step that morning left a deeper mark. And, so full of
his thought was Ahab, that at every uniform turn that he made, now
at the main-mast and now at the binnacle, you could almost see that

Ch. XXXVI.

thought turn in him as he turned, and pace in him as he paced; so completely possessing him, indeed, that it all but seemed the inward mould of every outer movement.

"D'ye mark him, Flask?" whispered Stubb; "the chick that's in him pecks the shell. 'Twill soon be out."

The hours wore on;—Ahab now shut up within his cabin; anon, pacing the deck, with the same intense bigotry of purpose in his aspect.

It drew near the close of day. Suddenly he came to a halt by the bulwarks, and inserting his bone leg into the auger-hole there, and with one hand grasping a shroud, he ordered Starbuck to send everybody aft.

"Sir!" said the mate, astonished at an order seldom or never given on ship-board except in some extraordinary case.

"Send everybody aft," repeated Ahab. "Mast-heads, there! come down!"

When the entire ship's company were assembled, and with curious and not wholly unapprehensive faces, were eyeing him, for he looked not unlike the weather horizon when a storm is coming up, Ahab, after rapidly glancing over the bulwarks, and then darting his eyes among the crew, started from his standpoint; and as though not a soul were nigh him resumed his heavy turns upon the deck. With bent head and half-slouched hat he continued to pace, unmindful of the wondering whispering among the men; till Stubb cautiously whispered to Flask, that Ahab must have summoned them there for the purpose of witnessing a pedestrian feat. But this did not last long. Vehemently pausing, he cried:—

"What do ye do when ye see a whale, men?"

"Sing out for him!" was the impulsive rejoinder from a score of clubbed voices.

"Good!" cried Ahab, with a wild approval in his tones; observing the hearty animation into which his unexpected question had so magnetically thrown them.

"And what do ye next, men?"

"Lower away, and after him!"

"And what tune is it ye pull to, men?"

"A dead whale or a stove boat!"

More and more strangely and fiercely glad and approving, grew the countenance of the old man at every shout; while the mariners began to gaze curiously at each other, as if marvelling how it was that they themselves became so excited at such seemingly purpose-less questions.

But, they were all eagerness again, as Ahab, now half-revolving in his pivot-hole, with one hand reaching high up a shroud, and tightly, almost convulsively grasping it, addressed them thus:—

"All ye mast-headers have before now heard me give orders about a white whale. Look ye! d'ye see this Spanish ounce of gold?"—holding up a broad bright coin to the sun—"it is a sixteen dollar piece, men. D'ye see it? Mr. Starbuck, hand me yon top-maul."

While the mate was getting the hammer, Ahab, without speaking, was slowly rubbing the gold piece against the skirts of his jacket, as if to heighten its lustre, and without using any words was meanwhile lowly humming to himself, producing a sound so strangely muffled and inarticulate that it seemed the mechanical humming of the wheels of his vitality in him.

Receiving the top-maul from Starbuck, he advanced towards the main-mast with the hammer uplifted in one hand, exhibiting the gold with the other, and with a high raised voice exclaiming: "Whosoever of ye raises me a white-headed whale with a wrinkled brow and a crooked jaw; whosoever of ye raises me that white-headed whale, with three holes punctured in his starboard fluke—look ye, whosoever of ye raises me that same white whale, he shall have this gold ounce, my boys!"

"Huzza! huzza!" cried the seamen, as with swinging tarpaulins they hailed the act of nailing the gold to the mast.

"It's a white whale, I say," resumed Ahab, as he threw down the top-maul: "a white whale. Skin your eyes for him, men; look sharp for white water; if ye see but a bubble, sing out."

All this while Tashtego, Daggoo, and Queequeg had looked on with even more intense interest and surprise than the rest, and at the mention of the wrinkled brow and crooked jaw they had started as if each was separately touched by some specific recollection.

"Captain Ahab," said Tashtego, "that white whale must be the same that some call Moby Dick."

"Moby Dick?" shouted Ahab. "Do ye know the white whale then, Tash?"

"Does he fan-tail a little curious, sir, before he goes down?" said the Gay-Header deliberately.

"And has he a curious spout, too," said Daggoo, "very bushy, even for a parmacetty, and mighty quick, Captain Ahab?"

"And he have one, two, tree—oh! good many iron in him hide, too, Captain," cried Queequeg disjointedly, "all twiske-tee be-twisk, like him—him—" faltering hard for a word, and screwing his hand round and round as though uncorking a bottle—"like him—him——"

"Corkscrew!" cried Ahab, "aye, Queequeg, the harpoons lie all twisted and wrenched in him; aye, Daggoo, his spout is a big one, like a whole shock of wheat, and white as a pile of our Nantucket wool after the great annual sheep-shearing; aye, Tashtego, and he fan-tails like a split jib in a squall. Death and devils! men, it is Moby Dick ye have seen—Moby Dick—Moby Dick!"

"Captain Ahab," said Starbuck, who, with Stubb and Flask, had thus far been eyeing his superior with increasing surprise, but at last seemed struck with a thought which somewhat explained all the wonder. "Captain Ahab, I have heard of Moby Dick—but it was not Moby Dick that took off thy leg?"

"Who told thee that?" cried Ahab; then pausing, "Aye, Starbuck; aye, my hearties all round; it was Moby Dick that dismasted me; Moby Dick that brought me to this dead stump I stand on now. Aye, aye," he shouted with a terrific, loud, animal sob, like that of a heart-stricken moose; "Aye, aye! it was that accursed white whale that razeed me; made a poor pegging lubber for me for ever and a day!" Then tossing both arms, with measureless imprecations he shouted out: "Aye, aye! and I'll chase him round Good Hope, and round the Horn, and round the Norway Maelstrom, and round perdition's flames before I give him up. And this is what ye have shipped for, men! to chase that white whale on both sides of land, and over all sides of earth, till he spouts black blood and rolls fin out. What say ye, men, will ye splice hands on it, now? I think ye do look brave."

"Aye, aye!" shouted the harpooneers and seamen, running closer to the excited old man: "A sharp eye for the white whale; a sharp lance for Moby Dick!"

"God bless ye," he seemed to half sob and half shout. "God bless ye, men. Steward! go draw the great measure of grog. But what's this long face about, Mr. Starbuck; wilt thou not chase the white whale? art not game for Moby Dick?"

"I am game for his crooked jaw, and for the jaws of Death too, Captain Ahab, if it fairly comes in the way of the business we follow; but I came here to hunt whales, not my commander's vengeance. How many barrels will thy vengeance yield thee even if thou gettest it, Captain Ahab? it will not fetch thee much in our Nantucket market."

"Nantucket market! Hoot! But come closer, Starbuck; thou requirest a little lower layer. If money's to be the measurer, man, and the accountants have computed their great counting-house the globe, by girdling it with guineas, one to every three parts of an inch; then, let me tell thee, that my vengeance will fetch a great premium *here!*"

"He smites his chest," whispered Stubb, "what's that for? methinks it rings most vast, but hollow."

"Vengeance on a dumb brute!" cried Starbuck, "that simply smote thee from blindest instinct! Madness! To be enraged with a dumb thing, Captain Ahab, seems blasphemous."

"Hark ye yet again—the little lower layer. All visible objects, man, are but as pasteboard masks. But in each event—in the living act, the undoubted deed—there, some unknown but still reasoning thing puts forth the mouldings of its features from behind the unreasoning mask. If man will strike, strike through the mask! How can the prisoner reach outside except by thrusting through the wall? To me, the white whale is that wall, shoved near to me. Sometimes I think there's naught beyond. But 'tis enough. He tasks me; he heaps me; I see in him outrageous strength, with an inscrutable malice sinewing it. That inscrutable thing is chiefly what I hate; and be the white whale agent, or be the white whale principal, I will wreak that hate upon him. Talk not to me of blasphemy, man; I'd strike the sun if it insulted me. For could the sun do that, then could I do the other; since there is ever a sort of fair play herein, jealousy presiding over all creations. But not my master, man, is even that fair play. Who's over me? Truth hath no confines. Take off thine eye! more intolerable than fiends' glarings is a doltish stare! So, so; thou reddenest and palest; my heat has melted thee to anger-glow. But look ye, Starbuck, what is said in heat, that thing unsays itself. There are men from whom warm words are small indignity. I meant not to incense thee. Let it go. Look! see yonder Turkish cheeks of spotted tawn—living, breathing pictures painted by the sun. The Pagan leopards—the unrecking and unworshipping things, that live; and seek, and give no reasons for the torrid life they feel! The crew, man, the crew! Are they not one and all with Ahab, in this matter of the whale? See Stubb! he laughs! See yonder Chilian! he snorts to think of it. Stand up amid the general hurricane, thy one tost sapling cannot, Starbuck! And what is it? Reckon it. 'Tis but to help strike a fin; no wondrous feat for Starbuck. What is it more? From this one poor hunt, then, the best lance out of all Nantucket, surely he will not hang back, when every foremast-hand has clutched a whetstone.

Ah! constrainings seize thee; I see! the billow lifts thee! Speak, but speak!—Aye, aye! thy silence, then, *that* voices thee. (*Aside*) Something shot from my dilated nostrils, he has inhaled it in his lungs. Starbuck now is mine; cannot oppose me now, without rebellion."

"God keep me!—keep us all!" murmured Starbuck, lowly.

But in his joy at the enchanted, tacit acquiescence of the mate, Ahab did not hear his foreboding invocation; nor yet the low laugh from the hold; nor yet the presaging vibrations of the winds in the cordage; nor yet the hollow flap of the sails against the masts, as for a moment their hearts sank in. For again Starbuck's downcast eyes lighted up with the stubbornness of life; the subterranean laugh died away; the winds blew on; the sails filled out; the ship heaved and rolled as before. Ah, ye admonitions and warnings! why stay ye not when ye come? But rather are ye predictions than warnings, ye shadows! Yet not so much predictions from without, as verifications of the foregoing things within. For with little external to constrain us, the innermost necessities in our being, these still drive us on.

"The measure! the measure!" cried Ahab.

Receiving the brimming pewter, and turning to the harpooneers, he ordered them to produce their weapons. Then ranging them before him near the capstan, with their harpoons in their hands, while his three mates stood at his side with their lances, and the rest of the ship's company formed a circle round the group; he stood for an instant searchingly eyeing every man of his crew. But those wild eyes met his, as the bloodshot eyes of the prairie wolves meet the eye of their leader, ere he rushes on at their head in the trail of the bison; but, alas! only to fall into the hidden snare of the Indian.

"Drink and pass!" he cried, handing the heavy charged flagon to the nearest seamen. "The crew alone now drink. Round with it, round! Short draughts—long swallows, men; 'tis hot as Satan's hoof. So, so; it goes round excellently. It spiralizes in ye; forks out at the serpent-snapping eye. Well done; almost drained. That way it went, this way it comes. Hand it me—here's a hollow! Men, ye seem the years; so brimming life is gulped and gone. Steward, refill!

"Attend now, my braves. I have mustered ye all round this capstan; and ye mates, flank me with your lances; and ye harpooneers, stand there with your irons; and ye, stout mariners, ring me in, that I may in some sort revive a noble custom of my fishermen fathers before me. O men, you will yet see that—Ha! boy, come back? bad pennies come not sooner. Hand it me. Why, now, this pewter had run brimming again, wer't not thou St. Vitus' imp—away, thou ague!

"Advance, ye mates! Cross your lances full before me. Well done! Let me touch the axis." So saying, with extended arm, he grasped the three level, radiating lances at their crossed centre; while so doing, suddenly and nervously twitched them; meanwhile glancing intently from Starbuck to Stubb; from Stubb to Flask. It seemed as though, by some nameless, interior volition, he would fain have shocked into them the same fiery emotion accumulated within the Leyden jar of his own magnetic life. The three mates quailed before his strong, sustained, and mystic aspect. Stubb and Flask looked sideways from him; the honest eye of Starbuck fell downright.

"In vain!" cried Ahab; "but, maybe, 'tis well. For did ye three but once take the full-forced shock, then mine own electric thing, *that* had perhaps expired from out me. Perchance, too, it would have dropped ye dead. Perchance ye need it not. Down lances! And now, ye mates, I do appoint ye three cupbearers to my three pagan kinsmen there—yon three most honorable gentlemen and noblemen, my valiant harpooneers. Disdain the task? What, when the great Pope washes the feet of beggars, using his tiara for ewer? Oh, my sweet cardinals! your own condescension, *that* shall bend ye to it. I do not order ye; ye will it. Cut your seizings and draw the poles, ye harpooneers!"

Silently obeying the order, the three harpooneers now stood with the detached iron part of their harpoons, some three feet long, held, barbs up, before him.

"Stab me not with that keen steel! Cant them; cant them over! know ye not the goblet end? Turn up the socket! So, so; now, ye cup-bearers, advance. The irons! take them; hold them while I fill!" Forthwith, slowly going from one officer to the other, he brimmed the harpoon sockets with the fiery waters from the pewter.

"Now, three to three, ye stand. Commend the murderous chalices! Bestow them, ye who are now made parties to this indissoluble league. Ha! Starbuck! but the deed is done! Yon ratifying sun now waits to sit upon it. Drink, ye harpooneers! drink and swear, ye men that man the deathful whaleboat's bow—Death to Moby Dick! God hunt us all, if we do not hunt Moby Dick to his death!" The long, barbed steel goblets were lifted; and to cries and maledictions against the white whale, the spirits were simultaneously quaffed down with a hiss. Starbuck paled, and turned, and shivered. Once more, and finally, the replenished pewter went the rounds among the frantic crew; when, waving his free hand to them, they all dispersed; and Ahab retired within his cabin.

THE NEUROSIS OF SUBMISSION

Heinrich Mann

From *Little Superman*

During those icy cold days of February, 1892, he went about the streets a great deal, in the expectation of great events. Along Unter den Linden something was afoot, but what it was could not yet be seen. Mounted police held the ends of the streets and waited. Pedestrians pointed to this display of force. "The unemployed!" People stood still to watch them approaching. They came from a northerly direction, marching slowly in small sections. When they reached Unter den Linden they hesitated, as if lost, took counsel by an exchange of glances, and turned off towards the Castle. There they stood in silence, their hands in their pockets, while the wheels of the cars splashed them with mud, and they hunched up their shoulders beneath the rain which fell on their faded overcoats. Many of them turned to look at passing officers, at the ladies in their carriages, at the long fur coats of the gentlemen hurrying from Burgstrasse. Their faces were expressionless, neither threatening nor even curious: not as if they wanted to see, but as if they wanted to be seen. Others never moved an eye from the windows of the Castle. The rain trickled down from their upturned faces. The horse of a shouting policeman drove them on further across the street to the next corner—but they stood still again, and the world seemed to sink down between those broad hollow faces, lit by the livid gleam of evening, and the stern walls beyond them which were already enveloped in darkness.

"I do not understand," said Diederich, "why the police do not take more energetic measures. That is certainly a rebellious crew."

"Don't you worry," Wiebel replied, "they have received exact instructions. Believe me, the authorities have their own well-developed plans. It is not always desirable to suppress at the outset such excrescences on the body politic. When they have been allowed to ripen, then a radical operation can be performed."

The ripening process to which Wiebel referred increased daily, and on the 26th it was completed. The demonstrations of the unemployed seemed more conscious of their objective. When they were driven back into one of the northern streets they overflowed into the next, and, before they could be cut off, they surged forward again in increased numbers. The processions all met at Unter den Linden, and as often as they were separated they ran together again. They reached the Castle, were driven back, and reached it again, silent and irresistible, like a river overflowing its banks. The traffic was blocked, the stream of pedestrians was banked up until it flowed over slowly into the flood which submerged the square; into this turbid, discoloured sea of poverty, rolling up in clammy waves, emitting subdued noises and throwing up, like the masts of sunken ships, poles bearing banners: "Bread! Work!" Here and there a more distinct rumbling broke out of the depths: "Bread! Work!" Swelling above the crowd it rolled off like a thunder-cloud: "Bread! Work!" The mounted police attack, the sea foams up and subsides, while women's voices shrilly cry like signals above the uproar: "Bread! Work!"

They are swept along, carrying with them the curious spectators standing on the Friederich monument. Their mouths are wide open; dust rises from the minor officials whose way to the office has been blocked, as if their clothes had been beaten. A distorted face, unknown to Diederich, shouts at him: "Here's something different! Now we are going for the Jews!"—and the face disappears before he remembers that it is Herr von Barnim. He tries to follow him, but in a big rush is thrown far across the road in front of a café, where he hears the crash of the broken windows and a workman shouting: "They fired me out of here lately with my thirty pfennig, because I had not got a silk hat on."—With him Diederich is forced in through the window, between the overturned tables and on to the floor, where they trip over broken glass, crushing against one another and howling. "No more in here! We must have air!" But still they clamber in. "The police are charging!" In the middle of the street, a free passage is miraculously made, as if for a triumphant procession. Then someone cries: "There goes Emperor William!"

Diederich found himself once more on the street. No one knew how it happened that they could suddenly move along in a solid mass the whole width of the street, and on both sides, right up to the flanks of the horse on which the Emperor sat—the Emperor himself. The people looked at him and followed him. Shouting masses were dissolved and swept along. Every one looked at him. A dark pushing mob without form, without plan, without limit, and bright above it a young man in a helmet: the Emperor. They looked. They had brought him down from his Castle. They had shouted: "Bread! Work!" until he had come. Nothing had been changed, except that he was there, and yet they were marching as if to a review of the troops at the Tempelhof.

On the outskirts, where the crowds were thinner, respectable people were saying to each other: "Well, thank God, he knows what he wants!"

"What does he want then?"

"To show that mob who is master! He tried treating them kindly. He even went too far in remitting sentences two years ago; they have become impertinent."

"It certainly must be admitted that he is not afraid. My word, this is an historical moment!

Diederich listened and was thrilled. The old gentleman who had spoken turned to him. He had white side-whiskers and wore an iron cross.

"Young man," said he, "what our magnificent young Emperor is now doing will be learned one day by the children in their schoolbooks. Wait till you see!"

Many people threw out their chests with an air of reverence. The gentlemen who rode behind the Emperor kept their eyes fixed in front of them, but they guided their horses through the crowd as if all these folk were supers ordered to appear in some royal spectacle. At times they glanced sideways at the public to see how the latter were impressed. The Emperor himself saw only his own personality and his own performance. Profound seriousness was stamped upon his features and his eyes flashed over the thousands whom he had fascinated. He measured himself against them, he, the master by the grace of God, and his rebellious slaves. Alone and unprotected he had dared to come amongst them, strong only in the sense of his mission. They might lay violent hands upon him if that were the will of the Almighty. He offered himself as sacrifice to his sacred trust. He would show them whether God was on his side. Then they would carry away the impression of his action and the eternal memory of their own powerlessness.

A young man wearing a wide-brimmed hat passed near Diederich and said: "Old stuff. Napoleon in Moscow fraternising alone with the people."

"But it is fine," asserted Diederich, and his voice faltered with emotion. The other shrugged his shoulders.

"Melodrama, and no good, at that."

Diederich looked at him and tried to flash his eyes like the Emperor.

"I suppose you are one of that rabble yourself."

He could not have explained what the rabble was. He simply felt that here, for the first time in his life, he had to defend law and order against hostile criticism. In spite of his agitation, he had another look at the man's shoulders; they were not imposing. The bystanders, too, were expressing disapproval. Then Diederich asserted himself. With his huge stomach he pressed the enemy against the wall and battered in his hat. Others joined in pummelling him, his hat fell to the ground, and soon the man himself lay there. As he moved on, Diederich remarked to his fellow-combatants: "That fellow has certainly not done his military service. He hasn't even got scars on his face; he has never fought a duel."

The old gentleman with the side-whiskers and the iron cross turned up again and shook Diederich's hand.

"Bravo, young man, bravo!"

"Isn't it enough to make you mad," said Diederich, still furious, "when the fellow tries to spoil our historical moment?"

"You have been in the army?" queried the old gentleman.

"I would have liked nothing better than to stay there," Diederich replied.

"Ah, yes, it isn't every day that we have a Sedan." The old gentleman touched his iron cross. "That's what we did!"

Diederich stretched himself and pointed to the Emperor and the subdued crowd.

"That is as good as Sedan!"

"Hm, hm," said the old gentleman.

"Allow me, sir," cried some one, waving a notebook. "We must get that. A touch of atmosphere, y'understand? I suppose it was a damned radical you bashed?"

"Oh, a mere trifle"—Diederich was still boiling. "As far as I am concerned this would be the time to go straight for the domestic enemy. We have our Emperor with us."

"Fine," said the reporter as he wrote: "In the wildly agitated throng people of all classes were heard expressing their devoted loyalty and unshakable confidence in His Majesty."

"Hurrah!" shouted Diederich, for every one was shouting, and, caught in a great surge of shouting people, he was carried right along to the Brandenburger Tor. A few steps in front of him rode the Emperor. Diederich could see his face, its stony seriousness and flashing eyes, but he was shouting so much that his sight was blurred. An intoxication, higher and nobler than that which beer procured, raised his feet off the ground and carried him into the air. He waved his hat high above all heads, in a sphere of enthusiastic madness, in a heaven where our finest feelings move. There on the horse rode Power, through the gateway of triumphal entries, with dazzling features but graven as in stone. The Power which transcends us and whose hoofs we kiss, the Power which is beyond the reach of hunger, spite and mockery! Against it we are impotent, for we all love it! We have it in our blood, for in our blood is submission. We are an atom of that Power, a diminutive molecule of something it has given out. Each one of us is as nothing, but massed in ranks as Neo-Teutons, soldiers, bureaucrats, priests and scientists, as economic organisations and unions of power, we taper up like a pyramid to the point at the top where Power itself stands, graven and dazzling. In it we live and have our being, merciless towards those who are remote beneath us, and triumphing even when we ourselves are crushed, for thus does power justify our love for it!

LEADERSHIP REDISCOVERED

Arthur Koestler

From *The Gladiators*

Each group built its own camp in the crescent-shaped valley named "Hell's Ante-room." They cooked their own meals, sang their own songs. They spoke Celtic, Thracian, Oscian, Syrian, Latin, Cimbric, German. They did not care for one another, and clashes were rather frequent. They swapped bacon for clubs, wine for shoes, women for weapons, weapons for money.

Reprinted with permission of The Macmillan Company and A. D. Peters & Co. From *The Gladiators* by Arthur Koestler, Book II, Ch. 1. Copyright 1939 by Arthur Koestler; renewed 1967 by Edith Simon.

The members of the original horde walked about the camp with a bad grace, and looked at the throng, silent and annoyed. The gladiators had put on airs; they wore the best clothes, uniforms of Roman officers; one could recognize them at first glance and pointed them out to new-comers. There were still fifty gladiators left from Lentulus's school in Capua; their horde, known as the gladiators' horde, soon embraced five thousand.

The camp boasted a number of celebrities; people turned and stared after them. Zozimos the rhetorician wandered from group to group, joked and squandered learned phrases, was applauded and gibed at; he was the only one in the whole camp who wore a toga. Hermios the shepherd played the great man towards his compatriots, the uncivilized Lucanians, flashed his teeth and bragged about his service with the Campanian army, he who had seen the world. Castus, the little fellow, minced affectedly past the crowds, stopped by a group here and there, played with his silver necklace, spoke of the Old Horde's exploits in the swamps of the Clanius; was admired and very little loved. The women ran after Oenomaus, enamoured of his girlish face: it was said he had never lain with a woman yet, and that he made poetry though he was a gladiator. Crixus inspired abashed deference; when he walked through the camp—fat, inert, dull-and-slow-eyed, conversation became unnatural, and the young people avoided his glance. Scurrilous tales circulated about him: it was said he slept with Jack to-day and Jill to-morrow: in itself there was nothing wrong with that, but you ought to look different if you did it.

And then there was Spartacus.

Many of the new-comers wondered after the first few days what thing about him was so special: it was a popular topic for evening chatter, and they chattered much for they had time.

Some said the special thing was his eyes; others, his cleverness. Women said it was his voice or his freckles. But there were others among them who had the same kind of eyes and were maybe just as clever, and there was no dearth in pleasant voices or freckles.

Philosophers and learned people said that it was not one trait or the other, but the Whole that did it: that certain something called "personality." Well, yes, it did sound learned, and pulpy as everything learned—but in the end everybody had a "personality," one in this way, the next in another; that did not explain a thing.

Zozimos put a finger to his nose, said: "Man's will it is, that force which giveth power," and more such comely, rhythmic sentences.

But when you thought it over and were not taken in by the rhythm: where was the man who did not *will*, and if all that mattered was the strength of your will, every landowner in Italy would have died of pestilence long ago, and every maiden in Italy would have her belly great.

Well, said Zozimos, he had not meant quite *that*, not the will of desire mattered, but the will of action. Action? There had been the brothers Eunus of Beneventum, the three of them had killed their master and harangued their colleagues to the effect that they should all become free bandits instead of remaining servants. And what happened? They were hanged, were these Eunus brothers, hanged, all three of them, together with their will, their action and personality.

In short, if you looked close, one man was like the next; one was a little plumper, the next a little cleverer, the third could talk like an angel, a fourth had a crooked nose—all this did not in the least explain what was so special about Spartacus. And if you thought it over and thrashed it out you might find that in the end there wasn't anything special about him at all. Spartacus was Spartacus: he went about the camp, tall, slightly hunched like a wood-cutter in his fur-skin; let his eyes wander, said little—but what he did say was exactly that which scorched your own tongue, and if he said the opposite, it seemed at once as though the opposite had been scorching your tongue. He smiled seldom and when he did smile he certainly had good reason, and it positively warmed your heart. He had little time, and when he came to sit with one group—say, the servants of Fannius or the herdsmen of Lucania—you did not make a fuss, but you were glad, and it seemed as though at last you knew why you were busy killing time on this mad mountain, instead of continuing your life according to reason, order, and your station in life.

When Castus ordered you to do something you obeyed because it was ill-advised to disagree with the Hyaenas. When Crixus issued a command, you obeyed because you shrank from the heavy, dismal man. But when Spartacus said anything you never dreamt of a contradiction—simply because none occurred to you. Where was the sense in wanting something different from Spartacus; did he not want exactly the same as everybody wanted?

It must, of course, not be forgotten that every one did want something different. One man wanted to stay here for ever and gorge his fill to the end of his days. Another wanted them all to march to Puteoli to burn his master's house with the master in it. A third wanted them all to conquer and take a ship on which to go to Alexandria where women were plentiful. A fourth wanted them to go to Capua, raze the city to the ground and erect a new one. A fifth wanted to make war on Rome. The sixth wanted to go home, to his flocks—what in hell had they come for? The seventh wanted to go to Sicily where the slaves had stood up to Rome once before. The eighth wanted to join the pirates of Cilicia, the ninth wanted communal wives, a tenth man wanted to enforce the prohibition of eating fish. Everybody wanted something different, and talked, quarreled or kept silence about it. But each one felt and knew that the man with the fur-skin who had nothing special about him, wanted exactly the same as he himself—that he was the common denominator of all their opposed hopes and desires—and nothing else.

But maybe that was the special thing about him.

The rains were approaching.

Half a month had passed since they vanquished Clodius Glaber; counted from the flight of the Seventy from Capua, nearly three had gone by.

Provisions were dwindling on Mount Vesuvius. Expeditions into the valleys yielded less and less; the entire district, including Herculaneum, Nola and Pompeii, had been laid waste. In a circuit of ten miles the plain of Campania, the paradise, lay bald and bare as though eaten by locusts. The cities were closed, their garrisons reinforced, and their walls repaired.

And still humanity came flocking up the mountain, bearded, ragged, with branding scars on their shoulders and sore feet. They plundered the estates on their way and avoided the towns. They brought scythes, shovels, hatchets, sticks. They were the dregs of the blessed country, the refuse that fertilized her fields: they stank and there was no health left in their bodies. They carried disease and bad habits into camp, brought a dower of hunger and nebulous hopes.

They were not kindly received. Those who had lived in the camp for ten days looked down on the three-day-olds, those who had come three days ago regarded themselves as old inmates and treated newcomers accordingly. People in the camp began to get bored; there they were, waiting, and did not know for what. They began to grumble, some went home. No one prevented them. Five thousand people lived on the mountain, spoke various languages, ate, argued, talked, quarrelled about booty or women, formed friendships, sang, killed one another. They were waiting, and knew not for what.

Even the gladiators were at variance over what should be done. They held meetings to which none but the Fifty were admitted, conferences preceded by mysterious preparations, held inside the crater. Fannius's servants had to fetch up many bags of wine before it commenced, and the gladiators wore important-looking faces like Senators, as they went to a conference. But nothing much was ever decided; for, each time they drew near to the question of what was to be done, it was evaded, unimportant subjects discussed, quarrel or laughter raised, and the necessity of coming to a decision forgotten.

Spartacus never took sides to the projects that sprouted up every day. In silence he listened to the others, and only towards the end, when everything threatened to be lost in confused back-chat, did he speak briefly on subordinate questions which could not be postponed: provisions, the sharing out of arms, camping sites for newcomers. He was never once contradicted, for his suggestions were sensible and simple; but all were disappointed as they expected him to supply the deciding cue, which he did not seem to notice.

Instead, he achieved the gradual re-formation of the divers groups into cohorts and centuries, with one gladiator at the head of each column. Then he told them of the ways in which the hunters of the Thracian mountains made their arms: round shields of wickerwork covered with fresh hide, and wooden lances whose points were hardened in fire. Finally he divided them up into categories: vanguard, reserves, and regular infantry; heavy cavalry with the armour and spears of the fallen Romans; light cavalry armed with swords and slings.

All of this took time; day followed day, hardly one without discord and killings; food supply diminished, and the rains approached ever closer.

But when two months had passed after the defeat of Clodius Glaber, he had accomplished it; from the shapeless clay on Mount Vesuvius he had moulded an army.

One fine day two months after the defeat of Clodius Glaber, the servants of Fannius went from one group to another with the same message: "Elect aldermen and representatives of every ten among you," they said, "and send them to the crater. A general meeting is going to be held."

Commotion went through the camp. The groups mingled, they voted, argued, conjectured, lapped up rumours. The camp had woken and shook the waiting off like a deep sleep.

An endless procession ascended the path leading to the rim of the cavity. Only aldermen and delegates of every ten were supposed to attend, but the entire camp crowded the path; the boldest climbed over naked rock. When they arrived at the summit, they beheld for the first time the inside crater with its charred rock and queer-shaped, corroded blocks of stone. They scurried down through loose pebbles and rubble, streamed together at the bottom, fidgeted excitedly and showed new-comers the memorials of the siege: the Thracian basin, the Celtic basin, the skeletons of the slaughtered mules. The sun sent harsh rays into the crater and on the growing multitude at the bottom, whom he melted into a piebald, sweating massive lump. Even the crater walls were studded with people; they sat on blackened rocks, clutching the tough mesh of wild vines which grew all over the rubble. Some littered the rim and looked down. Like a giant sea-shell, the crater sent a hollow buzzing up into the broiling air.

When Spartacus started to speak, his voice was drowned in the hum. Clothed in his fur-skin, he stood on a large, projecting tooth of rock half-way up the wall; with him were Crixus, and some of the gladiators and of Fannius's servants. The odour of the many became one odour, their expectation mobbed him as one expectation. Clumsily he raised his arm—immediately the gladiators and bull-necks behind him raised theirs, and silence descended. For the second time Spartacus began; the walls of the crater caught and amplified his voice.

"The rains are on their way," said Spartacus, "and food is getting scarce; we must have winter quarters."

"He's right," thought Hermios the shepherd, who huddled in the rubble on the other side. "That's just what worried me too," he thought, bared his teeth approvingly and looked at Spartacus on his rock, tall and very splendid in his fur-skin. His voice was not much louder than usual, and calm, as though he were speaking to the shepherd alone.

"Maybe the Romans will send another army," said Spartacus. "We must have a town for the winter, a town with walls around it, a town of our own."

That was not what he had meant to say. It was impossible to take a walled city without appropriate siege machines. Crixus who stood, fat and heavy, by his side, turned his head and looked at him cloudily. He knew that you could not take a city without siege-machinery, and those Five Thousand in the crater knew it as well.

But the Five Thousand were quiet, heard the wheezing breath of the Many, their own breath, smelled the smell of the Many, their own smell, and they knew that this man Spartacus up on his rock was right, and that everything became possible as soon as they willed it.

"A town," said Spartacus, "a town of houses and firm walls, a town of our own. Then, when the Romans come, they will break their heads against the walls of the town which belongs to us—a gladiators' town, a slaves' town."

Only now he felt the silence. He heard his own voice rebounding from every side of the crater. He heard the breath of the Many as one breath, as he felt the one expectation of the multitude.

"And the name of this Town shall be the Town of Slaves," said Spartacus and perceived his own alien voice resounding through the crater. "Remember that we'll get what we want and that no one will serve in our town. But maybe we will not have one town only, but many, a brotherhood of Slave Towns. Don't think I am just talking, for such a thing existed once before, a long, long time ago. It was called The Sun State . . ."

All the time he was thinking of the siege machines they did not have. They were what he meant to talk of, but he talked of the Sun State. As through a dancing hot veil he saw the Essene sitting on a stone opposite and wagging his head with the stern lips in listening. He saw Hermios the shepherd bare his teeth and stare. And the smell of the crowd was in his nostrils.

"Why should the strong serve the weak?" he roared at them, his arms suddenly flung high as though invisibly pulled up. "Why should the hard serve the soft, the Many serve the Few? We guard their cattle and drag the bloody calf out of its mother, but not into our herds. We build them ponds and may not bathe in them. We are the Many and are to serve the Few—why, tell me, why?"

Now he was no longer thinking of siege machinery, he listened to the words that spurted out of him from an unknown source; they became a stream which swirled around those in the crater, swallowing them in its whirlpool. The words frothed in their ears, and their eyes drank in the sight of the man in the fur-skin, sharply outlined against the bare wall of rock.

"We are the Many," said Spartacus, "and we have served them because we were blind and did not ask for reasons. But once we start asking they have no more power over us. And I tell you, when we start asking it is the end of them, and they rot away like the body of a man whose arms and legs have been sawed off. And we will go our own way and laugh at them. If we will it, all Italy will laugh, from Gaul to Tarentum and Africa. And behold, what laughter that will be, and what cries will go up before the Eastern Gate and what alarm at the other gates, what loud laments from the seven hills! For then they will be as nothing before us, and the walls of their cities will crumble without siege machinery."

He paused to listen in astonishment to the echo of his own words. Again the horde grew indistinct; all he saw was the bullet-headed Essene over on the other side, sitting on his stone, his head asway. Then the siege machines came back into his thoughts:

"Again I tell you: we must have a walled town, a town of our own. A town that is ours, whose walls protect us. But we have no siege machines . . ."

A wave of restlessness passed over the multitude. Those who were herded at the bottom shuffled and stirred, as though waking from a great enchanted silence, and testing their limbs.

". . . We have no siege machines, and it is not true that the walls of cities tumble on their own accord. But we will camp in front of their gates and through every gate and gap we will send our message to the serfs of the town, and will repeat and repeat it until the message fills their ears: 'The gladiators of Lentulus Batuatus of Capua want to ask you why the strong should serve the weak and the Many serve the Few.' This question will rain on them like stony hail from mighty catapults, and the serfs in the city will hear it, and they will raise their voices and unite their strength with ours. And then there will be no walls."

Now he could distinguish several women. From their eyes which never left him he saw that their breath went haltingly and that he touched them with his voice. And there the men stood, and if he wished it they would kill Crixus; and if he wished it they would start off.

He spoke of the distant beginnings of the horde, and how the Fifty became Five Thousand. He spoke of the anger of the fettered and oppressed which weighed down heavily over Italy, told them how this wrath had dug roads to roam like the brooks that spring forth from the pressure and sweat of the mountains. And how they, Lentulus's fifty gladiators, dug one broad bed for all the small angry brooks, so that they united in one mighty stream which drowned Glaber and his army. And how necessary it was to dam the flow and guide it, so its force might not be wasted. And that therefore they must conquer the first fortified town before the rains set in, how the brotherhood of Slave Towns would grow up in Italia; the great state of justice and goodwill, which will be called—and here he said it for the second time—which will be called the *Sun State*.

A PARABLE OF REVOLUTIONARY LEADERSHIP

Isaac Babel

"Line and Color"

I met Alexander Fyodorovich Kerensky for the first time on December 20, 1916, in the dining-room of the Olila Sanatorium.

We were introduced to one another by Zatzareny, the lawyer from Turkestan. All that I knew of Zatzareny was that he had had himself circumcised at the age of forty. The Grand Duke Nicholas Constantinovich, off his head, in disgrace and exiled to Tashkent, had made much of his friendship with the lawyer. This Grand Duke used to walk about the streets of Tashkent with his buttons undone. He had a Caucasian woman as wife; used to burn candles before the portrait of Voltaire as though it were an icon, and had arranged for an immense stretch of the Amur-Darya to be dried up. Zatzareny was his friend.

We were at the Olila, then. Ten kilometers away we could see the great blue lights of Helsingfors. O Helsingfors, dream of my heart! And thou, azure sky, dripping with light above the esplanade and losing thyself in the infinite!

So we were at the Olila. In vases flowers from the north were dying. Elk-horns blurred the somber ceiling. The dining-room smelled of pine trees, of the Countess Tyszkiewicz's fresh shoulders, and of the English officers' silk underwear.

At the table Kerensky was seated next to a converted Jew from the Police Department, an extremely polished individual. On his right Nikkelsen the Norwegian, owner of a whaler; close at hand the Countess Tyszkiewicz, beautiful as Marie Antoinette. When he had eaten three cakes, Kerensky rose and took me by the arm, and we went for a walk in the forest. *Fröken* Kirsti swept past us on skis.

"Who was that?" asked Alexander Fyodorovich.

"Nikkelsen's daughter Kirsti," I told him. "Good-looking, isn't she?"

Then old Johann drove past on his sledge.

"Who was that?"

"Old Johann," I said. "He carts fruit and brandy to Helsingfors. Is it possible you don't know Johann the sledge-driver?"

"I know everyone here," replied Kerensky, "but I can't distinguish one from t'other."

"You're shortsighted, eh?"

"Quite so."

"Alexander Fyodorovich, you ought to wear glasses."

"Never!"

Then, bubbling over like a mere boy, I said to him:

"Just think: you're not merely blind, you're practically dead! Line, that divine trait, mistress of the world, eternally escapes you. Here we are, you and I, walking about in this magic garden, this Finnish forest that almost baffles description. All our lives we shall never see anything more beautiful. And you can't see the pink edges of the frozen waterfall, over there by the stream! You are blind to the Japanese chiseling of the weeping willow leaning over the waterfall. The red trunks of the pines are covered by snow in which a thousand sparks are gleaming. The snow, shapeless when it fell, has draped itself along the branches, lying on their surfaces that undulate like a line drawn by Leonardo. In the snow flaming clouds are reflected. And think what you'd have to say about *Fröken* Kirsti's silk stockings; about the line of her leg, that lovely line! I beseech you, Alexander Fyodorovich, buy a pair of glasses!"

"My child," he replied, "don't waste your time. Forty copecks for spectacles are the only forty copecks I've no wish to squander. I don't need your line, vulgar as truth is vulgar. You live your life as though you were a teacher of trigonometry, while I for my part live in a world of miracles, even when I'm only at Klyazma. What do I need to see *Fröken* Kirsti's freckles for, if even when I can scarcely make her out I can see in her all I wish to see? What do I need Finnish clouds for, when above my head I see a moving ocean? What do I need line for, when I have color? To me the whole universe is a gigantic theater, and I am the only member of the audience who hasn't glued opera glasses to his eyes. The orchestra is playing the overture to the third act; the stage is far away, just as in a dream; my heart swells with ecstasy. I see Juliet's purple velvet, Romeo's lilac silk, and not a single false beard. And you want me to blind myself with forty-copeck spectacles!"

That evening I left for Helsingfors. O Helsingfors, refuge of my dreams!

Six months later I saw Alexander Fyodorovich once more; it was June 1917, and he was now supreme god of our armies and arbiter of our destinies.

That day the Troitsky bridge had been dismantled. The workers of the Putilov Factory were marching on the Arsenal. Streetcars lay like dead horses in the streets. A rally had been called at the House of the People, and there Alexander Fyodorovich made a speech about Russia—Russia, mystic mother and spouse. The animal passion of the crowd stifled him. Could he, the only member of the audience without opera glasses, see how their hackles were rising? I do not know. But after him Trotsky climbed to the speaker's tribune, twisted his mouth, and in an implacable voice began:

"Comrades!"

Chapter VIII

Political Economy

The interaction of economic and political ambition, of the pursuit of wealth and property and the pursuit of power—for which we have adopted the old phrase political economy—has long been a primary focus of both theoretical analysis and literary exploration. The state is, of course, an arena within which every sort of human purpose can be and has been acted out: The aspirations to be wealthy, to be powerful, to be good, to be loved, to be honored—none of these are alien to political men (as the selections on leadership show). But the obsession with money has a certain pride of place, not because it ranks first in the list of human passions, but because so many men have believed it to be—whole cultures have been based on the proposition that it is —the means to every other goal. Money is, as Karl Marx wrote, the universal pander, mediating between everyman and his most cherished dream. Shakespeare's Timon sums up its extraordinary powers: It can bring adoration to the ugly, a husband to the aging widow, honor to criminals. But precisely because it is a universal means to an endless number of ends, it becomes an end in itself and every other end becomes its means. If money is a way to buy beauty or power or celebrity, so all these are means to win riches.

Political power is one of the most important means to the acquisition of money and also one of the greatest threats to acquired wealth. Powerful men win from the state subsidies, grants, franchises, tax rebates, and endless opportunities for profitable investment. Other men, temporarily or permanently deprived of power, must deal as best they can with heavy taxation, forced loans, outright confiscation. An enormous amount of ordinary political activity can be explained in terms of one or both of these two processes, the pursuit and the defense of money and property. (This is so even though the most significant and critical political activities may well require some further or different explanation, a delicate analysis of the entanglements of all the passions and all the complex rationalizations of human desire.) Thus Gustave Flaubert's usual psychological subtlety is hardly needed in his quick sketch of the adjustment of the banker Dambreuse to the revolution of 1848. Dambreuse's decision to sponsor a candidate in the coming elections is a simple reflex of his fear for his property. Similarly, Theodore Dreiser's description of a financier's struggle to win a municipal franchise, though harsh, simplistic, and psychologically flat, is nevertheless realistic: Cowperwood is a political man, as he is a philanthropist, only in order to make money. If pressed, Cowperwood would doubtlessly claim public purposes, arguing that his activities are aimed at municipal improvement as well as self-enrichment. It would be an automatic or a casual argument, however, an obvious rationalization; for Cowperwood's idealism is intensely private, centered exclusively on himself.

But the power of money is strange. It can assume many shapes and give rise to the most extraordinary fantasies and the most intense public zeal and commitment. It can become a fetish, to be worshipped openly like a god—for are not the gods also universal means to all good things, and don't they sometimes require the most extreme sacrifices from their worshippers? Joseph Conrad's Nostromo is first and foremost a novel about imperialism, a subject directly relevant to the theme of political economy. But it is also a novel about the sheer power of money, vividly symbolized by the great San Tomé silver mine. The mine inspires, as Irving Howe has suggested, "a vision of nothing less than capitalism itself." Like capitalism, it promises wealth and peace of mind to everyone within its reach, yet somehow its aggrandizement serves only itself, robbing even its most devout votaries. The ultimate sense of the mine's frightening sovereignty comes not to some poor miner, but to Mrs. Gould, wife of the owner: "She saw the San Tomé mountain hanging over the Campo, over the whole land, feared, hated, wealthy, more soulless than any tyrant, more pitiless and autocratic than the worst government, ready to crush innumerable lives in the expansion of its greatness." But that vision comes only at the end of the novel. Our excerpt is from the beginning, when the mine is like a young god and Charles Gould its neophyte priest. "I pin my faith," he says, "to material interests." He hopes that business, above all the development of the mine, will bring security and order to the republic of Costaguana. In fact, Gould is ready to sacrifice every real human interest, including security and order, to that supposed embodiment of them all, the mine, which is simultaneously his property, his passion, and his master.

Not only in political economy do human inventions (like money) and possessions (property) take on an existence of their own and dominate over the men who use or own them. The same thing can happen in religious life—where it is called idolatry—and in politics—where it is called absolutism. The process as Conrad illustrates it, however, is the one best known in the West; and it is also, as his novel suggests, the one we have most successfully exported. But there is no need to suggest the many "San Tomé mines" around the world to which human interests have been sacrificed. Every reader can make his own list.

GOLD, GLITTERING GOLD

William Shakespeare

From *Timon of Athens*

ACT IV

Scene 3: [Woods and cave near the sea-shore.]

Enter TIMON IN THE WOODS [*from the Cave.*]

TIM. O blessed breeding sun, draw from the earth
Rotten humidity; below thy sister's orb
Infect the air! Twinn'd brothers of one womb,
Whose procreation, residence and birth,
Scarce is dividant, touch them with several fortunes,
The greater scorns the lesser: not nature,
To whom all sores lay siege, can bear great fortune
But by contempt of nature.
Raise me this beggar, and deny 't that lord,
The senator shall bear contempt hereditary,
The beggar native honour.
It is the pasture lards the rother's sides,
The want that makes him lean. Who dares, who dares,
In purity of manhood stand upright,
And say, "This man's a flatterer"? If one be,
So are they all; for every grize of fortune
Is smooth'd by that below: the learned pate
Ducks to the golden fool: all is oblique;
There's nothing level in our cursed natures
But direct villainy. Therefore, be abhorr'd
All feasts, societies, and throngs of men!
His semblance, yea, himself, Timon disdains:
Destruction fang mankind! Earth, yield me roots!

[*Digging.*]

Who seeks for better of thee, sauce his palate
With thy most operant poison! What is here?

Gold? yellow, glittering, precious gold? No, gods,
I am no idle votarist: roots, you clear heavens!
Thus much of this will make black white, foul fair,
Wrong right, base noble, old young, coward valiant.
Ha, you gods! why this? what this, you gods? Why, this
Will lug your priests and servants from your sides,
Pluck stout men's pillows from below their heads:
This yellow slave
Will knit and break religions; bless the accurs'd;
Make the hoar leprosy ador'd; place thieves,
And give them title, knee, and approbation,
With senators on the bench; this is it
That makes the wappen'd widow wed again;
She, whom the spital-house and ulcerous sores
Would cast the gorge at, this embalms and spices
To the April day again. Come, damned earth,
Thou common whore of mankind, that putt'st odds
Among the rout of nations, I will make thee
Do thy right nature. (March afar off.) Ha! a drum? thou'rt quick,
But yet I'll bury thee: thou'lt go, strong thief,
When gouty keepers of thee cannot stand:
Nay, stay thou out for earnest.

                                                [Keeping some gold.]

THE DEFENSE OF WEALTH

Gustave Flaubert

From *Sentimental Education*

Then Property rose in their regard to the level of Religion, and
was confounded with God. The attacks made on it appeared to them
a sacrilege; almost a species of cannibalism. In spite of the most
humane legislation that ever existed, the spectre of '93 reappeared,
and the chopper of the guillotine vibrated in every syllable of the
word "Republic," which did not prevent them from despising it for
its weakness. France, no longer feeling herself mistress of the situ-

From Ch. 14.

ation, was beginning to shriek with terror, like a blind man without his stick or an infant that had lost its nurse.

Of all Frenchmen, M. Dambreuse was the most alarmed. The new condition of things threatened his fortune, but, more than anything else, it deceived his experience. A system so good! a king so wise! was it possible? The ground was giving way beneath their feet! Next morning he dismissed three of his servants, sold his horses, bought a soft hat to go out into the streets, thought even of letting his beard grow; and he remained at home, prostrated, reading over and over again newspapers most hostile to his own ideas, and plunged into such a gloomy mood that even the jokes about the pipe of Flocon * had not the power to make him smile.

As a supporter of the last reign, he was dreading the vengeance of the people so far as concerned his estates in Champagne when Frederick's effusion fell into his hands. Then it occurred to his mind that his young friend was a very useful personage, and that he might be able, if not to serve him, at least to protect him, so that, one morning, M. Dambreuse presented himself at Frederick's residence, accompanied by Martinon.

This visit, he said, had no object save that of seeing him for a little while, and having a chat with him. In short, he rejoiced at the events that had happened, and with his whole heart adopted "our sublime motto, *Liberty, Equality, and Fraternity,*" having always been at bottom a Republican. If he voted under the other *régime* with the Ministry, it was simply in order to accelerate an inevitable downfall. He even inveighed against M. Guizot, "who has got us into a nice hobble, we must admit!" By way of retaliation, he spoke in an enthusiastic fashion about Lamartine, who had shown himself "magnificent, upon my word of honour, when, with reference to the red flag——"

"Yes, I know," said Frederick. After which he declared that his sympathies were on the side of the working-men.

"For, in fact, more or less, we are all working-men!" And he carried his impartiality so far as to acknowledge that Proudhon had a certain amount of logic in his views. "Oh, a great deal of logic, deuce take it!"

Then, with the disinterestedness of a superior mind, he chatted about the exhibition of pictures, at which he had seen Pellerin's work. He considered it original and well-painted.

Martinon backed up all he said with expressions of approval; and

* Editors' note: Flocon was a well-known member of the Ministry of the day.

likewise was of his opinion that it was necessary to rally boldly to
the side of the Republic. And he talked about the husbandman, his
father, and assumed the part of the peasant, the man of the people.
They soon came to the question of the elections for the National
Assembly, and the candidates in the arrondissement of La Fortelle.
The Opposition candidate had no chance.

"You should take his place!" said M. Dambreuse.

Frederick protested.

"But why not?" For he would obtain the suffrages of the Extrem-
ists owing to his personal opinions, and that of the Conservatives
on account of his family. "And perhaps also," added the banker,
with a smile, "thanks to my influence, in some measure."

Frederick urged as an obstacle that he did not know how to set
about it.

There was nothing easier if he only got himself recommended to
the patriots of the Aube by one of the clubs of the capital. All he
had to do was to read out, not a profession of faith such as might
be seen every day, but a serious statement of principles.

"Bring it to me; I know what goes down in the locality; and you
can, I say again, render great services to the country—to us all—to
myself."

In such times people ought to aid each other, and, if Frederick
had need of anything, he or his friends——

"Oh, a thousand thanks, my dear Monsieur!"

"You'll do as much for me in return, mind!"

Decidedly, the banker was a decent man.

CORRUPTION

Theodore Dreiser

From *The Titan*

It was plain that these rumors against Cowperwood in New York,
unless offset promptly by favorable events in Chicago, might mean
—in the large banking quarters, anyhow—the refusal of all subse-

quent Cowperwood issues. It might even close the doors of minor banks and make private investors nervous.

Addison's report of all this annoyed Cowperwood no little. It made him angry. He saw in it the work of Schryhart, Hand, and others who were trying their best to discredit him. "Let them talk," he declared, crossly. "I have the street-railways. They're not going to rout me out of here. I can sell stocks and bonds to the public direct if need be! There are plenty of private people who are glad to invest in these properties."

At this psychological moment enter, as by the hand of Fate, the planet Mars and the University. This latter, from having been for years a humble Baptist college of the cheapest character, had suddenly, through the beneficence of a great Standard Oil multimillionaire, flared upward into a great university, and was causing a stir throughout the length and breadth of the educational world. It was already a most noteworthy spectacle, one of the sights of the city. Millions were being poured into it; new and beautiful buildings were almost monthly erected. A brilliant, dynamic man had been called from the East as president. There were still many things needed—dormitories, laboratories of one kind and another, a great library; and, last but not least, a giant telescope—one that would sweep the heavens with a hitherto unparalleled receptive eye, and wring from it secrets not previously decipherable by the eye and the mind of man.

Cowperwood had always been interested in the heavens and in the giant mathematical and physical methods of interpreting them. It so happened that the war-like planet, with its sinister aspect, was just at this time to be seen hanging in the west, a fiery red; and the easily aroused public mind was being stirred to its shallow depth by re-reflections and speculations regarding the famous canals of the luminary. The mere thought of the possibility of a larger telescope than any now in existence, which might throw additional light on this evasive mystery, was exciting not only Chicago, but the whole world. Late one afternoon Cowperwood, looking over some open fields which faced his new power-house in West Madison Street, observed the planet hanging low and lucent in the evening sky, a warm, radiant bit of orange in a sea of silver. He paused and surveyed it. Was it true that there were canals on it, and people? Life was surely strange.

One day not long after this Alexander Rambaud called him up on the 'phone and remarked, jocosely:

"I say, Cowperwood, I've played a rather shabby trick on you just now. Doctor Hooper, of the University, was in here a few minutes ago asking me to be one of ten to guarantee the cost of a telescope lens that he thinks he needs to run that one-horse school of his out there. I told him I thought you might possibly be interested. His idea is to find some one who will guarantee forty thousand dollars, or eight or ten men who will guarantee four or five thousand each. I thought of you, because I've heard you discuss astronomy from time to time."

"Let him come," replied Cowperwood, who was never willing to be behind others in generosity, particularly where his efforts were likely to be appreciated in significant quarters.

Shortly afterward appeared the doctor himself—short, rotund, rubicund, displaying behind a pair of clear, thick, gold-rimmed glasses, round, dancing, incisive eyes. Imaginative grip, buoyant, self-delusive self-respect were written all over him. The two men eyed each other—one with that broad-gage examination which sees even universities as futile in the endless shift of things; the other with that faith in the balance for right which makes even great personal forces, such as financial magnates, serve an idealistic end.

"It's not a very long story I have to tell you, Mr. Cowperwood," said the doctor. "Our astronomical work is handicapped just now by the simple fact that we have no lens at all, no telescope worthy of the name. I should like to see the University do original work in this field, and do it in a great way. The only way to do it, in my judgment, is to do it better than any one else can. Don't you agree with me?" He showed a row of shining white teeth.

Cowperwood smiled urbanely.

"Will a forty-thousand-dollar lens be a better lens than any other lens?" he inquired.

"Made by Appleman Brothers, of Dorchester, it will," replied the college president. "The whole story is here, Mr. Cowperwood. These men are practical lens-makers. A great lens, in the first place, is a matter of finding a suitable crystal. Large and flawless crystals are not common, as you may possibly know. Such a crystal has recently been found, and is now owned by Mr. Appleman. It takes about four or five years to grind and polish it. Most of the polishing, as you may or may not know, is done by the hand—smoothing it with the thumb and forefinger. The time, judgment, and skill of an optical expert is required. To-day, unfortunately, that is not cheap. The laborer is worthy of his hire, however, I suppose"—he waved a soft, full, white hand—"and forty thousand is little enough. It would be a great honor if the University could have the largest, most serviceable, and most perfect lens in the world. It would reflect great credit, I take it, on the men who would make this possible."

Cowperwood liked the man's artistically educational air; obviously here was a personage of ability, brains, emotion, and scientific enthusiasm. It was splendid to him to see any strong man in earnest, for himself or others.

"And forty thousand will do this?" he asked.

"Yes, sir. Forty thousand will guarantee us the lens, anyhow."

"And how about land, buildings, a telescope frame? Have you all those things prepared for it?"

"Not as yet, but, since it takes four years at least to grind the lens, there will be time enough, when the lens is nearing completion, to look after the accessories. We have picked our site, however—Lake Geneva—and we would not refuse either land or accessories if we knew where to get them."

Again the even, shining teeth, the keen eyes boring through the glasses.

Cowperwood saw a great opportunity. He asked what would be the cost of the entire project. Dr. Hooper presumed that three hundred thousand would do it all handsomely—lens, telescope, land machinery, building—a great monument.

"And how much have you guaranteed on the cost of your lens?"

"Sixteen thousand dollars, so far."

"To be paid when?"

"In instalments—ten thousand a year for four years. Just enough to keep the lens-maker busy for the present."

Cowperwood reflected. Ten thousand a year for four years would be a mere salary item, and at the end of that time he felt sure that he could supply the remainder of the money quite easily. He would be so much richer; his plans would be so much more mature. On such a repute (the ability to give a three-hundred-thousand-dollar telescope out of hand to be known as the Cowperwood telescope) he could undoubtedly raise money in London, New York, and elsewhere for his Chicago enterprise. The whole world would know him in a day. He paused, his enigmatic eyes revealing nothing of the splendid vision that danced before them. At last! At last!

"How would it do, Mr. Hooper," he said, sweetly, "if, instead of ten men giving you four thousand each, as you plan, one man were to give you forty thousand in annual instalments of ten thousand each? Could that be arranged as well?"

"My dear Mr. Cowperwood," exclaimed the doctor, glowing, his eyes alight, "do I understand that you personally might wish to give the money for this lens?"

"I might, yes. But I should have to exact one pledge, Mr. Hooper, if I did any such thing."

"And what would that be?"

"The privilege of giving the land and the building—the whole telescope, in fact. I presume no word of this will be given out unless the matter is favorably acted upon?" he added, cautiously and diplomatically.

The new president of the university arose and eyed him with a peculiarly approbative and grateful gaze. He was a busy, over-worked man. His task was large. Any burden taken from his shoulders in this fashion was a great relief.

"My answer to that, Mr. Cowperwood, if I had the authority, would be to agree now in the name of the University, and thank you. For form's sake, I must submit the matter to the trustees of the University, but I have no doubt as to the outcome. I anticipate nothing but grateful approbation. Let me thank you again."

They shook hands warmly, and the solid collegian bustled forth. Cowperwood sank quietly in his chair. He pressed his fingers together, and for a moment or two permitted himself to dream. Then he called a stenographer and began a bit of dictation. He did not care to think even to himself how universally advantageous all this might yet prove to be.

The result was that in the course of a few weeks the proffer was formally accepted by the trustees of the University, and a report of the matter, with Cowperwood's formal consent, was given out for publication. The fortuitous combination of circumstances already described gave the matter a unique news value. Giant reflectors and refractors had been given and were in use in other parts of the world, but none so large or so important as this. The gift was sufficient to set Cowperwood forth in the light of a public benefactor and patron of science. Not only in Chicago, but in London, Paris, and New York; wherever, indeed, in the great capitals scientific and intellectual men were gathered, this significant gift of an apparently fabulously rich American became the subject of excited discussion. Banking men, among others, took sharp note of the donor, and when Cowperwood's emissaries came around later with a suggestion that the fifty-year franchises about to be voted him for elevated roads should be made a basis of bond and mortgage loans, they were courteously received. A man who could give three-hundred-thousand-dollar telescopes in the hour of his greatest difficulties must be in a rather satisfactory financial condition. He must have great wealth in reserve. After some preliminaries, during which Cowperwood paid a flying visit to Threadneedle Street in London, and to Wall Street in New York, an arrangement was made with an English-American banking company by which the majority of the bonds for his proposed roads were taken over by them for sale in Europe and elsewhere, and he was given ample means wherewith to proceed. Instantly the stocks of his surface lines bounded in price, and those who had been scheming to bring about Cowperwood's downfall gnashed impotent teeth. Even Haeckelheimer & Co. were interested.

Anson Merrill, who had only a few weeks before given a large field for athletic purposes to the University, pulled a wry face over this sudden eclipse of his glory. Hosmer Hand, who had given a chemical laboratory, and Schryhart, who had presented a dormitory, were depressed to think that a benefaction less costly than theirs should create, because of the distinction of the idea, so much more notable comment. It was merely another example of the brilliant fortune which seemed to pursue the man, the star that set all their plans at defiance.

. . .

The money requisite for the construction of elevated roads having been thus pyrotechnically obtained, the acquisition of franchises remained no easy matter. It involved, among other problems, the taming of Chaffee Thayer Sluss, who, quite unconscious of the evidence stored up against him, had begun to fulminate the moment it was suggested in various secret political quarters that a new ordinance was about to be introduced, and that Cowperwood was to be the beneficiary. "Don't you let them do that, Mr. Sluss," observed Mr. Hand, who for purposes of conference had courteously but firmly bidden his hireling, the mayor, to lunch. "Don't you let them pass that if you can help it." (As chairman or president of the city council Mr. Sluss held considerable manipulative power over the machinery of procedure.) "Raise such a row that they won't try to pass it over your head. Your political future really depends on it—your standing with the people of Chicago. The newspapers and the respectable financial and social elements will fully support you in this. Otherwise they will wholly desert you. Things have come to a handsome pass when men sworn and elected to perform given services turn on their backers and betray them in this way!"

Mr. Hand was very wroth.

Mr. Sluss, immaculate in black broadcloth and white linen, was very sure that he would fulfill to the letter all of Mr. Hand's suggestions. The proposed ordinance should be denounced by him; its legislative progress heartily opposed in council.

"They shall get no quarter from me!" he declared, emphatically. "I know what the scheme is. They know that I know it."

He looked at Mr. Hand quite as one advocate of righteousness should look at another, and the rich promoter went away satisfied that the reins of government were in safe hands. Immediately afterward Mr. Sluss gave out an interview in which he served warning on all aldermen and councilmen that no such ordinance as the one in question would ever be signed by him as mayor.

At half past ten on the same morning on which the interview appeared—the hour at which Mr. Sluss usually reached his office—his private telephone bell rang, and an assistant inquired if he would be willing to speak with Mr. Frank A. Cowperwood. Mr. Sluss, somehow anticipating fresh laurels of victory, gratified by the front-page display given his announcement in the morning papers, and swelling internally with civic pride, announced, solemnly: "Yes; connect me."

"Mr. Sluss," began Cowperwood, at the other end, "this is Frank A. Cowperwood."

"Yes. What can I do for you, Mr. Cowperwood?"

"I see by the morning papers that you state that you will have nothing to do with any proposed ordinance which looks to giving me a franchise for any elevated road on the North or West Side?"

"That is quite true," replied Mr. Sluss, loftily. "I will not."

"Don't you think it is rather premature, Mr. Sluss, to denounce something which has only a rumored existence?" (Cowperwood, smiling sweetly to himself, was quite like a cat playing with an unsuspicious mouse.) "I should like very much to talk this whole matter over with you personally before you take an irrevocable attitude. It is just possible that after you have heard my side you

may not be so completely opposed to me. From time to time I have
sent to you several of my personal friends, but apparently you do
not care to receive them."

"Quite true," replied Mr. Sluss, loftily; "but you must remember
that I am a very busy man, Mr. Cowperwood, and, besides, I do
not see how I can serve any of your purposes. You are working for
a set of conditions to which I am morally and temperamentally
opposed. I am working for another. I do not see that we have any
common ground on which to meet. In fact, I do not see how I can
be of any service to you whatsoever."

"Just a moment, please, Mr. Mayor," replied Cowperwood, still
very sweetly, and fearing that Sluss might choose to hang up the receiver, so superior was his tone. "There may be some common ground
of which you do not know. Wouldn't you like to come to lunch at
my residence or receive me at yours? Or let me come to your office
and talk this matter over. I believe you will find it the part of wisdom as well as of courtesy to do this."

"I cannot possibly lunch with you to-day," replied Sluss, "and I
cannot see you, either. There are a number of things pressing for my
attention. I must say also that I cannot hold any back-room conferences with you or your emissaries. If you come you must submit to
the presence of others."

"Very well, Mr. Sluss," replied Cowperwood, cheerfully. "I will
not come to your office. But unless you come to mine before five
o'clock this afternoon you will face by noon to-morrow a suit for
breach of promise, and your letters to Mrs. Brandon will be given
to the public. I wish to remind you that an election is coming on,
and that Chicago favors a mayor who is privately moral as well as
publicly so. Good morning."

Mr. Cowperwood hung up his telephone receiver with a click, and
Mr. Sluss sensibly and visibly stiffened and paled. Mrs. Brandon!
The charming, lovable, discreet Mrs. Brandon who had so ungen-
erously left him! Why should she be thinking of suing him for breach
of promise, and how did his letters to her come to be in Cowperwood's hands? Good heavens—those mushy letters! His wife! His
children! His church and the owlish pastor thereof! Chicago! And
its conventional, moral, religious atmosphere! Come to think of it,
Mrs. Brandon had scarcely if ever written him a note of any kind.
He did not even know her history.

At the thought of Mrs. Sluss—her hard, cold, blue eyes—Mr. Sluss
arose, tall and distrait, and ran his hand through his hair. He walked

to the window, snapping his thumb and middle finger and looking eagerly at the floor. He thought of the telephone switchboard just outside his private office, and wondered whether his secretary, a handsome young Presbyterian girl, had been listening, as usual. Oh, this sad, sad world! If the North Side ever learned of this—Hand, the newspapers, young MacDonald—would they protect him? They would not. Would they run him for mayor again? Never! Could the public be induced to vote for him with all the churches fulminating against private immorality, hypocrites, and whited sepulchers? Oh, Lord! Oh, Lord! And he was so very, very much respected and looked up to—that was the worst of it all. This terrible demon Cowperwood had descended on him, and he had thought himself so secure. He had not even been civil to Cowperwood. What if the latter chose to avenge the discourtesy?

Mr. Sluss went back to his chair, but he could not sit in it. He went for his coat, took it down, hung it up again, took it down, announced over the 'phone that he could not see any one for several hours, and went out by a private door. Wearily he walked along North Clark Street, looking at the hurly-burly of traffic, looking at the dirty, crowded river, looking at the sky and smoke and gray buildings, and wondering what he should do. The world was so hard at times; it was so cruel. His wife, his family, his political career. He could not conscientiously sign any ordinances for Mr. Cowperwood—that would be immoral, dishonest, a scandal to the city. Mr. Cowperwood was a notorious traitor to the public welfare. At the same time he could not very well refuse, for here was Mrs. Brandon, the charming and unscrupulous creature, playing into the hands of Cowperwood. If he could only meet her, beg of her, plead; but where was she? He had not seen her for months and months. Could he go to Hand and confess all? But Hand was a hard, cold, moral man also. Oh, Lord! O, Lord! He wondered and thought, and sighed and pondered—all without avail.

Pity the poor earthling caught in the toils of the moral law. In another country, perhaps, in another day, another age, such a situation would have been capable of a solution, one not utterly destructive to Mr. Sluss, and not entirely favorable to a man like Cowperwood. But here in the United States, here in Chicago, the ethical verities would all, as he knew, be lined up against him. What Lake View would think, what his pastor would think, what Hand and all his moral associates would think—ah, these were the terrible, the incontrovertible consequences of his lapse from virtue.

At four o'clock, after Mr. Sluss had wandered for hours in the snow and cold, belaboring himself for a fool and a knave, and while Cowperwood was sitting at his desk signing papers, contemplating a glowing fire, and wondering whether the mayor would deem it advisable to put in an appearance, his office door opened and one of his trim stenographers entered announcing Mr. Chaffee Thayer Sluss. Enter Mayor Sluss, sad, heavy, subdued, shrunken, a very different gentleman from the one who had talked so cavalierly over the wires some five and a half hours before. Gray weather, severe cold, and much contemplation of seemingly irreconcilable facts had reduced his spirits greatly. He was a little pale and a little restless. Mental distress has a reducing, congealing effect, and Mayor Sluss seemed somewhat less than his usual self in height, weight, and thickness. Cowperwood had seen him more than once on various political platforms, but he had never met him. When the troubled mayor entered he arose courteously and waved him to a chair.

"Sit down, Mr. Sluss," he said, genially. "It's a disagreeable day out, isn't it? I suppose you have come in regard to the matter we were discussing this morning?"

Nor was this cordiality wholly assumed. One of the primal instincts of Cowperwood's nature—for all his chicane and subtlety—was to take no rough advantage of a beaten enemy. In the hour of victory he was always courteous, bland, gentle, and even sympathetic; he was so to-day, and quite honestly, too.

Mayor Sluss put down the high sugar-loaf hat he wore and said, grandiosely, as was his manner even in the direst extremity: "Well, you see, I am here, Mr. Cowperwood. What is it you wish me to do, exactly?"

"Nothing unreasonable, I assure you, Mr. Sluss," replied Cowperwood. "Your manner to me this morning was a little brusque, and, as I have always wanted to have a sensible private talk with you, I took this way of getting it. I should like you to dismiss from your mind at once the thought that I am going to take an unfair advantage of you in any way. I have no present intention of publishing your correspondence with Mrs. Brandon." (As he said this he took from his drawer a bundle of letters which Mayor Sluss recognized at once as the enthusiastic missives which he had some time before penned to the fair Claudia. Mr. Sluss groaned as he beheld this incriminating evidence.) "I am not trying," continued Cowperwood, "to wreck your career, nor to make you do anything which you do

not feel that you can conscientiously undertake. The letters that I
have here, let me say, have come to me quite by accident. I did not
seek them. But, since I do have them, I thought I might as well mention them as a basis for a possible talk and compromise between us."

Cowperwood did not smile. He merely looked thoughtfully at
Sluss; then, by way of testifying to the truthfulness of what he had
been saying, thumped the letters up and down, just to show that they
were real.

"Yes," said Mr. Sluss, heavily, "I see."

He studied the bundle—a small, solid affair—while Cowperwood
looked discreetly elsewhere. He contemplated his own shoes, the
floor. He rubbed his hands and then his knees.

Cowperwood saw how completely he had collapsed. It was ridiculous, pitiable.

"Come, Mr. Sluss," said Cowperwood, amiably, "cheer up. Things
are not nearly as desperate as you think. I give you my word right
now that nothing which you yourself, on mature thought, could say
was unfair will be done. You are the mayor of Chicago. I am a citizen.
I merely wish fair play from you. I merely ask you to give me your
word of honor that from now on you will take no part in this fight
which is one of pure spite against me. If you cannot conscientiously
aid me in what I consider to be a perfectly legitimate demand for
additional franchises, you will, at least, not go out of your way to
publicly attack me. I will put these letters in my safe, and there they
will stay until the next campaign is over, when I will take them out
and destroy them. I have no personal feeling against you—none in
the world. I do not ask you to sign any ordinance which the council
may pass giving me elevated-road rights. What I do wish you to
do at this time is to refrain from stirring up public sentiment against
me, especially if the council should see fit to pass an ordinance over
your veto. Is that satisfactory?"

"But my friends? The public? The Republican party? Don't you
see it is expected of me that I should wage some form of campaign
against you?" queried Sluss, nervously.

"No, I don't," replied Cowperwood, succinctly, "and, anyhow,
there are ways and ways of waging a public campaign. Go through
the motions, if you wish, but don't put too much heart in it. And,
anyhow, see some one of my lawyers from time to time when they
call on you. Judge Dickensheets is an able and fair man. So is General Van Sickle. Why not confer with them occasionally?—not pub-

licly, of course, but in some less conspicuous way. You will find both of them most helpful."

Cowperwood smiled encouragingly, quite beneficently, and Chaffee Thayer Sluss, his political hopes gone glimmering, sat and mused for a few moments in a sad and helpless quandary.

"Very well," he said, at last, rubbing his hands feverishly. "It is what I might have expected. I should have known. There is no other way, but—" Hardly able to repress the hot tears now burning beneath his eyelids, the Hon. Mr. Sluss picked up his hat and left the room. Needless to add that his preachings against Cowperwood were permanently silenced.

THE FETISHISM OF PROPERTY

Joseph Conrad

"The Silver of the Mine"

Mrs. Gould knew the history of the San Tomé mine. Worked in the early days mostly by means of lashes on the backs of slaves, its yield had been paid for in its own weight of human bones. Whole tribes of Indians had perished in the exploitation; and then the mine was abandoned, since with this primitive method it had ceased to make a profitable return, no matter how many corpses were thrown into its maw. Then it became forgotten. It was rediscovered after the war of independence. An English company obtained the right to work it, and found so rich a vein that neither the exactions of successive governments, nor the periodical raids of recruiting officers upon the population of paid miners they had created, could discourage their perseverance. But in the end, during the long turmoil of pronunciamentos that followed the death of the famous Guzmán Bento, the native miners, incited to revolt by the emissaries sent out from the capital, had risen upon their English chiefs and murdered them to a man. The decree of confiscation which appeared immediately afterwards in the *Diario Oficial*, published in Santa Marta, began with the words:

From *Nostromo*, Ch. VI. Reprinted by permission of J. M. Dent & Sons Ltd.; Publishers; Doubleday & Co.; and the Trustees of the Joseph Conrad Estate.

> Justly incensed at the grinding oppression of foreigners, actuated
> by sordid motives of gain rather than by love for a country where
> they come impoverished to seek their fortunes, the mining popula-
> tion of San Tomé, etc. . . .

and ended with the declaration:

> The chief of the state has resolved to exercise to the full his power
> of clemency. The mine, which by every law, international, human,
> and divine, reverts now to the government as national property,
> shall remain closed till the sword drawn for the sacred defence of
> liberal principles has accomplished its mission of securing the hap-
> piness of our beloved country.

And for many years this was the last of the San Tomé mine. What
advantage that government had expected from the spoliation, it is
impossible to tell now. Costaguana was made with difficulty to pay
a beggarly money compensation to the families of the victims, and
then the matter dropped out of diplomatic despatches. But afterwards another government bethought itself of that valuable asset.
It was an ordinary Costaguana government—the fourth in six years—
but it judged of its opportunities sanely. It remembered the San
Tomé mine with a secret conviction of its worthlessness in their own
hands, but with an ingenious insight into the various uses a silver
mine can be put to, apart from the sordid process of extracting the
metal from under the ground. The father of Charles Gould, for a
long time one of the most wealthy merchants of Costaguana, had
already lost a considerable part of his fortune in forced loans to the
successive governments. He was a man of calm judgment, who never
dreamed of pressing his claims; and when, suddenly, the perpetual
concession of the San Tomé mine was offered to him in full settlement, his alarm became extreme. He was versed in the ways of governments. Indeed, the intention of this affair, though no doubt deeply
meditated in the closet, lay open on the surface of the document
presented urgently for his signature. The third and most important
clause stipulated that the concession-holder should pay at once to
the government five years' royalties on the estimated output of the
mine.

Mr. Gould, senior, defended himself from this fatal favour with
many arguments and entreaties, but without success. He knew nothing of mining; he had no means to put his concession on the European market; the mine as a working concern did not exist. The buildings had been burnt down, the mining plant had been destroyed, the
mining population had disappeared from the neighourhood years

and years ago; the very road had vanished under a flood of tropical vegetation as effectually as if swallowed by the sea; and the main Gallery had fallen in within a hundred yards from the entrance. It was no longer an abandoned mine; it was a wild, inaccessible, and rocky gorge of the sierra, where vestiges of charred timber, some heaps of smashed bricks, and a few shapeless pieces of rusty iron could have been found under the matted mass of thorny creepers covering the ground. Mr. Gould, senior, did not desire the perpetual possession of that desolate locality; in fact, the mere vision of it arising before his mind in the still watches of the night had the power to exasperate him into hours of hot and agitated insomnia.

It so happened, however, that the finance minister of the time was a man to whom, in years gone by, Mr. Gould had, unfortunately, declined to grant some small pecuniary assistance, basing his refusal on the ground that the applicant was a notorious gambler and cheat, besides being more than half suspected of a robbery with violence on a wealthy ranchero in a remote country district, where he was actually exercising the function of a judge. Now, after reaching his exalted position, that politician had proclaimed his intention to repay evil with good to Señor Gould—the poor man. He affirmed and reaffirmed this resolution in the drawing rooms of Santa Marta, in a soft and implacable voice, and with such malicious glances that Mr. Gould's best friends advised him earnestly to attempt no bribery to get the matter dropped. It would have been useless. Indeed, it would not have been a very safe proceeding. Such was also the opinion of a stout, loud-voiced lady of French extraction, the daughter, she said, of an officer of high rank (*officier supérieur de l'armée*), who was accommodated with lodgings within the walls of a secularized convent next door to the ministry of finance. That florid person, when approached on behalf of Mr. Gould in a proper manner, and with a suitable present, shook her head despondently. She was good-natured, and her despondency was genuine. She imagined she could not take money in consideration of something she could not accomplish. The friend of Mr. Gould, charged with the delicate mission, used to say afterwards that she was the only honest person closely or remotely connected with the government he had ever met. "No go," she had said with a cavalier, husky intonation which was natural to her, and using turns of expression more suitable to a child of parents unknown than to the orphaned daughter of a general officer. "No; it's no go. *Pas moyen, mon garçon. C'est dommage, tout de même. Ah!*

zut! Je ne vole pas mon monde. Je ne suis pas ministre—moi! Vous pouvez emporter votre petit sac."

For a moment, biting her carmine lip, she deplored inwardly the tyranny of the rigid principles governing the sale of her influence in high places. Then, significantly, and with a touch of impatience, "*Allez,*" she added, "*et dites bien à votre bonhomme—entendez-vous? —qu'il faut avaler la pilule.*"

After such a warning there was nothing for it but to sign and pay. Mr. Gould had swallowed the pill, and it was as though it had been compounded of some subtle poison that acted directly on his brain. He became at once mine-ridden, and as he was well read in light literature it took to his mind the form of the Old Man of the Sea fastened upon his shoulders. He also began to dream of vampires. Mr. Gould exaggerated to himself the disadvantages of his new position, because he viewed it emotionally. His position in Costaguana was no worse than before. But man is a desperately conservative creature, and the extravagant novelty of this outrage upon his purse distressed his sensibilities. Everybody around him was being robbed by the grotesque and murderous bands that played their game of governments and revolutions after the death of Guzmán Bento. His experience had taught him that, however short the plunder might fall of their legitimate expectations, no gang in possession of the presidential palace would be so incompetent as to suffer itself to be baffled by the want of a pretext. The first casual colonel of the barefooted army of scarecrows that came along was able to expose with force and precision to any mere civilian his titles to a sum of ten-thousand dollars; the while his hope would be immutably fixed upon a gratuity, at any rate, of no less than a thousand. Mr. Gould knew that very well, and, armed with resignation, had waited for better times. But to be robbed under the forms of legality and bus - ness was intolerable to his imagination. Mr. Gould, the father, had one fault in his sagacious and honourable character: he attached too much importance to form. It is a failing common to mankind, whose views are tinged by prejudices. There was for him in that affair a malignancy of perverted justice which, by means of a moral shock, attacked his vigorous physique. "It will end by killing me," he used to affirm many times a day. And, in fact, since that time he began to suffer from fever, from liver pains, and mostly from a worrying inability to think of anything else. The finance minister could have formed no conception of the profound subtlety of his revenge. Even Mr. Gould's letters to his fourteen-year-old boy Charles, then away in England for his education, came at last to talk of practically nothing but the mine. He groaned over the injustice, the persecution, the outrage of that mine; he occupied whole pages in the exposition of the fatal consequences attaching to the possession of that mine from every point of view, with every dismal inference, with words of horror at the apparently eternal character of that curse. For the Concession had been granted to him and his descendants for ever. He implored his son never to return to Costaguana, never to claim any part of his inheritance there, because it was tainted by the infamous Concession; never to touch it, never to approach it, to forget that America existed, and pursue a mercantile career in Europe. And each letter ended with bitter self-reproaches for having stayed too long in that cavern of thieves, intriguers, and brigands.

To be told repeatedly that one's future is blighted because of the possession of a silver mine is not, at the age of fourteen, a matter of prime importance as to its main statement, but in its form it is calculated to excite a certain amount of wonder and attention. In course of time the boy, at first only puzzled by the angry jeremiads, but rather sorry for his dad, began to turn the matter over in his mind in such moments as he could spare from play and study. In about a year he had evolved from the lecture of the letters a definite conviction that there was a silver mine in the Sulaco province of the republic of Costaguana, where poor Uncle Harry had been shot by soldiers a great many years before. There was also connected closely with that mine a thing called the "iniquitous Gould Concession," apparently written on a paper which his father desired ardently to "tear and fling into the faces" of presidents, members of judicature, and ministers of state. And this desire persisted, though the names of these people, he noticed, seldom remained the same for a whole year together. This desire (since the thing was iniquitous) seemed quite natural to the boy, though why the affair was iniquitous he did not know. Afterwards, with advancing wisdom, he managed to clear the plain truth of the business from the fantastic intrusions of the Old Man of the Sea, vampires, and ghouls, which had lent to his father's correspondence the flavour of a gruesome Arabian Nights tale. In the end, the growing youth attained to as close an intimacy with the San Tomé mine as the old man who wrote these plaintive and enraged letters on the other side of the sea. He had been made several times already to pay heavy fines for neglecting to work the mine, he reported, besides other sums extracted from him on account of future royalties, on the ground that a man with such a valuable concession in his pocket could not refuse his financial assistance to the government of the republic. The last of his fortune was passing away from him against worthless receipts, he wrote, in a rage, whilst he was being pointed out as an individual who had known how to secure enormous advantages from the necessities of his country. And the young man in Europe grew more and more interested in that thing which could provoke such a tumult of words and passion.

He thought of it every day; but he thought of it without bitterness. It might have been an unfortunate affair for his poor dad, and the whole story threw a queer light upon the social and political life of Costaguana. The view he took of it was sympathetic to his father, yet calm and reflective. His personal feelings had not been outraged, and it is difficult to resent with proper and durable indignation the physical or mental anguish of another organism, even if that other organism is one's own father. By the time he was twenty Charles Gould had, in his turn, fallen under the spell of the San Tomé mine. But it was another form of enchantment, more suitable to his youth, into whose magic formula there entered hope, vigour, and self-confidence, instead of weary indignation and despair. Left after he was twenty to his own guidance (except for the severe injunction not to return to Costaguana), he had pursued his studies in Belgium and France with the idea of qualifying for a mining engineer. But this scientific aspect of his labours remained vague and imperfect in his mind. Mines had acquired for him a dramatic interest. He studied their peculiarities from a personal point of view, too, as one would study the varied characters of men. He visited them as one goes with curiosity to call upon remarkable persons. He visited mines in Germany, in Spain, in Cornwall. Abandoned workings had for him strong fascination. Their desolation appealed to him like the sight of human misery, whose causes are varied and profound. They might have been worthless, but also they might have been misunderstood. His future wife was the first, and perhaps the only person to detect this secret mood which governed the profoundly sensible, almost voiceless attitude of this man towards the world of material things. And at once her delight in him, lingering with half-open wings like those birds that cannot rise easily from a flat level, found a pinnacle from which to soar up into the skies.

They had become acquainted in Italy, where the future Mrs. Gould was staying with an old and pale aunt who, years before, had married a middle-aged, impoverished Italian marquis. She now mourned that man, who had known how to give up his life to the independence and unity of his country, who had known how to be as enthusiastic in his generosity as the youngest of those who fell for that very cause of which old Giorgio Viola was a drifting relic, as a broken spar is suffered to float away disregarded after a naval victory. The *marchesa* led a still, whispering existence, nunlike in her black robes and a white band over the forehead, in a corner of the first floor of an ancient and ruinous palace, whose big, empty halls downstairs sheltered under their painted ceilings the harvests, the fowls, and even the cattle, together with the whole family of the tenant farmer.

The two young people had met in Lucca. After that meeting Charles Gould visited no mines, though they went together in a carriage, once, to see some marble quarries, where the work resembled mining insofar that it also was the tearing of the raw material of treasure from the earth. Charles Gould did not open his heart to her in any set speeches. He simply went on acting and thinking in her sight. This is the true method of sincerity. One of his frequent remarks was, "I think sometimes that poor father takes a wrong view of that San Tomé business." And they discussed that opinion long and earnestly, as if they could influence a mind across half the globe; but in reality they discussed it because the sentiment of love can enter into any subject and live ardently in remote phrases. For this natural reason these discussions were precious to Mrs. Gould in her engaged state. Charles feared that Mr. Gould, senior, was wasting his strength and making himself ill by his efforts to get rid of the Concession. "I fancy that this is not the kind of handling it requires," he mused aloud, as if to himself. And when she wondered frankly that a man of character should devote his energies to plotting and intrigues, Charles would remark, with a gentle concern that understood her wonder, "You must not forget that he was born there."

She would set her quick mind to work upon that, and then make the inconsequent retort, which he accepted as perfectly sagacious, because, in fact, it was so—

"Well, and you? You were born there, too."

He knew his answer.

"That's different. I've been away ten years. Dad never had such a long spell; and it was more than thirty years ago."

She was the first person to whom he opened his lips after receiving the news of his father's death.

"It has killed him!" he said.

He had walked straight out of town with the news, straight out before him in the noonday sun on the white road, and his feet had brought him face to face with her in the hall of the ruined *palazzo*, a room magnificent and naked, with here and there a long strip of damask, black with damp and age, hanging down on a bare panel of the wall. It was furnished with exactly one gilt armchair, with a broken back, and an octagon columnar stand bearing a heavy marble vase ornamented with sculptured masks and garlands of flowers, and cracked from top to bottom. Charles Gould was dusty with the white dust of the road lying on his boots, on his shoulders, on his cap with two peaks. Water dripped from under it all over his face, and he grasped a thick oaken cudgel in his bare right hand.

She went very pale under the roses of her big straw hat, gloved, swinging a clear sunshade, caught just as she was going out to meet him at the bottom of the hill, where three poplars stand near the wall of a vineyard.

"It has killed him!" he repeated. "He ought to have had many years yet. We are a long-lived family."

She was too startled to say anything; he was contemplating with a penetrating and motionless stare the cracked marble urn as though he had resolved to fix its shape forever in his memory. It was only when, turning suddenly to her, he blurted out twice, "I've come to you . . . I've come straight to you . . . ," without being able to finish his phrase, that the great pitifulness of that lonely and tormented death in Costaguana came to her with the full force of its misery. He caught hold of her hand, raised it to his lips, and at that she dropped her parasol to pat him on the cheek, murmured "Poor boy," and began to dry her eyes under the downward curve of her hatbrim, very small in her simple, white frock, almost like a lost child crying in the degraded grandeur of the noble hall, while he stood by her, again perfectly motionless in the contemplation of the marble urn.

Afterwards they went out for a long walk, which was silent till he exclaimed suddenly—

"Yes. But if he had only grappled with it in a proper way!"

And then they stopped. Everywhere there were long shadows lying on the hills, on the roads, on the enclosed fields of olive trees, the shadows of poplars, of wide chestnuts, of farm buildings, of stone walls; and in midair the sound of a bell, thin and alert, was like the throbbing pulse of the sunset glow. Her lips were slightly parted as though in surprise that he should not be looking at her with his usual expression. His usual expression was unconditionally approving and attentive. He was in his talks with her the most anxious and deferential of dictators, an attitude that pleased her immensely. It affirmed her power without detracting from his dignity. That slight girl, with her little feet, little hands, little face attractively overweighted by great coils of hair, with a rather large mouth, whose mere parting seemed to breathe upon you the fragrance of frankness and generosity, had the fastidious soul of an experienced woman. She was, before all things and all flatteries, careful of her pride in the object of her choice. But now he was actually not looking at her at all; and his expression was tense and irrational, as is natural in a man who elects to stare at nothing past a young girl's head.

"Well, yes. It was iniquitous. They corrupted him thoroughly, the poor old boy. Oh! Why wouldn't he let me go back to him? But now I shall know how to grapple with this."

After pronouncing these words with immense assurance, he glanced down at her, and at once fell a prey to distress, incertitude, and fear.

The only thing he wanted to know now, he said, was whether she did love him enough—whether she would have the courage to go with him so far away? He put these questions to her in a voice that trembled with anxiety—for he was a determined man.

She did. She would. And immediately the future hostess of all the Europeans in Sulaco had the physical experience of the earth falling away from under her. It vanished completely, even to the very sound of the bell. When her feet touched the ground again, the bell was still ringing in the valley; she put her hands up to her hair, breathing quickly, and glanced up and down the stony lane. It was reassuringly empty. Meantime, Charles, stepping with one foot into a dry and dusty ditch, picked up the open parasol, which had bounded away from them with a martial sound of drum taps. He handed it to her soberly, a little crestfallen.

They turned back, and after she had slipped her hand on his arm, the first words he pronounced were—

"It's lucky that we shall be able to settle in a coast town. You've heard its name. It is Sulaco. I am so glad poor father did get that house. He bought a big house three years ago, in order that there should always be a Casa Gould in the principal town of what used to be called the Occidental province. I lived there once, as a small boy, with my dear mother, for a whole year, while poor father was away in the United States on business. You shall be the new mistress of the Casa Gould."

And later, in the inhabited corner of the *palazzo* above the vineyards, the marble hills, the pines and olives of Lucca, he also said—

"The name of Gould has been always highly respected in Sulaco. My Uncle Harry was chief of the state for some time, and has left a great name amongst the first families. By this I mean the pure Creole families, who take no part in the miserable farce of governments. Uncle Harry was no adventurer. In Costaguana we Goulds are no adventurers. He was of the country, and he loved it, but he remained essentially an Englishman in his ideas. He made use of the political cry of his time. It was 'federation.' But he was no politician. He simply stood up for social order out of pure love for rational liberty and from his hate of oppression. There was no nonsense about him. He went to work in his own way because it seemed right, just as I feel I must lay hold of that mine."

In such words he talked to her because his memory was very full of the country of his childhood, his heart of his life with that girl, and his mind of the San Tomé Concession. He added that he would have to leave her for a few days to find an American, a man from San Francisco, who was still somewhere in Europe. A few months before he had made his acquaintance in an old historic German town, situated in a mining district. The American had his womankind with him, but seemed lonely while they were sketching all day long the old doorways and the turreted corners of the mediæval houses. Charles Gould had with him the inseparable companionship of the mine. The other man was interested in mining enterprises, knew something of Costaguana, and was no stranger to the name of Gould. They had talked together with some intimacy which was made possible by the difference of their ages. Charles wanted now to find that capitalist of shrewd mind and accessible character. His father's fortune in Costaguana, which he had supposed to be still considerable, seemed to have melted in the rascally crucible of revolutions. Apart from some ten thousand pounds deposited in England, there appeared to be nothing left except the house in Sulaco, a vague right of forest exploitation in a remote and savage district, and the San Tomé Concession, which had attended his poor father to the very brink of the grave.

He explained those things. It was late when they parted. She had never before given him such a fascinating vision of herself. All the eagerness of youth for a strange life, for great distances, for a future in which there was an air of adventure, of combat—a subtle thought of redress and conquest, had filled her with an intense excitement, which she returned to the giver with a more open and exquisite display of tenderness.

He left her to walk down the hill, and directly he found himself alone he became sober. That irreparable change a death makes in the course of our daily thoughts can be felt in a vague and poignant discomfort of mind. It hurt Charles Gould to feel that never more, by no effort of will, would he be able to think of his father in the same way he used to think of him when the poor man was alive. His breathing image was no longer in his power. This consideration, closely affecting his own identity, filled his breast with a mournful and angry desire for action. In this his instinct was unerring. Action is consolatory. It is the enemy of thought and the friend of flattering illusions. Only in the conduct of our action can we find the sense of mastery over the Fates. For his action, the mine was obviously the only field. It was imperative sometimes to know how to disobey the solemn wishes of the dead. He resolved firmly to make his disobedience as thorough (by way of atonement) as it well could be. The mine had been the cause of an absurd moral disaster; its working must be made a serious and moral success. He owed it to the dead man's memory. Such were the—properly speaking—emotions of Charles Gould. His thoughts ran upon the means of raising a large amount of capital in San Francisco or elsewhere; and incidentally there occurred to him also the general reflection that the counsel of the departed must be an unsound guide. Not one of them could be aware beforehand what enormous changes the death of any given individual may produce in the very aspect of the world.

The latest phase in the history of the mine Mrs. Gould knew from personal experience. It was in essence the history of her married life. The mantle of the Gould's hereditary position in Sulaco had descended amply upon her little person; but she would not allow the peculiarities of the strange garment to weigh down the vivacity of her character, which was the sign of no mere mechanical sprightliness, but of an eager intelligence. It must not be supposed that Mrs. Gould's mind was masculine. A woman with a masculine mind is not a being of superior efficiency; she is simply a phenomenon of imperfect differentiation—interestingly barren and without importance. Doña Emilia's intelligence being feminine led her to achieve the conquest of Sulaco, simply by lighting the way for her unselfishness and sympathy. She could converse charmingly, but she was not talkative. The wisdom of the heart, having no concern with the erection or demolition of theories any more than with the defence of prejudices, has no random words at its command. The words it pronounces have the value of acts of integrity, tolerance, and compassion. A woman's true tenderness, like the true virility of man, is expressed in action of a conquering kind. The ladies of Sulaco adored Mrs. Gould. "They still look upon me as something of a monster," Mrs. Gould had said pleasantly to one of the three gentlemen from San Francisco she had to entertain in her new Sulaco house just about a year after her marriage.

They were her first visitors from abroad, and they had come to look at the San Tomé mine. She jested most agreeably, they thought; and Charles Gould, besides knowing thoroughly what he was about, had shown himself a real hustler. These facts caused them to be well disposed towards his wife. An unmistakable enthusiasm, pointed by a slight flavour of irony, made her talk of the mine absolutely fascinating to her visitors, and provoked them to grave and indulgent smiles in which there was a good deal of deference. Perhaps had they known how much she was inspired by an idealistic view of success they would have been amazed at the state of her mind as the Spanish American ladies had been amazed at the tireless activity of her body. She would—in her own words—have been for them "something of a monster." However, the Goulds were in essentials a reticent couple, and their guests departed without the suspicion of any other purpose but simple profit in the working of a silver mine. Mrs. Gould had out her own carriage, with two white mules, to drive them down to the harbour, whence the *Ceres* was to carry them off into the Olympus of plutocrats. Captain Mitchell had snatched at the occasion of leave-taking to remark to Mrs. Gould, in a low, confidential mutter, "This marks an epoch."

Mrs. Gould loved the patio of her Spanish house. A broad flight of stone steps was overlooked silently from a niche in the wall by a Madonna in blue robes with the crowned child sitting on her arm. Subdued voices ascended in the early mornings from the paved well of the quadrangle, with the stamping of horses and mules led out in pairs to drink at the cistern. A tangle of slender bamboo stems drooped its narrow, bladelike leaves over the square pool of water, and the fat coachman sat muffled up on the edge, holding lazily the ends of halters in his hand. Barefooted servants passed to and fro, issuing from dark, low doorways below; two laundry girls with baskets of washed linen; the baker with the tray of bread made for the day; Leonarda—her own *camerista*—bearing high up, swung from her hand raised above her raven black head, a bunch of starched underskirts dazzlingly white in the slant of sunshine. Then the old porter would hobble in, sweeping the flagstones, and the house was ready for the day. All the lofty rooms on three sides of the quadrangle opened into each other and into the *corredor*, with its wrought-iron railings and a border of flowers, whence, like the lady of the mediæval castle, she could witness from above all the departures and arrivals of the casa, to which the sonorous arched gateway lent an air of stately importance.

She had watched her carriage roll away with the three guests from the north. She smiled. Their three arms went up simultaneously to their three hats. Captain Mitchell, the fourth, in attendance, had already begun a pompous discourse. Then she lingered. She lingered, approaching her face to the clusters of flowers here and there, as if to give time to her thoughts to catch up with her slow footsteps along the straight vista of the corridor.

A fringed Indian hammock from Aroa, gay with coloured feather-work, had been swung judiciously in a corner that caught the early sun; for the mornings are cool in Sulaco. The cluster of *flor de noche-buena* blazed in great masses before the open glass doors of the reception rooms. A big green parrot, brilliant like an emerald in a cage that flashed like gold, screamed out ferociously, "*Viva Costaguana!*", then called twice mellifluously, "Leonarda! Leonarda!" in imitation of Mrs. Gould's voice, and suddenly took refuge in immobility and silence. Mrs. Gould reached the end of the gallery and put her head through the door of her husband's room.

Charles Gould, with one foot on a low wooden stool, was already strapping his spurs. He wanted to hurry back to the mine. Mrs. Gould, without coming in, glanced about the room. One tall, broad bookcase, with glass doors, was full of books; but in the other, without shelves, and lined with red baize, were arranged firearms: Winchester carbines, revolvers, a couple of shotguns, and even two pairs of double-barrelled holster pistols. Between them, by itself, upon a strip of scarlet velvet, hung an old cavalry sabre, once the property of Don Enrique Gould, the hero of the Occidental province, presented by Don José Avellanos, the hereditary friend of the family.

Otherwise, the plastered white walls were completely bare, except for a water-colour sketch of the San Tomé mountain—the work of Doña Emilia herself. In the middle of the red-tiled floor stood two long tables littered with plans and papers, a few chairs, and a glass showcase containing specimens of ore from the mine. Mrs. Gould, looking at all these things in turn, wondered aloud why the talk of these wealthy and enterprising men, discussing the prospects, the working, and the safety of the mine, rendered her so impatient and uneasy, whereas she could talk of the mine by the hour with her husband with unwearied interest and satisfaction.

And dropping her eyelids expressively, she added—

"What do *you* feel about it, Charley?"

Then, surprised at her husband's silence, she raised her eyes, opened wide, as pretty as pale flowers. He had done with the spurs, and, twisting his moustache with both hands, horizontally, he contemplated her from the height of his long legs with a visible appreciation of her appearance. The consciousness of being thus contemplated pleased Mrs. Gould.

"They are considerable men," he said.

"I know. But have you listened to their conversation? They don't
"They have seen the mine. They have understood that to some
seem to have understood anything they have seen here."
purpose," Charles Gould interjected, in defence of the visitors; and then his wife mentioned the name of the most considerable of the three. He was considerable in finance and in industry. His name was familiar to many millions of people. He was so considerable that he would never have travelled so far away from the centre of his activity if the doctors had not insisted, with veiled menaces, on his taking a long holiday.

"Mr. Holroyd's sense of religion," Mrs. Gould pursued, "was shocked and disgusted at the tawdriness of the dressed-up saints in the cathedral—the worship, he called it, of wood and tinsel. But it seemed to me that he looked upon his own God as a sort of influential partner, who gets his share of profits in the endowment of churches. That's a sort of idolatry. He told me he endowed churches every year, Charley."

"No end of them," said Mr. Gould, marvelling inwardly at the mobility of her physiognomy. "All over the country. He's famous for that sort of munificence."

"Oh, he didn't boast," Mrs. Gould declared scrupulously. "I believe he's really a good man, but so stupid! A poor cholo who offers a little silver arm or leg to thank his God for a cure is as rational and more touching."

"He's at the head of immense silver and iron interests," Charles Gould observed.

"Ah, yes! The religion of silver and iron. He's a very civil man, though he looked awfully solemn when he first saw the Madonna on the staircase, who's only wood and paint; but he said nothing to me. My dear Charley, I heard those men talk among themselves. Can it be that they really wish to become, for an immense consideration, drawers of water and hewers of wood to all the countries and nations of the earth?"

"A man must work to some end," Charles Gould said vaguely.

Mrs. Gould, frowning, surveyed him from head to foot. With his riding breeches, leather leggings (an article of apparel never before seen in Costaguana), a Norfolk coat of grey flannel, and those great flaming moustaches, he suggested an officer of cavalry turned gentleman farmer. This combination was gratifying to Mrs. Gould's tastes. "How thin the poor boy is!" she thought. "He overworks himself." But there was no denying that his fine-drawn, keen red face, and his whole, long-limbed, lank person had an air of breeding and distinction. And Mrs. Gould relented.

"I only wondered what you felt," she murmured gently.

During the last few days, as it happened, Charles Gould had been kept too busy thinking twice before he spoke to have paid much attention to the state of his feelings. But theirs was a successful match, and he had no difficulty in finding his answer.

"The best of my feelings are in your keeping, my dear," he said lightly; and there was so much truth in that obscure phrase that he experienced towards her at the moment a great increase of gratitude and tenderness.

Mrs. Gould, however, did not seem to find this answer in the least obscure. She brightened up delicately; already he had changed his tone.

"But there are facts. The worth of the mine—as a mine—is beyond doubt. It shall make us very wealthy. The mere working of it is a matter of technical knowledge, which I have—which ten thousand other men in the world have. But its safety, its continued existence as an enterprise, giving a return to men—to strangers, comparative strangers—who invest money in it, is left altogether in my hands. I have inspired confidence in a man of wealth and position. You seem to think this perfectly natural—do you? Well, I don't know.

I don't know why I have; but it is a fact. This fact makes everything possible, because without it I would never have thought of disregarding my father's wishes. I would never have disposed of the Concession as a speculator disposes of a valuable right to a company—for cash and shares, to grow rich eventually if possible, but at any rate to put some money at once in his pocket. No. Even if it had been feasible—which I doubt—I would not have done so. Poor father did not understand. He was afraid I would hang on to the ruinous thing, waiting for just some such chance, and waste my life miserably. That was the true sense of his prohibition, which we have deliberately set aside."

They were walking up and down the corridor. Her head just reached to his shoulder. His arm, extended downwards, was about her waist. His spurs jingled slightly.

"He had not seen me for ten years. He did not know me. He parted from me for my sake, and he would never let me come back. He was always talking in his letters of leaving Costaguana, of abandoning everything and making his escape. But he was too valuable a prey. They would have thrown him into one of their prisons at the first suspicion."

His spurred feet clinked slowly. He was bending over his wife as they walked. The big parrot, turning its head askew, followed their pacing figures with a round, unblinking eye.

"He was a lonely man. Ever since I was ten years old he used to talk to me as if I had been grown up. When I was in Europe he wrote to me every month. Ten, twelve pages every month of my life for ten years. And, after all, he did not know me! Just think of it—ten whole years away, the years I was growing up into a man. He could not know me. Do you think he could?"

Mrs. Gould shook her head negatively, which was just what her husband had expected from the strength of the argument. But she shook her head negatively only because she thought that no one could know her Charles—really know him for what he was but herself. The thing was obvious. It could be felt. It required no argument. And poor Mr. Gould, senior, who had died too soon to ever hear of their engagement, remained too shadowy a figure for her to be credited with knowledge of any sort whatever.

"No, he did not understand. In my view this mine could never have been a thing to sell. Never! After all his misery I simply could not have touched it for money alone," Charles Gould pursued; and she pressed her head to his shoulder approvingly.

These two young people remembered the life which had ended wretchedly just when their own lives had come together in that splendour of hopeful love, which to the most sensible minds appears like a triumph of good over all the evils of the earth. A vague idea of rehabilitation had entered the plan of their life. That it was so vague as to elude the support of argument made it only the stronger. It had presented itself to them at the instant when the woman's instinct of devotion and the man's instinct of activity receive from the strongest of illusions their most powerful impulse. The very prohibition imposed the necessity of success. It was as if they had been morally bound to make good their vigorous view of life against the unnatural error of weariness and despair. If the idea of wealth was present to them it was only insofar as it was bound with that other success. Mrs. Gould, an orphan from early childhood and without fortune, brought up in an atmosphere of intellectual interests, had never considered the aspects of great wealth. They were too remote, and she had not learned that they were desirable. On the other hand, she had not known anything of absolute want. Even the very poverty of her aunt, the *marchesa*, had nothing intolerable to a refined mind; it seemed in accord with a great grief; it had the austerity of a sacrifice offered to a noble ideal. Thus even the most legitimate touch of materialism was wanting in Mrs. Gould's character. The dead man of whom she thought with tenderness (because he was Charley's father) and with some impatience (because he had been weak) must be put completely in the wrong. Nothing else would do to keep their prosperity without a stain on its only real, on its immaterial side!

Charles Gould, on his part, had been obliged to keep the idea of wealth well to the fore; but he brought it forward as a means, not as an end. Unless the mine was good business it could not be touched. He had to insist on that aspect of the enterprise. It was his lever to move men who had capital. And Charles Gould believed in the mine. He knew everything that could be known of it. His faith in the mine was contagious, though it was not served by a great eloquence; but businessmen are frequently as sanguine and imaginative as lovers. They are affected by a personality much oftener than people would suppose; and Charles Gould, in his unshaken assurance, was absolutely convincing. Besides, it was a matter of common knowledge to the men to whom he addressed himself that mining in Costaguana was a game that could be made considerably more than worth the candle. The men of affairs knew that very well. The real difficulty in touching it was elsewhere. Against that there was an implication of calm and implacable resolution in Charles Gould's very voice. Men of affairs venture sometimes on acts that the common judgment of the world would pronounce absurd; they make their decisions on apparently impulsive and human grounds. "Very well," had said the considerable personage to whom Charles Gould on his way out through San Francisco had lucidly exposed his point of view. "Let us suppose that the mining affairs of Sulaco are taken in hand. There would then be in it: first, the house of Holroyd, which is all right; then, Mr. Charles Gould, a citizen of Costaguana, who is also all right; and, lastly, the government of the republic. So far, this resembles the first start of the Atacama nitrate fields, where there was a financing house, a gentleman of the name of Edwards, and a government—or, rather, two governments—two South American governments. And you know what came of it. War came of it; devastating and prolonged war came of it, Mr. Gould. However, here we possess the advantage of having only one South American government hanging around for plunder out of the deal. It is an advantage; but then there are degrees of badness, and that government is the Costaguana government."

Thus spoke the considerable personage, the millionaire endower of churches on a scale befitting the greatness of his native land—the same to whom the doctors used the language of horrid and veiled menaces. He was a big-limbed, deliberate man, whose quiet burliness lent to an ample silk-faced frock coat a superfine dignity. His hair was iron-grey, his eyebrows were still black, and his massive profile was the profile of a Caesar's head on an old Roman coin. But his parentage was German and Scotch and English, with remote strains of Danish and French blood, giving him the temperament of a puritan and an insatiable imagination of conquest. He was completely unbending to his visitor, because of the warm introduction the visitor had brought from Europe, and because of an irrational liking for earnestness and determination wherever met, to whatever end directed.

"The Costaguana government shall play its hand for all it's worth—and don't you forget it, Mr. Gould. Now, what is Costaguana? It is the bottomless pit of ten per cent loans and other fool investments. European capital had been flung into it with both hands for years. Not ours, though. We in this country know just about enough to keep indoors when it rains. We can sit and watch. Of course, someday we shall step in. We are bound to. But there's no hurry. Time itself has got to wait on the greatest country in the whole of God's universe. We shall be giving the word for everything: industry, trade, law, journalism, art, politics, and religion, from Cape Horn clear over to Smith's Sound, and beyond, too, if anything worth taking hold of turns up at the North Pole. And then we shall have the leisure to take in hand the outlying islands and continents of the earth. We shall run the world's business whether the world likes it or not. The world can't help it—and neither can we, I guess."

By this he meant to express his faith in destiny in words suitable to his intelligence, which was unskilled in the presentation of general ideas. His intelligence was nourished on facts; and Charles Gould, whose imagination had been permanently affected by the one great fact of a silver mine, had no objection to this theory of the world's future. If it had seemed distasteful for a moment it was because the sudden statement of such vast eventualities dwarfed almost to nothingness the actual matter in hand. He and his plans and all the mineral wealth of the Occidental province appeared suddenly robbed of every vestige of magnitude. The sensation was disagreeable; but Charles Gould was not dull. Already he felt that he was producing a favourable impression; the consciousness of that flattering fact helped him to a vague smile, which his big interlocutor took for a smile of discreet and admiring assent. He smiled quietly, too; and immediately Charles Gould, with that mental agility mankind will display in defence of a cherished hope, reflected that the very apparent insignificance of his aim would help him to success. His personality and his mine would be taken up because it was a matter of no great consequence, one way or another, to a man who referred his action to such a prodigious destiny. And Charles Gould was not humiliated by this consideration, because the thing remained as big as ever for him. Nobody else's vast conceptions of destiny could diminish the aspect of his desire for the redemption of the San Tomé mine. In comparison to the correctness of his aim, definite in space and absolutely attainable within a limited time, the other man appeared for an instant as a dreamy idealist of no importance.

The great man, massive and benignant, had been looking at him thoughtfully; when he broke the short silence it was to remark that concessions flew about thick in the air of Costaguana. Any simple soul that just yearned to be taken in could bring down a concession at the first shot.

"Our consuls get their mouths stopped with them," he continued, with a twinkle of genial scorn in his eyes. But in a moment he became grave. "A conscientious, upright man, that cares nothing for boodle, and keeps clear of their intrigues, conspiracies, and factions, soon gets his passports. See that, Mr. Gould? *Persona non grata.* That's the reason our government is never properly informed. On the other hand, Europe must be kept out of this continent, and for proper interference on our part the time is not yet ripe, I dare say. But we here—we are not this country's government, neither are we simple souls. Your affair is all right. The main question for us is whether the second partner, and that's you, is the right sort to hold his own against the third and unwelcome partner, which is one or another of the high and mighty robber gangs that run the Costaguana government. What do you think, Mr. Gould, eh?"

He bent forward to look steadily into the unflinching eyes of Charles Gould, who, remembering the large box full of his father's letters, put the accumulated scorn and bitterness of many years into the tone of his answer—

"As far as the knowledge of these men and their methods and their politics is concerned, I can answer for myself. I have been fed on that sort of knowledge since I was a boy. I am not likely to fall into mistake from excess of optimism."

"Not likely, eh? That's all right. Tact and a stiff upper lip is what you'll want; and you could bluff a little on the strength of your backing. Not too much, though. We will go with you as long as the thing runs straight. But we won't be drawn into any large trouble. This is the experiment which I am willing to make. There is some risk, and we will take it; but if you can't keep up your end, we will stand our loss, of course, and then—we'll let the thing go. This mine can wait; it has been shut up before, as you know. You must understand that under no circumstances will we consent to throw good money after bad."

Thus the great personage had spoken then, in his own private office, in a great city where other men (very considerable in the eyes of a vain populace) waited with alacrity upon a wave of his hand. And rather more than a year later, during his unexpected appearance in Sulaco, he had emphasized his uncompromising attitude with a freedom of sincerity permitted to his wealth and influence. He did this with the less reserve, perhaps, because the inspection of what had been done, and more still the way in which successive steps had been taken, had impressed him with the conviction that Charles Gould was perfectly capable of keeping up his end.

"This young fellow," he thought to himself, "may yet become a power in the land."

This thought flattered him, for hitherto the only account of this young man he could give to his intimates was—

"My brother-in-law met him in one of these one-horse old German towns, near some mines, and sent him on to me with a letter. He's one of the Costaguana Goulds, pure-bred Englishmen, but all born in the country. His uncle went into politics, was the last provincial president of Sulaco, and got shot after a battle. His father was a prominent businessman in Santa Marta, tried to keep clear of their politics, and died ruined after a lot of revolutions. And that's your Costaguana in a nutshell."

Of course, he was too great a man to be questioned as to his motives, even by his intimates. The outside world was at liberty to wonder respectfully at the hidden meaning of his actions. He was so great a man that his lavish patronage of the "purer forms of Christianity" (which in its naïve form of church-building amused Mrs. Gould) was looked upon by his fellow citizens as the manifestation of a pious and humble spirit. But in his own circles of the financial world the taking up of such a thing as the San Tomé mine was regarded with respect, indeed, but rather as a subject for discreet jocularity. It was a great man's caprice. In the great Holroyd building (an enormous pile of iron, glass, and blocks of stone at the corner of two streets, cobwebbed aloft by the radiation of telegraph wires) the heads of principal departments exchanged humorous glances, which meant that they were not let into the secrets of the San Tomé business. The Costaguana mail (it was never large—one fairly heavy envelope) was taken unopened straight into the great man's room, and no instructions dealing with it had ever been issued thence. The office whispered that he answered personally—and not by dictation either, but actually writing in his own hand, with pen and ink, and, it was to be supposed, taking a copy in his own private press copybook, inaccessible to profane eyes. Some scornful young men, insignificant pieces of minor machinery in that eleven-storey-high workshop of great affairs, expressed frankly their private opinion that the great chief had done at last something silly, and was ashamed of his folly; others, elderly and insignificant, but full of romantic reverence for the business that had devoured their best years, used to mutter darkly and knowingly that this was a portentous sign, that the Holroyd connection meant by-and-by to get hold of the whole republic of Costaguana, lock, stock, and barrel. But, in fact, the hobby theory was the right one. It interested the great man to attend personally to the San Tomé mine; it interested him so much that he allowed this hobby to give a direction to the first complete holiday he had taken for quite a startling number of years. He was not running a great enterprise there; no mere railway board or industrial corporation. He was running a man! A success would have pleased him very much on refreshingly novel grounds; but, on the other side of the same feeling, it was incumbent upon him to cast it off utterly at the first sign of failure. A man may be thrown off. The papers had unfortunately trumpeted all over the land his journey to Costaguana. If he was pleased at the way Charles Gould was going on, he infused an added grimness into his assurances of support. Even at the very last interview, half an hour or so before he rolled out of the patio, hat in hand, behind Mrs. Gould's white mules, he had said in Charles's room—

"You go ahead in your own way, and I shall know how to help you as long as you hold your own. But you may rest assured that in a given case we shall know how to drop you in time."

To this Charles Gould's only answer had been: "You may begin sending out the machinery as soon as you like."

And the great man had liked this imperturbable assurance. The secret of it was that to Charles Gould's mind these uncompromising terms were agreeable. Like this the mine preserved its identity, with which he had endowed it as a boy; and it remained dependent on himself alone. It was a serious affair, and he, too, took it grimly.

"Of course—" he said to his wife, alluding to this last conversation with the departed guest, while they walked slowly up and down the corridor, followed by the irritated eye of the parrot—"of course, a man of that sort can take up a thing or drop it when he likes. He will suffer from no sense of defeat. He may have to give in, or he may have to die tomorrow, but the great silver and iron interests shall survive, and some day shall get hold of Costaguana along with the rest of the world."

They had stopped near the cage. The parrot, catching the sound of a word belonging to his vocabulary, was moved to interfere. Parrots are very human.

"*Viva Costaguana!*" he shrieked, with intense self-assertion, and, instantly ruffling up his feathers, assumed an air of puffed-up somnolence behind the glittering wires.

"And do you believe that, Charley?" Mrs. Gould asked. "This seems to me most awful materialism, and——"

"My dear, it's nothing to me," interrupted her husband, in a reasonable tone. "I make use of what I see. What's it to me whether his talk is the voice of destiny or simply a bit of claptrap eloquence? There's a good deal of eloquence of one sort or another produced in both Americas. The air of the New World seems favourable to the art of declamation. Have you forgotten how dear Avellanos can hold forth for hours here——?"

"Oh, but that's different," protested Mrs. Gould, almost shocked. The allusion was not to the point. Don José was a dear good man, who talked very well, and was enthusiastic about the greatness of the San Tomé mine. "How can you compare them, Charles?" she exclaimed reproachfully "He has suffered—and yet he hopes."

The working competence of men—which she never questioned—was very surprising to Mrs. Gould, because upon so many obvious issues they showed themselves strangely muddle-headed.

Charles Gould, with a careworn calmness which secured for him at once his wife's anxious sympathy, assured her that he was not comparing. He was an American himself, after all, and perhaps he could understand both kinds of eloquence—"if it were worth while to try," he added grimly. But he had breathed the air of England longer than any of his people had done for three generations, and really he begged to be excused. His poor father could be eloquent, too. And he asked his wife whether she remembered a passage in one of his father's last letters where Mr. Gould had expressed the conviction that "God looked wrathfully at these countries or else He would let some ray of hope fall through a rift in the appalling darkness of intrigue, bloodshed, and crime that hung over the 'queen of continents.' "

Mrs. Gould had not forgotten. "You read it to me, Charley," she murmured. "It was a striking pronouncement. How deeply your father must have felt its terrible sadness!"

"He did not like to be robbed. It exasperated him," said Charles Gould. "But the image will serve well enough. What is wanted here is law, good faith, order, security. Anyone can declaim about these things, but I pin my faith to material interests. Only let the material interests once get a firm footing, and they are bound to impose the conditions on which alone they can continue to exist. That's how your money-making is justified here in the face of lawlessness and disorder. It is justified because the security which it demands must be shared with an oppressed people. A better justice will come afterwards. That's your ray of hope." His arm pressed her slight form closer to his side for a moment. "And who knows whether in that sense even the San Tomé mine may not become that little rift in the darkness which poor father despaired of ever seeing?"

She glanced up at him with admiration. He was competent; he had given a vast shape to the vagueness of her unselfish ambitions.

"Charley," she said, "you are splendidly disobedient."

He left her suddenly in the *corredor* to go and get his hat, a soft, grey sombrero, an article of national costume which combined unexpectedly well with his English get-up. He came back, a riding whip under his arm, buttoning up a dogskin glove; his face reflected the resolute nature of his thoughts. His wife had waited for him at the head of the stairs, and before he gave her the parting kiss he finished the conversation—

"What should be perfectly clear to us," he said, "is the fact that there is no going back. Where could we begin life afresh? We are in now for all that there is in us."

He bent over her upturned face very tenderly and a little remorsefully. Charles Gould was competent because he had no illusions. The Gould Concession had to fight for life with such weapons as could be found at once in the mire of corruption that was so universal as to almost lose its significance. He was prepared to stoop for his weapons. For a moment he felt as if the silver mine, which had killed his father, had decoyed him further than he meant to go; and with the roundabout logic of emotions, he felt that the worthiness of his life was bound up with success. There was no going back.

Personality, Politics, and Social Structure

Whatever their merits, scientific studies of political behavior have on the whole caught only the typical, the numerically representative case; deviant actors have most often been either slighted or treated as though they were failing to behave properly. Thus, for example, from various voting and attitude studies of the United States one is virtually led to conclude that a poor Irish Catholic living in a big city whose parents are Democrats and who himself votes Republican is making an incomprehensible error, or has somehow missed the point of his whole life. Yet such deviant cases may in the end be as significant for our understanding as the typical case; they may be in tune with hidden, underlying trends in a society that are missed by studies limited to a small sample of individual attitudes at one brief historical moment.

On the other hand, of course, there may be no such hidden trends to spot: the typical case may be truly typical. How can we know what the truth is in this regard—which cases are significant for our understanding? Only, it seems, by having, above and beyond our behavioral studies, a theory about society's dynamics: what a given society is becoming, as well as what it is and does. We need, that is, a theory about the long-run impact that a political system has on individual lives. Because questions about the long run are not usually answered well by voting surveys, attitude studies, and so forth, social scientists often attempt to answer questions of this sort by leaping to large-scale studies of the political or social system, ignoring individuals and trying to detect broad patterns of behavior and change.

Where the literary imagination can be of special help is in providing one method to link individual behavior—and ultimately any social science must have something to say about the lives of individuals—to the organization and direction of the political system. This linkage is created by the tendency of art, especially written art, to derive the universal from the particular. In effect, every political novel or story poses an implicit theory about the meaning of political life for individuals in the social system depicted. No doubt such fictions are not behavioral statements of a scientific kind; at first glance they are even less likely to help us discover a system's essential nature, because their "samples" of the political universe are even more limited than those of a typical attitude study. But they do provide us with a kind of knowledge, and it is indeed a kind of knowledge that can only rarely be duplicated by the formal techniques of social science. To be sure, it is hard to define with any precision exactly of what this "unscientific" sort of knowledge consists; yet in everyday life we rely on it all the time. We may call it the appeal to experience, and especially to one's experience of one's own inmost being. "Whosoever looks into himself," wrote Thomas Hobbes in his Leviathan, "and considers what he does when he does think, opine, reason, hope, fear, etc., and upon what grounds, he shall thereby read and know what are the thoughts and passions of all other men on like occasions." When done with insight, this kind of art produces a feeling of internal conviction that we have seen the truth—or a truth—of some matter; a sense of recognition from having witnessed someone behave in a believable way, from having seen things happen in a way we are certain they ought to happen. In the absence of any more fruitful approach—and for the most part statistical studies convey little or no feeling for why people behave the way they do—such material, even though it stems wholly from the imagination, is invaluable.

The materials in this chapter, then, are intended to illuminate a few (only a few) of the important aspects of political life. The selections, dictated largely by our own interests and concerns, may be divided roughly into three groups. The passages from Jorge Amado's The Violent Land and Peter Abraham's Tell Freedom, as well as Albert Maltz's short story "The Happiest Man on Earth," show how political systems can impinge on individuals' lives in a variety of ways that may be generally described as instances of exploitation or oppression. The range of experiences that can be understood in this light, as revealed by the literary imagination, is broad indeed: the direct brutality of power in a traditional or premodern society; the special nature of racial oppression in a modern society that is, for the master race, civilized and even "free"; and the potential exploitativeness of even "freedom" itself—in the case of Albert Maltz's story, that economic freedom which once was thought to be the very fundament of liberal democracy.

The remaining selections convey a feeling for the long-term effects of a political system on people's lives. One group of these selections touches on the relationship between social class identifications and political attitudes. Thus the political apathy of Doris Lessing's friend Rose (In Pursuit of the English) and the irrelevant attitudinizing of Henry James's upper-class reformer Lord Warburton (The Portrait of a Lady) give evidence of some of the unexpected forms this relationship may take. The selection from Lionel Trilling's Middle of the Journey is especially revealing: In one of the most subtle passages in recent literature, Trilling exposes the tension felt by so many middle-class liberal intellectuals between a rhetorical commitment to "peace" and an emotional commitment to the violence that may be necessary for revolutionary social change.

We have also included, finally, some brief pictures of various personality types that are commonplace in the academic literature of political science and social psychology: Richard Wright's alienated American Bigger Thomas, whose outlook is surely a logical outcome of the type of relationship described by Abrahams in Tell Freedom; Heinrich Mann's authoritarian personality Diederich Hessling, whose portrait was presciently drawn twenty years before the rise of Naziism; Christopher Isherwood's docile conformists; Joseph Conrad's imperialist Kurtz, corrupted by absolute power; and Feodor Dostoevski's rebel Ivan Karamazov, who angrily expresses a perennial response to the inadequacy of both political philosophy and political action—their inability to solve once and for all the problems raised throughout this reader. Indeed, the argument of Ivan, if taken seriously—and even in a liberal democracy it is hard not to take it seriously—confronts us with the provocative question whether politics as we so far know it in thought and deed may not be ultimately unsatisfactory.

Taken together, these selections are not intended to be typical of anything (except, perhaps, the variety and power of the art of fiction). Rather, they are intended to portray significant portions of political reality: that is, imaginable behavior that could be critical in the proper circumstances. Our assumption is that if one person can respond in a certain way to the pressure of events and of environment, then perhaps many persons will so respond when subjected to that particular kind of pressure. Thus our emphasis on dramatic cases is deliberate; for these, when they carry conviction, increase our appreciation of what can happen to a political system and to the people who live in it, and thus expand our view of political possibility.

DOMINATION

Jorge Amado

From *The Violent Land*

Once upon a time there were three sisters: Maria, Lucia, and
Violeta. Three sisters who were as one in the lives that they led and
in their light-hearted laughter. Lucia of the black braids, Violeta of
the lacklustre eyes, and Maria who was the youngest of the three.
Once upon a time there were three sisters who were as one in the
fate that awaited them.

They cut off Lucia's braids, her breasts grew round, and her cinna-
mon-coloured thighs were like two brown columns. The boss came
and took her. A cedarwood bed and a feather mattress, bolsters and
coverlets. Once upon a time there were three sisters.

Violeta's eyes were wide-opened on the world, her breasts were
pointed, her big, youthful buttocks were waves as she walked. The
overseer came and took her. An iron bed and a horsehair mattress,
sheets, and the Virgin Mary. Once upon a time there were three
sisters.

Maria, youngest of the three, had tiny breasts and a belly that was
sleek and smooth. Came the boss; he did not want her. Came the
overseer; he did not take her. There was left Pedro, a worker on the
plantation. A cowhide bed without sheet or coverlets, no cedarwood,
no feathers. Maria and her love.

Once upon a time there were three sisters: Maria, Lucia, Violeta.
Three sisters who were as one in the lives that they led and in their
light-hearted laughter. Lucia with her boss, Violeta with her overseer, and Maria with her love. Once upon a time there were three
sisters whom destiny had parted.

Lucia's braids grew again, her rounded breasts sank in, and her
column-like thighs were covered with black-and-blue marks. The
boss rode away in an automobile, taking with him the cedarwood
bed, the bolsters, and the coverlets. Once upon a time there were
three sisters.

Violeta's wide eyes were closed from fear of looking at the world

From Part III. Translated by Samuel Putnam. Reprinted by permission of Alfred
A. Knopf, Inc.

about her, her breasts were flaccid, and she had a child to suckle.
On his sorrel horse the overseer left one day, never to return. The
iron bed went also. Once upon a time there were three sisters.

Maria, youngest of the three, went with her husband to the field,
to the cacao plantations. When she came back from the field, she was
the oldest of the three. Pedro went away one day, for he was neither
a boss nor an overseer; he went away in a casket, a plain wooden
box, leaving behind him the cowhide bed and Maria with her love.
Once upon a time there were three sisters.

Where now are Lucia's braids, Violeta's breasts, Maria's love?

Once upon a time there were three sisters in a cheap whorehouse.
Three sisters who were as one in their suffering and in their despair.
Maria, Lucia, Violeta: three sisters who were as one in the fate that
awaited them.

RACIAL OPPRESSION

Peter Abrahams

From *Tell Freedom*

A couple of white men came down the path and ended our possible fight. We hurried past them to the distant shed where a queue
had already formed. There were grown-ups and children. All the
grown-ups and some of the children were from places other than our
location.

The line moved slowly. The young white man who served us did
it in leisurely fashion, with long pauses for a smoke. Occasionally
he turned his back.

At last, after what seemed hours, my turn came. Andries was
behind me. I took the sixpenny piece from the square of cloth and
offered it to the man.

"Well?" he said.

"Sixpence crackling, please."

Andries nudged me in the back. The man's stare suddenly became
cold and hard. Andries whispered into my ear.

"Well?" the man repeated coldly.

"Please *baas*," I said.

"What d'you want?"

"Sixpence crackling, please."

"What?"

Andries dug me in the ribs.

"Sixpence crackling, please, *baas*."

"What?"

"Sixpence crackling, please, *baas*."

"You new here?"

"Yes, *baas*." I looked at his feet, while he stared at me.

At last he took the sixpenny piece from me. I held my bag open while he filled it with crackling from a huge pile on a large canvas sheet on the ground. Turning away, I stole a fleeting glance at his face. His eyes met mine, and there was amused, challenging mockery in them. I waited for Andries at the back of the queue, out of the reach of the white man's mocking eyes.

The cold day was at its mildest as we walked home along the sandy road. I took out my piece of bread and, with a small piece of greasy crackling, still warm, on it, I munched as we went along. We had not yet made our peace, so Andries munched his bread and crackling on the other side of the road.

"Dumb fool!" he mocked at me for not knowing how to address the white man.

"Scare arse!" I shouted back.

Thus, hurling curses at each other, we reached the fork. Andries saw them first and moved over to my side of the road.

"White boys," he said.

There were three of them, two of about our own size and one slightly bigger. They had school bags and were coming towards us up the road from the siding.

"Better run for it," Andries said.

"Why?"

"No, that'll draw them. Let's just walk along, but quickly."

"Why?" I repeated.

"Shut up," he said.

Some of his anxiety touched me. Our own scrap was forgotten. We marched side by side as fast as we could. The white boys saw us and hurried up the road. We passed the fork. Perhaps they would take the turning away from us. We dared not look back.

"Hear them?" Andries asked.

"No." I looked over my shoulder. "They're coming," I said.

"Walk faster," Andries said. "If they come closer, run."

"Hey, *klipkop!*"

"Don't look back," Andries said.

"Hottentot!"

We walked as fast as we could.

"Bloody Kaffir!"

Ahead was a bend in the road. Behind the bend were bushes. Once there, we could run without them knowing it till it was too late.

"Faster," Andries said.

They began pelting us with stones.

"Run when we get to the bushes," Andries said.

The bend and the bushes were near. We would soon be there.

A clear young voice carried to us: "Your fathers are dirty black bastards of baboons!"

"Run!" Andries called.

A violent, unreasoning anger suddenly possessed me. I stopped and turned.

"You're a liar!" I screamed it.

The foremost boy pointed at me. "An ugly black baboon!"

In a fog of rage I went towards him.

"Liar!" I shouted. "My father was better than your father!"

I neared them. The bigger boy stopped between me and the one I was after.

"My father was better than your father! Liar!"

The big boy struck me a mighty clout on the side of the face. I staggered, righted myself, and leaped at the boy who had insulted my father. I struck him on the face, hard. A heavy blow on the back of my head nearly stunned me. I grabbed at the boy in front of me. We went down together.

"Liar!" I said through clenched teeth, hitting him with all my might.

Blows rained on me—on my head, my neck, the side of my face, my mouth—but my enemy was under me and I pounded him fiercely, all the time repeating:

"Liar! Liar! Liar!"

Suddenly stars exploded in my head. Then there was darkness. I emerged from the darkness to find Andries kneeling beside me.

"God, man! I thought they'd killed you."

I sat up. The white boys were nowhere to be seen. Like Andries, they'd probably thought me dead and run off in panic. The inside of my mouth felt sore and swollen. My nose was tender to the touch. The back of my head ached. A trickle of blood dripped from my nose. I stemmed it with the square of coloured cloth. The greatest damage was to my shirt. It was ripped in many places. I remembered the crackling. I looked anxiously about. It was safe, a little off the road on the grass. I relaxed. I got up and brushed my clothes. I picked up the crackling.

"God, you're dumb!" Andries said. "You're going to get it! Dumb arse!"

I was too depressed to retort. Besides, I knew he was right. I was dumb. I should have run when he told me to.

"Come on," I said.

One of many small groups of children, each child carrying his little bag of crackling, we trod the long road home in the cold winter afternoon.

There was tension in the house that night. When I got back, Aunt Liza had listened to the story in silence. The beating or scolding I expected did not come. But Aunt Liza changed while she listened, became remote and withdrawn. When Uncle Sam came home she told him what had happened. He, too, just looked at me and became more remote and withdrawn than usual. They were waiting for something; their tension reached out to me, and I waited with them, anxious, apprehensive.

The thing we waited for came while we were having our supper. We heard a trap pull up outside.

"Here it is," Uncle Sam said, and got up.

Aunt Liza leaned back from the table and put her hands in her lap, fingers intertwined, a cold, unseeing look in her eyes.

Before Uncle Sam reached the door, it burst open. A tall, broad, white man strode in. Behind him came the three boys. The one I had attacked had swollen lips and a puffy left eye.

"Evening, *baas*," Uncle Sam murmured.

"That's him," the bigger boy said, pointing at me.

The white man stared till I lowered my eyes.

"Well?" he said.

"He's sorry, *baas*," Uncle Sam said quickly. "I've given him a hiding he won't forget soon. You know how it is, *baas*. He's new here, the child of a relative in Johannesburg, and they don't all know how to behave there. You know how it is in the big towns, *baas*."

The plea in Uncle Sam's voice had grown more pronounced as he went on. He turned to me. "Tell the *baas* and the young *basies* how sorry you are, Lee."

I looked at Aunt Liza and something in her lifelessness made me stubborn in spite of my fear.

"He insulted my father," I said.

The white man smiled.

"See, Sam, your hiding couldn't have been good."

There was a flicker of life in Aunt Liza's eyes. For a brief moment she saw me, looked at me, warmly, lovingly; then her eyes went dead again.

"He's only a child, *baas*," Uncle Sam murmured.

"You stubborn too, Sam?"

"No, *baas*."

"Good. Then teach him, Sam. If you and he are to live here, you must teach him. Well—?"

"Yes, *baas*."

Uncle Sam went into the other room and returned with a thick leather thong. He wound it once round his hand and advanced on me. The man and the boys leaned against the door, watching. I looked at Aunt Liza's face. Though there was no sign of life or feeling on it, I knew suddenly, instinctively, that she wanted me not to cry.

Bitterly, Uncle Sam said: "You must never lift your hand to a white person. No matter what happens, you must never lift your hand to a white person. . . ."

He lifted the strap and brought it down on my back. I clenched my teeth and stared at Aunt Liza. I did not cry with the first three strokes. Then, suddenly, Aunt Liza went limp. Tears showed in her eyes. The thong came down on my back again and again. I screamed and begged for mercy. I grovelled at Uncle Sam's feet, begging him to stop, promising never to lift my hand to any white person. . . .

At last the white man's voice said: "All right, Sam."

Uncle Sam stopped. I lay whimpering on the floor. Aunt Liza sat like one in a trance.

"Is he still stubborn, Sam?"

"Tell the *baas* and *basies* you are sorry."

"I'm sorry," I said.

"Bet his father is one of those who believe in equality."

"His father is dead," Aunt Liza said.

"Good night, Sam."

"Good night, *baas*. Sorry about this."

"All right, Sam." He opened the door. The boys went out first, then he followed. "Good night, Liza."

Aunt Liza did not answer. The door shut behind the white folk, and soon we heard their trap moving away. Uncle Sam flung the thong viciously against the door, slumped down on the bench, folded his arms on the table, and buried his head on his arms. Aunt Liza moved away from him, sat down on the floor beside me, and lifted me into her large lap. She sat rocking my body. Uncle Sam began to sob softly. After some time he raised his head and looked at us.

"Explain to the child, Liza," he said.

"You explain," Aunt Liza said bitterly. "You are the man. You did the beating. You are the head of the family. This is a man's world. You do the explaining."

"Please, Liza."

"You should be happy. The whites are satisfied. We can go on now."

With me in her arms, Aunt Liza got up. She carried me into the other room. The food on the table remained half-eaten. She laid me on the bed on my stomach, smeared fat on my back, then covered me with the blankets. She undressed and got into bed beside me. She cuddled me close, warmed me with her own body. With her big hand on my cheek, she rocked me, first to silence, then to sleep.

For the only time during my stay there, I slept on a bed in Elsburg.

When I woke next morning, Uncle Sam had gone. Aunt Liza only once referred to the beating he had given me. It was in the late afternoon, when I returned with the day's cow dung.

"It hurt him," she said. "You'll understand one day."

That night Uncle Sam brought me an orange, a bag of boiled sweets, and a dirty old picture book. He smiled as he gave them to me, rather anxiously. When I smiled back at him, he seemed to relax. He put his hand on my head, started to say something, then changed his mind and took his seat by the fire.

Aunt Liza looked up from the floor, where she dished out the food.

"It's all right, old man," she murmured.

"One day . . ." Uncle Sam said.

"It's all right," Aunt Liza repeated insistently.

THE TYRANNY OF THE MARKET

Albert Maltz

"The Happiest Man On Earth"

Jesse felt ready to weep. He had been sitting in the shanty waiting for Tom to appear, grateful for the chance to rest his injured foot, quietly, joyously anticipating the moment when Tom would say, "Why of course, Jesse, you can start whenever you're ready!"

For two weeks he had been pushing himself, from Kansas City, Missouri, to Tulsa, Oklahoma, through nights of rain and a week of scorching sun, without sleep or a decent meal, sustained by the vision of that one moment. And then Tom had come into the office. He had come in quickly, holding a sheaf of papers in his hand; he had glanced at Jesse only casually, it was true—but long enough. He had not known him. He had turned away. . . . And Tom Brackett was his brother-in-law.

Was it his clothes? Jesse knew he looked terrible. He had tried to spruce up at a drinking fountain in the park, but even that had gone badly; in his excitement he had cut himself shaving, an ugly gash down the side of his cheek. And nothing could get the red gumbo dust out of his suit even though he had slapped himself till both arms were worn out. . . . Or was it just that he *had* changed so much?

True, they hadn't seen each other for five years; but Tom looked five years older, that was all. He was still Tom. God! was *he* so different?

Brackett finished his telephone call. He leaned back in his swivel chair and glanced over at Jesse with small, clear blue eyes that were suspicious and unfriendly. He was a heavy, paunchy man of forty-five, auburn-haired, rather dour-looking; his face was meaty, his features pronounced and forceful, his nose somewhat bulbous and reddish-hued at the tip. He looked like a solid, decent, capable business man who was commander of his local branch of the American Legion—which he was. He surveyed Jesse with cold indiffer-

Reprinted by permission of Albert Maltz.

ence, manifestly unwilling to spend time on him. Even the way he chewed his toothpick seemed contemptuous to Jesse.

"Yes?" Brackett said suddenly. "What do you want?"

His voice was decent enough, Jesse admitted. He had expected it to be worse. He moved up to the wooden counter that partitioned the shanty. He thrust a hand nervously through his tangled hair.

"I guess you don't recognize me, Tom," he said falteringly, "I'm Jesse Fulton."

"Huh?" Brackett said. That was all.

"Yes, I am, and Ella sends you her love."

Brackett rose and walked over to the counter until they were face to face. He surveyed Fulton incredulously, trying to measure the resemblance to his brother-in-law as he remembered him. This man was tall, about thirty. That fitted! He had straight good features and a lank erect body. That was right too. But the face was too gaunt, the body too spiny under the baggy clothes for him to be sure. His brother-in-law had been a solid, strong young man with muscle and beef to him. It was like looking at a faded, badly taken photograph and trying to recognize the subject: the resemblance was there but the difference was tremendous. He searched the eyes. They at least seemed definitely familiar, gray, with a curiously shy but decent look in them. He had liked that about Fulton.

Jesse stood quiet. Inside he was seething. Brackett was like a man examining a piece of broken-down horseflesh: there was a look of pure pity in his eyes. It made Jesse furious. He knew he wasn't as far gone as all that.

"Yes, I believe you are," Brackett said finally, "but you sure have changed."

"By God, it's five years, ain't it?" Jesse said resentfully. "You only saw me a couple of times anyway." Then, to himself, with his lips locked together, in mingled vehemence and shame, What if I have changed? Don't everybody? I ain't no corpse.

"You was solid-looking," Brackett continued softly, in the same tone of incredulous wonder. "You lost weight, I guess?"

Jesse kept silent. He needed Brackett too much to risk antagonizing him. But it was only by deliberate effort that he could keep from boiling over. The pause lengthened, became painful. Brackett flushed. "Jiminy Christmas, excuse me," he burst out in apology. He jerked the counter up. "Come in. Take a seat. Good God, boy"—he grasped Jesse's hand and shook it—"I *am* glad to see you; don't think anything else! You just looked so peaked."

"It's all right," Jesse murmured. He sat down, thrusting his hand through his curly, tangled hair.

"Why are you limping?"

"I stepped on a stone; it jagged a hole through my shoe." Jesse pulled his feet back under the chair. He was ashamed of his shoes. They had come from the Relief originally, and two weeks on the road had about finished them. All morning, with a kind of delicious, foolish solemnity, he had been vowing to himself that before anything else, before even a suit of clothes, he was going to buy himself a brand-new strong pair of shoes.

Brackett kept his eyes off Jesse's feet. He knew what was bothering the boy and it filled his heart with pity. The whole thing was appalling. He had never seen anyone who looked more down and out. His sister had been writing to him every week, but she hadn't told him they were as badly off as this.

"Well, now, listen," Brackett began, "tell me things. How's Ella?"

"Oh, she's pretty good," Jesse replied absently. He had a soft, pleasing, rather shy voice that went with his soft gray eyes. He was worrying over how to get started.

"And the kids?"

"Oh, they're fine. . . . Well, you know," Jesse added, becoming more attentive, "the young one has to wear a brace. He can't run around, you know. But he's smart. He draws pictures and he does things, you know."

"Yes," Brackett said. "That's good." He hesitated. There was a moment's silence. Jesse fidgeted in his chair. Now that the time had arrived, he felt awkward. Brackett leaned forward and put his hand on Jesse's knee. "Ella didn't tell me things were so bad for you, Jesse. I might have helped."

"Well, goodness," Jesse returned softly, "you been having your own troubles, ain't you?"

"Yes," Brackett leaned back. His ruddy face became mournful and darkly bitter. "You know I lost my hardware shop?"

"Well, sure, of course," Jesse answered, surprised. "You wrote us. That's what I mean."

"I forgot," Brackett said. "I keep on being surprised over it myself. Not that it was worth much," he added bitterly. "It was running downhill for three years. I guess I just wanted it because it was mine." He laughed pointlessly, without mirth. "Well, tell me about yourself," he asked. "What happened to the job you had?"

Jesse burst out abruptly, with agitation. "Let it wait, Tom, I got something on my mind."

"It ain't you and Ella?" Brackett interrupted anxiously.

"Why, no!" Jesse sat back. "Why, however did you come to think that? Why, Ella and me"—he stopped, laughing. "Why, Tom, I'm just crazy about Ella. Why she's just wonderful. She's just my whole life, Tom."

"Excuse me. Forget it." Brackett chuckled uncomfortably, turned away. The naked intensity of the youth's burst of love had upset him. It made him wish savagely that he could do something for them. They were both too decent to have had it so hard. Ella was like this boy too, shy and a little soft.

"Tom, listen," Jesse said, "I come here on purpose." He thrust his hand through his hair. "I want you to help me."

"Damn it, boy," Brackett groaned. He had been expecting this. "I can't much. I only get thirty-five a week and I'm damn grateful for it."

"Sure, I know," Jesse emphasized excitedly. He was feeling once again the wild, delicious agitation that had possessed him in the early hours of the morning. "I know you can't help us with money! But we met a man who works for you! He was in our city! He said you could give me a job!"

"Who said?"

"Oh, why didn't you tell me?" Jesse burst out reproachfully. "Why, as soon as I heard it I started out. For two weeks now I been pushing ahead like crazy."

Brackett groaned aloud. "You come walking from Kansas City in two weeks so I could give you a job?"

"Sure, Tom, of course. What else could I do?"

"God Almighty, there ain't no jobs, Jesse! It's a slack season. And you don't know this oil business. It's special. I got my Legion friends here but they couldn't do nothing now. Don't you think I'd ask for you as soon as there was a chance?"

Jesse felt stunned. The hope of the last two weeks seemed rolling up into a ball of agony in his stomach. Then, frantically, he cried, "But listen, this man said *you* could hire! He *told* me! He drives trucks for you! He said you *always* need men!"

"Oh! . . . You mean *my* department?" Bracket said in a low voice.

"*Yes*, Tom. That's it!"

"Oh, no, you don't want to work in my department," Brackett told him in the same low voice. "You don't know what it is."

"Yes, I do," Jesse insisted. "He told me all about it, Tom. You're a dispatcher, ain't you? You send the dynamite trucks out?"

"Who was the man, Jesse?"

"Everett. Everett, I think."

"Egbert? Man about my size?" Brackett asked slowly.

"Yes, Egbert. He wasn't a phony, was he?"

Brackett laughed. For the second time his laughter was curiously without mirth. "No, he wasn't a phony." Then, in a changed voice: "Jiminy, boy, you should have asked me before you trekked all the way down here."

"Oh, I didn't want to," Jesse explained with naïve cunning. "I knew you'd say 'no.' He told me it was risky work, Tom. But I don't care."

Brackett locked his fingers together. His solid, meaty face became very hard. "I'm going to say 'no' anyway, Jesse."

Jesse cried out. It had not occurred to him that Brackett would not agree. It had seemed as though reaching Tulsa were the only problem he had to face. "Oh, no," he begged, "you can't. Ain't there any jobs, Tom?"

"Sure there's jobs. There's even Egbert's job if you want it."

"He's quit?"

"He's dead!"

"Oh!"

"On the job, Jesse. Last night, if you want to know."

"Oh!". . . Then, "I don't care!"

"Now you listen to me," Brackett said. "I'll tell you a few things that you should have asked before you started out. It ain't dynamite you drive. They don't use anything as safe as dynamite in drilling oil wells. They wish they could, but they can't. It's nitroglycerin! Soup!"

"But I know," Jesse told him reassuringly. "He advised me, Tom. You don't have to think I don't know."

"Shut up a minute," Brackett ordered angrily. "Listen! You just have to *look* at this soup, see? You just *cough* loud and it blows! You know how they transport it? In a can that's shaped like this, see, like a fan? That's to give room for compartments, because each compartment has to be lined with rubber. That's the only way you can even *think* of handling it."

"Listen, Tom——"

"Now wait a minute, Jesse. For God's sake just put your mind to this. I know you had your heart set on a job, but you've got to understand. This stuff goes only in special trucks! At night! They got to follow a special route! They can't go through any city! If they lay over, it's got to be in a special garage! Don't you see what that means? Don't that tell you how dangerous it is?"

"I'll drive careful," Jesse said. "I know how to handle a truck. I'll drive slow."

Brackett groaned. "Do you think Egbert didn't drive careful or know how to handle a truck?"

"Tom," Jesse said earnestly, "you can't scare me. I got my mind fixed on only one thing: Egbert said he was getting a dollar a mile. He was making five to six hundred dollars a month for half a month's work, he said. Can I get the same?"

"Sure, you can get the same," Brackett told him savagely. "A dollar a mile. It's easy. But why do you think the company has to pay so much? It's easy—until you run over a stone that your headlights didn't pick out, like Egbert did. Or get a blowout! Or get something in your eye, so the wheel twists and you jar the truck! Or any other God damn thing that nobody ever knows! We can't ask Egbert what happened to him. There's no truck to give any evidence. There's no corpse. There's nothing! Maybe tomorrow somebody'll find a piece of twisted steel way off in a cornfield. But we never find the driver. Not even a finger nail. All we know is that he don't come in on schedule. Then we wait for the police to call us. You know what happened last night? Something went wrong on a bridge. Maybe Egbert was nervous. Maybe he brushed the side with his fender. Only there's no bridge any more. No truck. No Egbert. Do you understand now? That's what you get for your God damn dollar a mile!"

There was a moment of silence. Jesse sat twisting his long thin hands. His mouth was sagging open, his face was agonized. Then he shut his eyes and spoke softly. "I don't care about that, Tom. You told me. Now you got to be good to me and give me the job."

Brackett slapped the palm of his hand down on his desk. "No!"

"Listen, Tom," Jesse said softly, "you just don't understand." He opened his eyes. They were filled with tears. They made Brackett turn away. "Just look at me, Tom. Don't that tell you enough. What did you think of me when you first saw me? You thought: 'Why don't that bum go away and stop panhandling?' Didn't you, Tom?

Tom, I just can't live like this any more. I got to be able to walk down the street with my head up."

"You're crazy," Brackett muttered. "Every year there's one out of five drivers gets killed. That's the average. What's worth that?"

"Is my life worth anything now? We're just starving at home, Tom. They ain't put us back on relief yet."

"Then you should have told me," Brackett exclaimed harshly. "It's your own damn fault. A man has no right to have false pride when his family ain't eating. I'll borrow some money and we'll telegraph it to Ella. Then you go home and get back on relief."

"And then what?"

"And then wait, God damn it! You're no old man. You got no right to throw your life away. Sometime you'll get a job."

"No!" Jesse jumped up. "No. I believed that too. But I don't now," he cried passionately. "I ain't getting a job no more than you're getting your hardware store back. I lost my skill, Tom. Linotyping is skilled work. I'm rusty now. I've been six years on relief. The only work I've had is pick and shovel. When I got that job this spring I was supposed to be an A-1 man. But I wasn't. And they got new machines now. As soon as the slack started they let me out."

"So what?" Brackett said harshly. "Ain't there other jobs?"

"How do I know?" Jesse replied. "There ain't been one for six years. I'd even be afraid to take one now. It's been too hard waiting so many weeks to get back on relief."

"Well, you got to have some courage," Brackett shouted. "You've got to keep up hope."

"I got all the courage you want," Jesse retorted vehemently, "but no, I ain't got no hope. The hope has dried up in me in six years' waiting. You're the only hope I got."

"You're crazy," Brackett muttered. "I won't do it. For God's sake think of Ella for a minute."

"Don't you *know* I'm thinking about her?" Jesse asked softly. He plucked at Brackett's sleeve. "That's what decided me, Tom." His voice became muted into a hushed, pained whisper. "The night Egbert was at our house I looked at Ella like I'd seen her for the first time. *She ain't pretty any more, Tom!*" Brackett jerked his head and moved away. Jesse followed him, taking a deep, sobbing breath. "Don't that tell you, Tom? Ella was like a little doll or something, you remember. I couldn't walk down the street without somebody turning to look at her. She ain't twenty-nine yet, Tom, and she ain't pretty no more."

Brackett sat down with his shoulders hunched up wearily. He gripped his hands together and sat leaning forward, staring at the floor.

Jesse stood over him, his gaunt face flushed with emotion, almost unpleasant in its look of pleading and bitter humility. "I ain't done right for Ella, Tom. Ella deserved better. This is the only chance I see in my whole life to do something for her. I've just been a failure."

"Don't talk nonsense," Brackett commented, without rancor. "You ain't a failure. No more than me. There's millions of men in the identical situation. It's just the depression, or the recession, or the God damn New Deal, or . . . !" He swore and lapsed into silence.

"Oh, no," Jesse corrected him, in a knowing, sorrowful tone, "those things maybe excuse other men. But not me. It was up to me to do better. This is my own fault!"

"Oh, beans!" Brackett said. "It's more sun spots than it's you!"

Jesse's face turned an unhealthy mottled red. It looked swollen. "Well, I don't care!" he cried wildly. "I don't care! You got to give me this! I got to lift my head up. I went through one stretch of hell, but I can't go through another. You want me to keep looking at my little boy's legs and tell myself if I had a job he wouldn't be like that? Every time he walks he says to me, 'I got soft bones from the rickets and you give it to me because you didn't feed me right.' Jesus Christ, Tom, you think I'm going to sit there and watch him like that another six years?"

Brackett leaped to his feet. "So what if you do?" he shouted. "You say you're thinking about Ella. How's she going to like it when you get killed?"

"Maybe I won't," Jesse pleaded. "I've got to have some luck sometime."

"That's what they all think," Brackett replied scornfully. "When you take this job your luck is a question mark. The only thing certain is that sooner or later you get killed."

"Okay, then," Jesse shouted back. "Then I do! But meanwhile I got something, don't I? I can buy a pair of shoes. Look at me! I can buy a suit that don't say 'Relief' by the way it fits. I can smoke cigarettes. I can buy some candy for the kids. I can eat some myself. Yes, by God, I want to eat some candy. I want a glass of beer once a day. I want Ella dressed up. I want her to eat meat three times a week, four times maybe. I want to take my family to the movies."

Brackett sat down. "Oh, shut up," he said wearily.

"No," Jesse told him softly, passionately, "you can't get rid of me. Listen, Tom," he pleaded, "I got it all figured out. On six hundred a month look how much I can save! If I last only three months, look how much it is—a thousand dollars—more! And maybe I'll last longer. Maybe a couple years. I can fix Ella up for life!"

"You said it," Brackett interposed. "I suppose you think she'll enjoy living when you're on a job like that?"

"I got it all figured out," Jesse answered excitedly. "She don't know, see? I tell her I make only forty. You put the rest in a bank account for her, Tom."

"Oh, shut up," Brackett said. "You think you'll be happy? Every minute, waking and sleeping, you'll be wondering if tomorrow you'll be dead. And the worst days will be your days off, when you're not driving. They have to give you every other day free to get your nerve back. And you lay around the house eating your heart out. That's how happy you'll be."

Jesse laughed. "I'll be happy! Don't you worry, I'll be so happy, I'll be singing. Lord God, Tom, I'm going to feel *proud* of myself for the first time in seven years!"

"Oh, shut up, shut up," Brackett said.

The little shanty became silent. After a moment Jesse whispered: "You got to, Tom. You got to. You got to."

Again there was silence. Brackett raised both his hands to his head, pressing the palms against his temples.

"Tom, Tom——" Jesse said.

Brackett sighed. "Oh, God damn it," he said finally, "all right, I'll take you on, God help me." His voice was low, hoarse, infinitely weary. "If you're ready to drive tonight, you can drive tonight."

Jesse didn't answer. He couldn't. Brackett looked up. The tears were running down Jesse's face. He was swallowing and trying to speak, but only making an absurd, gasping noise.

"I'll send a wire to Ella," Brackett said in the same hoarse, weary voice. "I'll tell her you got a job, and you'll send her fare in a couple of days. You'll have some money then—that is, if you last the week out, you jackass!"

Jesse only nodded. His heart felt so close to bursting that he pressed both hands against it, as though to hold it locked within his breast.

"Come back here at six o'clock," Brackett said. "Here's some money. Eat a good meal."

"Thanks," Jesse whispered.

"Wait a minute," Brackett said. "Here's my address." He wrote it on a piece of paper. "Take any car going that way. Ask the conductor where to get off. Take a bath and get some sleep."

"Thanks," Jesse said. "Thanks, Tom."

"Oh, get out of here," Brackett said.

"Tom."

"What?"

"I just——" Jesse stopped. Brackett saw his face. The eyes were still glistening with tears, but the gaunt face was shining now, with a kind of fierce radiance.

Brackett turned away. "I'm busy," he said.

Jesse went out. The wet film blinded him, but the whole world seemed to have turned golden. He limped slowly, with the blood pounding his temples and a wild, incommunicable joy in his heart. "I'm the happiest man in the world," he whispered to himself. "I'm the happiest man on the whole earth."

Brackett sat watching till finally Jesse turned the corner of the alley and disappeared. Then he hunched himself over, with his head in his hands. His heart was beating painfully, like something old and clogged. He listened to it as it beat. He sat in desperate tranquillity, gripping his head in his hands.

A WORKING-CLASS CYNIC

Doris Lessing

From *In Pursuit of the English*

One evening I was reading, while Rose smoked and worried opposite me. Rosemary began to cry. Rose instantly lifted her head to listen, although she had not heard the last remark I made.

"Leave her alone," said Ronnie Skeffington. "She'll go to sleep again."

"I've got to stop her. Mrs. Bolt'll be complaining." Her feet dragged across the floor. "Oh, Rosemary, Rosemary," she said, as the child wailed.

"Come to bed and leave her alone, she'll be all right," said Ronnie Skeffington, in an efficient voice. "Let her cry."

"But where are we going to live, if they turn us out?"

"Oh, we'll find somewhere."

"*We* will? That's good. Who wore their feet out for months trying to find a place that would take a kid?"

"Don't start that now."

Rosemary cried herself to sleep again, and Mrs. Skeffington crept back to bed.

"Oh no, leave me alone, I'm so tired."

"Come on, don't make a fuss."

"But, Ronnie, I'm so tired."

"Oh, come on."

"No, I won't."

"Oh, so you won't!" He laughed, and she cried miserably while the bed creaked. Rose said: "Listen to that! Just listen to it." At last, silence; and Rose said: "Thank God for that, perhaps we'll have some peace." But she sat listening tensely.

A few minutes later Rosemary began crying again. We sat still while the thing repeated itself. But when Mrs. Skeffington got back into bed she cried out in hysteria: "No, I won't, Ronnie. Don't make me."

"Oh, come on, what fun is there in life?"

"Fun for who?" Then she screamed out: "You've bitten me." Rosemary and her mother wailed together.

Rose got up, her lips narrowed into a vindictive line.

"Where are you going?"

"You'll see."

"Leave them alone."

"They don't leave us alone, do they?"

Rose went up and hammered on the door. "Let me in," she shouted.

"Who's that?"

"Let me in." The door opened. "You ought to be ashamed of yourself," said Rose. "Have you got to bite your wife just because she won't sleep with you fifty times a night? You dirty beast. And what about Rosemary? What's it like for her hearing all this non-sense. Give her to me."

"We'll keep her quiet, we will really."

"Give her to me," said Rose again.

Rosemary began sobbing, as a child does when it finds a refuge.

"Now you go to bed," said Rose. "You leave your wife alone. Anyway, why do you have to make love tonight? Friday and Saturday's for making love. Everyone has to work tomorrow, and you just go on and on."

Husband and wife crept into their bed. Rose took the child into the other room and covered her up on the sofa. She was upstairs a long time. When she came down her eyes were red.

"Yes," she said. "If I had a kid I'd know what to do. But who gets them? Dirty beasts like them Skeffingtons."

"You're hard on them."

"Now don't you start on your talk. Just don't talk. I don't want to think about nothing at all. Because when I start thinking I begin to think about what might happen. Suppose I don't marry Dickie, what then?"

"You'll marry someone else."

"Yes? They're all the same, when you get down to it."

"Things are different from they used to be. You don't have to get married."

"They might be different for you, but they're not for me."

This was how she always put an end to our discussions about socialism. "You're different," she had concluded, listening to me exhort about the system. "You're middle-class—you don't mind me saying it, I've got nothing against you personally, see? So if you want to talk about socialism, you're welcome."

"Rose, socialism is for the working people, not for us."

"Yes?"

"Yes. You won't get it until you fight for it."

"Yes? I'm not going to waste my time getting excited. Things will last out my time. In the newspapers they're always talking about a new this and new that. Well, there's one thing I know, my mother worked all her life, and I'm no better off than she was."

"Yes, you are. You won't starve, for one thing?"

"Starve? Who's talking about starving? She never starved either. There's always someone to help you out if you're in trouble. You would, if I was in trouble. But I know her life and I know mine. And I know the difference, not much."

"It's your fault, because you won't fight."

"Yes? Well you talk, if you enjoy it, I'll think my own thoughts."

"We're supposed to have a new society."

"Yes?"

"Do you get angry because there are still rich and powerful people when all that is supposed to be finished?"

"Who said it was?"

"A lot of people."

"Well, if you want to believe all them lies, who's stopping you?"

"I didn't say I believed it."

"Then you're talking sense for once."

"All the same. The reason they are saying it, is they want to put something over on you."

"Yes? Well, they're not. As for them with their parties and their good times and their money here and their money there, I say, good luck to them. They've either got brains, which I haven't, or they've done something dirty to get it. Well, I don't envy their consciences. Would you like to be Bobby Brent or Dan or Flo?"

"Much rather, than being virtuous and poor."

"Then you're not my friend. Excuse me for saying so. I don't like you talking like that. Then why don't you put money into their dirty deals?"

"Because I haven't any."

"Don't give me that talk. I don't believe it, for one. And for another, I don't like to hear it. And I'll tell you something else. Sometimes I'm sorry you're my friend, because you make me think about things."

"Good. That's what friends are for."

"Yes? But not if it makes you unhappy. I've told you before, there's one thing wrong with you. You think it's enough to say things are wrong to change them. Well, it isn't. I'll tell you something else. My stepfather was Labour. Well, it stands to reason, he had unemployment and all that. And who's Labour Party in this house? The Skeffingtons upstairs."

"Good for them," I said.

"Yes? That pair of no-goods? They have everything bad, and so they vote Labour." Suddenly she giggled. "It made me laugh. When we had that election, Flo and Dan, they had Tory posters all over. Well, that makes sense, they're doing all right. And the Skeffingtons stuck a Labour in their window. Flo went up and tore it down. So the Skeffingtons made a fuss about their rights. They make me laugh. Lucky they pay the rent regular. He said to Flo: All right, then we'll leave. And she said: All right, then leave. Then she thought about the rent, and her heart broke. So for weeks, you can

imagine how it was, all the house plastered up and down with Vote
for Churchill, and just one window, Vote for Labour."

"And you?"

"Me?"

"You have the vote."

"Don't make me laugh. I know what's what. I just watch them
at it and laugh to myself."

"Well, you make me angry."

"Yes I know I do, and I don't care."

"For one thing, you make me cross because you hang about
waiting for Churchill to speak. What has he ever done for you?"

"Whoever said he had?"

Rose would listen to Churchill talk with a look of devotion I
entirely misunderstood. She would emerge at the end of half an
hour's fiery peroration with a dreamy and reminiscent smile, and
say: "He makes me laugh. He's just a jealous fat man, I don't take
any notice of him. Just like a girl he is, saying to a friend: No dear,
you don't look nice in that dress, and the next thing is, he's wearing
it himself."

"Then why do you listen to him?"

"Why should I care? He makes me remember the war, for one
thing. I don't care what he says about Labour. I don't care who
gets in, I'll get a smack in the eye either way. When they come in
saying Vote for Me, Vote for Me, I just laugh. But I like to hear
Churchill speak, with his dirty V-Sign and everything, he enjoys
himself, say what you like."

Similarly she would listen to programmes about the war and say:
"Well, to think all those exciting things were going on all the time.
They didn't happen to us. Did I ever tell you about the bomb we
had on the factory?"

But there were programmes she refused to listen to at all. Or she
would return from the cinema sometimes in a mood of sullen rage,
saying: "They make me sick, they do."

"Who?"

To begin with she was vague, saying, "I don't know."

But later on, when she knew me, and we had begun to fight
about what we thought, she would say: "Oh, I know what I say'll
be grist to your mill, but I don't care. Those films. They make fun
of us."

There was a certain wireless programme that I thought was
funny, but if Rose came in when I was listening she would say

politely: "You think that's funny, do you? Well, I don't," and go out until it was over.

"I don't think it's funny people talk in different ways," she said to me at last. "That's what that programme is, isn't it? Just to make people feel above themselves because they talk well and people like me don't. Listen to them laughing, just because someone uses the wrong grammar. I'm surprised at you, dear, I am really."

I have seen her return from a film so angry she would smoke several cigarettes before she could bring herself to speak about it

"They make me sick. It was a British film, see. I don't know why I ever go to them sometimes. If it's an American film, well, they make us up all wrong, but it's what you'd expect from them. You don't take it serious. But the British films make me mad. Take the one tonight. It had what they call a cockney in it. I hate seeing cockneys in films. Anyway, what is a cockney? There aren't any, except around Bow Bells, so they say, and I've never been there. And then the barrow-boys, or down in Petticoat Lane. They just put it on to be clever, and sell things if they see an American or a foreigner coming. 'Watcher, cock,' and all that talk all over the place. They never say Watcher, cock! unless there's someone stupid around to laugh. Them film people just put it in to be clever, like the barrow-boys, it makes the upper-class people laugh. They think of the working-class as dragged up. Dragged up and ignorant and talking vulgar-ugly. I've never met anyone who spoke cockney. I don't and no one I know does, not even Flo, and God knows she's stupid enough and on the make to say anything. Well, that's what I think and I'll stick to it. And the bloody British can keep their films. I don't mind when they have a film about rich people. You can go and have a nice sit-down and take the weight off your feet and think: I wish that was me. But when they make pictures for people to laugh at, then they've had me and my money. I'll keep my money for the Americans. You don't take them serious, and anyway they don't laugh at people with different voices in America. That's because America is all foreigners, the way I look at it, and they can't all laugh at each other, can they? Sometimes when I've got the 'ump I think I'll go to America and to hell with England, that's what I think, anyway."

"You'd hate it in America," I said.

"How do I know? Well, the way I look at it is, America must be like England was during the war."

Rose, now she was depressed, talked about the war all the time.

At this distance—it was 1950 now—those six years of hardship meant to her warmth, comradeship, a feeling of belonging and being wanted, a feeling she had never been given before or since. She could talk about the war for hours and never mention death, fear, food shortages or danger.

"Eight hundred people we were, in the factory. We got to know each other, by face, anyway. It was funny, everyone not knowing what'd happen next day, if their house was still standing or not, by the time they got home at nights, but at least, we were all together, if you know what I mean. I used to be sorry for myself, with all the night-work and everything. I used to say: When will the war be over—and not think it'd ever be over. But now I wish it was back. I don't mean the killing part of it, but I didn't know anyone who was killed, much, not much more than in peacetime—I mean, I know they were killed, but I didn't know them. But then people liked each other. You could talk to people, if you felt like it, even upper-class people, and no one would think the worse. You got to know people. You'd think about some lardyda person, they're not so bad, when you get to know them, they can't help it, poor sods, it's the way they're brought up. I remember when I got scared and the raids were bad, I used to go down to the shelters and the air was foul, and I couldn't sleep and the ground was shaking all around, and I wished it would all end. But it was nice, too. You could talk to the man sitting next to you in the Underground at night, and share your blanket with him if he hadn't got one, and he never thought the worse. You'd say goodbye in the morning and you'd know you'd never see him again, but you'd feel nice all day, because he was friendly, and you was friendly too. See? And if I got real shook-up and frightened and I couldn't take the shelters, I used to go home to my mother. My stepfather was giving her hell, because he was dying of tuberculosis, only he was keeping it quiet, and we didn't know he was so ill, otherwise we'd have had more patience with the old so-and-so, but he wouldn't have me in the house, he said I was a bad girl, because of being out at nights after ten o'clock—he just made me laugh with his dirty mind. So I'd creep all quiet into mother's room and she'd lock the door and say she had a headache and we'd get under the bed on a mattress because of the bombs and we'd talk. It was company, see, with the Germans overhead and the bombs. And I'd hear that old so-and-so crying for my mother, and I'd think, sod him. Of course if I'd known his lungs were rotting on him with T.B., I'd not have grabbed my mother when I had the chance, but I didn't know. If someone had told me I'd be glad to have the war back, I'd have laughed in their face. Now I think: That was a good time, say what you like. I earned eight pounds a week. Where am I going to earn eight pounds a week now? Lucky I had the sense to put some in the post office for my old age. Not that it'll be worth anything by then, the way money's melting to nothing week by week as we live. But I like to think I have something there. Without the war, I wouldn't. Yes, I know, dear, it's funny you can only get something nice these days when there's a war, but that's how things seem to me. People liked each other. Well, they don't now, do they? And so don't talk to me about your socialism, it just makes me sick and tired, and that's the truth."

A MIDDLE-CLASS INTELLECTUAL

Lionel Trilling

From *Middle of the Journey*

For a while Nancy gardened in silence. Then she asked, "Are you fond of flowers, John?"

It was one of those things that one friend can say to another only under such country circumstances—while one of them worked and the other idled, in the open air, with plenty of time ahead, with no particular concentration on each other, not wanting any special answer or any answer at all. It came like a greeting and suggested how valuable he could be without struggle, or ideas, or commitments. A hundred, a thousand other questions could be asked that would have the effect of making two people as simple and without strain as Laskell suddenly felt that he and Nancy were. It seemed to him that such conversations could go on for ever. "Are you fond of flowers?" "Do you like dogs?" "Do you like whisky?" "Do you like to read poetry?" And there were untold numbers of answers. "Yes, I am quite fond of flowers and my favourites are peonies but I also have a great feeling for delphinium." "Yes, I like dogs. If I had one, I would have an Irish terrier. I've also thought of dachschunds. Schnauzers I don't like, nor boxers, nor Scotch terriers. But I'd only have a dog if I lived in the country." It could go on for ever.

It would have been better if, lying there on the ground, with his hands clasped under his head, he had just stayed with one of those imbecile answers to Nancy's question, one of those responses that gently said no more than that he was alive and she was alive and that they were aware of this fact about each other. But instead he said, "It's funny you ask. Because I never gave it a thought until I got sick. But while I was sick I seem to have got myself enormously involved with a flower. It was a rose."

"Oh, roses!" said Nancy, wrinkling her nose. "Queen of the flowers."

"I could look at it for hours. I never knew what it meant when people talked about contemplation. But that's what I did with that rose—I contemplated it. My nurse Paine said—"

"I liked that Paine. Not the other nurse, not at all. But Paine I liked a great deal.

"She liked you too. She had a great admiration for both of you, you and Arthur. After I had been looking at that flower for days, she said, 'You seem to be having quite a love affair with that flower.' And I suppose she was right. It was a clever thing to say."

"You were quite a Ferdinand," Nancy said.

His eyes had been closed against the sun. Now he opened them and looked straight up into the sky. It was very blue, and the longer he looked the higher it became. He remembered that in Latin there was only one word for high and for deep. The Romans spoke of the heights of the sea and the depths of the sky. He tried to let this oddly remembered fact fill the whole of his mind.

But it would not fill the whole of his mind. It would not displace the strange, contracting pain he experienced at Nancy's calling him by the name of the hero of that children's book so popular with adults, about a young bull who liked to look at flowers and did not charge around like other bulls. When Ferdinand was sent to the bull-ring in Madrid, instead of resisting the matador and being hurt and killed, he sat down in the middle of the ring and enjoyed the flowers in the hair of the ladies who had come to see him fight. In consequence he was disgraced but safe, and he was sent back to the ranch where he spent the rest of his life looking at flowers. A good many political feelings became attached to the story and people chuckled over it as if it were a piece of folk-wisdom.

Laskell said, "Why do people like that story so much?" He was still looking deep into the sky.

"I do. I can't wait for Micky to get old enough so I can read it to him."

"Why do people like it? Why do you like it?"

"For its moral, I suppose."

"They seem to like the idea of a bull going against the nature of bulls."

"Oh, no, that's not it. The moral is that if people just refused to fight there would be no more wars. I suppose Ferdinand is just simple human reason, the reason of simple human people refusing to cooperate in their own exploitation and slaughter. After all, Ferdinand wasn't killed, the way all the other bulls were. He lived to enjoy himself."

"Is that something?"

"Well, isn't it?"

"If the Loyalists were to act like Ferdinand?"

"That's different. They're fighting for something."

When Laskell spoke again, he spoke carefully. "When you said just now that I was quite a Ferdinand, you were teasing me, weren't you, not praising me?"

"Why, John!" Nancy said. "Why, John Laskell!"

"No, I'm not being sensitive. But really, it's serious. You say you admire Ferdinand. But when you want to make fun of me, you say I am quite a Ferdinand. That puzzles me. It's like the people who give parties for Spain—they're the same people who admire the sissy bull."

Nancy was ruffling. "We have to make a distinction between immediate necessity and ultimate hope, don't we? We have to hope that eventually we will be able to change man's nature."

"I'm not so sure." But the conversation was becoming very heavily charged and Laskell felt tired. "I suppose," he said, "the bull who smells flowers and doesn't charge when he's attacked is the modern version of the lion who lies down with the lamb." Nancy made a gesture to show that she didn't quite accept the parallel. He had not yet been able to look at Nancy, he was still looking deep into the sky. "I think the old version was nicer. The lion was still a lion and whenever he lay down with the lamb it was a fresh surprise. I don't think we really admire Ferdinand, Nancy. I think we really despise him. What bothers me is that we praise something we really despise." And then he said, "I wonder if we're not developing a strange ambivalent kind of culture, people like us. I wonder if we don't rather like the idea of safety by loss of bullhood. A kind of Kingdom-come by emasculation."

He had successfully carried it away from himself. And the sudden pain he had felt when Nancy called him Ferdinand had sunk almost to nothing. He had talked very fast and he had headed, as the occasion seemed to require, towards generalities. He had talked with half his mind, loosely, and he was rather startled by the place he had come to. He had never before generalized in this adverse way about the people he lived with, the decent people, the people of goodwill. It frightened him a little. He wondered what Nancy would say.

Nancy had picked up her hand-rake and was thoughtfully scratching the grass with it. For the life of him Laskell could not think of anything to say that would carry their conversation in a new direction. He felt that he had said something for which Nancy might not easily forgive him.

A RADICAL ARISTOCRAT

Henry James

From *The Portrait of a Lady*

When Isabel was interested she asked a great many questions, and as her companion was a copious talker she urged him on this occasion by no means in vain. He told her he had four sisters and two brothers and had lost both his parents. The brothers and sisters were very good people—"not particularly clever, you know," he said, "but very decent and pleasant"; and he was so good as to hope Miss Archer might know them well. One of the brothers was in the Church, settled in the family living, that of Lockleigh, which was a heavy, sprawling parish, and was an excellent fellow in spite of his thinking differently from himself on every conceivable topic. And then Lord Warburton mentioned some of the opinions held by his brother, which were opinions Isabel had often heard expressed and that she supposed to be entertained by a considerable portion

From Ch. VIII.

of the human family. Many of them indeed she supposed she had held herself, till he assured her she was quite mistaken, that it was really impossible, that she had doubtless imagined she entertained them, but that she might depend that, if she thought them over a little, she would find there was nothing in them. When she answered that she had already thought several of the questions involved over very attentively he declared that she was only another example of what he had often been struck with—the fact that, of all the people in the world, the Americans were the most grossly superstitious. They were rank Tories and bigots, every one of them; there were no conservatives like American conservatives. Her uncle and her cousin were there to prove it; nothing could be more mediaeval than many of their views; they had ideas that people in England nowadays were ashamed to confess to; and they had the impudence moreover, said his lordship, laughing, to pretend they knew more about the needs and dangers of this poor dear stupid old England than he who was born in it and owned a considerable slice of it—the more shame to him! From all of which Isabel gathered that Lord Warburton was a nobleman of the newest pattern, a reformer, a radical, a contemner of ancient ways. His other brother, who was in the army in India, was rather wild and pig-headed and had not been of much use as yet but to make debts for Warburton to pay—one of the most precious privileges of an elder brother. "I don't think I shall pay any more," said her friend; "he lives a monstrous deal better than I do, enjoys unheard-of luxuries and thinks himself a much finer gentleman than I. As I'm a consistent radical I go in only for equality; I don't go in for the superiority of the younger brothers." Two of his four sisters, the second and fourth, were married, one of them having done very well, as they said, the other only so-so. The husband of the elder, Lord Haycock, was a very good fellow, but unfortunately a horrid Tory; and his wife, like all good English wives, was worse than her husband. The other had espoused a smallish squire in Norfolk and, though married but the other day, had already five children. This information and much more Lord Warburton imparted to his young American listener, taking pains to make many things clear and to lay bare to her apprehension the peculiarities of English life. Isabel was often amused at his explicitness and at the small allowance he seemed to make either for her own experience or for her imagination. "He thinks I'm a barbarian," she said, "and that I've never seen forks and spoons"; and she used to ask him artless questions for the pleasure of hearing him answer seriously. Then when he had fallen into the trap, "It's a pity you can't see me in my war-paint and feathers," she remarked; "if I had known how kind you are to the poor savages I would have brought over my native costume!" Lord Warburton had travelled through the United States and knew much more about them than Isabel; he was so good as to say that America was the most charming country in the world, but his recollections of it appeared to encourage the idea that Americans in England would need to have a great many things explained to them. "If I had only had you to explain things to me in America!" he said. "I was rather puzzled in your country; in fact I was quite bewildered, and the trouble was that the explanations only puzzled me more. You know I think they often gave me the wrong ones on purpose; they're rather clever about that over there. But when I explain you can trust me; about what I tell you there's no mistake." There was no mistake at least about his being very intelligent and cultivated and knowing almost everything in the world. Although he gave the most interesting and thrilling glimpses Isabel felt he never did it to exhibit himself, and though he had had rare chances and had tumbled in, as she put it, for high prizes, he was as far as possible from making a merit of it. He had enjoyed the best things of life, but they had not spoiled his sense of proportion. His quality was a mixture of the effect of rich experience—oh, so easily come by! —with a modesty at times almost boyish; the sweet and wholesome savour of which—it was as agreeable as something tasted—lost nothing from the addition of a tone of responsible kindness.

"I like your specimen English gentleman very much," Isabel said to Ralph after Lord Warburton had gone.

"I like him too—I love him well," Ralph returned. "But I pity him more."

Isabel looked at him askance. "Why, that seems to me his only fault—that one can't pity him a little. He appears to have everything, to know everything, to *be* everything."

"Oh, he's in a bad way!" Ralph insisted.

"I suppose you don't mean in health?"

"No, as to that he's detestably sound. What I mean is that he's a man with a great position who's playing all sorts of tricks with it. He doesn't take himself seriously."

"Does he regard himself as a joke?"

"Much worse; he regards himself as an imposition—as an abuse."

"Well, perhaps he is," said Isabel.

"Perhaps he is—though on the whole I don't think so. But in that case what's more pitiable than a sentient, self-conscious abuse planted by other hands, deeply rooted but aching with a sense of its injustice? For me, in his place, I could be as solemn as a statue of Buddha. He occupies a position that appeals to my imagination. Great responsibilities, great opportunities, great consideration, great wealth, great power, a natural share in the public affairs of a great country. But he's all in a muddle about himself, his position, his power, and indeed about everything in the world. He's the victim of a critical age; he has ceased to believe in himself and he doesn't know what to believe in. When I attempt to tell him (because if I were he I know very well what I should believe in) he calls me a pampered bigot. I believe he seriously thinks me an awful Philistine; he says I don't understand my time. I understand it certainly better than he, who can neither abolish himself as a nuisance nor maintain himself as an institution."

"He doesn't look very wretched," Isabel observed.

"Possibly not; though, being a man of a good deal of charming taste, I think he often has uncomfortable hours. But what is it to say of a being of his opportunities that he's not miserable? Besides, I believe he is."

"I don't," said Isabel.

"Well," her cousin rejoined, "if he isn't he ought to be!"

In the afternoon she spent an hour with her uncle on the lawn, where the old man sat, as usual, with his shawl over his legs and his large cup of diluted tea in his hands. In the course of conversation he asked her what she thought of their late visitor.

Isabel was prompt. "I think he's charming."

"He's a nice person," said Mr. Touchett, "but I don't recommend you to fall in love with him."

"I shall not do it then; I shall never fall in love but on your recommendation. Moreover," Isabel added, "my cousin gives me rather a sad account of Lord Warburton."

"Oh, indeed? I don't know what there may be to say, but you must remember that Ralph *must* talk."

"He thinks your friend's too subversive—or not subversive enough! I don't quite understand which," said Isabel.

The old man shook his head slowly, smiled and put down his cup. "I don't know which either. He goes very far, but it's quite possible he doesn't go far enough. He seems to want to do away with a good many things, but he seems to want to remain himself. I suppose that's natural, but it's rather inconsistent."

"Oh, I hope he'll remain himself," said Isabel. "If he were to be done away with his friends would miss him sadly."

"Well," said the old man, "I guess he'll stay and amuse his friends. I should certainly miss him very much here at Gardencourt. He always amuses me when he comes over, and I think he amuses himself as well. There's a considerable number like him, round in society; they're very fashionable just now. I don't know what they're trying to do—whether they're trying to get up a revolution. I hope at any rate they'll put it off till after I'm gone. You see they want to disestablish everything; but I'm a pretty big landowner here, and I don't want to be disestablished. I wouldn't have come over if I had thought they were going to behave like that," Mr. Touchett went on with expanding hilarity. "I came over because I thought England was a safe country. I call it a regular fraud if they are going to introduce any considerable changes; there'll be a large number disappointed in that case."

"Oh, I do hope they'll make a revolution!" Isabel exclaimed. "I should delight in seeing a revolution."

"Let me see," said her uncle, with a humorous intention; "I forget whether you're on the side of the old or on the side of the new. I've heard you take such opposite views."

"I'm on the side of both. I guess I'm a little on the side of everything. In a revolution—after it was well begun—I think I should be a high, proud loyalist. One sympathises more with them, and they've a chance to behave so exquisitely. I mean so picturesquely."

"I don't know that I understand what you mean by behaving picturesquely, but it seems to me that you do that always, my dear."

"Oh, you lovely man, if I could believe that!" the girl interrupted.

"I'm afraid, after all, you won't have the pleasure of going gracefully to the guillotine here just now," Mr. Touchett went on. "If you want to see a big outbreak you must pay us a long visit. You see, when you come to the point it wouldn't suit them to be taken at their word."

"Of whom are you speaking?"

"Well, I mean Lord Warburton and his friends—the radicals of the upper class. Of course I only know the way it strikes me. They talk about the changes, but I don't think they quite realise. You and I, you know, we know what it is to have lived under democratic institutions: I always thought them very comfortable, but I was used to them from the first. And then I ain't a lord; you're a lady, my dear, but I ain't a lord. Now over here I don't think it quite comes home to them. It's a matter of every day and every hour, and I don't think many of them would find it as pleasant as what they've got. Of course if they want to try, it's their own business; but I expect they won't try very hard."

"Don't you think they're sincere?" Isabel asked.

"Well, they want to *feel* earnest," Mr. Touchett allowed; "but it seems as if they took it out in theories mostly. Their radical views are a kind of amusement; they've got to have some amusement, and they might have coarser tastes than that. You see they're very luxurious, and these progressive ideas are about their biggest luxury. They make them feel moral and yet don't damage their position. They think a great deal of their position; don't let one of them ever persuade you he doesn't, for if you were to proceed on that basis you'd be pulled up very short."

Isabel followed her uncle's argument, which he unfolded with his quaint distinctness, most attentively, and though she was unacquainted with the British aristocracy she found it in harmony with her general impressions of human nature. But she felt moved to put in a protest on Lord Warburton's behalf. "I don't believe Lord Warburton's a humbug; I don't care what the others are. I should like to see Lord Warburton put to the test."

"Heaven deliver me from my friends!" Mr. Touchett answered. "Lord Warburton's a very amiable young man—a very fine young man. He has a hundred thousand a year. He owns fifty thousand acres of the soil of this little island and ever so many other things besides. He has half a dozen houses to live in. He has a seat in Parliament as I have one at my own dinner-table. He has elegant tastes —cares for literature, for art, for science, for charming young ladies. The most elegant is his taste for the new views. It affords him a great deal of pleasure—more perhaps than anything else, except the young ladies. His old house over there—what does he call it, Lockleigh?—is very attractive; but I don't think it's as pleasant as this. That doesn't matter, however—he has so many others. His views don't hurt any one as far as I can see; they certainly don't hurt himself. And if there were to be a revolution he would come off very easily. They wouldn't touch him, they'd leave him as he is: he's too much liked."

"Ah, he couldn't be a martyr even if he wished!" Isabel sighed. "That's a very poor position."

"He'll never be a martyr unless you make him one," said the old man.

Isabel shook her head; there might have been something laughable in the fact that she did it with a touch of melancholy. "I shall never make any one a martyr."

"You'll never be one, I hope."

"I hope not. But you don't pity Lord Warburton then as Ralph does?"

Her uncle looked at her a while with genial acuteness. "Yes, I do, after all!"

AN ALIEN

Richard Wright

From *Native Son*

He stretched his arms above his head and yawned; his eyes moistened. The sharp precision of the world of steel and stone dissolved into blurred waves. He blinked and the world grew hard again, mechanical, distinct. A weaving motion in the sky made him turn his eyes upward; he saw a slender streak of billowing white blooming against the deep blue. A plane was writing high up in the air.

"Look!" Bigger said.

"What?"

"That plane writing up there," Bigger said, pointing.

"Oh!"

They squinted at a tiny ribbon of unfolding vapor that spelled out the word: USE. . . . The plane was so far away that at times the strong glare of the sun blanked it from sight.

"You can hardly see it," Gus said.

"Looks like a little bird," Bigger breathed with childlike wonder.

"Them white boys sure can fly," Gus said.

"Yeah," Bigger said, wistfully. "They get a chance to do everything."

Noiselessly, the tiny plane looped and veered, vanishing and appearing, leaving behind it a long trail of white plumage, like coils of fluffy paste being squeezed from a tube; a plume-coil that grew and swelled and slowly began to fade into the air at the edges. The plane wrote another word: SPEED. . . .

"How high you reckon he is?" Bigger asked.

"I don't know. Maybe a hundred miles; maybe a thousand."

"I could fly one of them things if I had a chance," Bigger mumbled reflectively, as though talking to himself.

Gus pulled down the corners of his lips, stepped out from the wall, squared his shoulders, doffed his cap, bowed low and spoke with mock deference:

"Yessuh."

"You go to hell," Bigger said, smiling.

"Yessuh," Gus said again.

"I could fly a plane if I had a chance," Bigger said.

"If you wasn't black and if you had some money, and if they'd let you go to that aviation school, you could fly a plane," Gus said.

For a moment Bigger contemplated all the "ifs" that Gus had mentioned. Then both boys broke into hard laughter, looking at each other through squinted eyes. When their laughter subsided, Bigger said in a voice that was half-question and half-statement:

"It's funny how the white folks treat us, ain't it?"

"It better be funny," Gus said.

"Maybe they right in not wanting us to fly," Bigger said. " 'Cause if I took a plane up I'd take a couple of bombs along and drop 'em as sure as hell. . . ."

They laughed again, still looking upward. The plane sailed and dipped and spread another word against the sky: GASOLINE. . . .

"Use Speed Gasoline," Bigger mused, rolling the words slowly from his lips. "God, I'd like to fly up there in that sky."

"God'll let you fly when He gives you your wings up in heaven," Gus said.

They laughed again, reclining against the wall, smoking, the lids of their eyes drooped softly against the sun. Cars whizzed past on rubber tires. Bigger's face was metallically black in the strong sunlight. There was in his eyes a pensive, brooding amusement, as of a man who had been long confronted and tantalized by a riddle whose answer seemed always just on the verge of escaping him, but prodding him irresistibly on to seek its solution. The silence irked Bigger; he was anxious to do something to evade looking so squarely at this problem.

"Let's play 'white,' " Bigger said, referring to a game of play-acting in which he and his friends imitated the ways and manners of white folks.

"I don't feel like it," Gus said.

"General!" Bigger pronounced in a sonorous tone, looking at Gus expectantly.

"Aw, hell! I don't want to play," Gus whined.

"You'll be court-martialed," Bigger said, snapping out his words with military precision.

"Nigger, you nuts!" Gus laughed.

"General!" Bigger tried again, determinedly.

Gus looked wearily at Bigger, then straightened, saluted and answered:

"Yessuh."

"Send your men over the river at dawn and attack the enemy's left flank," Bigger ordered.

"Yessuh."

"Send the Fifth, Sixth, and Seventh Regiments," Bigger said, frowning. "And attack with tanks, gas, planes, and infantry."

"Yessuh!" Gus said again, saluting and clicking his heels.

For a moment they were silent, facing each other, their shoulders thrown back, their lips compressed to hold down the mounting impulse to laugh. Then they guffawed, partly at themselves and partly at the vast white world that sprawled and towered in the sun before them.

"Say, what's a 'left flank'?" Gus asked.

"I don't know," Bigger said. "I heard it in the movies."

They laughed again. After a bit they relaxed and leaned against the wall, smoking. Bigger saw Gus cup his left hand to his ear, as though holding a telephone receiver; and cup his right hand to his mouth, as though talking into a transmitter.

"Hello," Gus said.

"Hello," Bigger said. "Who's this?"

"This is Mr. J. P. Morgan speaking," Gus said.

"Yessuh, Mr. Morgan," Bigger said; his eyes filled with mock adulation and respect.

"I want you to sell twenty thousand shares of U.S. Steel in the market this morning," Gus said.

"At what price, suh?" Bigger asked.

"Aw, just dump 'em at any price," Gus said with casual irritation. "We're holding too much."

"Yessuh," Bigger said.

"And call me at my club at two this afternoon and tell me if the President telephoned," Gus said.

"Yessuh, Mr. Morgan," Bigger said.

Both of them made gestures signifying that they were hanging up telephone receivers; then they bent double, laughing.

"I bet that's *just* the way they talk," Gus said.

"I wouldn't be surprised," Bigger said.

They were silent again. Presently, Bigger cupped his hand to his mouth and spoke through an imaginary telephone transmitter.

"Hello."

"Hello," Gus answered. "Who's this?"

"This is the President of the United States speaking," Bigger said.

"Oh, yessuh, Mr. President," Gus said.

"I'm calling a cabinet meeting this afternoon at four o'clock and you, as Secretary of State, *must* be there.

"Well, now, Mr. President," Gus said, "I'm pretty busy. They raising sand over there in Germany and I got to send 'em a note. . . ."

"But this is important," Bigger said.

"What you going to take up at this cabinet meeting?" Gus asked.

"Well, you see, the niggers is raising sand all over the country," Bigger said, struggling to keep back his laughter. "We've got to do something with these black folks. . . ."

"Oh, if it's about the niggers, I'll be right there, Mr. President," Gus said.

They hung up imaginary receivers and leaned against the wall and laughed. A street car rattled by. Bigger sighed and swore.

"Goddammit!"

"What's the matter?"

"They don't let us do *nothing*."

"Who?"

"The *white* folks."

"You talk like you just now finding that out," Gus said.

"Naw. But I just can't get used to it," Bigger said. "I swear to God I can't. I know I oughtn't think about it, but I can't help it. Every time I think about it I feel like somebody's poking a red-hot iron down my throat. Goddammit, look! We live here and they live there. We black and they white. They got things and we ain't. They do things and we can't. It's just like living in jail. Half the time I feel like I'm on the outside of the world peeping in through a knot-hole in the fence. . . ."

"Aw, ain't no use feeling that way about it. It don't help none," Gus said.

"You know one thing?" Bigger said.

"What?"

"Sometimes I feel like something awful's going to happen to me." Bigger spoke with a tinge of bitter pride in his voice.

"What you mean?" Gus asked, looking at him quickly. There was fear in Gus's eyes.

"I don't know. I just feel that way. Every time I get to thinking about me being black and they being white, me being here and they being there, I feel like something awful's going to happen to me. . . ."

"Aw, for Chrissakes! There ain't nothing you can do about it. How come you want to worry yourself? You black and they make the laws. . . ."

"Why they make us live in one corner of the city? Why don't they let us fly planes and run ships. . . ."

Gus hunched Bigger with his elbow and mumbled good-naturedly, "Aw, nigger, quit thinking about it. You'll go nuts."

The plane was gone from the sky and the white plumes of floating smoke were thinly spread, vanishing. Because he was restless and had time on his hands, Bigger yawned again and hoisted his arms high above his head.

"Nothing ever happens," he complained.

"What you want to happen?"

"Anything," Bigger said with a wide sweep of his dingy palm, a sweep that included all the possible activities of the world.

Then their eyes were riveted; a slate-colored pigeon swooped down to the middle of the steel car tracks and began strutting to and fro with ruffled feathers, its fat neck bobbing with regal pride. A street car rumbled forward and the pigeon rose swiftly through the air on wings stretched so taut and sheer that Bigger could see the gold of the sun through their translucent tips. He tilted his head and watched the slate-colored bird flap and wheel out of sight over the edge of the high roof.

"Now, if I could only do that," Bigger said.

Gus laughed.

"Nigger, you nuts."

"I reckon we the only things in this city that can't go where we want to go and do what we want to do."

"Don't think about it," Gus said.

"I can't help it."

"That's why you feeling like something awful's going to happen to you," Gus said. "You think too much."

"What in hell can a man do?" Bigger asked, turning to Gus.

"Get drunk and sleep it off."

"I can't. I'm broke."

Bigger crushed his cigarette and took out another one and offered the package to Gus. They continued smoking. A huge truck swept past, lifting scraps of white paper into the sunshine; the bits settled down slowly.

"Gus?"

"Hunh?"

"You know where the white folks live?"

"Yeah," Gus said, pointing eastward. "Over across the 'line'; over there on Cottage Grove Avenue."

"Naw; they don't," Bigger said.

"What you mean?" Gus asked, puzzled. "Then, where do they live?"

Bigger doubled his fist and struck his solar plexus.

"Right down here in my stomach," he said.

Gus looked at Bigger searchingly, then away, as though ashamed.

"Yeah; I know what you mean," he whispered.

"Every time I think of 'em, I *feel* 'em," Bigger said.

"Yeah; and in your chest and throat, too," Gus said.

"It's like fire."

"And sometimes you can't hardly breathe. . . ."

Bigger's eyes were wide and placid, gazing into space.

"That's when I feel like something awful's going to happen to me. . . ." Bigger paused, narrowed his eyes. "Naw; it ain't like something going to happen to me. It's. . . . It's like I was going to do something I can't help. . . ."

"Yeah!" Gus said with uneasy eagerness. His eyes were full of a look compounded of fear and admiration for Bigger. "Yeah; I know what you mean. It's like you going to fall and don't know where you going to land. . . ."

Gus's voice trailed off. The sun slid behind a big white cloud and the street was plunged in cool shadow; quickly the sun edged forth again and it was bright and warm once more. A long sleek black car, its fenders glinting like glass in the sun, shot past them at high speed and turned a corner a few blocks away. Bigger pursed his lips and sang:

"Zoooooooooom!"

"They got everything," Gus said.

"They own the world," Bigger said.

"Aw, what the hell," Gus said. "Let's go in the poolroom."

"O.K."

They walked toward the door of the poolroom.

"Say, you taking that job you told us about?" Gus asked.

"I don't know."

"You talk like you don't want it."

"Oh, hell, yes! I want the job," Bigger said.

They looked at each other and laughed. They went inside. The poolroom was empty, save for a fat, black man who held a half-smoked, unlit cigar in his mouth and leaned on the front counter. To the rear burned a single green-shaded bulb.

"Hi, Doc," Bigger said.

"You boys kinda early this morning," Doc said.

"Jack or G.H. around yet?" Bigger asked.

"Naw," Doc said.

"Let's shoot a game," Gus said.

"I'm broke," Bigger said.

"I got some money "

"Switch on the light. The balls are racked," Doc said.

Bigger turned on the light. They lagged for first shot. Bigger won. They started playing. Bigger's shots were poor; he was thinking of Blum's, fascinated with the idea of the robbery, and a little afraid of it.

"Remember what we talked about so much?" Bigger asked in a flat, neutral tone.

"Naw."

"Old Blum."

"Oh," Gus said. "We ain't talked about that for a month. How come you think of it all of a sudden?"

"Let's clean the place out."

"I don't know."

"It was your plan from the start," Bigger said.

Gus straightened and stared at Bigger, then at Doc who was looking out of the front window.

"You going to tell Doc? Can't you never learn to talk low?"

"Aw, I was just asking you, do you want to try it?"

"Naw."

"How come? You scared 'cause he's a white man?"

"Naw. But Blum keeps a gun. Suppose he beats us to it?"

"Aw, you scared; that's all. He's a white man and you scared."

"The hell I'm scared," Gus, hurt and stung, defended himself.

Bigger went to Gus and placed an arm about his shoulders.

"Listen, you won't have to go in. You just stand at the door and keep watch, see? Me and Jack and G.H.'ll go in. If anybody comes along, you whistle and we'll go out the back way. That's all."

The front door opened; they stopped talking and turned their heads.

"Here comes Jack and G.H. now," Bigger said.

Jack and G.H. walked to the rear of the poolroom.

"What you guys doing?" Jack asked.

"Shooting a game. Wanna play?" Bigger asked.

"You asking 'em to play and I'm paying for the game," Gus said.

They all laughed and Bigger laughed with them but stopped quickly. He felt that the joke was on him and he took a seat alongside the wall and propped his feet upon the rungs of a chair, as though he had not heard. Gus and G.H. kept on laughing.

"You niggers is crazy," Bigger said. "You laugh like monkeys and you ain't got nerve enough to do nothing but talk."

"What you mean?" G.H. asked.

"I got a haul all figured out," Bigger said.

"What haul?"

"Old Blum's."

There was silence. Jack lit a cigarette. Gus looked away, avoiding the conversation.

"If Old Blum was a black man, you-all would be itching to go. 'Cause he's white, everybody's scared."

"I ain't scared," Jack said. "I'm with you."

"You say you got it all figured out?" G.H. asked.

Bigger took a deep breath and looked from face to face. It seeme1 to him that he should not have to explain.

"Look, it'll be easy. There ain't nothing to be scared of. Between three and four ain't nobody in the store but the old man. The cop is way down at the other end of the block. One of us'll stay outside and watch. Three of us'll go in, see? One of us'll throw a gun on old Blum; one of us'll make for the cash box under the counter; one of us'll make for the back door and have it open so we can make a quick get-away down the black alley. . . . That's all. It won't take three minutes."

"I thought we said we wasn't never going to use a gun," G.H. said. "And we ain't bothered no white folks before."

"Can't you see? This is something *big*," Bigger said.

He waited for more objections. When none were forthcoming, he talked again.

"We can do it, if you niggers ain't scared."

Save for the sound of Doc's whistling up front, there was silence. Bigger watched Jack closely; he knew that the situation was one in which Jack's word would be decisive. Bigger was afraid of Gus, because he knew that Gus would not hold out if Jack said yes. Gus stood at the table, toying with a cue stick, his eyes straying lazily over the billiard balls scattered about the table in the array of an unfinished game. Bigger rose and sent the balls whirling with a sweep of his hand, then looked straight at Gus as the gleaming balls kissed and rebounded from the rubber cushions, zig-zagging across the table's green cloth. Even though Bigger had asked Gus to be with him in the robbery, the fear that Gus would really go made the muscles of Bigger's stomach tighten; he was hot all over. He felt as if he wanted to sneeze and could not; only it was more nervous than wanting to sneeze. He grew hotter, tighter; his nerves were taut and his teeth were on edge. He felt that something would soon snap within him.

"Goddammit! Say something, somebody!"

"I'm in," Jack said again.

"I'll go if the rest goes," G.H. said.

Gus stood without speaking and Bigger felt a curious sensation—half-sensual, half-thoughtful. He was divided and pulled against himself. He had handled things just right so far; all but Gus had consented. The way things stood now there were three against Gus, and that was just as he had wanted it to be. Bigger was afraid of robbing a white man and he knew that Gus was afraid, too. Blum's store was small and Blum was alone, but Bigger could not think of robbing him without being flanked by his three pals. But even with his pals he was afraid. He had argued all of his pals but one into consenting to the robbery, and toward the lone man who held out he felt a hot hate and fear; he had transferred his fear of the whites to Gus. He hated Gus because he knew that Gus was afraid, as even he was; and he feared Gus because he felt that Gus would consent and then he would be compelled to go through with the robbery. Like a man about to shoot himself and dreading to shoot and yet knowing that he has to shoot and feeling it all at once and powerfully, he watched Gus and waited for him to say yes. But Gus did not speak. Bigger's teeth clamped so tight that his jaws ached. He edged toward Gus, not looking at Gus, but feeling the presence of Gus over all his body, through him, in and out of him, and hating himself and Gus because he felt it. Then he could not stand it any longer. The hysterical tensity of his nerves urged him to speak, to free himself. He faced Gus, his eyes red with anger and fear, his fists clenched and held stiffly to his sides.

"You black sonofabitch," he said in a voice that did not vary in tone. "You scared 'cause he's a white man."

"Don't cuss me, Bigger," Gus said quietly.

"I *am* cussing you!"

"You don't have to cuss me," Gus said.

"Then why don't you use that black tongue of yours?" Bigger asked. "Why don't you say what you going to do?"

"I don't have to use my tongue unless I *want* to!"

"You bastard! You scared bastard!"

"You ain't my boss," Gus said.

"You yellow!" Bigger said. "You scared to rob a white man."

"Aw, Bigger. Don't say that," G.H. said. "Leave 'im alone."

"He's yellow," Bigger said. "He won't go with us."

"I didn't say I wouldn't go," Gus said.

"Then, for Chrissakes, say what you going to do," Bigger said.

Gus leaned on his cue stick and gazed at Bigger and Bigger's stomach tightened as though he were expecting a blow and were getting ready for it. His fists clenched harder. In a split second he felt how his fist and arm and body would feel if he hit Gus squarely in the mouth, drawing blood; Gus would fall and he would walk out and the whole thing would be over and the robbery would not take place. And his thinking and feeling in this way made the choking tightness rising from the pit of his stomach to his throat slacken a little.

"You see, Bigger," began Gus in a tone that was a compromise between kindness and pride. "You see, Bigger, you the cause of all the trouble we ever have. It's your hot temper. Now, how come you want to cuss me? Ain't I got a right to make up my mind? Naw; that ain't your way. You start cussing. You say I'm scared. It's *you* who's scared. You scared I'm going to say yes and you'll have to go through with the job. . . ."

"Say that again! Say that again and I'll take one of these balls and sink it in your Goddamn mouth," Bigger said, his pride wounded to the quick.

"Aw, for Chrissakes," Jack said.

"You *see* how he is," Gus said.

"Why don't you say what you going to do?" Bigger demanded.

"Aw, I'm going with you-all," Gus said in a nervous tone that sought to hide itself; a tone that hurried on to other things. "I'm going, but Bigger don't have to act like that. He don't have to cuss me."

"Why didn't you say that at first?" Bigger asked; his anger amounted almost to frenzy. "You make a man want to sock you!"

". . . I'll help on the haul," Gus continued, as though Bigger had not spoken. "I'll help just like I always help. But I'll be Goddamn if I'm taking orders from *you.* Bigger! You just a scared coward! You calling me scared so nobody'll see how scared *you* is!"

Bigger leaped at him, but Jack ran between them. G.H. caught Gus's arm and led him aside.

"Who's asking you to take orders?" Bigger said. "I never want to give orders to a piss-sop like you!"

"You boys cut out that racket back there!" Doc called.

They stood silently about the pool table. Bigger's eyes followed Gus as Gus put his cue stick in the rack and brushed chalk dust from his trousers and walked a little distance away. Bigger's stomach burned and a hazy black cloud hovered a moment before his eyes, and left. Mixed images of violence ran like sand through his mind, dry and fast, vanishing. He could stab Gus with his knife; he could slap him; he could kick him; he could trip him up and send him sprawling on his face. He could do a lot of things to Gus for making him feel this way.

"Come on, G.H.," Gus said.

"Where we going?"

"Let's walk."

"O.K."

"What we gonna do?" Jack asked. "Meet here at three?"

"Sure," Bigger said. "Didn't we just decide?"

"I'll be here," Gus said, with his back turned.

When Gus and G.H. had gone Bigger sat down and felt cold sweat on his skin. It was planned now and he would have to go through with it. His teeth gritted and the last image he had seen of Gus going through the door lingered in his mind. He could have taken one of the cue sticks and gripped it hard and swung it at the back of Gus's head, feeling the impact of the hard wood cracking against the bottom of the skull. The tight feeling was still in him and he knew that it would remain until they were actually doing the job, until they were in the store taking the money.

"You and Gus sure don't get along none," Jack said, shaking his head.

Bigger turned and looked at Jack; he had forgotten that Jack was still there.

"Aw, that yellow black bastard," Bigger said.

"He's all right," Jack said.

"He's scared," Bigger said. "To make him ready for a job, you have to make him scared two ways. You have to make him more scared of what'll happen to him if he don't do the job than of what'll happen to him if he pulls the job."

"If we going to Blum's today, we oughtn't fuss like this," Jack said. "We got a job on our hands, a real job."

"Sure. Sure, I know," Bigger said.

Bigger felt an urgent need to hide his growing and deepening feeling of hysteria; he had to get rid of it or else he would succumb to it. He longed for a stimulus powerful enough to focus his attention and drain off his energies. He wanted to run. Or listen to some swing music. Or laugh or joke. Or read a *Real Detective Story Magazine.* Or go to a movie. Or visit Bessie. All that morning he had lurked behind his curtain of indifference and looked at things, snapping and glaring at whatever had tried to make him come out into the open. But now he was out; the thought of the job at Blum's and the tilt he had had with Gus had snared him into things and his self-trust was gone. Confidence could only come again now through action so violent that it would make him forget. These were the rhythms of his life: indifference and violence; periods of abstract brooding and periods of intense desire; moments of silence and moments of anger—like water ebbing, and flowing from the tug of a far-away, invisible force. Being this way was a need of his as deep as eating. He was like a strange plant blooming in the day and wilting at night; but the sun that made it bloom and the cold darkness that made it wilt were never seen. It was his own sun and darkness, a private and personal sun and darkness. He was bitterly proud of his swiftly changing moods and boasted when he had to suffer the results of them. It was the way he was, he would say; he could not help it, he would say, and his head would wag. And it was his sullen stare and the violent action that followed that made Gus and Jack and G.H. hate and fear him as much as he hated and feared himself.

AN AUTHORITARIAN PERSONALITY

Heinrich Mann

From *Little Superman*

Diederich Hessling was a dreamy, delicate child, frightened of everything, and troubled with constant earache. In winter he hated to leave the warm room, and in summer the narrow garden, which smelt of rags from the paper factory, and whose laburnum and elder-trees were overshadowed by the wooden roofs of the old houses. Diederich was often terribly afraid when he raised his eyes from his story book, his beloved fairy tales. A toad half as big as himself had been plainly sitting on the seat beside him! Or over there against the wall a gnome, sunk to his waist in the ground, was staring at him! His father was even more terrible than the gnome and the toad, and moreover he was compelled to love him. Diederich did love him. Whenever he had pilfered, or told a lie, he would come cringing shyly like a dog to his father's desk, until Herr Hessling noticed that something was wrong and took his stick from the wall. Diederich's submissiveness and confidence were shaken by doubts so long as any misdeed remained undiscovered. Once when his father, who had a stiff leg, fell downstairs the boy clapped his hands madly—and then ran away at full speed.

The workmen used to laugh when he passed the workshops after having been punished, crying loudly, his face swollen with tears. Then Diederich would stamp his feet and put out his tongue at them. He would say to himself: "I have got a beating, but from my papa. You would be glad to be beaten by him, but you are not good enough for that."

He moved amongst the men like a capricious potentate. Sometimes he would threaten to tell his father that they were bringing in beer, and at others he would coquetishly allow them to wheedle out of him the hour when Herr Hessling was expected to return. They were on their guard against the boss; he knew them, for he had been a workman himself. He had been a vat-man in the old mills where every sheet of paper was made by hand. During that time he had served in all the wars, and after the last one, when everybody made money, he was able to buy a paper machine. His plant consisted of one cylinder machine and one cutter. He himself counted the sheets. He kept his eye on the buttons which were taken from the rags. His little son often used to accept a few from the women, on condition that he did not tell on those who took some away with them. One day he had collected so many that he got the idea of exchanging them with the grocer for sweets. He succeeded—but in the evening Diederich knelt in his bed and, as he swallowed the last piece of barley sugar, he prayed to Almighty God to leave the crime undetected. He nevertheless allowed it to leak out. His father had always used the stick methodically, his weather-beaten face reflecting an old soldier's sense of honour and duty. This time his hand trembled and a tear rolled down, trickling over the wrinkles, onto one side of his grey upturned moustache. "My son is a thief," he said breathlessly, in a hushed voice, and he stared at the child as if he were a suspicious intruder. "You lie and you steal. All you have to do now is to commit a murder."

Frau Hessling tried to compel Diederich to fall on his knees before his father and beg his pardon, because his father had wept on his account. Diederich's instinct, however, warned him that this would only have made his father more angry. Hessling had no sympathy whatever with his wife's sentimental manner. She was spoiling the child for life. Besides he had caught her lying just like little Diederich. No wonder, for she read novels! By Saturday night her week's work was often not completed. She gossiped with the servant instead of exerting herself. . . . And even then Hessling did not know that his wife also pilfered, just like the child. At table she did not dare to eat enough and she crept surreptitiously to the cupboard. Had she dared to go into the workshop she would also have stolen buttons.

She prayed with the child "from the heart," and not according to the prescribed forms, and that always brought a flush to her face. She used to beat him also and gave him thorough thrashings, consumed with a desire for revenge. On such occasions she was frequently in the wrong, and then Diederich threatened to complain to his father. He would pretend to go into the office and, hiding somewhere behind a wall, would rejoice at her terror. He exploited his mother's tender moods, but felt no respect for her. Her resemblance to himself made that impossible, for he had no self-respect. The consequence was that he went through life with a conscience too uneasy to withstand the scrutiny of God.

Nevertheless mother and son spent twilight hours overflowing with sentiment. From festive occasions they jointly extracted the last drop of emotion by means of singing, piano-playing and story-telling. When Diederich began to have doubts about the Christ Child he let his mother persuade him to go on believing a little while longer, and thereby he felt relieved, faithful and good. He also believed obstinately in a ghost up in the Castle, and his father, who would not hear of such a thing, seemed too proud, and almost deserving of punishment. His mother nourished him with fairy tales. She shared with him her fear of the new, animated streets, and of the tramway which crossed them and took him past the city wall towards the Castle, where they enjoyed delightful thrills. At the corner of Meisestrasse you had to pass a policeman, who could take you off to prison if he liked. Diederich's heart beat nervously. How gladly he would have made a détour! But then the policeman would have noticed his uneasy conscience and have seized him. It was much better to prove that one felt pure and innocent—so with trembling voice Diederich asked the policeman the time.

After so many fearful powers, to which he was subjected; his father, God, the ghost of the Castle and the police; after the chimney sweep, who could slip him right up through the flue until he, too, was quite black, and the doctor, who could paint his throat and shake him when he cried—after all these powers, Diederich now fell under the sway of one even more terrible, which swallowed you up completely—the school. Diederich went there howling, and because he wanted to howl he could not give even the answers which he knew. Gradually he learnt how to exploit this tendency to cry whenever he had not learnt his lessons, for all his fears did not make him more industrious or less dreamy. And thus, until the teachers saw through the trick, he was able to avoid many of the evil consequences of his idleness. The first teacher who saw through it, at once earned his wholehearted respect. He suddenly stopped crying and gazed at him over the arm which he was holding bent in front of his face, full of timid devotion. He was always obedient and docile with the strict teachers. On the good-natured ones he played little tricks, which could with difficulty be proved against him and about which he did not boast. With much greater satisfaction he bragged of getting bad marks and great punishments. At table he would say: "To-day Herr Behnke flogged three of us again." And to the question: Whom? "I was one of them."

Diederich was so constituted that he was delighted to belong to an impersonal entity, to this immovable, inhumanly indifferent, mechanical organisation which was the college. He was proud of this power, this grim power, which he felt, if only through suffering. On the headmaster's birthday flowers were placed on the desk and the blackboard. Diederich actually decorated the cane.

In the course of the years two catastrophes, which befell the all-powerful, filled him with a holy and wonderful horror. An assistant master was called down in front of the class by the principal and dismissed. A senior master became insane. On these occasions still higher powers, the principal and the lunatic asylum, made fearful havoc of those who had hitherto wielded so much power. From beneath, insignificant but unharmed, one could raise one's eyes to these victims, and draw from their fate a lesson which rendered one's own lot more easy. In relation to his younger sisters Diederich replaced the power which held him in its mechanism. He made them take dictation, and deliberately make more mistakes than they naturally would, so that he could make furious corrections with red ink, and administer punishment. His punishments were cruel. The little ones cried—and then Diederich had to humble himself in order that they should not betray him.

He had no need of human beings in order to imitate the powers that be. Animals, and even inanimate objects, were sufficient. He would stand at the rail of the paper-making machine and watch the cylinder sorting out the rags. "So that one is gone! Look out, now, you blackguards!" Diederich would mutter, and his pale eyes glared. Suddenly he stepped back, almost falling into the tub of chlorine. A workman's footsteps had interrupted his vicious enjoyment.

Only when he himself received the punishment did he feel really big and sure of his position. He hardly ever resisted evil. At most he would beg a comrade: "Don't hit me on the back, that's dangerous." It was not that he was lacking in any sense of his rights and any love of his own advantage. But Diederich held that the blows which he received brought no practical profit to the striker and no real loss to himself. These purely ideal values seemed to him far less serious than the cream puff which the head waiter at the Netziger Hof had long since promised him, but had never produced. Many times Diederich wended his way, with earnest gait, up Meisestrasse to the market place, and called upon his swallow-tailed friend to deliver the goods. One day, however, when the waiter denied all knowledge of his promise, Diederich declared, as he stamped his foot in genuine indignation: "This is really too much of a good thing. If you don't give me it immediately, I'll report you to the boss!" Thereupon George laughed and brought him the cream puff.

That was a tangible success. Unfortunately Diederich could enjoy it only in haste and fear, for he was afraid that Wolfgang Buck, who was waiting outside, would come in on him and demand the share which had been promised to him. Meanwhile he found time to wipe his mouth clean, and at the door he broke out into violent abuse of George, whom he called a swindler who had no cream puffs at all. Diederich's sense of justice, which had just manifested itself so effectively to his own advantage, did not respond to the claims of his friend, who could not, at the same time, be altogether ignored. Wolfgang's father was much too important a personage for that. Old Herr Buck did not wear a stiff collar, but a white silk neckcloth, on which his great curly white beard rested. How slowly and majestically he tapped the pavement with his gold-topped walking-stick! He wore a silk hat, too, and the tails of his dress coat often peeped out under his overcoat, even in the middle of the day! For he went to public meetings, and looked after the affairs of the whole city. Looking at the bathing establishment, the prison and all the public institutions, Diederich used to think: "That belongs to Herr Buck." He must be tremendously wealthy and powerful. All the men, including Herr Hessling, took off their hats most respectfully to him. To deprive his son of something by force was a deed whose dangerous consequences could not be foretold. In order not to be utterly crushed by the mighty powers, whom he so profoundly respected, Diederich had to go quietly and craftily to work.

Only once did it happen, when he was in the Lower Third form, that Diederich forgot all prudence, acted blindly and became himself an oppressor, drunk with victory. As was the usual and approved custom, he had bullied the only Jew in his class, but then he proceeded to an unfamiliar manifestation. Out of the blocks which were used for drawing he built a cross on the desk and forced the Jew onto his knees before it. He held him tight, in spite of his resistance; he was strong! What made Diederich strong was the applause of the bystanders, the crowd whose arms helped him, the overwhelming majority within the building and in the world outside. He was acting on behalf of the whole Christian community of Netzig. How splendid it was to share responsibility, and to feel the sensation of collective consciousness.

When the first flush of intoxication had waned, it is true, a certain fear took its place, but all his courage returned to Diederich when he saw the face of the first master he met. It was so full of embarrassed good will. Others openly showed their approval. Diederich smiled up at them with an air of shy understanding. Things were easier for him after that. The class could not refuse to honour one who enjoyed the favour of the headmaster. Under him Diederich rose to the head of the class and secretly acted as monitor. At least, he laid claim, later on, to the latter of these honours also. He was a good friend to all, laughed when they planned their escapades, an unreserved and hearty laugh, as befitted an earnest youth who could yet understand frivolity—and then, during the lunch hour, when he brought his notebook to the professor, he reported everything. He also reported the nicknames of the teachers and the rebellious speeches which had been made against them. In repeating these things his voice trembled with something of the voluptuous terror which he had experienced as he listened to them with half-closed eyes. Whenever there was any disparaging comment on the ruling powers he had a guilty feeling of relief, as if something deep down in himself, like a kind of hatred, had hastily and furtively satisfied its hunger. By sneaking on his comrades he atoned for his own guilty impulses.

For the most part he had no personal feeling against the pupils whose advancement was checked by his activities. He acted as the conscientious instrument of dire necessity. Afterwards he could go to the culprit and quite honestly sympathise with him. Once he was instrumental in catching some one who had been suspected of copying. With the knowledge of the teacher, Diederich gave him a mathematical problem, the working out of which was deliberately wrong, while the final result was correct. That evening, after the cheater had been exposed, some of the students were sitting in the garden of a restaurant outside the gate singing, as they were allowed to do after gymnasium. Diederich had taken a seat beside his victim. Once, when they had emptied their glasses he slipped his right hand into that of his companion, gazed trustfully into his eyes, and began all alone to sing in a bass voice that quivered with emotion:

> Ich hatt' einen Kameraden,
> Einen bessern findst du nit. . . .*

* "I had a comrade / A better one you'll never find. . . ."

THE CONFORMISTS

Christopher Isherwood

"The Landauers"

When I returned to Berlin, in the autumn of 1932, I duly rang Bernhard up, only to be told that he was away, on business, in Hamburg. I blame myself now—one always does blame oneself afterwards—for not having been more persistent. But there was so much for me to do, so many pupils, so many other people to see; the weeks turned into months; Christmas came—I sent Bernhard a card but got no answer: he was away again, most likely; and then the New Year began.

Hitler came, and the Reichstag fire, and the mock-elections. I wondered what was happening to Bernhard. Three times I rang him up—from call-boxes, lest I should get Frl. Schroeder into trouble: there was never any reply. Then, one evening early in April, I went round to his house. The caretaker put his head out of the tiny window, more suspicious than ever: at first, he seemed even inclined to deny that he know Bernhard at all. Then he snapped: "Herr Landauer has gone away . . . gone right away."

"Do you mean he's moved from here?" I asked. "Can you give me his address?"

"He's gone away," the caretaker repeated, and slammed the window shut.

I left it at that—concluding, not unnaturally, that Bernhard was somewhere safe abroad.

On the morning of the Jewish boycott, I walked round to take a look at Landauers'. Things seemed very much as usual, superficially. Two or three uniformed S.A. boys were posted at each of the big entrances. Whenever a shopper approached, one of them would say: "Remember this is a Jewish business!" The boys were quite polite, grinning, making jokes among themselves. Little knots of passers-by collected to watch the performance—interested, amused

From *Goodbye To Berlin*. Reprinted by permission of The Hogarth Press, Ltd. and Curtis Brown, Ltd. Copyright 1945, 1954, by New Directions.

or merely apathetic; still uncertain whether or not to approve. There was nothing of the atmosphere one read of later in the smaller provincial towns, where purchasers were forcibly disgraced with a rubber ink-stamp on the forehead and cheek. Quite a lot of people went into the building. I went in myself, bought the first thing I saw—it happened to be a nutmeg-grater—and strolled out again, twirling my small parcel. One of the boys at the door winked and said something to his companion. I remembered having seen him once or twice at the Alexander Casino, in the days when I was living with the Nowaks.

In May, I left Berlin for the last time. My first stop was at Prague— and it was there, sitting one evening alone, in a cellar restaurant, that I heard, indirectly, my last news of the Landauer family.

Two men were at the next table, talking German. One of them was certainly an Austrian; the other I couldn't place—he was fat and sleek, about forty-five, and might well have owned a small business in any European capital, from Belgrade to Stockholm. Both of them were undoubtedly prosperous, technically Aryan, and politically neuter. The fat man startled me into attention by saying:

"You know Landauers'? Landauers' of Berlin?"

The Austrian nodded: "Sure, I do. . . . Did a lot of business with them, one time. . . . Nice place they've got there. Must have cost a bit. . . ."

"Seen the papers, this morning?"

"No. Didn't have time. . . . Moving into our new flat, you know. The wife's coming back."

"She's coming back? You don't say! Been in Vienna, hasn't she?"

"That's right."

"Had a good time?"

"Trust her! It cost enough, anyway."

"Vienna's pretty dear, these days."

"It is that."

"Food's dear."

"It's dear everywhere."

"I guess you're right." The fat man began to pick his teeth: "What was I saying?"

"You were saying about Landauers'."

"So I was. . . . You didn't read the papers, this morning?"

"No, I didn't read them."

"There was a bit in about Bernhard Landauer."

"Bernhard?" said the Austrian. "Let's see—he's the son, isn't he?"

"I wouldn't know. . . ." The fat man dislodged a tiny fragment of meat with the point of his toothpick. Holding it up to the light, he regarded it thoughtfully.

"I think he's the son," said the Austrian. "Or maybe the nephew . . . No, I think he's the son."

"Whoever he is," the fat man flicked the scrap of meat on to his plate with a gesture of distaste: "He's dead."

"You don't say!"

"Heart failure." The fat man frowned, and raised his hand to cover a belch. He was wearing three gold rings: "That's what the newspapers said."

"Heart failure!" The Austrian shifted uneasily in his chair: "You don't say!"

"There's a lot of heart failure," said the fat man, "in Germany these days."

The Austrian nodded: "You can't believe all you hear. That's a fact."

"If you ask me," said the fat man, "anyone's heart's liable to fail, if it gets a bullet inside it."

The Austrian looked very uncomfortable: "Those Nazis . . ." he began.

"They mean business." The fat man seemed rather to enjoy making his friend's flesh creep. "You mark my words: they're going to clear the Jews right out of Germany. Right out."

The Austrian shook his head: "I don't like it."

"Concentration camps," said the fat man, lighting a cigar. "They get them in there, make them sign things. . . . Then their hearts fail."

"I don't like it," said the Austrian. "It's bad for trade."

"Yes," the fat man agreed. "It's bad for trade."

"Makes everything so uncertain."

"That's right. Never know who you're doing business with." The fat man laughed. In his own way, he was rather macabre: "It might be a corpse."

The Austrian shivered a little: "What about the old man, old Landauer? Did they get him, too?"

"No, he's all right. Too smart for them. He's in Paris."

"You don't say!"

"I reckon the Nazis'll take over the business. They're doing that, now."

"Then old Landauer'll be ruined, I guess?"

"Not him!" The fat man flicked the ash from his cigar, contemptuously. "He'll have a bit put by, somewhere. You'll see. He'll start something else. They're smart, those Jews. . . ."

"That's right," the Austrian agreed. "You can't keep a Jew down."

The thought seemed to cheer him, a little. He brightened: "That reminds me! I knew there was something I wanted to tell you. . . . Did you ever hear the story about the Jew and the Goy girl with the wooden leg?"

"No." The fat man puffed at his cigar. His digestion was working well, now. He was in the right after-dinner mood: "Go ahead. . . ."

THE IMPERIALIST

Joseph Conrad

From "Heart of Darkness"

And the lofty frontal bone of Mr. Kurtz! They say the hair goes on growing sometimes, but this—ah—specimen, was impressively bald. The wilderness had patted him on the head, and, behold, it was like a ball—an ivory ball; it had caressed him, and—lo!—he had withered; it had taken him, loved him, embraced him, got into his veins, consumed his flesh, and sealed his soul to its own by the inconceivable ceremonies of some devilish initiation. He was its spoiled and pampered favorite. Ivory? I should think so. Heaps of it, stacks of it. The old mud shanty was bursting with it. You would think there was not a single tusk left either above or below the ground in the whole country. "Mostly fossil," the manager had remarked, disparagingly. It was no more fossil than I am; but they call it fossil when it is dug up. It appears these niggers do bury the tusks sometimes—but evidently they couldn't bury this parcel deep enough to save the gifted Mr. Kurtz from his fate. We filled the steamboat with it, and had to pile a lot on the deck. Thus he could see and enjoy as long as he could see, because the appreciation of his favor had remained with him to the last. You should have heard him say, "My ivory." Oh yes, I heard him. "My Intended, my ivory, my station, my river, my—" everything belonged to him. It made me hold my breath in expectation of hearing the wilderness burst into a prodigious peal of laughter that would shake the fixed stars in their places. Everything belonged to him—but that was a trifle. The thing was to know what he belonged to, how many powers of darkness claimed him for their own. That was the reflection that made you creepy all over. It was impossible—it was not good for one either—trying to imagine. He had taken a high seat amongst the devils of the land—I mean literally. You can't understand. How could you?—with solid pavement under your feet, surrounded by kind neighbors ready to cheer you or to fall on you, stepping delicately between the butcher and the policeman, in the holy terror of scandal and gallows and lunatic asylums—how can you imagine what particular region of the first ages a man's untrammeled feet may take him into by the way of solitude—utter solitude without a policeman—by the way of silence— utter silence, where no warning voice of a kind neighbor can be heard whispering of public opinion? These little things make all the great difference. When they are gone you must fall back upon your own innate strength, upon your own capacity for faithfulness. Of course you may be too much of a fool to go wrong—too dull even to know you are being assaulted by the powers of darkness. I take it, no fool ever made a bargain for his soul with the devil: the fool is too much of a fool, or the devil too much of a devil—I don't know which. Or you may be such a thunderingly exalted creature as to be altogether deaf and blind to anything but heavenly sights and sounds. Then the earth for you is only a standing place—and whether to be like this is your loss or your gain I won't pretend to say. But most of us are neither one nor the other. The earth for us is a place to live in, where we must put up with sights, with sounds, with smells, too, by Jove!—breathe dead hippo, so to speak, and not be contaminated. And there, don't you see? Your strength comes in, the faith in your ability for the digging of unostentatious holes to bury the stuff in— your power of devotion, not to yourself, but to an obscure, back-breaking business. And that's difficult enough. Mind, I am not trying to excuse or even explain—I am trying to account to myself for—for— Mr. Kurtz—for the shade of Mr. Kurtz. This initiated wraith from the back of Nowhere honored me with its amazing confidence before it vanished altogether. This was because it could speak English to me. The original Kurtz had been educated partly in England, and—as he was good enough to say himself—his sympathies were in the right place. His mother was half-English, his father was half-French. All Europe contributed to the making of Kurtz; and by and by I learned that, most appropriately, the International Society for the Suppression of Savage Customs had intrusted him with the making of a report, for its future guidance. And he had written it, too. I've seen it. I've read it. It was eloquent, vibrating with eloquence, but too high-strung, I think. Seventeen pages of close writing he had found time for! But this must have been before his—let us say—nerves, went wrong, and caused him to preside at certain midnight dances ending with unspeakable rites, which—as far as I reluctantly gathered from what I heard at various times—were offered up to him —do you understand?—to Mr. Kurtz himself. But it was a beautiful piece of writing. The opening paragraph, however, in the light of later information, strikes me now as ominous. He began with the argument that we whites, from the point of development we had arrived at, "must necessarily appear to them [savages] in the nature of supernatural beings—we approach them with the might as of a deity," and so on, and so on. "By the simple exercise of our will we can exert a power for good practically unbounded," etc., etc. From that point he soared and took me with him. The peroration was magnificent, though difficult to remember, you know. It gave me the notion of an exotic Immensity ruled by an august Benevolence. It made me tingle with enthusiasm. This was the unbounded power of eloquence—of words—of burning noble words. There were no practical hints to interrupt the magic current of phrases unless a kind of note at the foot of the last page, scrawled evidently much later, in an unsteady hand, may be regarded as the exposition of a method. It was very simple, and at the end of that moving appeal to every altruistic sentiment it blazed at you, luminous and terrifying, like a flash of lightning in a serene sky: "Exterminate all the brutes!" The curious part was that he had apparently forgotten all about that valuable postscriptum, because, later on, when he in a sense came to himself, he repeatedly entreated me to take good care of "my pamphlet" (he called it), as it was sure to have in the future a good influence upon his career.

THE REBEL

Feodor Dostoevski

From *The Brothers Karamazov*

"I must make you one confession," Ivan began. "I could never understand how one can love one's neighbours. It's just one's neighbours, to my mind, that one can't love, though one might love those at a distance. I once read somewhere of John the Merciful, a saint, that when a hungry, frozen beggar came to him, he took him into his bed, held him in his arms, and began breathing into his mouth, which was putrid and loathsome from some awful disease. I am convinced that he did that from 'self-laceration,' from the self-laceration of falsity, for the sake of the charity imposed by duty, as a penance laid on him. For any one to love a man, he must be hidden, for as soon as he shows his face, love is gone."

"Father Zossima has talked of that more than once," observed Alyosha; "he, too, said that the face of a man often hinders many people not practised in love, from loving him. But yet there's a great deal of love in mankind, and almost Christ-like love. I know that myself, Ivan."

"Well, I know nothing of it so far, and can't understand it, and the innumerable mass of mankind are with me there. The question is, whether that's due to men's bad qualities or whether it's inherent in their nature. To my thinking, Christ-like love for men is a miracle impossible on earth. He was God. But we are not gods. Suppose I, for instance, suffer intensely. Another can never know how much I suffer, because he is another and not I. And what's more, a man is rarely ready to admit another's suffering (as though it were a distinction). Why won't he admit it, do you think? Because I smell unpleasant, because I have a stupid face, because I once trod on his foot. Besides there is suffering and suffering; degrading, humiliating suffering such as humbles me—hunger, for instance—my benefactor will perhaps allow me; but when you come to higher suffering—for

Reprinted with permission of The Macmillan Company and William Heinemann, Ltd. from *The Brothers Karamazov* by Feodor Dostoevski, Book V Ch. 4, translated by Constance Garnett. Printed in Great Britain.

an idea, for instance—he will very rarely admit that, perhaps because my face strikes him as not at all what he fancies a man should have who suffers for an idea. And so he deprives me instantly of his favour, and not at all from badness of heart. Beggars, especially genteel beggars, ought never to show themselves, but to ask for charity through the newspapers. One can love one's neighbours in the abstract, or even at a distance, but at close quarters it's almost impossible. If it were as on the stage, in the ballet, where if beggars come in, they wear silken rags and tattered lace and beg for alms dancing gracefully, then one might like looking at them. But even then we should not love them. But enough of that. I simply wanted to show you my point of view. I meant to speak of the suffering of mankind generally, but we had better confine ourselves to the sufferings of the children. That reduces the scope of my argument to a tenth of what it would be. Still we'd better keep to the children, though it does weaken my case. But, in the first place, children can be loved even at close quarters, even when they are dirty, even when they are ugly (I fancy, though, children never are ugly). The second reason why I won't speak of grown-up people is that, besides being disgusting and unworthy of love, they have a compensation—they've eaten the apple and know good and evil, and they have become 'like god.' They go on eating it still. But the children haven't eaten anything, and are so far innocent. Are you fond of children, Alyosha? I know you are, and you will understand why I prefer to speak of them. If they, too, suffer horribly on earth, they must suffer for their fathers' sins, they must be punished for their fathers, who have eaten the apple; but that reasoning is of the other world and is incomprehensible for the heart of man here on earth. The innocent must not suffer for another's sins, and especially such innocents! You may be surprised at me, Alyosha, but I am awfully fond of children, too. And observe, cruel people, the violent, the rapacious, the Karamazovs are sometimes very fond of children. Children while they are quite little—up to seven, for instance—are so remote from grown-up people; they are different creatures, as it were, of a different species. I knew a criminal in prison who had, in the course of his career as a burglar, murdered whole families, including several children. But when he was in prison, he had a strange affection for them. He spent all his time at his window, watching the children playing in the prison yard. He trained one little boy to come up to his window and made great friends with him. . . . You don't know why I am telling you all this, Alyosha? My head aches and I am sad."

"You speak with a strange air," observed Alyosha uneasily, "as though you were not quite yourself."

"By the way, a Bulgarian I met lately in Moscow," Ivan went on, seeming not to hear his brother's words, "told me about the crimes committed by Turks and Circassians in all parts of Bulgaria through fear of a general rising of the Slavs. They burn villages, murder, outrage women and children, they nail their prisoners by the ears to the fences, leave them so till morning, and in the morning they hang them—all sorts of things you can't imagine. People talk sometimes of bestial cruelty, but that's a great injustice and insult to the beasts; a beast can never be so cruel as a man, so artistically cruel. The tiger only tears and gnaws, that's all he can do. He would never think of nailing people by the ears, even if he were able to do it. These Turks took a pleasure in torturing children, too; cutting the unborn child from the mother's womb, and tossing babies up in the air and catching them on the points of their bayonets before their mother's eyes. Doing it before the mother's eyes was what gave zest to the amusement. Here is another scene that I thought very interesting. Imagine a trembling mother with her baby in her arms, a circle of invading Turks around her. They've planned a diversion; they pet the baby, laugh to make it laugh. They succeed, the baby laughs. At that moment a Turk points a pistol four inches from the baby's face. The baby laughs with glee, holds out its little hands to the pistol, and he pulls the trigger in the baby's face and blows out its brains. Artistic, wasn't it? By the way, Turks are particularly fond of sweet things, they say."

"Brother, what are you driving at?" asked Alyosha.

"I think if the devil doesn't exist, but man has created him, he has created him in his own image and likeness."

"Just as he did God, then?" observed Alyosha.

"'It's wonderful how you can turn words,' as Polonius says in *Hamlet*," laughed Ivan. "You turn my words against me. Well, I am glad. Yours must be a fine God, if man created Him in His image and likeness. You asked just now what I was driving at. You see, I am fond of collecting certain facts, and, would you believe, I even copy anecdotes of a certain sort from newspapers and books, and I've already got a fine collection. The Turks, of course, have gone into it, but they are foreigners. I have specimens from home that are even better than the Turks. You know we prefer beating—rods and scourges—that's our national institution. Nailing ears is unthinkable for us, for we are, after all, Europeans. But the rod and the scourge

we have always with us and they cannot be taken from us. Abroad now they scarcely do any beating. Manners are more humane, or laws have been passed, so that they don't dare to flog men now. But they make up for it in another way just as national as ours. And so national that it would be practically impossible among us, though I believe we are being inoculated with it, since the religious movement began in our aristocracy. I have a charming pamphlet, translated from the French, describing how, quite recently, five years ago, a murderer, Richard, was executed—a young man, I believe, of three and twenty, who repented and was converted to the Christian faith at the very scaffold. This Richard was an illegitimate child who was given as a child of six by his parents to some shepherds on the Swiss mountains. They brought him up to work for them. He grew up like a little wild beast among them. The shepherds taught him nothing, and scarcely fed or clothed him, but sent him out at seven to herd the flock in cold and wet, and no one hesitated or scrupled to treat him so. Quite the contrary, they thought they had every right, for Richard had been given to them as a chattel, and they did not even see the necessity of feeding him. Richard himself describes how in those years, like the Prodigal Son in the Gospel, he longed to eat of the mash given to the pigs, which were fattened for sale. But they wouldn't even give him that, and beat him when he stole from the pigs. And that was how he spent all his childhood and his youth, till he grew up and was strong enough to go away and be a thief. The savage began to earn his living as a day labourer in Geneva. He drank what he earned, he lived like a brute, and finished by killing and robbing an old man. He was caught, tried, and condemned to death. They are not sentimentalists there. And in prison he was immediately surrounded by pastors, members of Christian brotherhoods, philanthropic ladies, and the like. They taught him to read and write in prison, and expounded the Gospel to him. They exhorted him, worked upon him, drummed at him incessantly, till at last he solemnly confessed his crime. He was converted. He wrote to the court himself that he was a monster, but that in the end God had vouchsafed him light and shown grace. All Geneva was in excitement about him—all philanthropic and religious Geneva. All the aristocratic and well-bred society of the town rushed to the prison, kissed Richard and embraced him; 'You are our brother, you have found grace.' And Richard does nothing but weep with emotion, 'Yes, I've found grace! All my youth and childhood I was glad of pigs' food, but now even I have found grace. I am dying in the

Lord.' 'Yes, Richard, die in the Lord; you have shed blood and must die. Though it's not your fault that you knew not the Lord, when you coveted the pig's food and were beaten for stealing it (which was very wrong of you, for stealing is forbidden); but you've shed blood and you must die.' And on the last day, Richard, perfectly limp, did nothing but cry and repeat every minute: 'This is my happiest day. I am going to the Lord.' 'Yes,' cry the pastors and the judges and philanthropic ladies. 'This is the happiest day of your life, for you are going to the Lord!' They all walk or drive to the scaffold in procession behind the prison van. At the scaffold they call to Richard: 'Die, brother, die in the Lord, for even thou hast found grace!' And so, covered with his brothers' kisses, Richard is dragged on to the scaffold, and led to the guillotine. And they chopped off his head in brotherly fashion, because he had found grace. Yes, that's characteristic. That pamphlet is translated into Russian by some Russian philanthropists of aristocratic rank and evangelical aspirations, and has been distributed gratis for the enlightenment of the people. The case of Richard is interesting because it's national. Though to us it's absurd to cut off a man's head, because he has become our brother and has found grace, yet we have our own specialty, which is all but worse. Our historical pastime is the direct satisfaction of inflicting pain. There are lines in Nekrassov describing how a peasant lashes a horse on the eyes, 'on its meek eyes,' every one must have seen it. It's peculiarly Russian. He describes how a feeble little nag had foundered under too heavy a load and cannot move. The peasant beats it, beats it savagely, beats it at last not knowing what he is doing in the intoxication of cruelty, thrashes it mercilessly over and over again. 'However weak you are, you must pull, if you die for it.' The nag strains, and then he begins lashing the poor defenceless creature on its weeping, on its 'meek eyes.' The frantic beast tugs and draws the load, trembling all over, gasping for breath, moving sideways, with a sort of unnatural spasmodic action—it's awful in Nekrassov. But that's only a horse, and God has given horses to be beaten. So the Tatars have taught us, and they left us the knout as a remembrance of it. But men, too, can be beaten. A well-educated, cultured gentleman and his wife beat their own child with a birch-rod, a girl of seven. I have an exact account of it. The papa was glad that the birch was covered with twigs. 'It stings more,' said he, and so he began stinging his daughter. I know for a fact there are people who at every blow are worked up to sensuality, to literal sensuality, which increases progressively at every blow they inflict. They beat for a minute, for five minutes, for ten minutes, more often and more savagely. The child screams. At last the child cannot scream, it gasps, 'Daddy! daddy!' By some diabolical unseemly chance the case was brought into court. A counsel is engaged. The Russian people have long called a barrister 'a conscience for hire.' The counsel protests in his client's defence. 'It's such a simple thing,' he says, 'an everyday domestic event. A father corrects his child. To our shame be it said, it is brought into court.' The jury, convinced by him, give a favourable verdict. The public roars with delight that the torturer is acquitted. Ah, pity, I wasn't there! I would have proposed to raise a subscription in his honour! . . . Charming pictures.

"But I've still better things about children. I've collected a great, great deal about Russian children, Alyosha. There was a little girl of five who was hated by her father and mother, 'most worthy and respectable people, of good education and breeding.' You see, I must repeat again, it is a peculiar characteristic of many people, this love of torturing children, and children only. To all other types of humanity these torturers behave mildly and benevolently, like cultivated and humane Europeans; but they are very fond of tormenting children, even fond of children themselves in that sense. It's just their defencelessness that tempts the tormentor, just the angelic confidence of the child who has no refuge and no appeal, that sets his vile blood on fire. In every man, of course, a demon lies hidden—the demon of rage, the demon of lustful heat at the screams of the tortured victim, the demon of lawlessness let off the chain, the demon of diseases that follow on vice, gout, kidney disease, and so on.

"This poor child of five was subjected to every possible torture by those cultivated parents. They beat her, thrashed her, kicked her for no reason till her body was one bruise. Then, they went to greater refinements of cruelty—shut her up all night in the cold and frost in a privy, and because she didn't ask to be taken up at night (as though a child of five sleeping its angelic, sound sleep could be trained to wake and ask), they smeared her face and filled her mouth with excrement, and it was her mother, her mother did this. And that mother could sleep, hearing the poor child's groans! Can you understand why a little creature, who can't even understand what's done to her, should beat her little aching heart with her tiny fist in the dark and the cold, and weep her meek unresentful tears to dear, kind God to protect her? Do you understand that, friend and brother, you pious and humble novice? Do you understand why this infamy must be and is permitted? Without it, I am told, man could not have existed on earth, for he could not have known good and evil. Why should he know that diabolical good and evil when it costs so much? Why, the whole world of knowledge is not worth that child's prayer to 'dear, kind God'! I say nothing of the sufferings of grown-up people, they have eaten the apple, damn them, and the devil take them all! But these little ones! I am making you suffer, Alyosha, you are not yourself. I'll leave off if you like."

"Never mind. I want to suffer too," muttered Alyosha.

"One picture, only one more, because it's so curious, so character-istic, and I have only just read it in some collection of Russian antiquities. I've forgotten the name. I must look it up. It was in the darkest days of serfdom at the beginning of the century, and long live the Liberator of the People! There was in those days a general of aristocratic connections, the owner of great estates, one of those men—somewhat exceptional, I believe, even then—who, retiring from the service into a life of leisure, are convinced that they've earned absolute power over the lives of their subjects. There were such men then. So our general, settled on his property of two thousand souls, lives in pomp, and domineers over his poor neighbours as though they were dependents and buffoons. He has kennels of hundreds of hounds and nearly a hundred dog-boys—all mounted, and in uni-form. One day a serf boy, a little child of eight, threw a stone in play and hurt the paw of the general's favourite hound. 'Why is my favourite dog lame?' He is told that the boy threw a stone that hurt the dog's paw. 'So you did it.' The general looked the child up and down. 'Take him.' He was taken—taken from his mother and kept shut up all night. Early that morning the general comes out on horseback, with the hounds, his dependents, dog-boys, and hunts-men, all mounted around him in full hunting parade. The servants are summoned for their edification, and in front of them all stands the mother of the child. The child is brought from the lock-up. It's a gloomy cold, foggy autumn day, a capital day for hunting. The general orders the child to be undressed; the child is stripped naked. He shivers, numb with terror, not daring to cry. . . . 'Make him run,' commands the general. 'Run! run!' shout the dog-boys. The boy runs. . . . 'At him!' yells the general, and he sets the whole pack of hounds on the child. The hounds catch him, and tear him to pieces before his mother's eyes! . . . I believe the general was after-wards declared incapable of administering his estates. Well—what did he deserve? To be shot? To be shot for the satisfaction of our moral feelings? Speak, Alyosha!"

"To be shot," murmured Alyosha, lifting his eyes to Ivan with a pale, twisted smile.

"Bravo!" cried Ivan delighted. "If even you say so . . . You're a pretty monk! So there is a little devil sitting in your heart, Alyosha Karamazov!"

"What I said was absurd, but——"

"That's just the point that 'but'!" cried Ivan. "Let me tell you, novice, that the absurd is only too necessary on earth. The world stands on absurdities, and perhaps nothing would have come to pass in it without them. We know what we know!"

"What do you know?"

"I understand nothing," Ivan went on, as though in delirium. "I don't want to understand anything now. I want to stick to the fact. I made up my mind long ago not to understand. If I try to understand anything, I shall be false to the fact and I have determined to stick to the fact."

"Why are you trying me?" Alyosha cried, with sudden distress. "Will you say what you mean at last?"

"Of course, I will; that's what I've been leading up to. You are dear to me, I don't want to let you go, and I won't give you up to your Zossima."

Ivan for a minute was silent, his face became all at once very sad.

"Listen! I took the case of children only to make my case clearer. Of the other tears of humanity with which the earth is soaked from its crust to its centre, I will say nothing. I have narrowed my subject on purpose. I am a bug, and I recognise in all humility that I cannot understand why the world is arranged as it is. Men are themselves to blame, I suppose; they were given paradise, they wanted freedom, and stole fire from heaven, though they knew they would become unhappy, so there is no need to pity them. With my pitiful, earthly, Euclidian understanding, all I know is that there is suffering and that there are none guilty; that cause follows effect, simply and directly; that everything flows and finds its level—but that's only Euclidian nonsense, I know that, and I can't consent to live by it! What comfort is it to me that there are none guilty and that cause follows effect simply and directly, and that I know it—I must have justice, or I will destroy myself. And not justice in some remote infinite time and space, but here on earth, and that I could see myself. I have believed in it. I want to see it, and if I am dead by then, let me rise again, for if it all happens without me, it will be too unfair. Surely I haven't suffered, simply that I, my crimes and my sufferings, may manure the soil of the future harmony for somebody else. I want to see with my own eyes the hind lie down with the lion and the victim rise up and embrace his murderer. I want to be there when every one suddenly understands what it has all been for. All the religions of the world are built on this longing, and I am a believer. But then there are the children, and what am I to do about them? That's a question I can't answer. For the hundredth time I repeat, there are numbers of questions, but I've only taken the children, because in their case what I mean is so unanswerably clear. Listen! If all must suffer to pay for the eternal harmony, what have children to do with it, tell me, please? It's beyond all comprehension why they should suffer, and why they should pay for the harmony. Why should they, too, furnish material to enrich the soil for the harmony of the future? I understand solidarity in sin among men. I understand solidarity in retribution, too; but there can be no such solidarity with children. And if it is really true that they must share responsibility for all their fathers' crimes, such a truth is not of this world and is beyond my comprehension. Some jester will say, perhaps, that the child would have grown up and have sinned, but you see he didn't grow up, he was torn to pieces by the dogs, at eight years old. Oh, Alyosha, I am not blaspheming! I understand, of course, what an upheaval of the universe it will be, when everything in heaven and earth blends in one hymn of praise and everything that lives and has lived cries aloud: 'Thou art just, O Lord, for Thy ways are revealed.' When the mother embraces the fiend who threw her child to the dogs, and all three cry aloud with tears, 'Thou art just, O Lord!' then, of course, the crown of knowledge will be reached and all will be made clear. But what pulls me up here is that I can't accept that harmony. And while I am on earth, I make haste to take my own measures. You see, Alyosha, perhaps it really may happen that if I live to that moment, or rise again to see it, I, too, perhaps, may cry aloud with the rest, looking at the mother embracing the child's torturer, 'Thou art just, O Lord!' but I don't want to cry aloud then. While there is still time, I hasten to protect myself and so I renounce the higher harmony altogether. It's not worth the tears of that one tortured child who beat itself on the breast with its little fist and prayed in its stinking outhouse, with its unexpiated tears to 'dear, kind God'! It's not worth it, because those tears are unatoned for. They must be atoned for, or there can be no harmony. But how? How are you going to atone for them? Is it possible? By their being avenged? But what do I care for avenging them? What do I care for a hell for oppressors? What good can hell do since those children have already been tortured? And what becomes of harmony, if there is hell? I want to forgive. I want to embrace. I don't want more suffering. And if the sufferings of children go to swell the sum of sufferings which was necessary to pay for truth, then I protest that the truth is not worth such a price. I don't want the mother to embrace the oppressor who threw her son to the dogs! She dare not forgive him! Let her forgive him for herself, if she will, let her forgive the torturer for the immeasurable suffering of her mother's heart. But the sufferings of her tortured child she has no right to forgive; she dare not forgive the torturer, even if the child were to forgive him! And if that is so, if they dare not forgive, what becomes of harmony? Is there in the whole world a being who would have the right to forgive and could forgive? I don't want harmony. From love for humanity I don't want it. I would rather be left with the unavenged suffering. I would rather remain with my unavenged suffering and unsatisfied indignation, *even if I were wrong.* Besides, too high a price is asked for harmony; it's beyond our means to pay so much to enter on it. And so I hasten to give back my entrance ticket, and if I am an honest man I am bound to give it back as soon as possible. And that I am doing. It's not God that I don't accept, Alyosha, only I most respectfully return Him the ticket."

"That's rebellion," murmured Alyosha, looking down.

"Rebellion? I am sorry you call it that," said Ivan earnestly. "One can hardly live in rebellion, and I want to live. Tell me yourself, I challenge you—answer. Imagine that you are creating a fabric of human destiny with the object of making men happy in the end, giving them peace and rest at last, but that it was essential and inevitable to torture to death only one tiny creature—that baby beating its breast with its fist, for instance—and to found that edifice on its unavenged tears, would you consent to be the architect on those conditions? Tell me, and tell the truth."

"No, I wouldn't consent," said Alyosha softly.